Tuning Diamonds

Electromagnetism &
Spiritual Evolution

A Study Guide

Susan Joy Rennison

Second Edition (International), published in the UK in 2008 by

Joyfire Publishing,

P. O. Box 7144,
Burton upon Trent,
Staffordshire
DE14 9BJ

First published by Joyfire Publishing in 2006,
reprinted with minor revisions and updates.

Printed and bound in the United Kingdom

A catalogue record for this book is available from the British Library

ISBN 978-0-9553216-0-3

www.joyfirepublishing.com

This book is

Dedicated

To Seekers of the Truth

Acknowledgements

I have a passion for truth, and so over the years I have been very grateful to many authors who have shown courage and dedication in sharing their enlightenment. For this book I have been delighted to indulge my thirst for knowledge, bringing together the discoveries of physics with insights from metaphysics

The following list is in no particular order of the best teachers of the Electric Universe theories. Wal Thornhill, Don Scott, and James McCanney. I would like to thank scientists in Russia for making the effort to translate Russian research and books into English, especially Dr. Alexey Dmitriev, Dr. Valery Uvarov and Dr. Krasnoholovets.

Thanks to scientist Candace Pert, another "Seeker of the Truth" who shared her enlightenment in the book "Molecules of Emotion." The physicist Bibhas De for his deep understanding of magnetism and his views on the true nature of the universe. I would like to thank the metaphysicians Tom Kenyon and Lee Carroll for their insights and willingness to share. David Wilcock gets special acknowledgement for his advanced research that greatly helped my process of integration.

In the production of this book, I would like to thank those who have responded to my requests for help and permissions, including Prof. William Tiller, Dr. John Milewski and Dr. Rollin McCraty at the Heartmath Institute. Dr Serge Barsamian and Mark Balfour, get thanks and appreciation for sending me an original slide of the historic discovery of the spiraling EM vortex. Thanks to Anne-Tora Svanes for allowing me to share her vision to the world.

A special thanks to my friend Oivind Gunnufsen in Oslo for his continuing support and PR efforts. Special thanks to my beautiful and dearest friend Janice Arnold for her love and support, and listening to me when I needed to talk about life and my new discoveries. To my wonderful new friend Heather Garrett, who illustrated the cover of my book and created the very special "rainbow diamond". I am immensely grateful for her love and support. Thanks to Laurie Soper, my Plain Language consultant and friends who helped me on the way deal with my idiosyncrasies with the English language. I thank my sons Jonathan & Christopher for their enthusiasm and interest in my book. Jonathan gets special thanks for being my brilliant technical consultant on computer related issues. Thanks to my sisters Joanne and Mary for their support. Finally, I would like to thank my mother for being a true "Pearl", she shows her love and concern by telling me to give my brain a rest!

Contents

Initiation

I am a "Seeker of the Truth," with over twenty-five years spent searching for knowledge. The feeling was that if enough information was acquired, the truth buried deep inside, would surface to help me in times of need. So for many years I would read and put information on a mental shelf, ready for the time it would serve me. I received no instruction to do this, it was purely intuitive. There was also the idea that I had to develop myself, and so in my quest, I read many self-help books. My passion for books developed from when I was about eight years old, this is the reason why I wear glasses now, my poor eyesight was the result of always being in a dark corner, quietly reading. This pastime was my escape from a seemingly hostile world. I was, and still am, a bookworm.

My mother sent me to Sunday school at age five and for that I am forever grateful. I learnt about God and the Bible and I was an enthusiastic believer. It helped me understand mystical experiences that started when I was about ten or eleven years old. If you have read the Bible, you will know it is full of weird stuff, so my logical mind was not alarmed when strange things happened to me. At age 15, I had the odd experience of myself asking myself to go to the church youth group to deliver a message. When this occurred, my consciousness was in two places at once, but I quite clearly understood it was two parts of me. Actually, the part of me that was being asked was rather put out! I had given up on the youth group because there was too much table tennis and not enough spirituality. The youth group belonged to the Elim Pentecostal Church, one of those happy clappy churches. I was not too impressed with the level of spirituality though, nobody ever invited me to their home. Once when I was in a prayer meeting, I cried all the way through it and afterwards someone asked if I was having a problem with new contact lenses!

Anyway, the day I went back to the church youth group, there was a change of format and the church organist asked if anybody had anything to say. Answering rather boldly that I did, it was exactly 8pm when the curtain fell. When I came back, looking at the clock again, it was 8.30pm. All I remember was the church organist saying, "I think she is right!" I did wonder, "right about what!" That one experience, has made me less skeptical about people who channel, I know it can be very easy!

After a while, I started to distance myself from church teachings. I still attended church meetings because I recognized that somehow being in a spiritual environment was helpful, but at the same time there was a nagging feeling that ordinary church members were not getting the full story and I was determined not to remain ignorant. This was the real start of my earnest search for truth. Even though I have had pictures and visions and strange mystical experiences, it has never stopped me using my brain. I have an honors degree in physics and geophysics from Liverpool University in the United Kingdom. I worked in the Oil Industry for a short while, but then I ended up specializing in Mainframe Computing for about ten years. I am very analytical, so it was natural for me to support and design software systems and develop my project management skills. My background working for large organizations gave me valuable insight into politics!

In 1997, I left the United Kingdom to start a new life as an expatriate in Italy. This gave me the opportunity to travel and I am grateful for the historical and cultural experience obtained whilst visiting different countries in Europe. Italy was particularly interesting, as I had an interest in Catholicism and so it was much easier for me to continue my research there. Seeing for myself the past power of the Church etched in stone, with the accompanying trappings, allowed me to fully comprehend the influence that the religious establishment had over ordinary people. Yet, at the same time, I came across historical places and monuments that intimated to me that there were other traditions and beliefs that were seemingly only known and understood by a few.

My quest for truth continued when I moved to Norway and at some point, I noticed that things broke very easily in my hands. For years, whilst asking the Universe for my purpose in life, there was always the same response—I was a healer. Actually, this reply never impressed me at all! There was no doubt in my mind of the existence of healing energies, but I did not want anyone thinking I was a clairvoyant type. The whole concept of being a healer was a severe blow to my self-esteem. So, after I had made a collection of "china" cups with no handles, there was denial for some time. I had decided it must be a mistake, rather like the stories you hear of toasters that when switched on, broadcast radio signals!

Eventually, I came across channeled information and the Seth books by Jane Roberts, which impressed me tremendously. One of my maxims states, "I am interested in the truth and I don't care where it comes from!" Still, my logical mind thought well, this material is quite old, is there anything around of value today? I found three Kryon books written by Lee Carroll by doing a search on the internet. My reasoning was if there are three books, then that means the first two must have been OK, so I ordered them! I was particularly impressed with the messages, to the extent that I was about 99% sure the information came from a "divine" source. Yet, I needed to check it out. This would be achieved by attending a weekend seminar, taking place October 2001, in Germany. This was a momentous occasion in my life, my first EVER attendance at a New Age meeting! I had absolutely no idea what to expect, but there was a need to *feel* the energy and then I would *know* whether I was right.

At this point, I must explain that I have always believed that brain information is not enough. Hence, I have always given my brain amply opportunity to supply information, but ultimately, I like to use my intuition. My only concern about attending the Kryon seminar was that if I was wrong, then I might be in a situation of being in a big auditorium with possibly hundreds of people with "bad" energy and I was very worried about ending up on the floor. Over the years, I have learnt that I am quite sensitive to "energies", and I have simply noted the effect on me as either being "good" or "bad". These abilities have been with me for quite some time, so even though there was a possibility that this was a risky venture, I was determined to check out Lee Carroll and the rest of the entourage.

Well, what actually happened in Hamburg, Germany was quite extraordinary. Within less that an hour of attending the seminar my back was "on fire" and this was aetheric fire, yes, BIG FLAMES! The seminar had started with energy exercises where we were invited to use our hands to draw up energies from the Earth. Obviously, my sensitivity was such that being in an auditorium of over four hundred people all raising Earth energies was just a bit too much for me! At the time, I had absolutely no idea what was happening. My assessment of the weekend was that Lee Carroll and company had passed the test, but the whole weekend had been rather overshadowed by my own big mystical experience

It has to be stated that I must be every guru's nightmare, I do not conform to any of the tenets purported by those who would wish to confer spiritual wisdom. Up until that Kryon seminar, I had only been to church which I completely stopped attending when I was about 25 years old, and after that I had only read books. That's it! There had been no meditation—or what I thought at the time was meditation—to give an explanation for why I had spiritual experiences. So it was of great interest to me when I came across books by the healer/medium Betty Shine who taught that "formal" meditation was not all that safe and that if people were too rigid in their practice, it could result in the aura closing down rather than expanding. When the aura closes down, depression will ensue. She taught that "day dreaming" and readings books, was a far safer meditation and that mind energy could link up to other mind energies throughout the Universe through books. Well, now I had an explanation for my occasional strange experiences. In fact, one meditation that Betty Shine outlined was virtually identical to a "vision" I had experienced whilst reading a book. Therefore, Betty Shine managed to pass my credibility test. Again, this is something NOT taught by the typical guru, New Age or otherwise!

Anyway, after research I discovered that the back-fire, (I hope you like the pun) was caused because I had awakened Kundalini energy and this had been achieved when I made a strong energetic connection to the Earth. Kundalini is energy that normally lies dormant at the base of the spine and the whole point of many different types of spiritual practices is to awaken this particular energy resource to enable enlightenment. I now consider that my Earth connection was cut-off as a child when I learnt in Sunday school that Hell was located in the center of the Earth. Obviously, as an adult, I realized this was not true, but the energetic connection had been lost and I was not consciously aware of the need to reconnect.

I will be truthful and say there was very little interest in the Earth or Earth energies until recently. Somewhere, I had acquired the impression that spirituality was something that went on in the head by linking up with divine energies. At age 39, a strong energetic connection to Earth was made and the consequences have been life changing. With continuous study, I have been able to unlock mysteries and deepen my understanding of the world around me. By integrating a vast database of knowledge, with my spiritual experiences, this book is only a part of what I have now come to understand. When I write about Universal Energies, I do so as someone who has seen energies coming from my hands, in lines and spirals. I have seen energy as golden, or more normally, like a white mist. Hence, for me this is not hypothetical. Due to my raised Kundalini, I deliver more energy than most. My personal energy field is strong and so sometimes sensitive clients tell me they experience a sensation of fire when I energy balance. In fact, I have frightened clients away because they find it very difficult to reconcile their experience with their understanding of universal energies.

In writing this book, I have been able to integrate my knowledge with my ability to examine processes from first principles, which has been a truly rewarding experience. It must be said that theory is not truth and in this book I make a very clear distinction. I do not seek to entertain, I seek to enlighten, so this book is about providing information. With this knowledge, vast swathes of esoteric teaching, mysticism and mythology can be re-interpreted. I have spent a great deal of effort providing references that can be looked up and easily checked, yet this is not written as a document to impress academics. There are enough highly coded research papers to entertain the academic community. I have written for the majority of intelligent and educated people who want to know how electromagnetism is related to their spirituality.

It has always been my belief, that the Universe never supplies important information to just one person. Therefore, this book puts together fragmented information into a cohesive body of knowledge and attempts to make sense of processes that are very important to the evolution of humanity. I do take an historical approach. It is well understood that history can provide lessons if we are wise and can learn from them. History proves that many seekers have held the truth for decades ahead of their peers, and subsequently they were only honored at the end of their lives or even after they died. This must mean that it is quite possible to have knowledge that is completely outside of the accepted paradigm but still be perfectly legitimate. For those who prefer to be part of the mainstream, the trade-off is being "safe" but deprived.

This book is the result of my brain and heart processing a HUGE amount of information. In my analysis, I have balanced the weight of evidence with the integrity of the person making the claim. I am much more likely to believe a scientist with 20, 30, 40 years experience who has gone against the grain to promote the truth, even if that means being ostracized from the scientific community, especially when they can prove undeniably that they are right. I provide information that is gathered from true Masters and I like to honor my sources who are often themselves "Seekers of the Truth".

This book serves as an initiation because it provides knowledge that will help raise human consciousness on Earth. In the past, this kind of knowledge was only available to a few. Now we are at the dawn of a New Golden Age, there can be barriers to sacred knowledge. My hope is that this book will empower you to create a more enlightened life.

Susan Joy Rennison

Introduction

We are living in extraordinary times! Humanity is in the midst of a massive transformation, taking place on Earth, one that has been predicted by spiritual elders and holders of esoteric wisdom from many traditions. Mankind is being invited to evolve and move into a New Golden Age. This requires that we live in balance and harmony with ourselves, in our relationships and most importantly with the Earth. Evolutionary change is energy driven and this book identifies *New Energy* to be coming from the center of our Milky Way Galaxy. A powerful alignment is taking place, which is increasing the frequency of planet Earth and providing a new source of energy for individuals who choose to raise their level of consciousness. Moreover, as we approach 2012, there has been a recent dramatic shift of energies and now planet Earth is experiencing a deluge of evolutionary energies. Incredibly, digital cameras are providing solid proof to ordinary people that aetheric energy, normally invisible to the eye, is literally raining on our heads. In the form of orbs and diamonds, this highly catalytic plasma energy, is serving to drive rapid evolutionary change.

Scientists are now observing planet-wide physical changes in all the planets that make up our solar system. This is occurring in a matter of decades and sometimes in only a few years. These changes are being driven by what scientists now define as *Space Weather.* Yet, these new conditions have been long predicted and welcomed by some as *New Energy*. This has provoked a flurry of scientific investigation, with thousands of scientists involved in international efforts to understand the consequences. The Sun is going berserk and delivering vast amounts of charged particles, thus transforming the Earth, but the Sun is not the primary source, it is only a conduit of universal energies. The recent dramatic increase in solar activity quickly commanded the attention of government organizations, satellite communication manufacturers and the power supply industry. Eruptions on the Sun are equivalent to a billion one-megaton nuclear bombs. When *New Energy* arrives and slams into our magnetosphere, our technological systems are not well able to withstand the onslaught. To cope with these hostile conditions, we now have an "armada" of satellites, one million miles from Earth watching the Sun. Their function is to provide an approximate 45 minute warning to satellite controllers, who then have sufficient time to put Earth bound satellites into "safe mode", hence protecting them against "killer electrons".

With the continuing onslaught of space weather, the inevitable can no longer be ignored. The highly delicate Earth environment is not able to withstand the pressure and so governments are conceding that global climatic change is underway. Scientists tell us that geological and geophysical changes are becoming irreversible. The bizarre weather and persistent breaking of weather records is now giving cause for concern, so we find that quietly, government organizations are planning for the possibility of a global disaster. In January 2006, the Norwegian government announced that they would build a vault to store seeds in a mountainside on the island of Svalbard 1,000 km (600 miles) from the North Pole. Described as a "Noah's Ark" by the Norwegian Agriculture and Food Minister, it is anticipated that completion would be in September 2007. The idea being that if a global disaster occurred, the survivors would be able to re-seed Earth [1]. This announcement was reported in various publications and one reason given for this planning was the possibility of a complete breakdown of global electricity supplies, but no mention is given of how this would occur. Well, this book reveals that the electrical conditions in our solar system have changed and hence there is a possibility that planet Earth could get zapped by "lose wires" in space! The universe has a *live* electrical network that links everything together. Energy is connected to energy – everyone to everyone – everything to everything – every planet to every planet – every solar body to every solar body. The electrical conditions in our galaxy and solar system are changing and we could get a shock! Our governments understand that change is occurring and since they do not know what will happen, they are planning for the worst case scenario.

There are electric fields in outer-space and we find that this has been known for decades, yet the electric properties of space are not taken fully in account. This explains why astronomical discoveries are constantly described as "surprising" and "amazing" and the Big Bang theory, consistently fails to explain observations brought back to Earth via satellite images and space probes. A major pillar of Big Bang theory is that gravity rules the universe. This outdated thinking is finally losing dominance as scientists slowly realize that the universe is not electrically neutral. Simply put, it is hard to comprehend why cosmologists believe that gravity rules the universe, when the electromagnetic force is 10^{39} times (a thousand billion, billion, billion, billion times) more powerful! Plasma physicists and electrical engineers accept that electromagnetism is the primary driver in the universe and they can explain how energy is delivered around by the cosmic web of electric power lines in space.

To understand how the universe really works, *Tuning the Diamonds: Electromagnetism and Spiritual Evolution,* highlights shifting scientific opinion. Scientists have come to believe that Einstein's relativity is flawed and that String

Theory, for years hailed as the most sophisticated predictive model ever developed by modern science, is now a failure. As humanity faces evolutionary challenge, we can choose to no longer listen to those scientists who can only offer abstract mathematics and no real answers. The changes that are happening on Earth are real, hence we need explanations that can be backed up with hard facts. The science of plasma physics explains the true nature of our universe and can provide many answers to astronomical enigmas. The Sun is just a huge mass of plasma, which is matter that exists in the most fundamental state of electrically charged particles. The ability to demonstrate plasma events, with laboratory experiments and supercomputer simulation, means that we can return to the true scientific tradition where predictions, observations and validations serve to enlighten. Mayan Elders predicted a new era dominated by space and the arrival of a "Serpent Rope". Now, with our modern day understanding of the behavior of plasma, we can now understand these old prophecies. These Mayan prophecies are now fulfilled with the arrival of space weather and a new space weather feature called, "The Equatorial Electrojet". A "huge" snake-like electrical current of millions of ampéres, currently dancing around the Earth's equator.

The Earth is undergoing transformation and Russian scientists tell us that the Earth's frequency which creates electromagnetic grid lines, commonly referred to as "ley lines" has changed in recent years. When we examine the overall shape of these grid lines, we find crystal-like geometry and a diamond! Geophysicists tell us the Earth's magnetic field appears to be in the process of reversing, but they cannot predict when a full flip will occur. On examination, it appears that the Earth's magnetism is still a mystery. Scientists are not certain how the Earth obtained its magnetic field in the first place and what exactly maintains the field we have now. Yet, if we take a closer look at the Earth's core, where the Earth's magnetic field originates, we get another surprise. The data suggests that the inner core is crystalline, just like one large diamond crystal, about the size of our moon!

There have been many amazing discoveries in space. One enigma is that galaxies are distributed in a diamond lattice formation! These discoveries reveal that geometry is fundamental to how the universe is organized and understanding the true state of the universe will help us understand the true nature of the human being. Diamond geometry is the signature of universal consciousness and it can be found at all levels from the truly macroscopic to the microscopic. Diamond geometry can even be found in the human energy field and its importance is highlighted in this book.

The true nature of our reality is now apparent. Physicists verify the presence of an underlying sea of electromagnetic energy, of almost inconceivable magnitude. The invisible aether was once widely believed to exist by mystics and scientists, but was largely discredited by one flawed experiment. Today the aether has now attained mainstream scientific acceptance by being passed off under the guise of zero-point energy! The new name was derived because there is always some energy in the background, even at absolute zero temperature, a constant fluctuation of energetic particles that appear and disappear. NASA is now seriously investigating this infinite supply of energy, as a possible power source for spacecraft.

Today, technology has reached places that only mystics have gone before. The magic eye of electrodes can detect frequencies only previously seen by the gifted and so now the human energy field has been detected and verified by science. Healing energies can be explained in scientific terms, but this requires that we understand the interplay of electromagnetic forces that make-up our reality. Again, scientists admit that humans must have the ability to interact with other realms of reality and now only the uneducated claim Extra Sensory Perception (ESP) is the domain of gypsies and fortune-tellers. Now, armchair techniques have been developed by military organizations and are employed for the practical purpose of ESPionage! Bolstered by their success, the United States military are now publicly investigating teleportation and have enthusiastically endorsed the power of yogis as real!

The evolutionary push encourages us to become more multi-dimensional. This concept is examined in the light of our current understanding of multi-dimensional realities, encapsulated within our modern scientific theories such as String Theory. The controversial book *The Da Vinci Code* by Dan Brown has recently introduced many to the concept that there is esoteric knowledge, preserved for many thousands of years, carefully blended into the background of culture and science. In the metaphysical world, it is understood that in the *New Energy* there can be no secrets. For the sake of humanity, those secrets are now being revealed in order to help us evolve in a gracious way. In this regard, *Tuning the Diamonds: Electromagnetism and Spiritual Evolution* introduces the science associated with "Sacred geometry". Here, the main focus is the octahedron, which can be described as two square based pyramids back to back, represented in two dimensions by the diamond shape. The unique properties of the octahedron are examined and the connection with universal consciousness is explored.

As the electromagnetic grid of planet Earth has changed, metaphysical tradition suggests that we will have to follow suit. Thus, as the presence of *New Energy* gets stronger on Earth, humans will have to maintain balance, when we talk about balance, we are referring to mental and emotional health as well as motor, sensory and intellectual capabilities. This is achieved by strengthening our core energy and energy field, whilst activating a specific diamond shaped layer of light held in our personal energy field. The relevance here is that space weather is delivering energy that we can use—if we are correctly "wired". When we take on a greater electromagnetic charge, it will also provide us with self-empowerment.

Russians scientists have been exploring the mystery of The Great Pyramid, placed in the geographical center of the world. Extensive research has satisfied them that the ancient Egyptians understood the need for balanced electromagnetic forces. Consequently, the Russians have been building massive pyramids for over 15 years and Egyptian techniques are being revived to prevent cancer in humans. They believe the balancing influence of these pyramids will benefit the whole world. My research suggests that The Great Pyramid was originally designed as a machine to provide balanced energies on Earth. At this time of accelerated change, the people of higher consciousness must provide the same balancing role intended by the builders of the Great Pyramid. We can use our consciousness to program the core of Earth and in doing so, lessen the climatic and geophysical upheaval that is a necessary part of change. We can take more responsibility and start *Tuning the Diamonds.*

Susan Joy Rennison

Tuning the Diamonds: A Study Guide

Tuning the Diamonds: Electromagnetism and Spiritual Evolution is defined as a "A Study Guide" and will be most useful for teachers. Hence, the material is presented in such a way that the book is easiest to follow for the majority of readers. Many concepts are introduced, but readers may have different levels of background knowledge and this has been taken into account. Hence, there are text boxes with additional information that can be ignored if the subject is already well understood. If there are technical words in the text, which do not have an immediate description, or more clarification is required, then the reader is directed to the glossary at the end of the book where definitions can be found. Small sections that are more technical have been denoted with the following symbols ✧❖◆❖✧ to signify that they can be skipped over by the less scientifically minded, with the intention that these sections can be re-read at a later time. Occasionally, details that are not pertinent to the discussion are supplied in the chapter notes and readers who want to study are encouraged to follow up subjects of interest. It is also important to point out that electromagnetism is an area of science that is poorly understood, so sources of information can vary tremendously. Hence, the sources provided in this book have been vetted for their credibility even if they are not deemed as mainstream.

Chapter One

The Electromagnetic Universe

"There is a highly catalytic energy coming from deep space, which is striking the Great Central Sun (of your galaxy) and the Sun of your solar system... This deep-space energy that is affecting both the Sun and your Earth is essentially an energy of accelerating self-awareness and spiritual evolution."
Tom Kenyon, Shaman

Space Weather: The Arrival of Evolutionary New Energy

In March 1989, our modern technological world was given a major initiation, thereafter called The Great Magnetic Storm. Space weather researchers watched in amazement as a massive sunspot developed over two days and finally measured *54 times* the size of the Earth. This sunspot region was the most complex – both magnetically and structurally – that any of these scientists had ever seen [1]. On March 6, when the sunspot exploded, X-rays travelling at the speed of light reached Earth in 8 minutes and 20 seconds. Chaos ensued. The sunspot generated 195 solar flares, 11 of them classified as the most intense "X-class." The stream of radiation from the initial explosion lasted 10 hours where 30 minutes is considered the norm. Under those conditions, the magnetosphere, the cosmic shield made up of trapped radiation protecting us from the Sun's harmful rays, was put under enormous strain. As energetic particles rained down from the Sun, the magnetosphere was squashed to less than half its normal size. On Earth the sky turned red and in parts of the world it was like night turning to day. The geomagnetic storm raged for 13 days and wrought havoc to sensitive electronic equipment.

During this historic event, military and commercial satellite communications failed and some dropped out of their normal orbit. The U.S. Air Force Space Command lost 1,300 of 8,000 orbiting objects it was tracking in space [2]. The Global Positioning System (GPS) gave erroneous information, power surges burned out generators and caused blackouts, power plants shut down, oil platforms stopped drilling, as compasses became unreliable. Anything that could carry an electric current such as transmission lines, railway lines, pipelines and cables induced ground potentials and currents causing further problems. The cost to repair the damage ran into billions of dollars. The polar aurora electrojet was pushed down over North America and reports of the aurora came in from brightly-lit skies in Portugal, Spain, The Netherlands, Britain and Hungary. In the Southern Hemisphere, the aurora australis was seen in New Zealand, Australia and South Africa. Mystified observers saw the aurora in Mexico, Cayman Islands, Honduras and Cuba. The world had received a major initiation.

In general, scientists calculate that the biggest solar flares are equivalent to a billion one-megaton nuclear bombs. When they occur, the initial explosion sends radiation to Earth in just over 8 minutes, then hours later, clouds of charged particles engulf the planet. If the magnetic field of a storm is oriented opposite to our planet's protective magnetic field, gaps are created and radiation leaks to the planet's surface. This has the potential of threatening astronauts aboard the International Space Station, shorting out satellites, and even causing terrestrial power grids to trip. In addition to the solar flares, there can be companion coronal mass ejections (CMEs), which shoot megatons of plasma (electrified particles) into space. CMEs occur when the entire surface of the Sun just lifts off and explodes into space, normally reaching Earth three or four days after the initial solar eruption. Highly energized particles from CMEs disrupt satellite signals and power grids, sometimes for hours or days at a time. Storms from the Sun are nothing new, but scientists are mystified because compared to historic records, the energy coming from the Sun has been different. At the University of Maryland, a team of researchers published a paper in January 1999 detailing the unusual composition of the May 2-3 1998 coronal mass ejection [3].

The Solar and Heliospheric Observatory (SOHO) spacecraft launched in December 1995, is a joint project of the European Space Agency (ESA) and the

National Aeronautics and Space Administration (NASA), which seeks to understand the fundamental processes of the Sun–Earth connection. This mission has been highly successful and some of the SOHO images taken of the Sun over the last few years have been spectacular, but they have also raised many questions. One particular enigmatic image forces us to wonder and ask:

> **How do solar physicists explain the highly unusual coronal mass ejection that is clearly helical and looks like DNA?** [4]

There have been attempts to explain this particular unusual CME occurrence, see plate 1. Some scientists have given vague suggestions that the "twist" was caused by magnetic variations generated from the fusion furnace at the Sun's core [5]. Another explanation comes from The Millennium Group (TMG), a group of independent scientists. They claim that two comets virtually simultaneously hit the Sun and they provide SOHO satellite images as evidence [6]. Regardless of how this event occurred, the spiral is a universal symbol throughout the world for ancient wisdom and the process of initiation.

On July 14 2000 (Bastille Day), a monstrous full "halo" CME detonated from the Sun at nearly 1,800km per second, (4 million miles per hour) [7]. There was a full assault on Earth orbiting spacecraft, and the Earth's magnetosphere was hit 26 hours later with three shock waves that arrived twice as fast as expected. There were of course many satellite casualties, but this time space weather forecasters had issued warnings and alerts to industry to mitigate the damage on Earth. These increasingly furious blasts from the Sun are now categorized as *Space Weather* and the technological impact on communication systems and the power supply industry has become a major concern.

Every Planet in our Solar System is Undergoing Transformation

Every single planet in our solar system has undergone massive change in the last few decades and there are a few reports that suggest ALL the planets are undergoing "Global Warming" [8]. Here are the highlights:

- Mercury: "Surprise" polar ice discovered, along with an "anomalous" strong intrinsic magnetic field – for a supposedly "dead" planet.
- Venus: Oxygen formation, 2500% increase in auroral brightness, and substantive global atmospheric changes in less than 30 years.
- Earth: Substantial and obvious worldwide weather and geophysical changes. A new electrojet and the magnetic field weakening in parts of the world at an "alarming" rate. There is new nitrogen in upper atmosphere and two

unexpected populations of cosmic particles found in the Van Allen radiation belts. The Earth's atmosphere is now emitting gamma ray bursts into space!

- Mars: Doubling of atmospheric density, "global warming", polar melting of ice caps, new appearance of planet-wide storms.
- Jupiter: Magnetic field intensity doubling and appearance of a "dark" spot. Over 200% increase in brightness of surrounding plasma clouds.
- Saturn: Saturn's famous ring spokes periodically disappear! 1000% increase in plasma toroidal field. Major decrease in equatorial jet stream velocities in only ~20 years, accompanied by a surprising surge of X-rays from the equator.
- Uranus: Massive growth of magnetosphere intensity. Vast increase of clouds and global cloud activity. Enormous changes in Uranian brightness. Magnetic polar shift.
- Neptune: 40% increase in atmospheric brightness and light spot dynamics in just several years. Magnetic polar shift.
- Pluto: 300% increase in atmospheric pressure and "global warming", even as it recedes farther from the Sun.

More and more scientists now debunk the commonly held views of the cause of global warming and the correlation has been made between increased levels of high-energy cosmic rays and climate change. Prominent scientist, Professor Jan Veizer, a geologist and paleoclimatologist from the University of Ottawa (now retired) and Nir Shaviv, an astrophysicist at the Hebrew University of Jerusalem, conducted an extensive study. Their 2003 report states:

> "Independent empirical evidence suggests that the galactic cosmic ray flux (CRF) is linked to climate variability." [9]

The data shows that when the Earth periodically experiences swings in temperature, violent weather and precipitation, at least 66 per cent of this "is likely due to solar system passages through the spiral arms of the galaxy." [9] Dr. Svensmark from the Solar-Terrestrial Physics Division, Danish Meteorological Institute, believes it is the interaction of the solar wind, a wave of charged particles from the sun and cosmic rays that determines the Earth's climate. These findings are in line with the views of a growing number of scientists, including those who have influential positions at many of the world's most prestigious scientific institutions [10]. The evidence suggests that all the warming Earth has experienced in the past 150 years, can be traced back to solar and cosmic factors and that human activity is not the sole cause of global warming.

In 1997, Dr. Alexey Dmitriev published a paper entitled *Planetophysical State of the Earth and Life*, which in 1998 was updated and translated into English, see Appendix I [11]. Dmitriev has impressive credentials as professor of geology and mineralogy, and he is the chief scientific member, at the Siberian department of the Russian Academy of Sciences. He is an expert on global ecology, and fast–processing Earth events. This highly informative paper tells us that: "Geological, geophysical and climatical alternations of the Earth are becoming more and more irreversible". Furthermore, it announced "high speed transformations" that are being caused by:

> "Highly charged material... which have broken into the interplanetary area of our Solar system. This "donation" of energy is producing hybrid processes and excited energy states in all planets, as well as the Sun."

We are informed that there is, "a general reorganization of the electro-magnetosphere (the electromagnetic skeleton) of our planet" and the report goes on to say in a rather prophetic manner:

> **"Each living representative on Earth will be getting a thorough "examination" or "quality control inspection" to determine it's ability to comply with these new conditions**. These evolutionary challenges always require effort, or endurance... It is not only the climate that is becoming new, but we as human beings are experiencing a global change in the vital processes of living organisms, or life itself." *[Bold added for emphasis]*

In conclusion, the paper makes some rather remarkable statements, indicating that human beings can directly influence and even lessen catastrophic events, associated with the transformation of Earth.

> "Our planet Earth is now in the process of a dramatic transformation; by altering the electromagnetic skeleton through a shift of the geomagnetic field poles, and through compositional changes in the ozone, and hydrogen, saturation levels of its gas-plasma envelopes. These changes in the Earth's physical state are being accompanied by resultant climatic/atmospheric, and biospheric, adaptation processes. These processes are becoming more and more intense, and frequent, as evidenced by the real time increase in "non-periodic transient events"; i.e., catastrophes. **There are reasons favoring, or pointing to, the fact that a growth in the ethical, or spiritual quality, of humanity would decrease the number and intensity of complex catastrophes."** *[Bold added for emphasis]*

Dmitriev is not alone in his assessment. Russian specialists in climatology, geophysics, planetophysics, and heliophysics all cite a cosmic cause for what is happening. The comment about the need for the evolution of humanity to spare the Earth from the worst catastrophe, is indeed the main aim of this book to explain. This report gives us fascinating detail into how the Earth is being reorganized, and this will be discussed at the end of the next chapter.

The beginning of this chapter highlighted the increased level of solar activity and the new phenomena of space weather. As a consequence, there is a transformation of our planet and solar system of genesis-like magnitude underway. The remainder of this chapter is devoted to explaining *The Electromagnetic Universe* and plasma – energy that exists in the most fundamental state of matter. Basic knowledge of how the universe works, is key to understanding what is happening to the Sun, our principal source of universal energies. Once the necessary background information is acquired, it will be far easier to appreciate how catalytic energy is being delivered to Earth and why there is change underway in our personal electromagnetic fields. Human beings are inextricably connected to the electromagnetic environment of Earth, our solar system and our galaxy. An appreciation of plasma physics will give new insights into many disciplines of science, history, and metaphysics and will unlock mysteries that have been existence for thousands of years.

Electrical Engineers Love Astronomy!

This is not well known, but there is a quiet revolution, taking place in astronomy. Progress is such that traditional astronomers privately worry their scientific field will be taken over by electrical engineers! [12] This has been going on for a few decades now, but with the latest technology in the form of artificial satellites, space probes and powerful telescopes, traditionalists are getting a shock, literally! The evidence points to the universe being electrically *alive* and what is being observed can only be explained in terms of matter, in the highly energetic state of plasma. Some scientists have coined the phrase, *The Plasma Universe*, to reflect the discovery that in volume, 99.9% of all the observable matter in the universe exists in the plasma state. In recognition of the contribution of plasma science to cosmology, the Institute of Electrical and Electronics Engineers (IEEE), the world's largest scientific and technical society, announced that it would recognize Plasma Cosmology as an official discipline in science, (see figure 1.1 for the official IEEE logo) [13]. The reason for this is simple. Electrical engineers and physicists, who have studied the behavior of plasmas in the laboratory since the beginning of the twentieth century, are applying their expertise to the behavior of plasma seen beyond Earth. With the scalability of plasma events, laboratory experiments and supercomputer simulation, plasma specialists can replicate stellar and galactic evolution, including many enigmatic formations only recently discovered in deep space.

Figure 1.1 The official logo of the Institute of Electronics and Electrical Engineers (IEEE). The arrow represents an electrical current and the associated magnetic field is shown as an anti-clockwise swirl created by that current. Note that a diamond antenna surrounds the emblem, which is an excellent emitter of electromagnetic radiation.

In 1979, Anthony Peratt a highly respected senior plasma scientist at Los Alamos National Laboratory, was the first to accurately match observations of ordinary and radio galaxies with computer simulations, modeling the evolution of galactic structures under the influence of electric currents [14]. Laboratory experiments confirm that the same phenomena can be applied to currents from micro to mega-amperes – a range of a trillion-fold. Hence, the same basic patterns will be seen at laboratory, planetary, stellar, and galactic levels.

It is argued that a spark that lasts for microseconds in the laboratory may continue for years at planetary or stellar scales, or for millions of years at galactic or intergalactic scales.

In contrast, gravitational models do not achieve the same level of success, and often completely fail. Yet, traditional cosmologists still adhere to gravitational modeling, with principles based on Albert Einstein's theory of general relativity. As cosmologists once thought that space was an empty void, it is not part of traditional training to study how space filled with matter in the plasma state would behave, therefore they have no hope in understanding what they actually see. Hence, that is why many new astronomical discoveries are often described as "enigmatic", "puzzling", "unbelievable", "stunning", "surprising" or even "mind-boggling". Nowadays, everywhere that astronomers look, they see magnetic fields at work and electricity flowing in filaments across immense distances in space. Recently, NASA released "surprising" studies showing lightning, thousands of miles into space. Astronomers were completely "stunned" by a photograph taken with NASA's Spitzer Space Telescope, of a cosmic tornado in space that was two trillion miles long! [15] Herbig Haro objects, or 'jetted stars' are an energetic outflow, known to be associated with the formation of young stars. The exact cause of the spiraling structure is described as "mysterious" by astronomers, but plasma physicists insist that the only force known to prevent a stream of plasma from rapidly dispersing in the near vacuum of space is magnetism, and only electric currents can generate magnetic fields. At both the stellar and galactic scales, astronomers are seeing features that defy their understanding of the Universe, that they believe is ruled by gravity, but these wonders can be easily compared to plasma discharge formations seen in the laboratory [16]. Moreover, these same discoveries can be predictable if the true nature of the Universe is understood. Shifts in scientific opinion always start with ideas that were once thought heretical and impossible, and so maybe it is not surprising to find that electric and plasma based theories of the cosmos have been around for a century. We will review the influence of two great Scandinavian pioneers whose contributions are only now being fully recognized.

(Here small sections denoted with ✧❖◆❖✧ provide slightly more technical details and can be skipped over by the less scientifically minded.)

Kristian Birkeland and The Early History of Plasma Physics

The founder of experimental astrophysics and the grandfather of plasma physics is the great Norwegian scientist Kristian Olaf Bernhard Birkeland, (1867-1917). He was a Professor at Oslo University at 31 and contributed many achievements in technology and applied physics and today in Norway, Birkeland's image adorns the front of the 200 Kroner note. Below we see an image that captures one of Birkeland's most famous experiments, Birkeland's terrella, or "little Earth". This experiment produced artificial northern lights using a magnetized metal globe to represent the Earth, see figure 1.2.

Figure 1.2 Kristian Birkeland works in his laboratory to simulate the aurora by shooting beams of electrons at his terrella or "little Earth". Photo from *The Norwegian Aurora Polaris Expedition*, 1902-1903, by Birkeland, published in Christiana, Norway in 1908.

At the end of the nineteenth century, Birkeland had laid out a compelling case – supported by theory, laboratory experiments, polar expeditions, and a chain of magnetic-field observatories around the world – that electric currents flowing down along the Earth's magnetic field into the atmosphere were the cause of the aurora and polar magnetic disturbances [17]. Birkeland demonstrated that when plasma escapes from the Sun and travels through space, the Earth's magnetic field compresses it on the daylight side of the Earth and stretches it into a tail on the night side, ultimately producing the northern lights, see figure 3.3. Birkeland explained the auroras as "pencils of cathode rays from the Sun", namely plasma. Actually, Nobel laureate Irving Langmuir first coined the term "plasma" in the early 20th century, when he studied electric plasmas in his laboratory following on from Birkeland's work.

> **The term "plasma" was chosen because it acted as if it were *alive*. These ionized gas clouds had self-organizing behavior in the presence of electrical currents and magnetic fields.**

Birkeland also discovered the twisted corkscrew shaped paths taken by electric currents when they exist in plasmas. The strength of the current being carried by the plasma determines whether these twisted shapes are visible or not. Today, these streams of ions and electrons are called "Birkeland Currents" and they are associated with a host of electrical phenomena in the plasma of our upper atmosphere. Birkeland believed that the electromagnetic influence of the Sun on near and distant space was as important as that of gravity. In an act of brilliance, he took the laws of electric and magnetic forces derived by Maxwell in the 19th century and applied them to space. It was a breakthrough in the understanding of the forces at work in the solar system. Some of his observations and theories have taken nearly a century to be verified! Birkeland was totally vindicated in 1966, when a US Navy satellite observed magnetic disturbances on nearly every pass over the polar regions [18]. Today, his understanding that the same charged particles that cause magnetic storms also cause the Northern and Southern Lights is fully accepted. The following quote shows us the depth of Birkeland's insight into the electrical nature of the Universe:

> "According to our manner of looking at the matter, every star in the universe would be the seat and field of activity of electric forces of a strength that no one could imagine. We have no certain opinion as to how the assumed enormous electric currents with enormous tension are produced, but it is certainly not in accordance with the principles we employ in technics on the Earth at the present time. One may well believe, however, that a knowledge in the future of the electrotechnics of the heavens would be of great practical value to our electrical engineers. It seems to be a natural consequence of our points of view to assume that the whole of space is filled with electrons and flying electric ions of all kinds. We have assumed that each stellar system in

> evolutions throws off electric corpuscles into space. It does not seem unreasonable therefore to think that the greater part of the material masses in the universe is found, not in the solar systems or nebulae, but in *empty* space." *K Birkeland, Norwegian Aurora Polaris Expedition 1902-1903* [19]

It is over one hundred years since the great Norwegian scientist Kristian Birkeland claimed that electromagnetic forces played a role as important as gravity in near and more distant regions of space. Today, the physics of plasmas and electromagnetic forces introduced by Birkeland have finally emerged to prominence and are challenging how astronomers view the cosmic environment. Space satellites show indisputable evidence supporting Birkeland's ideas of a flow of electric particles (plasma) from the Sun. A flow of electric particles is simply an electric current and when they occur in space, they are called Birkeland currents, named after Kristian Birkeland who first suggested their existence.

In 1962, NASA's Mariner II spacecraft on its way to Venus, recorded the presence of particles travelling through the space at speeds ranging from 300 to 700 kilometers *a second*. The Soviet Lunik 2 spacecraft had previously observed this phenomenon on its way to the moon, but western scientists arrogantly dismissed the Soviet data as unreliable. After Mariner, other craft were launched into space and soon it was acknowledged that "empty space" was not empty at all! Rather, there is a million-degree Celsius plasma blowing off the Sun at 1.5 million and even up to 3 million kilometers per hour through the solar system, now euphemistically called the solar wind! [20] Furthermore, evidence of these currents was found in 1979, when the Voyager spacecraft recorded enormous Birkeland currents connecting Jupiter and its moon Io. Again, Saturn is one of the planets in our solar system known for its beautiful rings. Yet, astronomers cannot explain why some of the rings are twisted! After decades of study, we still have these headlines which read, "Ring Riddles Baffle Saturn Scientists!" [21] The blatant ignorance of the electrical nature of space was exposed when Birkeland currents associated with Venus were described as "stringy things" [22]. The SOHO project partly sponsored by NASA, revealed that Venus has a tail which stretches some 45 million kilometers into space. This enigma has since been found repeated for comet Hyakutake, with its tail stretching half a billion kilometers across the solar system! Just imagine "electrified bare wires", whipping around lose in space! A New Scientist article stated:

> "Standard physics says that narrow plasma streams are unstable and should dissipate fast. No one can yet explain how they hold together over tens of millions of kilometers." [22]

Birkeland failed to be awarded a Nobel Prize in chemistry in recognition of contributions to science. Birkeland was sabotaged by the scheming of his politically influential business partner, Sam Eyde who was not a scientist, yet he still tried to get a joint nomination to establish his own credibility. The Swedish Nobel Prize committee would not permit a non-scientist to receive an award and so, for the sake of maintaining friendly relations between the two Scandinavian countries, the idea of giving Birkeland the Prize was quietly dropped.

Hannes Alfvén – Nobel Prize Winner and Heretic

"It is only the plasma that does not 'understand' how beautiful the theories are and absolutely refuses to obey them."
Hannes Alfvén, Nobel Lecture, 1970

The second great pioneer in the relatively unglamorous world of plasma physics is the Swedish Hannes Alfvén (1908-1995), winner of the 1970 Nobel Prize in Physics. Due to his many original ideas, Alfvén was regarded as a heretic by many physicists [23]. He made important contributions to astrophysics too, and his hypothesis formed in 1937 of a galactic magnetic field, forms the basis today for one of the fastest growing areas of research in astrophysics – Cosmic Magnetism. Most of Alfvén's theories in astrophysics and plasma physics only gained acceptance two or three decades after their publication. Much disputed, many of his theories about the solar system were only vindicated as late as the 1980s through measurements of cometary and planetary magnetospheres by artificial satellites and space probes.

Alfvén suggested that the galaxy contained a large-scale magnetic field and that cosmic rays moved in spiral orbits within the galaxy, owing to the forces exerted by the magnetic field. This novel idea was criticized for being too intuitive and not grounded in enough rational thought. Moreover, his theory was dismissed on the grounds that interstellar space was known to be a vacuum and that it certainly could not support the electrical currents and particle beams he was proposing. This viewpoint was widely accepted because space *looked* that way, being viewed using telescopes at optical wavelengths [24]. The electrical currents proposed by Alfvén could only be detected in the radio portions of the electromagnetic spectrum, so they could not be observed with the then existing instrumentation, hence the skepticism that electric currents existed in space. Alfvén still argued his case by stating that there could still be a pervading magnetic field if plasma was spread throughout the entire galaxy. This plasma could carry the electrical currents and create the galactic magnetic field. Alfvén's theories did start the scientific community thinking and so his ideas eventually became more accepted in the 1980s and 1990s. Yet, despite the skepticism amongst astronomers, we know this property of space was acknowledged at the highest level, as we find that in 1981, there was a report written for the Pentagon called *Electric Fields in Earth Orbital Space* [25]. This research is ongoing and in July 2006, NASA announced the award of space weather related contracts, to investigate "Electric Fields in Space."

Alfvén also proposed a new form of electromagnetic wave that could propagate in a perfect conductor with no attenuation or reflection. The attributes of Magnetohydrodynamic (MHD) waves, were described in his book *The New Astronomy* (1948), after they were discovered in mercury experiments. Today these waves are now known as Alfvén waves, and have three characteristics; they produce (1) mechanical motion, (2) a magnetic field, and (3) an electric field. Scientists had always assumed that the movement of gases in stars obeyed the laws of hydrodynamics, as they apply to ordinary liquids and gases. Based on his mercury experiments, Alfvén realized that a magnetic field would drastically change the properties of dense stellar gases, implying that the current models of stellar behavior required serious revision.

Alfvén also challenged the views of Sydney Chapman, the acknowledged leader in interplanetary and magnetospheric physics after the death of Birkeland. Chapman proposed, in opposition to Birkeland's ideas, that currents were restricted to flow only in the ionosphere of Earth, with no down flowing currents. His theories were mathematically "elegant" and so gained wide acceptance over Birkeland's theory. Alfvén, who became involved well after Chapman's ideas gained predominance, kept insisting that Birkeland's current system made more sense because down flowing currents following the Earth's magnetic field lines were required to drive most of the ionospheric currents. The issue was not settled until 1974, four years after Chapman's death, when Earth satellites measured down flowing currents for the first time.

"When a true genius appears, you can know him by this sign:
that all the dunces are in a confederacy against him."
Jonathan Swift

Obviously, when you disagree with the prevailing view, the peer review system seems a waste of time. Alfvén always had trouble, especially with Anglo-American astrophysical journals, but he never had any difficulty publishing with the Soviet versions! In retrospect, it is possible to explain the reason why Alfvén had difficulty getting his work accepted. Alfvén was an electrical power engineer and as such was considered an unwanted outsider. For 30 years, Alfvén and his colleagues proposed an alternative cosmology, based on plasma physics, to both the Steady State and the Big Bang cosmologies. The Big Bang theory is rapidly losing credibility due to the numerous contradictions between observation and theory, especially over the last decade. In particular, the discovery of coherent structures of galaxies hundreds of millions of light years in length and the large-scale streaming of superclusters of galaxies at velocities that may approach 1,000 kilometers per second, these present anomalies are difficult, if not impossible, to reconcile with the Big Bang theory. To Alfvén, the issues raised were not surprising and he is quoted as saying, "I have never thought that you could obtain the extremely clumpy, heterogeneous universe we have today, strongly affected by plasma processes, from the smooth, homogeneous one of the Big Bang, dominated by gravitation." In 1970, Alfvén used the occasion of his Nobel Prize acceptance speech to admonish the astronomical community for treating plasma in a way he had subsequently shown to be mistaken. He said:

> "The cosmical plasma physics... is to some extent the playground of theoreticians who have never seen a plasma in a laboratory. Many of them still believe in formulas we know from laboratory experiments to be wrong. The astrophysical... crisis has not yet come" [26].

Maybe, we can take this as a warning from a visionary, that not understanding how plasmas behave could have dire consequences.

The Electric Power Lines in Space

"Jehovih rolleth up the heavens, and braideth the serpents of the firmament into His cyclic coil."
Oahspe, A Kosmon Bible [27]

The universe is not "empty", it is made up of energy in the *fourth state of matter*. The first three states of matter are solid, liquid, and gas, which occur when plasma is cooled to make atoms and molecules. The fourth state of matter is composed of the basic building blocks, electrically charged particles of ions and electrons. Plasma exhibits characteristics not found in solids, liquids, or gases, and so it has also been called the *fundamental state of matter*. Electric currents in plasma form filaments that attract each other at long distances and repel each other at short distances. These filaments tend to braid themselves into "ropes" that act as power transmission lines, with virtually no limit to the distances over which they can operate, see figure 1.3. For an actual example in space, the Cygnus Loop is thought to be a middle-aged remnant of a nearby supernova. However, it shows all the intricacy of twisted Birkeland currents with characteristics that support an Electric Universe interpretation, thus providing the definitive example of cosmic string in space! See plate 2 [28]. Plasma studies reveal that there are three distinct modes in which plasma can operate:

1. **Dark Current** – Very low strength electrical current (flow of charged particles) within the plasma. As the plasma does not glow, it is essentially invisible. We would not know plasma was there at all unless we measured its electrical activity with sensitive instruments. The present day magnetospheres of the planets are examples of plasmas operating in the dark current mode.

2. **Normal Glow** – Significant strength of the electrical current (flow of charged particles). The entire plasma glows, with the brightness dependent on the intensity of the current in the plasma. Examples being any neon sign, emission nebulae, the Sun's corona.

3. **Arc** – High strength electrical current in the plasma, with the plasma radiating brilliantly over a wide spectrum. Current tends to form twisting filaments. Examples being an electric arc welding machine, lightning, and the Sun's photosphere.

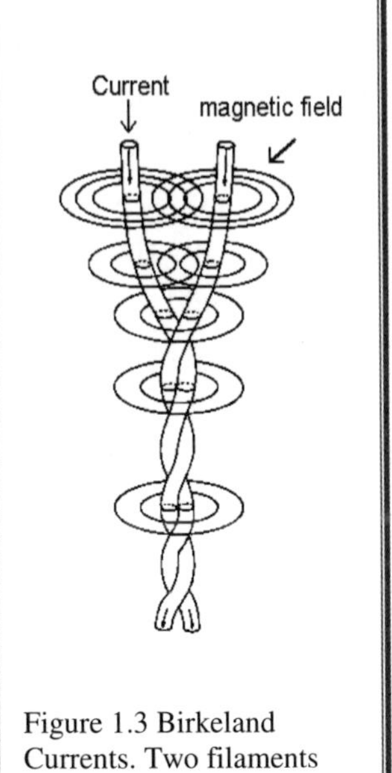

Figure 1.3 Birkeland Currents. Two filaments have been twisted into a single large filament. Credit: Unknown

Universal Energy is self-directing and self-regulating

One of the most important properties of any electrical plasma is its ability to "self-organize"– that is, to electrically isolate one section of itself from another. The (electrically) isolating wall between the two halves/parts of the plasma is called a double layer (DL). No electrostatic force is felt by particles on one side of the DL, due to charges on the other side. The total electric current, however, is the same throughout the plasma. Plasmas form double layers between regions of different densities, temperatures or magnetic field strengths. The signature of electromagnetic forces at work is called "doubleness". Wherever there are multiple strands of electric currents, they prefer to interact in pairs. The reason for this derives from Ampére's Law or the Biot-Savart Force Law which both state that currents in the same direction attract while currents in the opposite direction repel, they do so inversely as the distance between them. This results in a far larger ranging force of interaction than, say, the gravitational forces between two masses. This doubleness phenomena is observed in the laboratory when very high currents, passing through a plasma, explode into electrical discharges called "pinches" that often interact in pairs. There is a tendency for these pairs to compress between them any material (ionized or not) in the plasma. This is called the "z-pinch" effect. When the electric current is strong enough, the plasma formed by these discharges, electromagnetically "pinches" into a string of "sausages", "donuts" and plasma instabilities. The z-pinch effect explains "enigmatic" supernova structure and planetary nebula, see plates 3 & 4. Plasma scientists explain pinch filaments as vortices of current – plasma whirlwinds.

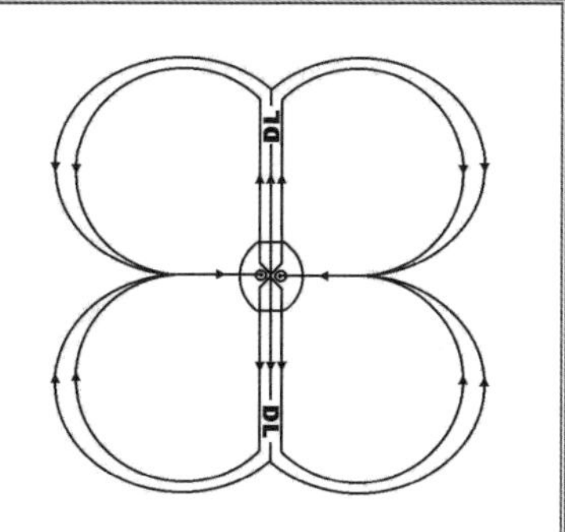

Figure 1.4 Galactic Circuit. Galaxy acting as unipolar inductor. Adapted from IEEE Transactions on Plasma Science (Vol. PS-14 No. 6). Dec. 1986

A vertical cross section of a galaxy is shown as a schematic in figure 1.4. The horizontal line at the center of the diagram represents a circular disk lying in the horizontal plane. The parallel vertical lines, (annotated as DL), along the galaxy's axis rotation represent the strong plasma current sometimes visible as jets. Double Layers (DL) within the jet plasma contain strong electric fields that are the source of radio frequency emissions, representing the typical "double radio source" that is observed in many galaxies, see figure 1.5. The plasma cosmology viewpoint presents that a galaxy spinning in the magnetic fields of intergalactic space generates electricity, as any conductor does when it moves through a magnetic field. (This is the same principal at work in any electrical generator). The huge electrical current produced by the galaxy flows in great filamentary spirals toward the center of the galaxy, where it turns and flows out along the spin axis. This galactic current then short-circuits, driving a vast amount of energy into the galactic core. The galaxy "blows a fuse" resulting in powerful electrical fields in the nucleus accelerating intense jets of electrons and ions out along the axis. The helical or braided energy shown in figure 1.5, as a vertical outburst of energy, is described by astronomers as a galactic jet [29]

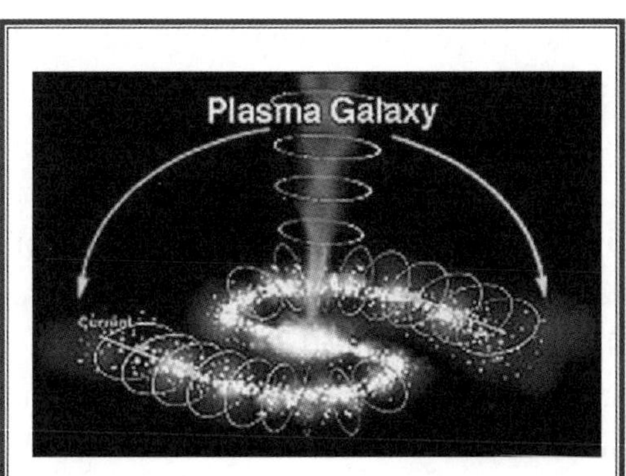

Figure 1.5 M82 Galaxy magnetic vector map. Courtesy: Holoscience.com

The Most Powerful Force in the Universe is Electromagnetic!

The universe is everything that exists, from galaxies to subatomic particles, and that includes forces and energies, as matter is exchangeable with energy as denoted by Einstein's famous equation, $E=mc^2$. Whether matter or energy can be detected by our senses or sophisticated instrumentation, the universe is everything we can perceive and more. Cosmology is the science of the origins of the Universe and this is often represented by the popular but disputed Big Bang theory, which postulates that some 12-15 billion years ago there was a suddenly expansion and explosion of all matter and energy out of an original point – out of literally nothing – and that not only space but even time began at this moment. This literally means that there was no previous space because space did not exist, there was no time at which this could be measured either – space and time are intrinsic properties of the universe rather than something absolute. Yet, the universe presents many enigmas, which cannot be explained by the generally accepted laws of physics and Big Bang theory. For example, the initial rate of expansion of the universe is calculated to be up to $3x10^{41}$ *times* the speed of light. Skeptics believe that this fantastic velocity indicates that we lack the true understanding of how the Universe really works [30].

"The Force" is Electromagnetic!

Scientists have defined that there are only four fundamental forces that rule the universe and gravity is believed to be the dominant force. Gravity is an attracting force that exists between all things with mass or energy. The electromagnetic force is associated with electrically charged particles, with oppositely charged particles attracting each other, and similarly charged particles repelling each other. The electromagnetic force binds negatively charged electrons to positively charged atomic nuclei and plays a major part in any chemical reaction, and of course, electrical and magnetic effects. The remaining two forces are the strong nuclear force, and the weak nuclear force. The latter two forces only play a role in the nuclei of atoms, where they are important for nuclear processes and radioactivity. The question arises: why do cosmologists think that gravity is the most powerful force in the universe? If we take the criteria of the effect of these forces changing with distance, the most important characteristic of electromagnetism is that it obeys the longest-range force law in the universe, see the small section, "The Laws of Attraction" [31]. Gravity is a very weak force and we can prove this with a simple experiment, where a small iron object can be lifted against gravity from the ground with a small magnet.

The Laws of Attraction

When two or more non-plasma bodies interact gravitationally, their force varies inversely as the square of the distance between them. Hence for 2 unit measurements apart the attraction is 1/4; for 3 unit measurements apart, the attraction is 1/9; for 4 unit measurements apart the attraction is 1/16 and so on. When plasma as streams of charged particles interact electromagnetically, their force law varies inversely as the distance between them. Hence for 2 unit measurements apart the attraction is 1/2; for 3 unit measurements apart the attraction is 1/3; for 4 unit measurements apart the attraction is 1/4. So at 4 unit measurements apart, the electromagnetic force is 4 times greater than that of gravitation, relatively speaking, and at 100 units, apart, the electromagnetic force is 100 times that of gravitation.

This means that the magnetic force of the small magnet is stronger than the gravitational force exerted by the whole planet Earth! Cosmologists argue that gravity is the most important force at the astronomical scales, because gravity can only attract whereas the electromagnetic force can attract and repel. This argument hinges on the concept that there is a balance of positive and negative electrical charges. If this is correct, the idea suggests that the electromagnetic forces of attraction and repulsion would even out at large scales and hence play no large role in how the universe operates. This scenario translates in scientific terms as the universe being electrically neutral. It does seem a fairly large assumption, especially when we discover that the electromagnetic force is 10^{39} times (a thousand billion, billion, billion, billion times) more powerful than gravity! This means that it does not matter if the universe is balanced overall, even a small variation in the distribution of electrical charge will override gravitational affects at a local level [31].

Searching for the "Dark" Force

"Newton was unaware of plasma. Today his disciples spend years in training learning when and how to shut their eyes to it. It's not just the Big Bang, General Relativity, and Quantum Mechanics that are in trouble but the foundation of them all: Gravity is an exhausted and bankrupt concept."
Mel Acheson, amateur astronomer

It is no surprise that cosmologists face many problems explaining the titanic forces that are calculated to operate in the Universe, when they only consider the weak force of gravity. To illustrate this point, the beautiful Whirlpool Galaxy (M51) is typical of 70% of observed galaxies that display spiral arms, see plate 5. What interests us here, is that only about 10% of the gravity necessary to hold the spiral arms together can be accounted for by known gravitational sources. This has led to the theorizing of dark (hidden) matter of exotic and unknown form, which would be responsible for the excess gravity [32].

Gravity based models are inadequate, which means that astrophysicists are continually "surprised" by new data and are forced to "revise" their theories to maintain their validity. Astrophysicists have achieved this by creating invisible entities such as neutron stars, weakly interacting massive particles (WIMPs), strange energy, and black holes [33]. Surprised? Yes, even black holes are largely theoretical, and we find that the respected Princeton University cosmologist Jim Peebles is quoted as saying, "It's an embarrassment that the dominant forms of matter in the universe are hypothetical." In August 2001, Astronomy Magazine cynically lambasted theorist. This is a snippet:

> "What's more, astronomers have gone to great lengths to affectionately name, define, and categorize this zoo of invisible stuff called dark matter. There are the MAssive Compact Halo Objects (MACHOs) – things like ... black holes, and neutron stars that purportedly populate the outer reaches of galaxies like the Milky Way. Then there are the Weakly Interacting Massive Particles (WIMPs), which possess mass, yet don't interact with ordinary matter - baryons such as protons and neutrons – because they are composed of something entirely foreign and unknown. Dark matter even comes in two flavors, hot (HDM) and cold (CDM)....."
>
> "Astronomers and physicists have refined their dark matter theories without ever getting their hands on a single piece of it. But where is all of this dark matter? The truth is that after more than 30 years of looking for it, there's still no definitive proof that WIMPs exist or that MACHOs will ever make up more than five percent of the total reserve of missing dark stuff."

In review, electric universe theorist, Dr. Donald Scott, provided a new category for these "invisible" particles, which he described as, "Fabricated Ad hoc Inventions Repeatedly Invoked in Efforts to Defend Untenable Scientific Theories", FAIRIE DUST! Maybe, Astronomy magazine were expressing frustration at the failure of scientists to detect even a single WIMP after one year of trying! [34] The detector was developed by the Cryogenic Dark Matter Search (CDMS), by a collaboration of 10 institutions and researchers from around the world. Even five years later, it was reported in May 2004 that they still have not found any! Even with this deafening silence, undaunted astrophysicists are still making attempts to find this dark matter, and even bigger detectors are envisaged. The Times newspaper of the United Kingdom reported that, "It remains possible that the WIMP is a phantom and does not exist, although this would require a revision of many fundamental theories of physics." In response, a researcher was quoted as saying, "One tries not to worry about that."

Big Bang Warfare

"There are some ideas so wrong that only a very intelligent person could believe in them."
George Orwell

We now have a situation of "open warfare" in the astronomy community. The Australian plasma physicist Wal Thornhill puts it bluntly: "Forget the glossy astronomy books and magazines – the Big Bang is pure fiction" [35]. Critics have been seeing flaws in the Big Bang Theory for over 30 years. The famous astronomer Halton Arp, known for his classic work in *Arp's Atlas of Peculiar Galaxies*, became a modern day Galileo when he dared to contradict orthodox cosmology. For some forty years Halton Arp has been a keen observer of strange galaxies. He concluded that supposedly remote quasars (galaxies with extremely bright nuclei) are actually connected to nearby galaxies *by observable streams of plasma*. This news was not welcomed and so he was branded a heretic and exiled from academia in the USA. His downfall came about because he exposed major weakness in prevailing theory, like redshift is not an indicator of velocity, quasars are not the brightest and most remote objects in the universe but are nearby, and hence the reasoning behind redshifts and the Big Bang hypothesis immediately collapses. Arp found scientific asylum at the Max Planck Institute for Physics and Astrophysics in West Germany, but his reputation was such that he was still referred to as "the most feared astronomer on Earth" [36].

When Arp was refused telescope time and publication in standard journals, he responded by writing the books, *Quasars, Redshifts and Controversies* (1987), and *Seeing Red* (1998). This rebellion has been joined by other authors who have written titles such as *The Big Bang Never Happened (*1992) and *Bye Bye Big Bang – Hello Reality* (2002). The unorthodox are writing books, articles and setting up websites to demonstrate that something has gone wrong in the field of astronomy. Many widely held beliefs fly in the face of *observational evidence.* The Meta Research website keeps up to date "The top 30 problems with the Big Bang". The lead astronomer Tom Van Flandern states that his website "is dedicated to bringing some common sense back to this field [astronomy]" [37]. War broke out when a group of 33 "concerned" scientists signed, *An Open Letter to the Scientific Community* that was published in New Scientist, May 22, 2004 [38]. Of course, the subject of the skirmish was the Big Bang theory and the opening salvo started as follows:

> "The Big Bang today relies on a growing number of hypothetical entities, things that we have never observed – inflation, dark matter and dark energy are the most prominent examples. Without them, there would be a fatal

contradiction between the observations made by astronomers and the predictions of the Big Bang theory."

"What is more, the Big Bang theory can boast **of no quantitative predictions that have subsequently been validated by observation.** The successes claimed by the theory's supporters consist of its ability to retrospectively fit observations with a steadily increasing array of adjustable parameters, just as the old Earth-centered cosmology of Ptolemy needed layer upon layer of epicycles." *[Bold added for emphasis]*

The accusation being made is that pure mathematicians, with little or no interest in experimental science and only a passing regard for direct observation, have indulged in "a carnival of speculation" [39]. A "Crisis in Cosmology" meeting took place in Portugal, June 2005. The agenda was to highlight the inconsistencies between data and Big Bang theory. Special concern was directed at the properties of the Cosmic Microwave Background (CMB) – the so-called "echo" of the Big Bang – where theory and predictions was particularly difficult to reconcile [40]. It was reported that astrophysicists were unhappy that cosmologists have had to introduce weird concepts like dark matter and dark energy to explain the universe. Others hit back, saying that they just needed to tweak the Big Bang model and tie up "loose ends". The question is: when does the tweaking turn into a concerto, and what's more, when do we get the finale?

"The fact that an opinion has been widely held is no evidence whatever that it is not utterly absurd."
Bertrand Russell

Now that astronomers can peek into the womb of a newly forming star, they are astounded at what they see. Traditional cosmology says that stars are born by "gravitational collapse" of vast precursor clouds over great spans of time in dead cold conditions estimated at 400 degrees below zero Fahrenheit (minus 240 degrees Celsius). After millions of years, the collapse will cause the clouds to sufficiently "ignite the nuclear fusion" of a new star. Well, that's the theory, but what they actually observe is extremely high energies at work, strong enough to produce X-rays! This latest blow to orthodoxy was reported by NASA-funded research at the Goddard Space Flight Center in March 2005. The "surprise" was reported as, "The detection of X-rays this early indicates that gravity alone is not the only force shaping young stars" [41]. Investigators were watching the electrical birth of the new star R Corona Australis and they concluded, "some previously unrealized energetic process, likely related to magnetic fields, is superheating parts of the cloud, nudging it to become a star". Basic physics tells us that you cannot have a magnetic field without the electrical component, but this force is traditionally *never* considered in cosmology. Plasma physicists propose that you don't even need a cloud of hydrogen because space is nearly all plasma, all that is required is a separation of charge. A weak electric field will drive an electric current, which will create a magnetic field, the whole thing will start to feed on itself and before you know it, a star is born! The electromagnetic force is doing the work and this explains why events can occur very rapidly, "10 times faster than gravity could account for". Let's think: why would the Universe use gravity when electricity is much more efficient?

Black holes that exist at the center of many galaxies are very much in vogue, but skeptics compare this belief along with Big Bang theory, as a form of religious mania [42]. It does appear, looking at the contrary evidence, that Big Bang orthodoxy has now become a matter of faith for many scientists. In this regard, it is interesting to know that the idea was first proposed by a Belgian priest and astronomer, Abbe Georges Lemaître, in 1927, and in 1951 it even received the blessing of Pope Pius XII! What is agreed amongst astrophysicists is that there *is* evidence for the existence of highly condensed aggregates of matter which produce very strong gravitational fields. But the fact remains that what is taken to represent a black hole actually appears to be undergoing *explosive* activity rather than swallowing things up! [43] Yet, another "surprise" occurred for European astronomers when they discovered a vast "jet-powered bubble" formed in the "gas" around a black hole in the Milky Way [44]. It was reported as:

> "Remarkably, it also means that, after a massive star dies and turns into a black hole, it is still capable of energizing its surroundings, *by means of completely different mechanisms*." *[Emphasis added]*
>
> "The importance of this result is that it demonstrates that black holes such as Cygnus X-1, of which there may be millions within our galaxy alone, do not swallow all of the infalling matter and energy, but rather redirect a considerable fraction of it back into space."
>
> "We knew about jets from black holes and expected to discover some interaction of the jet's energy with the gas in our Milky Way, but the size and energy content of this bubble came as a surprise."

Skeptics believe that the public is largely being fed with speculation and propaganda. Wal Thornhill suggests that, "Without the checks and balances of experiment and direct observation of black holes, astrophysicists long ago slipped their leash" [45].

The recent observation of copious emissions of X-rays and gamma rays in space, initially puzzled conventional astronomers, but now new theories are emerging, offering this initial "surprise" as evidence of black holes. Here are the differing explanations for the recent discovery of high energy in the form of gamma rays and X-rays in space:

Plasma Electro-Dynamics – Plasma experts gloat that they can recreate the same effects in the laboratory, and they simply suggest it is the way that nature concentrates electrical power in a plasma to produce the powerful beam of gamma and particle radiation seen *coming out of* what have been described as black holes. This is a known effect and is termed the 'plasma gun' or plasma focus. This effect explains the spectacular pictures of quasar ejection from the core of active galaxies, see plate 6. These produce 'jets', with velocities of more than 99.995 per cent of the speed of light! Black holes are not needed to explain this phenomena and are dismissed as imaginary. According to Los Alamos National Laboratory a slightly more technical view would be:

> "Plasma tends to separate into regions according to temperature, density, magnetic field strength, chemical constituency, and other physical properties. Wherever these regions are in relative motion, they are coupled by electrical currents that they drive in each other. Like all electrical currents, the circuit paths are closed, sometimes over very great distances. Thus plasmas in relative motion in one part of the universe can produce prodigious amounts of electrical energy. This energy may be transferred over many billions of light years to burst suddenly from a very small and localized region representing the circuit load." [46]

Gravity Dynamics – Gamma ray emissions from black holes were a "surprise" to researchers, so at the Max Planck Institute for Astrophysics they have been busy developing new relativistic models. It is thought that the gigantic energy which powers the gamma-ray burst is caused as follows:

> "...a rapidly spinning black hole, which forms when the central core of a dying star becomes unstable and collapses under its own gravity. This newly formed black hole then swallows much of the infalling stellar matter and thereby releases enormous amounts of energy in two "jets". These expand "highly relativistically", i.e. with almost the speed of light, along the rotation axis of the star. Before they break out from the stellar surface, they have to drill their way through thick layers of stellar material, thus getting collimated into very narrow beams with an opening angle of only a few degrees." [47]

The Max Planck approach is a good example of an old idea being revamped to fit observation, which is not strictly scientific. A good theory is one where predictions can be made and the theory can be tested, if possible, by experiment and eventually validated by data and/or the predictions being observed. Anything else can be viewed with suspicion. For those who want to judge the merits of what have been called black holes, if you need a reminder, gravity is a very weak force! It would also appear from these accounts, that to fully understand the universe and universal energies, we have to understand the properties of plasma and the science of electromagnetism. Thus, a recent discovery by astronomers at the Harvard-Smithsonian Center for Astrophysics in Cambridge, Massachusetts, US, has led them to believe that black holes do not exist and are in fact "bizarre" compact balls of plasma called Magnetospheric Eternally Collapsing Objects (MECOs) [47+]. Incredibly, these scientists have come up with a scientific theory that completely negates the current paradigm and is much more closely aligned to theories associated with multi-dimensional aetheric plasma. Quasars are usually thought to be, "a bright, compact object, whose radiation is usually thought to be generated by a giant black hole devouring its surrounding matter". In July 2006, New Scientist magazine reported that scientists had probed the structure of a quasar in much finer detail than is normally possible, the report stated:

> "According to the MECO theory, objects in our universe can never actually collapse to form black holes. When an object gets very dense and hot, subatomic particles start popping in and out of existence inside it in huge numbers, producing copious amounts of radiation. Outward pressure from this radiation halts the collapse so the object remains a hot ball of plasma rather than becoming a black hole."

Finally, we are reminded to be cautious of scientific conclusions by Nobel Prize-winning chemist Irving Langmuir who coined the term *Pathological Science* [48]. This is defined as a psychological process in which a scientist, originally conforming to the scientific method unconsciously veers from that method, and begins a pathological process of wishful data interpretation. Maybe this explains why most scientists appear to be willfully ignoring the facts, regardless of the data staring them in the face. Not understanding that the electromagnetic force rules the Universe, has now reached pathological status.

The Inside Info on Cosmic Power

Since the 1980s, astronomers have been mapping the universe. They knew that galaxies are concentrated into enormous clusters, but observers also discovered that the clusters are themselves concentrated into vast sheets, or walls. In between the walls are giant voids almost free of galaxies. The size of the cosmic voids ranges from tens to hundreds of millions of light years. On these scales, the universe looks like Swiss cheese or a sponge, more hole than substance. Astronomers have since struggled to explain the origin of these observed structures and hence are starting to propose new theories to explain the precise distribution of the clusters and voids, which some refer to as "The Honeycombed Universe" [49]. Yet, there is plasma theory and so we find this explanation from Hannes Alfvén, who is quoted as saying:

> "Space is filled with a network of currents which transfer energy and momentum over large or very large distances. The currents often pinch to filamentary or surface currents. The latter are likely to give space, as also interstellar and intergalactic space, a cellular structure."
>
> "One of the notable characteristics of space plasma, revealed by satellites and space probes, is its tendency to form *sharp boundaries* between plasmas with different properties. This tendency towards "*cellular structure*" can have profound astrophysical implications such as generating electric fields in space and providing sources of energy for driving electric currents over very large distances" [50].

The computer simulation image shown in plate 7 represents the large-scale structure in the universe, known as "The Cosmic Web". Galaxies line filaments of matter like pearls on a string, and galaxy clusters arise where filaments meet. According to plasma physicists, this image is distorted because the galaxies have been placed by the computer at their redshift distances [51]. However, galaxies do form linear chains. Such structure is not expected from gravity-driven formation of the Universe, however, it is expected from plasma cosmology, where galaxies form at the intersection of two intergalactic Birkeland current filaments.

In metaphysical circles, there is much talk of *Energy,* and this is attributed to the "sea" of invisible energy that is accessible to every human. The mystic Lee Carroll, has given structure to this invisible realm he has called, "The Cosmic Lattice". We are told that this energy source can be considered the common denominator of the unified energy source of the Universe. Carroll says:

> "Everything that you can see and everything you cannot see contains The Lattice. From the smallest particles of your physics, and from the electron haze forward, the Cosmic Lattice is present."
>
> "The Cosmic Lattice is what you would call the consciousness of God, yet it is physics and it is energy and it contains conscious love." [52]
>
> "The Cosmic Lattice is now responding to something it never did before on your planet. Energy is being created and time is being altered — all through human intent. There is no greater power in the Universe than human intent and love, and we have told you this fact repeatedly…This is the night we finally have to correlate and equate it with the physics of love!"
>
> "Now you begin to understand why New Age energy facilitators can do so much! They are tapping into The Cosmic Lattice. There is no longer mystery

regarding this, instead it will be someday… replaced with good solid science... God given, and Universal."

"I will not be the only channel to bring forth this principle, and it will be known by many names, and will be the source of tremendous power—actual physical power—power that you can use for travel and energy... power that you can use for life sustenance… There is no cleaner power anywhere than the lattice. This is physics, and it is known even by the enlightened that travel from here to there within the cosmos... **in fact they often "ride" the lattice strings**."

"We brought you the concept years ago of The Cosmic Lattice. I want you to take a look at the lattice for a moment. **Gaze into that vast area of strings connected to strings**. The Lattice is profound in its shape. Energy is connected to energy – everyone to everyone – everything to everything – every planet to every planet – every solar body to every solar body." *[Bold added for emphasis]* [53]

The strings of the Cosmic Lattice are now observed in space, appearing at vastly different scales. Scientists searching for missing matter have predicted that this material could be in giant cosmic strings in dark mode connecting superclusters in approximately straight lines [54]. In the search for "missing" matter, they theorize how a reservoir of hot gas would organize into a web of filaments, like those seen in computer simulations of structure formation, see plate 7. Largely, undetected by current instruments, the description given is *The Hot Cosmic Web*. Scientists admit that the existence of strings would provide the answer to many astrophysical enigmas. Cosmic strings are thought to be a consequence of the emerging Universe, as it expanded and cooled rapidly, from the original Big Bang. It is postulated that this event would have created features known as "topological defects", which can be compared to how ice on a freezing pond forms plates with zig-zag boundaries between them. This theory holds that these defects would create cosmic strings, curiously microscopic and massive at the same time. The theory has credibility because the processes can be simulated in the laboratory, what's more, as astronomical measurements are refined, its predictions can be tested by observation [55]. For further insight, *The Cosmic String Tutorial*, Appendix II provides more detail.

The Cosmic Lattice is also envisaged as "a celestial superhighway". Mathematicians are now mapping "a network of tubes crisscrossing through the solar system." This is achieved by studying the mathematics underlying subtle gravitational interactions between planetary bodies. At the same time, engineers are currently designing trajectories to send spacecraft along these routes to make voyages that were previously unimaginable. Thus, we find:

> "Unlike terrestrial highway systems, the interplanetary superhighway is not static. The Earth-Sun Lagrange points and tubes, for instance, are stationary only when considered in the Earth-Sun rotating frame. In reality, the tubes flail about "like streams from a crazy garden sprinkler,"... and the patterns of highway interchanges keep shifting." [56]

Even more surprising, scientists speculate that the web in space could be used for extraterrestrial communications as a galactic internet! Amongst scientists, CETI refers to Communications from ExtraTerrestrial Intelligences and is distinguished from SETI, Search for (or Signals from) ExtraTerrestrial Intelligences. SETI assumes that the ETs have set up a beacon to attract our attention. CETI assumes that the ETs don't really care whether or not they attract our attention, but are busily communicating among themselves and that we might be able to eavesdrop on their conversations! So, we find that scientists think:

> "The network of tubes of light would be a natural foundation for the ETs to build on to construct their galactic CETI Internet." [57]

In 1963, U.S. military Vela satellites were launched with the intention to monitor Soviet compliance with the nuclear test ban treaty. Instead, they picked up gamma ray bursts (GRBs) and it took until 1967 to realize that the gamma rays were originating from space. In the usual manner, this information was not made public until 1973 [58]. In the report *Gamma Ray Bursts and CETI,* from 1993 it states, "If GRBs are the gamma ray CETI signals from such a galactic Internet, then the duration of each message is ~30 sec, and there are about 2 messages/day." [57]

Diamonds in the Heavens: As Above, So Below

Galaxies are defined as large groupings of stars, planets, moons, comets, asteroids, nebulae, dust, neutron stars, and black holes, in fact most of the objects that cosmologists study in space. Since most of the space between galaxies is thought to be empty, a galaxy is essentially an oasis in space. Our own solar system is located within a galaxy that we call the Milky Way, which consists of over 100 billion stars. The Milky Way is a gigantic spiral disk, with a bright, central bulge, and our solar system is located about 3/4 of the way out from the center in one of the galaxy's spiral arms. The stars and our solar system within the Milky Way are revolving around the central core. There is nothing static in the universe, and our Milky Way, seems to be moving, spreading away from other galaxies at tremendous speeds. There are billions of galaxies in the universe, but they are not randomly distributed at all and the universe appears to have an overall shape and structure on the large scale. Galaxies tend to be part of groups called clusters and our Milky Way is part of a group of about 40 galaxies known as the Local Group, which is actually quite a small grouping. Most clusters tend to be part of larger groupings called superclusters and our Local Group is part of the massive Virgo supercluster, which contains over 2000 member galaxies. As astronomers map the locations of these galaxies, an

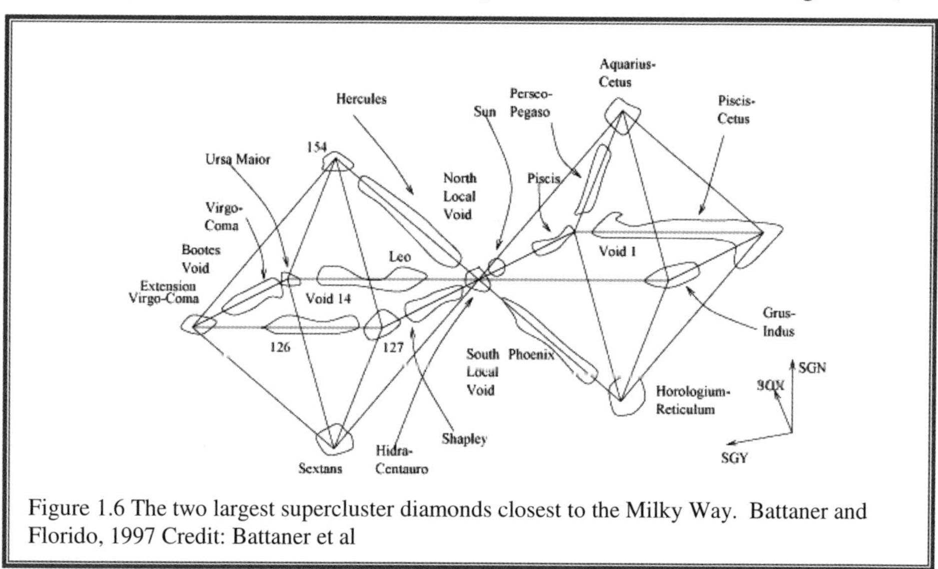

Figure 1.6 The two largest supercluster diamonds closest to the Milky Way. Battaner and Florido, 1997 Credit: Battaner et al

amazing big picture is emerging. What was once assumed to be random distribution of galaxies is now revealing itself to be a complicated design. Astronomers give many names to what they see and we have already mentioned the 'honeycomb', 'Swiss cheese' and 'sponge-like' arrangement, of the galaxies. Large galactic superclusters are gathered around what appears to be giant voids or bubbles, which reveal an octahedron structure on a huge scale, see figures 1.6 & 1.7. Thus, what astronomers have actually discovered is *The Diamond Lattice of the Universe!* In the paper *The Egg-Carton Universe*, Spanish scientists Drs. E. Battaner and E. Florido, write:

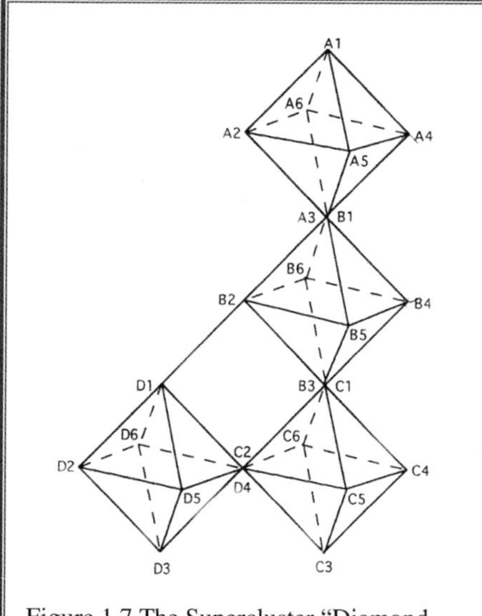

Figure 1.7 The Supercluster "Diamond Lattice". Schematic outline showing "A" and "B" 3-D octahedra superclusters closest to us, while "C" and "D" are farther away. Credit: Battaner et al.

> "The distribution of superclusters in the Local Supercluster neighborhood presents such a remarkable periodicity [i.e. ordered pattern] that some kind of network must fit the observed large-scale structure. A three-dimension chessboard has been suggested. The existence of this network is really a challenge for currently-suggested theoretical models... In this case, however, the identification of real octahedra is so clear and the network is so noticeably well-defined that a direct inspection is straightforward" [59].

Scientists are now busy trying to explain what they see as the fractal nature of the universe. They see diamonds within diamonds within diamonds [60].

"So the Cosmic Microwave Background Radiation is not the afterglow of some mythical 'Big Bang', in which all matter and energy, and even and space time, were created out of nothing, but the signature of the ongoing generation of matter out of the aether."
David Pratt

There was also another "surprise" for scientists who were looking for validation for the Big Bang theory from the Cosmic Microwave Background (CMB), the so-called "echo" of the Big Bang. Analysis has shown that even the most basic predictions of the Big Bang theory were contradicted by the data. Big Bang predicts that tiny fluctuations in radiation intensity would be randomly scattered across the sky, as a leftover from the original Big Bang. In March 2003, it was announced that the CMB was anything but random and measurements displayed symmetry, see plate 8. These are comments from Dr. Max Tegmark, of the University of Pennsylvania, US, who processed the WMAP satellite data of high resolution data and produced images of the radiation intensity across the sky [61].

> "We found something very bizarre; there is some extra, so far unexplained structure in the CMB. We had expected that the microwave background would be truly isotropic, with no preferred direction in space but that may not be the case."
>
> "The octopole and quadrupole components are arranged in a straight line across the sky, along a kind of cosmic equator. That's weird."
>
> "We don't think this is due to foreground contamination. It could be telling us something about the shape of space on the largest scales. We did not expect this and we cannot yet explain it."

This discovery provides stunning confirmation for scientists who do not believe in the existence of hypothetical "dark matter" and propose simpler theories based on geometry and the frequency of vibration. This latest discovery has set the astronomical community alight and the phrase "Axis of evil" has been

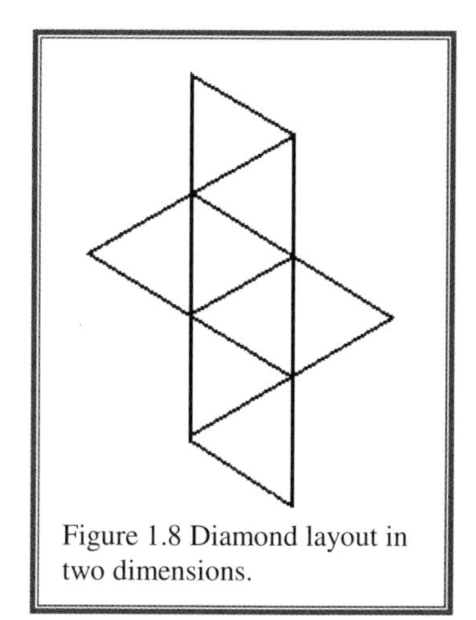
Figure 1.8 Diamond layout in two dimensions.

coined to describe the apparent "warping" of the cosmic background radiation [62]. The "axis" is just one way of illustrating data and can be compared to the two-dimensional, flat representation of a diamond, see figure 1.8. According to a NASA commentator:

"A visual image of the Universe reveals only the superficial appearances, but plasma studies will reveal the invisible structure of space and the processes that may have formed the solar system from dust and plasma." [65]

So is there evidence of other diamonds at a star and planetary level? Well, the planets reveal diamond fields too, and a good example is our Sun, which demonstrates an octopolar magnetic field, see figure 1.9. There are four evenly spaced points along the equator of the Sun that are known to emit showers of charged energy particles like a slowly-rotating lawn sprinkler. Four times each month, the Earth passes through another wave of these particles, which are either positively or negatively charged. The four coordinate points of this energetic emergence along the Sun's equator and its North and South Pole define an octahedron. The energy streaming out of all of its points are where aetheric energies are the most focused [63].

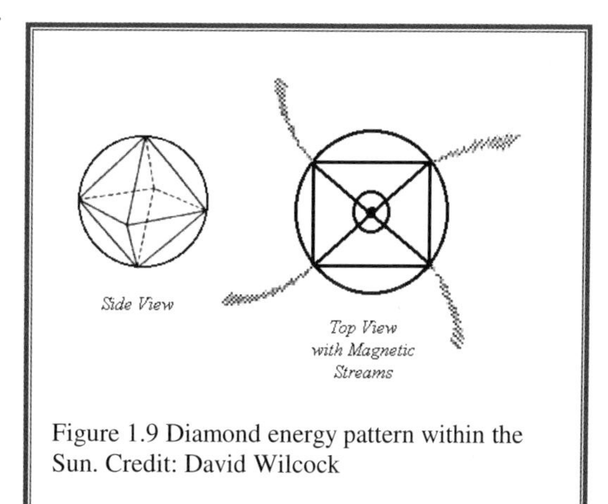

Figure 1.9 Diamond energy pattern within the Sun. Credit: David Wilcock

A consortium of fifty astronomers known as the Whole Earth Telescope Group reported the discovery of a carbon planet with a huge cosmic diamond interior [64]. For more than four decades, astronomers suspected that the interiors of white dwarfs – the name for a star that has used all up its internal nuclear fuel – become crystallized. A pulsating white dwarf called the Diamond Star is the first direct observational evidence and was found to have a crystal interior the size of our moon. Physics theory makes the assertion that, "Once a white dwarf becomes crystalline, it lives forever." From a metaphysical point of view that is quite interesting! At vastly different scales, the universe displays diamond geometry. Here, we have discovered one of the rules of the universe and this same diamond geometry can be found much closer to home!

It has to be understood that these new discoveries are occurring at exactly the same time that many theories, even the most sacrosanct, are being challenged. For example, the suggestion that gravity is just an electromagnetic side-effect is being seriously considered [66]. An article with the following headline seems to be some acknowledgement:

> "Gravity may not be working as advertised. Spacecraft hurtling through the Solar System have been behaving so bizarrely that some scientists wonder whether our theories of gravity are wrong" [67].

Today, even as many gravity-based theories abound, they are gradually losing steam in the face of cosmic features, which defy conventional beliefs. The importance of this has to be underlined, as electrical conditions in our solar system change. For instance, previously stable comets are breaking up for reasons that are totally inexplicable by conventional theory. Yet, plasma cosmology can offer us a simple explanation [68].

This all adds up to illustrate a few themes that run through this book. We are still learning! Brilliant minds, decades ahead of their peers, are normally proven right—eventually, but usually in their time were ignored or treated with skepticism. Mathematics, or any field of science that "appears" to work on paper, is not the same as the whole picture of theoretical, observational and experimental evidence. Ideology can become entrenched and minds can be closed, so that the obvious can be ignored, even in the face of incontrovertible evidence. Sudden paradigm shifts can occur, but often truths are suppressed to maintain the status quo, taking decades to become established. In this situation, truth seekers have to be proactive and use intuition as well as knowledge to gain new insights.

> *"Suddenly, the 'big picture' has changed. For decades we believed that gravity alone rules the macrocosm. Then a crescendo of space age discoveries revealed one of the great surprises of the twentieth century--a universe driven by electric currents and punctuated by cosmic violence."*
>
> *"From the smallest particle to the largest galactic formations, a web of circuitry connects and unifies all of nature, organizing galaxies, energizing stars, giving birth to planets and, on our world, controlling weather and animating biological organisms. There are no isolated islands in space."*

David Talbott & Wallace Thornhill, 'Thunderbolts of the Gods'

Chapter Two

The Sun-Earth-Core Connection

The Sun is Playing Havoc with our Satellites

Our world is changing and thousand of scientists are now focused on the activity of our Sun. The Sun is "freaking out" and one observer has stated it will be "news" when the Sun starts to behave normally! Scientists are telling us that the Sun has been more active in the last 70 years than for the previous 8000. This was the startling conclusion reported in the science journal Nature, dated 28 October 2004, by an international team of scientists from the Max Planck Institute for Solar System Research in Germany. The scientists analyzed the radioactive isotopes in trees preserved in riverbeds and bogs that date back 11,400 years, and by doing so produced the most precise study yet of sunspot history [1].

> "We are living in extraordinary times as far as solar activity is concerned… Extended periods of high activity seem to be much more rare than we previously thought."

This tree ring study also confirmed a previous study of polar ice core samples reported in the November 2003. That report showed that the Sun has been more active since the 1940s than in the previous 1,150 years combined [2]. Three days after the report was issued, the Earth was directly hit by the biggest Sun flare ever recorded – that solar event only served to emphasize the point. The activity of the Sun has been increasing over many decades, but recently the outbursts are getting more and more intense. Between 1901 and 2000, the Sun's magnetic field has increased in strength by 230 percent, at the same time the Earth's field has been decreasing [3]. Furthermore, since the late 1970s, the Sun's overall radiation emissions have increased by 0.5% per decade, which one NASA scientist said could cause "significant" climate change if such effects were to continue over several decades [4].

Solar Flare Ratings

Solar physicists have scales for ranking the magnitude of Solar flares in much the same way that geologists use the Richter Scale to measure the impact of earthquakes. There are actually two magnitude scales in use at the present time. The oldest scale measures how much brighter the flare's X-ray energy is than the average brightness of the Sun's surface. There are four main classes, B, C, M and X, and each is broken into 10 numerical sub-categories: 0-9. Like the Richter Scale used in earthquakes, an M5.5-class flare is 10 times more powerful than a C5.5-class flare, and 1/10 as powerful as an X5.5-class flare relative to the brightness of the solar surface. The second scale, recently adopted by NOAA for its space weather alerts, ranks flares on the basis of their energetic particle flows measured at the Earth. A S2 flare has 10 times the particle flow as an S1 flare, so now the classification of a flare is based on the actual number of particles, not a relative number as for the B, C, M and X-classes.

Powerful solar flares are given an "X" designation and the X ratings are just getting bigger and bigger, see the small section, "Solar Flare Ratings" [5]. Prior to 2003, the two strongest solar flares on record occurred in 1989 and 2001 and were rated at a previously unheard-of X20. Then in November 2003, a flare was so powerful it actually blinded the X-ray detector aboard the National Oceanic and Atmospheric Administration's (NOAA) GOES satellite that monitors the Sun. It was given an initial rating of a massive X28, see plate 9 [6]. Later, a team of physicists from New Zealand re-rated the solar flare to X45, twice as large as any previously recorded flare [7].

"I have not seen anything like it in my entire career as a solar physicist"
John Kohl, Harvard-Smithsonian Center for Astrophysics [8]

As we have a major drama going on in our solar system, cell phones and pagers not working are one of the few hints given to the general public that something is awry. In April 1998, the $200 million Galaxy IV Communication Satellite loss was the first failure in 35 years of pager service and was widely reported as "The Day The Bleepers Died" [9]. As 80% of the cellular phone users in North America were affected, the media could not ignore the failure. Satellite manufacturers are dealing with these failures by blaming engineering standards where possible, for insurance reasons. Meanwhile, independent researchers are compiling chronologies of satellite failures, sometimes from sources that wish to remain anonymous. These researchers have alternative views and put the failures down to "killer electrons", loose in the ionosphere for up to a month after geomagnetic storms [10]. Yet, these same researchers admit that the lists are incomplete because of "vendor concerns" [11]. In 2002, The Wall Street Journal reported that space insurance companies anticipated $1.5 billion in new claims, and that insurance premiums had almost doubled since 1998. This cost now accounts for about 20% of the estimated $250 million outlay for buying and launching a satellite [12]. This is just the cost for a "standard" satellite. A research satellite can cost in the region of $450 million. In October 2003, Japan lost 2 new research satellites in a week, due to a solar flare!

In December 2004, the website space.com wrote a frank article headlined, *There Is No Safe Place For Satellites* [12]. The article served to debunk the notion that there were "safe zones" in the slot between the pair of concentric toroidal (doughnut shaped) Van Allen Belts which are part of the magnetosphere (the protective bubble of radiation around Earth). The problem is that storms from the Sun pour so many particles into the magnetosphere that the slot fills up and the two belts become one. This is not good news for the multi-billion dollar satellite communication industry. NASA articles soon appeared accompanied by video animation that suggested there was a small area between the Van Allen belts that was regularly "cleared" by lightning, hence making them habitable by Global Positioning System (GPS) satellites that skirt the edge of the "safe zone", see figure 2.1 [13]. These conflicting reports illustrate that the electromagnetic environment surrounding Earth has become a major headache for researchers and designers who have the responsibility of working out where to place satellites in the least hazardous locations [14].

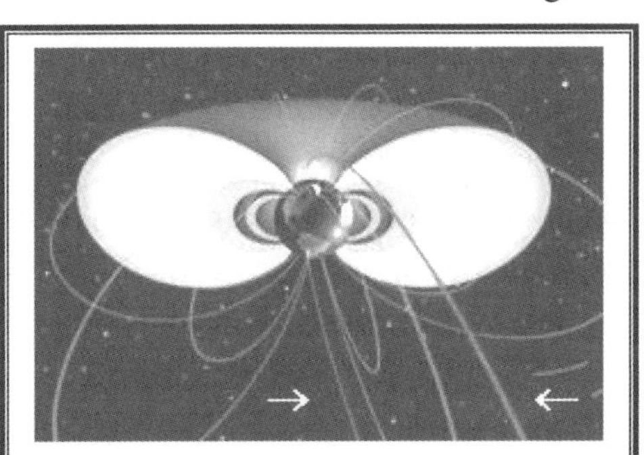

Figure 2.1 Schematic image of the toroidal/doughnut shaped Van Allen Belts. The orbit of the IMAGE satellite which dips into the "safe zone" every few days is marked with arrows. Credit: NASA/Tom Bridgman)

Obviously, this is coming as a shock to various corporations and institutions that have heavily invested in satellite communications. The U.S. Airforce Space Command has taken an unambiguous stance [15]. A 2003 report titled *Space Environment Impacts on Department of Defence (DOD) Operations,* stated in conclusion:

> "Clearly the near-Earth space environment is neither empty nor benign. Solar and geo-physical activity can produce some quite significant and unpleasant impacts on DoD [Department of Defence] systems that operate in or through the near-Earth environment. However, careful planning, accurate forecasts, detailed environmental specifications, rapid notification of actual events, and timely anomaly post-analyses can all help a designer, operator, or user of these systems to work around unfavorable environmental conditions or, at times, even take advantage of such conditions. They also allow one to avoid potentially harmful or ineffective actions, or to recover more quickly when adverse events occur."

Brigadier General Douglas M. Fraser, The Director of Air and Space Operations issued the above report in order to provide "Space Environmental Support". They have set up Combat Weather Teams (CWT) and supporting Operational Weather Squadrons (OWS) to advise designers, operators, and users of radar, communications, or space systems. Around the world, there is a rash of new government agencies set up to provide space weather support [16]. In the United States, in the interest of space weather forecasting, NOAA, NASA and the Department of Defence pooled resources to secure the capability of receiving quasi-continuous, real-time solar wind and Interplanetary Magnetic Field (IMF) data from NASA's WIND and Advance Composition Explorer (ACE) spacecraft.

There is now an "armada" of space monitors watching the Sun providing early warnings to protect Earth-orbiting spacecraft.

There is now a fleet of monitors parked up in space, a technological armada, ready to provide early warnings to protect Earth-orbiting spacecraft. At short notice, Earth satellites can be put into "safe mode" to protect them from *the massive onslaught of radiation.* As a matter of priority, it appears that space probes on purely scientific missions were commandeered to provide this advanced warning service [17]. SOHO and ACE actually orbit around a Lagrangian point, known as L1, about 1.5 million kilometers away from the Earth towards the Sun. From its L1 orbit location, SOHO is able to give scientists an uninterrupted view of the Sun [18]. The ACE satellite monitors the solar wind density and speed, and also the Interplanetary Magnetic Field. From these interplanetary measurements, forecasters have just 45 minutes, if they are lucky, to provide warnings of *hostile magnetospheric-ionospheric conditions.*

There are human considerations with this solar rain. Astronauts at the International Space Station, are now regularly having to take cover in a more heavily shielded section of the station when warned of the next "storm". The lower ionosphere acts as a shield filtering out most of the harmful radiation that could effect Earth inhabitants, but astronauts in the space stations, 225 miles (360 km) above the Earth, do not have the same level of protection. Speculation exists that the worsening space environment was the main reason the MIR Space Station was abandoned. The "Save MIR" campaign was rebutted by Russian space officials and designers, who stated by letter that the proposals aimed at rescuing MIR, "may lead to the loss of control of MIR space station and, as a result, to catastrophic consequences not only for Russia but for the whole world" [19]. Apparently, the main computer on the MIR space station had to be changed out nearly a half dozen times, due to the problems of charging by solar storms. The computers were being literally fried over and over again.

In January 2005, NASA admitted that its space weather theory had been "shattered" by a "new type of storm" which arrived "in minutes" rather than days [20]. The NASA article revealed the existence of a "superhighway for protons leading all the way from sunspot 720 to our planet". NASA cited the theory of "Magnetic Reconnection" as the explanation for the accelerated particles. This particular theory is highly disputed by plasma physicists, because it is based on the belief that magnetic field lines somehow "break". Since we define magnetic field "lines" as a mathematical abstraction, like contours on a map, this caused the great Hannes Alfvén to refer to the theory of "Magnetic Reconnection" as "pseudo-science" [21].

Solar physicists are also starting to dispel the myth of "solar minimum", which occurs as part of the 11 year solar cycle of increasing and decreasing solar activity. The truth is, solar activity never stops. The most powerful X-class solar flares, associated with bright auroras and intense radiation storms, occurred at least once during each of the last three solar minima [22]. The current ferocity of the energy hitting the Earth in the form of cosmic and galactic rays, solar flares and corona mass ejections (CMEs), even during the time of solar minimum is making scientists warn against complacency.

The whimsical sounding NASA program called *Living With A Star,* is the embodiment of a new strategic plan for NASA. It was introduced in 2000 by George Withbroe, the Director of NASA's Office of Space Science. *Living With A Star* has a strong emphasis on improving space weather forecasting ability, and providing the satellite resources to keep a constant watch on the Sun. Particularly, there is a need to be ready for the next solar maximum in 2012, when the new round of solar activity is expected to rise to a climax. In fact, a 2003 report from the European Space agency, *ESA sees stardust storms heading for Solar System,* tells us that the current magnetic configuration of the Sun is permitting two to three times more stardust than at the end of the 1990s. Moreover, this influx could increase by as much as ten times until the end of the current solar cycle in 2012. This discovery by the Ulysses space probe was described as a "flood" and will cause increased flaring of the Sun [23].

In March 2006, NASA announced, a breakthrough "solar climate" forecast technique. Helioseismology allows researchers to "see" inside the Sun by tracing reverberating sound waves. Thus creating a picture of the interior, like ultrasound creates a picture of an unborn baby. Scientists predict that the next solar cycle will begin with an increase in solar activity in late 2007 or early 2008, and there will be 30 to 50 percent *more* sunspots, flares, and CMEs [24]. This was widely reported with headlines such as, *Huge Solar Storms Could Zap Earth, Scientists Warn.* In summary, solar scientists admit they do not understand the factors that determine the behavior of the Sun in relation to the 11-year solar cycle. As Cycle 23 did not conform to predictions, they are beginning to suspect that a much bigger cycle of maybe thousands or even hundreds of thousands of years is now influencing the Sun's behavior. Hence the concern about what will happen at the peak of cycle 24 in 2012.

How Does the Sun Work? There's some con-FUSION!

The recent behavior of our Sun has attracted much scientific investigation, but it may come as some surprise, that there are many basic facts that scientists don't understand, such as what causes sunshine! We are told that the Sun radiates as much energy every second as 100 billion tons of exploding dynamite, but on examination, the Sun has some very strange properties which remain unresolved by conventional models. It has been nearly 70 years since the discovery that the *outer* atmosphere of the Sun, the corona (meaning crown), is three hundred times hotter than the surface! See plates 10 & 11.

The SOHO spacecraft launched in December 1995 aims to understand the fundamental processes of the Sun-Earth system. Within the first year, the space mission discovered "a continuously erupting magnetic carpet on the Sun", see figure 2.2 [25]. In 1999, European Space Agency (ESA) scientists announced they had identified regions on the Sun where the high-speed solar wind originates. They had observed solar wind flows coming from the edges of "honeycomb-shaped patterns of magnetic fields at the

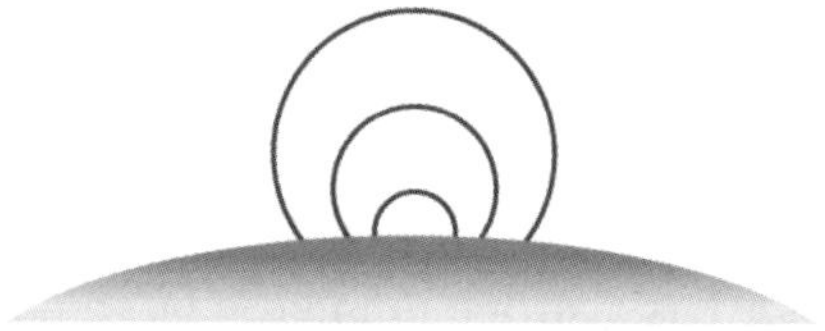

Figure 2.2 Drawing of a "magnetic loop" on the Sun. The visible surface of the Sun appears to be carpeted with tens of thousands of magnetic north and south poles joined by looping field lines which extend outward into the Solar Corona.

surface of the Sun." These are comments from the scientists involved:

> "If one thinks of these cells as paving stones in a patio, then the solar wind is breaking through like grass around the edges, concentrated in the corners where the paving stones meet."
>
> "We can now focus our attention on the plasma conditions and the dynamic processes seen in the corners of the magnetic field structures."

This is a particularly interesting observation because it matches the description given of the Cosmic Lattice, which is also described as "honeycombed energy cells" [26]. In July 2002, researchers at the Royal Swedish Academy of Sciences in Stockholm revealed the most detailed pictures ever taken of the Sun. Electrical activity in the form of Birkeland currents were captured, providing stunning evidence for the Electric Sun model proposed by plasma scientists, see plates 12 & 13 [27]. The only way to interpret these discoveries is that our scientists are identifying geometry with electromagnetism, and these have absolutely nothing in common with established theory!

The Thermonuclear (Fusion) model states that at the core of the Sun, the tremendous gravitational field produces intense pressure and heat, (estimated to be about 16 million degrees Celsius (16 million Kelvin), which causes the nuclei of hydrogen atoms to fuse together to produce helium. In this process, additional energy is generated, which radiates and convects to the surface of the Sun. Historically, this unproven theory was first proposed by Sir Arthur Eddington, who stated that the Sun *must* be getting its energy from inside itself. He simply argued that since the energy had not exhausted itself after billions of years, therefore, it had to be nuclear fusion.

"The certainty that the Sun generates its prodigious outpourings of energy through thermonuclear reactions deep in its interior has been with us for about half a century."
Ralph Juergens

Regardless of the dominance of these long held views, there are problems associated with the Fusion model, which critics claim can be explained by alternative theories. As we now live in "unprecedented" times in regard to the activity of the Sun, maybe, the Electric Sun model could provide a suitable explanation. Here is a short critique of the Fusion model and the main points raised by proponents of the Electric Universe. (Here small sections denoted with ✧❖◆❖✧ provide slightly more technical details and can be skipped over by the less scientifically minded.)

The Fusion Model – Critique

- **Fireside Anomaly**. The deepest observable surface of the Sun yields a temperature of about 6,000 Kelvin. But moving outward to the Sun's corona, the temperature jumps spectacularly to almost 2 million Kelvin. A typical source of radiant energy is expected to obey an inverse square law. That is to say, the farther we get away from it, the less energy we receive per unit area. This can be compared to feeling less heat as we stand further away from a fireplace. However, scientist say paradoxically, this is NOT what is happening at the Sun [28].
- **Acceleration of the Solar "Wind" Ions.** The positive ions that are the main constituent of the solar "wind" accelerate the farther away from the Sun they get. There is no explanation for this in the standard model and it remains one of the "unsolved problems of solar physics". However charges that accelerate is what happens when you apply an electric field! [29]
- **Missing Neutrinos.** Thermonuclear reactions in the core of the Sun are supposed to generate neutrally charged particles called neutrinos. However, after 30 years of experiments, scientists cannot find the requisite number of neutrinos predicted by theory. In June 2001, Sudbury Neutrino Observatory (SNO) in Ontario, Canada claimed that the deficit does not lie with the fusion model. Instead, they claim that measurable neutrinos turn into non-measurable ones enroute from the Sun and this circumstance explains the deficit [30]. This suggestion is offered with no definitive proof, hence the continuation of doubts that solar scientists really understand the details of energy generation in main-sequence stars.
- **Convection of Energy Up from the Core.** The Fusion model states that the Sun transports its energy from its central core outward and this would take hundreds of thousands of years. However, observations show that changes can occur within a period of hours.
- **Sunspots are Magnetic Depressions in the Photosphere.** Sunspots are areas of intense magnetic energy where we can see down deeper into the surface of the Sun. They seem to act like temporary caps on upwelling matter but they do permit occasional eruptions of tremendous amounts of light and plasma. If energy is really flowing upward toward the surface of the Sun from a 16 million Kelvin core, these holes in the photosphere should be much hotter than the outer layers of the photosphere, but in fact they are cooler.

The usual explanation is that *strange magnetic waves* down below the surface prevent heat energy from flowing up at these points.

- **Periodic Fluctuations in the Sun's Output and Size.** There is evidence that the Sun vibrates in a way that throws doubt on both the assumed convection process for heat transportation and the thermonuclear reaction process itself.
- **The Sun Rotates Faster at its Equator than at Higher Latitudes.** This is yet another problem that the accepted thermonuclear model cannot explain.

The Electric Sun Hypothesis

Why are we discussing the electromagnetic properties of the Sun? Well, the activity of the Sun is transforming the Earth and according to Russian scientists humans will face "evolutionary challenges" [31]. The standard model for the Sun cannot provide any reasonable suggestions for the wild behavior of the Sun. Plausible scientific theories are examined first, before we discuss metaphysical sources of information that are very clear about what is happening on Earth, within our solar system and our galaxy. The Electric Sun model is detailed because it suggests that as the Sun moves around the galactic center, it may come into regions of higher or lower total current and so its output may vary both periodically and randomly.

The Electric Sun model originated in the 1970s, by the late engineer Ralph E. Juergens of Flagstaff, Arizona. The theory proposes that the Sun is powered, not from within itself, but from outside, by the electric (Birkeland) currents that flow in our arm of our galaxy. Fusion is up at the surface and NOT in the core. The Sun's radiated power at any instant is due to the difference between incoming cosmic electrons and outgoing positive ions, the resultant is a net positive current leaving the Sun. Plasma scientists argue that this mechanism constitutes a plasma arc discharge, which is analogous in every way (except size) to those that have been observed in laboratories for decades [32] [29]. It is argued that the Electric Sun model is inherently predictive of all observed phenomena and has scientific integrity in that it does not violate Maxwell's electromagnetic equations as the fusion model does. Now, this is considered to be complete heresy, even by people who consider themselves heretics! There is no doubt that there *are* electric currents in space, but the issue is, whether there is *sufficient* quantity to power the Sun. Astrophysicists who do understand the electrical nature of the universe, think that the amount of energy warranted for the transmission lines to power the sun would make them visible!

The astrophysicist James McCanney is well known for his Plasma Discharge Comet Model [33]. His predictions made back in 1979 are being vindicated and he claims that his theories are taught to astrophysicists at Russian universities [34]. McCanney regularly appears on radio programs and even has his own radio show with a large audience of listeners [35]. McCanney teaches the electrical nature of our Universe and believes that magnetic fields are generated by rivers of electrical currents that flow constantly between the planets and beyond. He calls these "the electrical rivers or highways to the stars" [36]. This is what he had to say in an interview with The SPECTRUM news magazine about our Sun:

> "To understand Earth weather, you first have to understand that the Sun fusion is not in the core; it's up at the surface of the Sun. That translates into tremendous electrical energy in the Solar System. The planets and the comets and the moons of the Solar System all are discharging this battery or capacitor that's built-up around the Sun. In the process of discharging this capacitor, the electrical energy is blowing through the Solar System all the time and is, basically, the cause of our weather."
>
> "One of the fundamental properties of fusion is that it separates charge and the protons go out. It's a rather complicated situation but, basically, the Sun is like a "super atom". It has a corona of very high-energy electrons which are in orbit, literally at very high velocities, around the central, positively charged core of the Sun. So, you have the super-atom state. When the proton streamers come off of the Sun, they are accelerated through the corona, which is NEGATIVELY charged; then they come blasting out. This is the cause of solar flaring. In fact, you would not even have solar flaring with the solar core fusion model, where fusion is IN the core."
>
> "In fact, before SOHO and these solar satellites were up in orbit, the standard concept of the Sun was that it was just a very smooth, glowing, orange ball. That's what would be predicted if you had the core model of fusion IN the Sun. When they got up there, all of the data contradicted that model, yet they kept the model, which is one of the big problems in astronomy." [37]

McCanney has backed up his claims with Russian research that also finds that the Sun's fusion is up at the surface and *not* in the core [38]. There is also a relatively new "Iron Sun" theory proposed by nuclear chemist Oliver Manuel, which also provides solid evidence that fusion is up at the surface and so threatens the standard model [39]. What is suggested here, is that there is enough evidence to show that the standard model is incorrect, fusion takes place at the surface of the Sun and that energy can *also* be transmitted via the Sun by Birkeland currents which will influence or modify the Sun's behavior. Interestingly, record high temperatures can be produced in a laboratory setting with plasmas and a very strong magnetic field, yet scientists admit they do not understand how more energy is released than was originally put in, something that they believe should only occur in nuclear reactions [39]. Hence, we do have verifiable alternative explanations for how energy is generated by the Sun, but again, it does not comply with conventional scientific thinking.

Redshift and Space Domains 

Plasma based theories provide an explanation for the variation in the Sun's behavior that could be periodic and dependent on the region of space being traversed by the Sun around the galactic center. Yet, this means that any variation in space invalidates certain assumptions in cosmology. The main parameter under threat would be redshift. This is generally attributed to the Doppler effect, a change in wavelength that results when a given source of waves (e.g. light or radio waves) and an observer are in rapid motion with respect to each other. There is no dispute that the redshift of *ordinary* galaxies is closely correlated with the distance of those galaxies, but it is not well established that the redshift is caused by an increase in that distance. This simple assumption, which has reigned in the astronomical community for decades, is now in some doubt. There are 20 non-velocity redshift mechanisms that have been found that can cause light to lose energy and hence will cause it to redshift [40].

Some astronomers believe that redshift is a function of space-density and youth, NOT the prevailing view that it is a measure of distance from the time of the original Big Bang. Halton Arp and others have found 500 examples of high-redshift quasars that are *physically connected* to low-redshift galaxies by "bridges" of plasma. Arp explains the juxtaposition of low and high redshift as caused by galaxies 'giving birth' to new galaxies which we call quasars and he provides many examples of high redshift quasars that are symmetrically located on either side of what he suggests are their parent, low redshift galaxies. Such pairings occur much more often than would be expected from random placement. Obviously, this contradicts the standard explanation for the cause of astronomical redshift as being always due to receding stellar objects. There is also another problem for proponents of the Big Bang theory, the distribution of redshifts is quantized, that means it occurs in discreet values. This is more normally associated with quantum physics, the world of sub-atomic particles, and yet we are seeing this being demonstrated on the galactic level!

Dr. Harold Aspden of Cambridge University made the case for space having varying levels of density in 1972, proving mathematically the existence of what he called "space domains" [41]. When Aspden tried to publish a follow-up paper in 1996, complete with the *direct observational evidence* to prove that these areas of higher density exist in the Universe, his paper was rejected. Aspden based this new validation on the work of William Tifft, at the University of Arizona. The following was reported in THE TIMES newspaper (UK), on October 14, 1996.

> "The story began with the discovery in the 1970s by William Tifft, of the University of Arizona, that the speeds of the galaxies he studied were always multiples of 72 kilometres per second."
>
> "Red shifts should be able to take any value, but Dr. Tifft seemed to show they were 'quantized' – restricted to certain values."
>
> "This appeared impossible, but more recent research by Bill Napier at Oxford and Bruce Guthrie of the Edinburgh Royal Observatory confirmed it. Explaining why is very tricky, unless you assume that red shifts don't really tell us anything about speed or distance and that would undermine the whole basis of cosmology."

So, we have undisputed scientific work that completely falsifies and discredits The Big Bang theory, but due to convenience this is completely ignored, see the small section "What is the Falsifiability Criteria?" [42].

What is the Falsifiability Criteria?

The falsifiability criteria, is the cornerstone of twentieth-century scientific method. Philosopher Karl Popper argued that one could never prove a scientific theory to be correct, because only an infinite number of confirming results could constitute definitive proof. Popper proposed instead to test theories in ways to contradict, or falsify them; the absence of contradictory evidence thereby becomes proof of the theory's validity. People who believe that a theory has to be falsifiable, otherwise it's just metaphysics, are now referred to as "popperazzi"!

The NASA Space Physics Division have been very hostile to the notion of the variation of space density and so in the past, NASA have been accused of "bias" [43]. Key support for Aspden's work has come from Russian research. The 1997, *Planetophysical State of the Earth and Life* report by Dmitriev et al. concludes that as our Sun and solar system travels through interstellar space, it has met a variation of matter and energy. It seems the Russians are confirming that we are traversing a highly charged region of space or even a boundary that is organized with Birkeland currents or cosmic string. Specifically the report informs us:

> "This kind of interstellar space dispersed plasma is presented by magnetized strip structures and striations."

Earth is *Alive* with Electrical Activity

"This planet [Earth], with all its appalling immensity,
is to electric currents virtually no more than a small metal ball."
Nikola Tesla

The Earth is an electrified body, moving in plasma, and as such is "hard-wired" to the rest of the Universe! This has come as a complete surprise to scientists who believed that the Earth was isolated from the rest of the universe by a featureless vacuum. The Earth environment is *alive* with electrical activity, influenced by the activity of the Sun and the alignments of the planets and cometary bodies. The plasma state is not often considered on Earth, yet the most obvious examples are the auroras and lightning, see figure 2.3 & 2.4 and small section, "More about the Aurora".

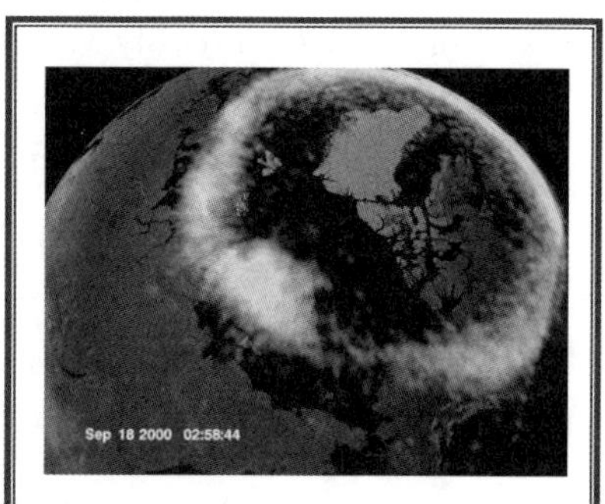

Figure 2.3 Aurora in ultraviolet at Earth's North Pole. Credit: NASA, IMAGE spacecraft.

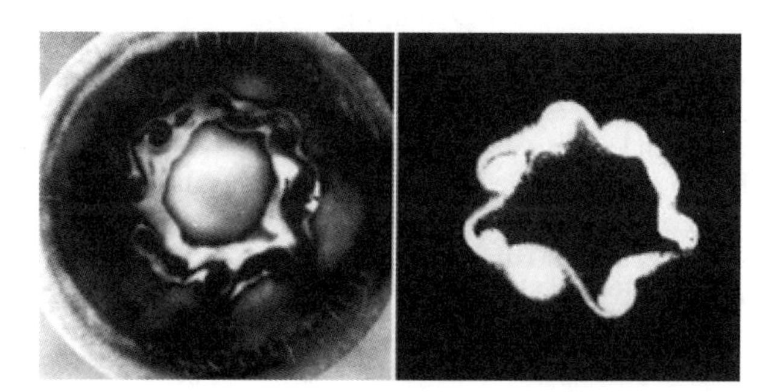

Figure 2.4 Plasma Instabilities. Credits: H. Davis, H. F. Webster.

Plasma Instabilities. The peculiar shape found in plasma instabilities could represent cosmic string. The undulating auroral curtains show this strange shape and the effect is believed to scale up to planetary, and even to galactic dimensions. These two images show in cross-section what happens to a beam of electrons that is following an axial magnetic field. The image on the left is due to a 90 kiloamp current striking a carbon witness plate. The other image is due to a 58 microamp current striking a fluorescent screen. So in the laboratory the effect is scaleable over 12 orders of magnitude of beam current.

More about the Aurora

Aurora usually occur within rings around the magnetic poles, with each ring up to about 3500 km in diameter and a few hundred kilometres deep. This "auroral oval" contains discrete aurora, which form curtain or ray shapes that are often easily visible with the naked eye, and diffuse aurora, which are fainter and lack sharp spatial boundaries. These particles collide with atmospheric gases, which become excited or ionized. When the atoms and molecules return to a lower energy state, electromagnetic (radio, infrared, visible, or ultraviolet) energy is emitted. Aurora are most intense, and are observed closer toward the equator, at times of geomagnetic storms. Aurora occur simultaneously at high northern and southern latitudes, and are sometimes called the Northern and Southern Lights, aurora borealis and aurora australis, respectively.

Due to free electrons, plasma is a good conductor of electricity, better than copper, silver, or gold and so lightning offers a dramatic manifestation of this property. The complex patterns of electric currents and magnetic fields surrounding the Earth are how the Earth's electric charge adjusts to the Sun's electric field. Scientists now also suspect that many other meteorological events are electrically driven. It can be easily shown that an electrical field is needed to generate clouds and rain, see the small section "How do Clouds Form?" [44]

How Do clouds Form?

The standard explanation for clouds and rain is that when moisture-laden warm air is heated, it begins to rise, the air bubbles expand, causing cooling of the moisture which eventually condenses to form clouds. As the cloud cools further, more moisture condenses and the water droplets making up the cloud grow and merge until some become so large and heavy that the air currents within the cloud can no longer support them. This traditional explanation was never offered with experimental observation to back it up! The only science experiment that is in anyway relevant is the cloud chamber, which was one of the very early forms of detecting subatomic particles. The subatomic particles would move through the cloud chamber, ionize the water, leaving a little trace, and therefore the subatomic particles could be seen moving around and spinning in the magnetic field. This means that in our atmosphere, clouds could form, but the big Cumulonimbus, storm-type clouds and the hurricane-type clouds, could not form at all, if there was not some kind of significant electric field. It is only very recent cloud chamber experiments, such as the Sky research by Svensmark at the Danish National Space Center, which duplicate the Earth's atmosphere and electric field, prove that cosmic rays create condensation nuclei on which cloud droplets could form. Further CLOUD (Cosmics Leaving Outdoor Droplets) experiments are being attempted by the world's top scientists, at the biggest particle-physics laboratory in the world CERN in Geneva, Switzerland.

Many Meteorological Events are Electrically Driven

Lightning has always been recognized as an electrical phenomenon, but now there is a growing realization that tornadoes and hurricanes are electrical too [45]. This includes spectacular weather conditions like dust devils and waterspouts, and larger weather patterns, like the jet streams and El Niño. Meteorologists admit they are not sure how tornadoes form, but they do know that they are often associated with severe electrical storms. We know that earthquakes can be induced by pumping electricity into the Earth and natural quakes are often accompanied by, or preceded by, electrical glows called earthquake lights and radio frequency static. Again, volcanic eruptions are often accompanied by copious amounts of lightning. There is even a strange report of a tornado, which was photographed rising out of the caldera of the Mount Etna volcano in Italy. Certainly, a meteorologist would have no explanation for this occurrence, as it occurred in a clear blue sky! [46] Question: have you ever wondered why there are so many reports of tornadoes tearing through caravan trailer parks in the United States? Answer: maybe it has something to do with all those little metal boxes, neatly placed in rows for the tornado to GROUND its electrical energy! So as the debate goes on, we are left without an adequate explanation for many aspects of mainstream theory. Yet, as the close relationship between solar activity and weather become more and more obvious, a few meteorologists have found methods that have enabled them to predict severe weather, up to nine months ahead of time [47]. Others admit that current weather forecasting for the general public is lacking. Chief Meteorologist Paul Barys stated in a radio interview:

> "Garbage In, Garbage Out! ...They do not take into effect in global models the Sun... they take it as a constant... and it is NOT! ...Forecasting is an educated guessing process." [48]

Along with the other electrical manifestations, there has been a noted rise in intense, destructive hurricanes worldwide [49]. In September 2005, the Reuters news agency reported:

> "Twice as many of the most powerful hurricanes, those ranked Category 4 or 5, have been detected since 1990 as were seen in the period from 1970 to 1985, scientists found in a global survey."

The standard explanation of "hotter seas" caused by global warming does not explain the trend of hurricanes forming over land and some forming over "freezing cold" oceans such as the Atlantic in December! We are witnessing hurricane after hurricane forming over the same water, but the sea temperatures never drop! Yet, the 2006 hurricane season proved once and for all that "warm seas" do not power hurricanes. Predictions were hopelessly incorrect even after an unprecedented "continent to continent" heat-wave, which failed to generate the requisite number of hurricanes in the Atlantic Ocean [50]. Therefore, the ferocity of some recent hurricanes is forcing scientists to suspect there *are* other factors! Scientists are monitoring a curious new trend in hurricanes – they are producing more lightning – lots of it. During the record-breaking hurricane season of 2005, three of the most powerful storms – Rita, Katrina, and Emily – had lightning in the hurricane's eye. Scientists exploring hurricane Emily, using NASA's ER-2 aircraft, noted the lightning and measured huge electric fields over the storm, "the strongest ever measured by the aircraft's sensors over any storm."

> "We observed steady fields in excess of 8 kilovolts per meter. That is huge—comparable to the strongest fields we would expect to find over a large land-based 'mesoscale' thunderstorm." [51]

Considering on a fair weather day you would only expect to find a potential difference of 100 volts per meter, 8,000 volts per meter can rightly be described as huge! The flight over Emily was part of a 30-day science data-gathering campaign, organized and sponsored by NASA headquarters to improve scientists' understanding of hurricanes. This is just one project amongst others, investigating the link between hurricanes and tropical storms with activity in the ionosphere. This is at the same time that NASA are funding research associated with the "Living With A Star" program. A priority is the "Distribution of electric currents connecting the magnetosphere to the ionosphere" [52]. We can presume by these scientific endeavors, that scientists are now starting to acknowledge the electric origin of our weather and universe, as indicated by areas of solar and Geospace research sponsored by NASA.

A new electrical theory highlights the correlation between sunspots and earthquakes. The idea being proposed is that certain changes in the Sun-Earth environment affect the magnetic field of the Earth, which then triggers earthquakes in vulnerable areas [53]. This theory has found favor with NASA and the European Geosciences Union have also given approval. Yet, historically many have noticed strange phenomena that precede large earthquakes. Some have been reported for centuries, even millennia and careful research has been conducted, notably by scientists from China and Turkey. There is a long and diverse list of pre-earthquake phenomena: bulging of the Earth's surface, changing well water levels, ground-hugging fog, low frequency electromagnetic emission, earthquake lights from ridges and mountain tops, and strange animal behavior. Dr. Friedemann Freund is a professor in the Department of Physics, San Jose State University, and a senior researcher at NASA Ames Research

Center who wrote a paper titled, *Rocks That Crackle and Sparkle and Glow: Strange Pre-Earthquake Phenomena.* Freund explains the existence of electrical current at a depth of 10-20km in the Earth's crust that is in the order of "millions" of amps. From laboratory experiments, Freund believes that the explanation is in the realm of semiconductor physics, so geoscientists do not have the expertise to consider the merits of this theory, and that is why the paper appears in a speculative journal. Freud's report is very important because it confirms the existence of electric currents in the Earth's crust that flow with no externally applied voltage, which by definition is a plasma.

Let us compare the Whirlpool Galaxy, which is 37 million light-years away, see plate 5, with hurricane Frances, see plate 14. Whilst Frances is hundreds of miles across, the Whirlpool Galaxy spans approximately 50,000 light-years. So, even though they are vastly dissimilar in scale, they do look amazingly alike, both exhibiting the shape of a simple and beautiful mathematical curve known as a logarithmic spiral. This is a spiral whose separation grows in a geometric way with increasing distance from the center. These rotating bodies should look alike because they are organized by the same electrical force!

Figure 2.5. A Seashell showing the logarithmic spiral. Courtesy: Pacific Northwest National Laboratory.

Maybe it is not surprising to find that the much-maligned scientist, Dr. Wilhelm Reich, was way ahead of his time. He postulated in his book *Cosmic Superimposition* (1951), that the combination of two orgone energy systems were involved in the formation of spiral galaxies, hurricanes, and the aurora borealis! Reich was proven right, when Anthony Peratt used a new computer program to simulate the action of two currents on a galactic scale, generating the graceful forms of spiral galaxies, as predicted by Alfvén [54]. Nowadays, we have the reportedly brilliant theoretical mathematician Christopher Illert, bachelor science and IQ over 200, who believes the same equations that govern the geometrics of sea shells and flowers can also be applied to the Cosmos! Yet, Illert has found that using computer simulation and the current laws of physics, as accepted by consensus, he CANNOT reproduce a seashell!

The revelation of the electromagnetic properties of the Universe and the role of 'alive' plasma present a new paradigm of understanding. We are moving back to science that is based more solidly on observation rather than mathematical conjecture.

The Earth's True Frequency

There are natural waves that continuously circle the Earth, they are often compared to the Earth's heartbeat, yet these waves do not originate within the Earth. The eccentric genius and master of electricity, Nikola Tesla, first discovered these signals, and he tried to exploit this electrical potential. Unfortunately, his discovery of the earth's natural frequency was not understood at the time and so he was not taken seriously. It wasn't until more than half a century later, in 1952, that the concept of the Earth having a natural frequency was established. Professor Wolfgang O. Schumann¸ a German physicist of the Technical University of Munich, predicted electromagnetic standing waves in the atmosphere, within the cavity formed by the surface of the earth and the ionosphere see figure 2.6. This was confirmed in 1954 when measurements by Schumann and König detected the resonance at a main frequency of 7.83 Hertz (Hz) [55]. It is the harmonics at 14, 20, 26, 33, 39 and 45 Hz, with a daily variation of about +/- 0.5 Hz, that generate the whole range of Schumann Resonances.

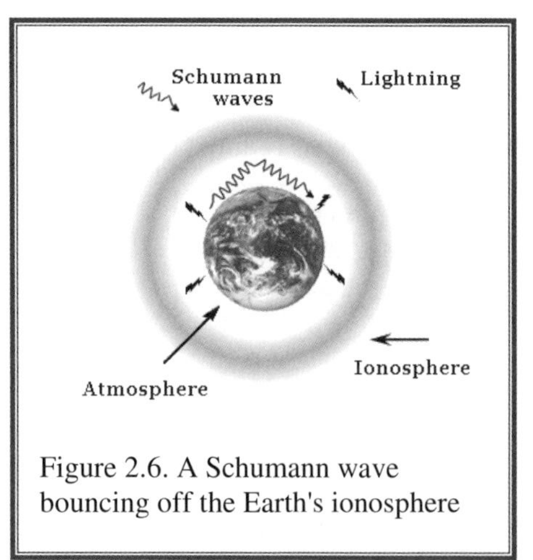

Figure 2.6. A Schumann wave bouncing off the Earth's ionosphere

Since the Earth's atmosphere is charged, maintaining a current and a voltage, it is not surprising to find such electromagnetic waves. The Schumann waves are powered by lightning bolts, which hit the Earth 50 - 100 times per second in the 2,000 concurrent thunderstorms that occur on planet Earth. Much of this energy is dissipated quickly, but the extremely low frequency, long-wavelength category, is able to circumnavigate the earth without serious degradation. These waves do not vary very much, as this is restricted by the size of the cavity. The parameters that do matter though, include **the electrical parameters of the atmosphere, and the state (height, ionization level) of the ionosphere** [56]. In summary, the Schumann Resonance is not the same as the frequency of the Earth. The Schumann Resonance is a measurement based on "resonance" between the Earth and the lower ionosphere and it will fluctuate based on known parameters.

The electromagnetic grids reflect the *true* Earth frequency!

Richard Buckminster Fuller (1895-1983) was an engineer, mathematician and architect, famed for his invention of the geodesic dome. Simple experiments conducted in the 1970s by his students, demonstrate perfectly how the Earth's frequency creates electromagnetic grid lines. These experiments involved submerging a balloon in a blue dye liquid, which are then both vibrated at a particular frequency. This results in the dye collecting at specific points on the surface of the balloon and thin lines forming that join the points in geometric arrangements. If the frequency is changed and turned higher, the original dye points will quickly dissolved and then a greater number of dye points will slowly form, joined by lines in a more complex configuration. These experiments have been repeated by many researchers and taken to new levels [57].

These experiments demonstrate how the Earth has its own energy centers, much like the human body has chakras and acupuncture points, but the energy centers are arranged in crystal-like configurations. When the Earth periodically moves into a higher energy state, the planetary energy patterns will shift into new crystal configurations. There is evidence that this has been going on for a very long period of time. Interestingly, ancient Egyptians described the earth as two twelve-sided pyramids joined together at the equator. Obviously, the Egyptians were not referring to the physical shape of the planet, but rather to an invisible energetic pattern that is related to the internal structure of the Earth [58].

Military pilot Bruce Cathie (now retired), first discovered the Earth had a diamond energy grid, see figure 2.7. He became fascinated when he realized that UFO sightings always followed specific straight-line paths that were always the same. Studying the work of other UFO researchers he eventually worked out that UFOs were following magnetic energy lines that circle the globe. In his first book called Harmonic 33, he revealed that these lines created a cube and octahedron within a sphere! Cathie has written several books and his work has been covered by many other researchers [59].

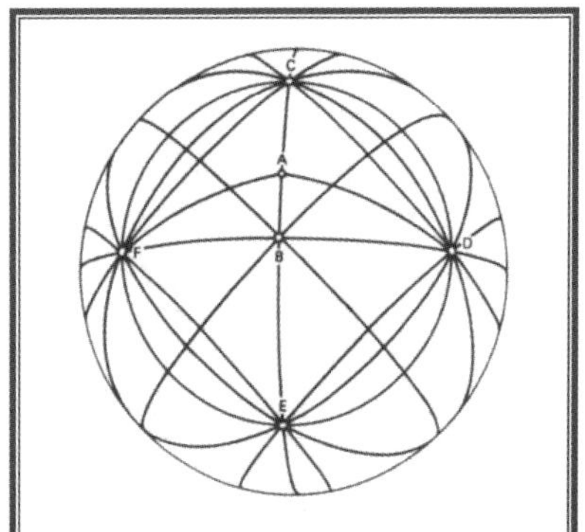

Figure 2.7. The Bruce Cathie Energy Grid, displaying the Cube and Octahedron. Credit: Bruce Cathie.

Russian geophysical evidence points to the core of the Earth as a growing crystal that influences planetary events.

Russian research reveals another Earth grid, which they believe is derived from a crystalline core, see figure 2.8 [60]. This was first proposed in January 1981, by a magazine article published in the former Soviet Union titled, *In the Earth's Crystal Rays*. After ten years of study, the authors suggested that geophysical evidence pointed to the core of the Earth as a growing crystal that influences planetary events. The crystal rays are lines of magnetic force that can be detected as a matrix on the surface of the Earth [61]. These lines have many different names. Here is a selection: *Heilige Linien* to the Germans, *Fairy Paths* to the Irish, *Dragon Lines* to the Chinese, *Spirit Lines* to Peruvians and *Dream Paths* (Turingas) to the Australian Aborigines – and so on around the world.

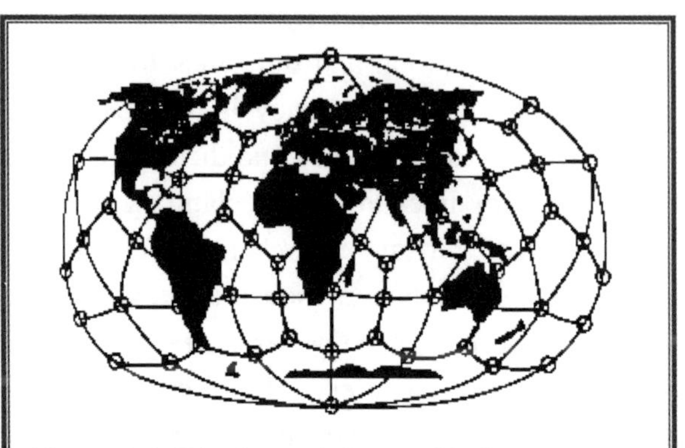

Figure 2.8 The icosa-dodeca grid discovered by Goncharov, Morozov and Makarov's, circa 1981.

Joseph Jochmans, a historian and anthropologist, believed that we would see a new grid, also referred to as the "Christ Grid" [62]. Jochmans wrote about his vision of a New Golden Age, where we would have a new grid with a crystalline form that is made up of twelve double-pentacles equally spaced across the surface of the globe, see figure 2.9. He believed this was the true meaning of the prophetic visions of the future, by the apostle John, writing in his Book of Revelation. John describes the coming New Jerusalem as having the light like the light unto a crystal, and being as long as it is wide as it is high, or geometric in shape. Jochman suggests that John is describing crowns or node points, and indicated that its structure would be based on a golden measure or the golden mean proportion of 1 to 1.617. Significantly, the only geometric figure that is composed entirely of golden mean proportions is a five-pointed star, the pentacle. Jochman writes:

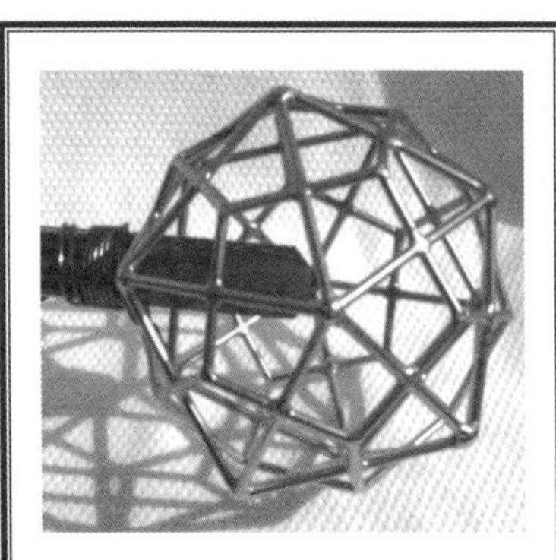

Figure 2.9 Sky Vajra demonstrating the "Christ Grid" geometry and a pentacle within a pentacle [63].

> "What the prophet may have been portraying is the future New Earth with the new Penta-Dodeca crystal energy grid fully in place. The twelve gemstones and twelve gates of the New Jerusalem would be the twelve double-pentacle faces of the Penta-Dodeca crystal form".

Now, we have scientific confirmation that the grids have changed. It is understood this will eventually allow the shift to a higher level of consciousness for mankind. This is welcomed by those who seek peace on Earth.

Earth's Diamond Core

"My hypothesis is that it's like a diamond in the center of the earth, just one single crystal"
Dr. Ronald E. Cohen

When shock waves from earthquakes ripple through Earth, sensitive instruments at many locations on the surface can detect the effect. After studying earthquake records for decades, seismologists concluded in 1996 that deep inside the Earth, spinning inside a pool of iron, the Earth's inner core is a giant iron crystal slightly smaller but more dense than the moon, see figure 2.10. Geophysicists were forced to consider this possibility because of two anomalies. Firstly, seismic waves travel faster north-south than east-west, this is measured to be about four seconds faster pole-to-pole than through the equator, revealing slight variations in their paths. Secondly, the natural vibration or "ringing" frequencies of the earth are "split" so that instead of a series of single "tones", what is detected is a series of closely paired frequencies. This confirms that the inner core is "anisotropic" – it has a directional quality, a texture similar to the grain in wood that allows sound waves to go faster when they travel in a certain direction. Thus to understand what was happening, scientists decided to use super-computers and predict the properties of iron at high temperatures and pressure. There are three standard crystalline forms known to scientists as body-centered cubic (bcc), face-centered cubic (fcc) and hexagonal close-packed (hcp). The data fitted the hcp format, see figure 2.11, but hexagonal crystals have a unique directionality, which must be aligned and oriented with Earth's spin axis

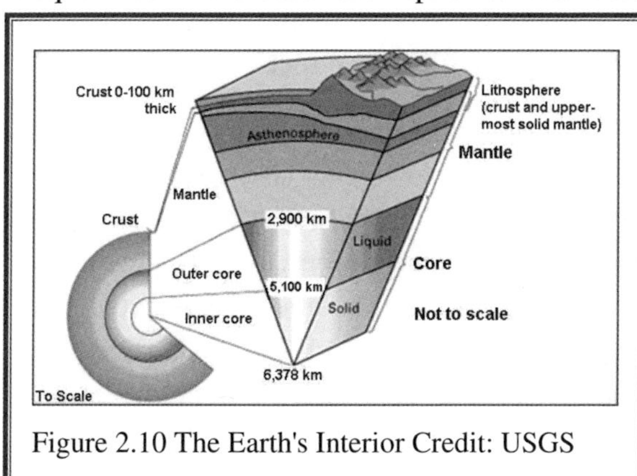

Figure 2.10 The Earth's Interior Credit: USGS

for every crystal in the inner core. So this lead geophysicists to the startlingly conclusion – was there just one big crystal in the core? Lars Stixrude of the Georgia Institute of Technology and Ronald E. Cohen of the Carnegie Institution of Washington noted that whatever texturing mechanism operates to form the anisotropic grain of the inner core, it must be almost 100 percent efficient. Otherwise the seismic anisotropy would not be as large as measured [64].

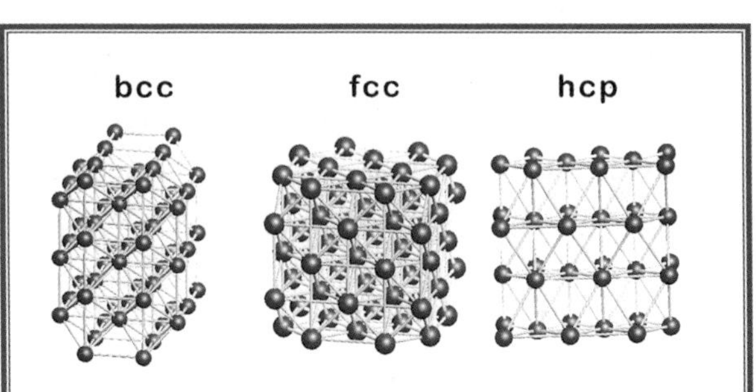

Figure 2.11 Standard crystalline forms, body-centered cubic (bcc), face-centered cubic (fcc) and hexagonal close-packed (hcp), lines show bonds between iron atoms.

> **"The very strong texturing indicated by our results suggests the possibility that the inner core is a very large single crystal."**

As amazing as it may seem, this interpretation is the simplest and most convincing explanation for the observed seismic data [65]. Similarly, J. Tromp of Harvard agrees but queries how the core material assumed this crystalline character [66].

Just imagine one gargantuan crystal nearly the size of the moon underneath your feet!

What is fascinating is that scientists say the diamond crystalline core is also spinning faster than the Earth's surface! Scientists calculate the inner core rotates an extra 0.3 degrees or so on average each year. In approximately 1200 years, the inner core completes an extra lap [67]. This speed of rotation is not always constant and some scientists believe there maybe a correlation between the inner core speeding up and the magnetic field responding with a "jerk". Hence, the speculation exists that the inner core may also influence magnetic field reversals. The thinking is that the outer core may produce the magnetic field, but somehow, the diamond like crystalline center may modify it in important ways. Maybe, there is geological evidence that shows some kind of *diamond energy* emanates from the Earth's inner core. Geologists cannot explain the mechanism for "kimberlite pipes". These are created by a sudden explosion and heat surge in the Earth's crust. If this occurs close enough to the surface then the location can be found and examined by drilling down into the impact. If the investigators are lucky, they will discover an elongated hollow tube completely lined with diamonds! Eskimos have been known to hand-dig their way down to such sites to claim sudden fortune. Obviously, the story that diamonds take thousands of years to form under great pressure and stress, is NOT what is going on here! Scientists tell us the Earth's core is crystalline and the existence of kimberlite pipes hints that the energy that originates from the core can heavily influence the structure of matter. Dmitriev et al. wrote the report *Physical Model of Kimberlite Pipe Formation: New Constraints From Theory of Non-Homogenous Physical Vacuum* (1998), which explains kimberlite pipes in terms of plasma phenomena that originates from the Earth's core [68].

The Earth Management Team

The Russian *Planetophysical State of the Earth and Life* report gives us a fascinating description of how the Earth is being changed [69]. The report states:

> "Moreover, the increase in the frequency, and scope, of natural self-luminous formations in the atmosphere and geospace forces us to wake up, and take notice. The processes of generation, and the existence of such formations, spreading all over the Earth, represents a remarkable physical phenomenon. What is most unusual about these natural self-luminous formations is that while they have distinct features of well-known physical processes, they are in entirely unusual combinations, and are accompanied by process features which cannot be explained on the basis of existing physical knowledge."
>
> "Hundreds of thousands of these natural self-luminous formations are exerting an increasing influence upon Earth's geophysic fields and biosphere. We suggest that the presence of these formations is the mainstream precedent to the transformation of Earth;"
>
> "These structures, or objects, then interact with the heliosensitive zones producing deep and powerful effects upon the environment such as the alteration of seismic activities, and chemical compositions. Because these non-homogeneous vacuum domain objects display not-of-this-physical-world characteristics such as "liquid light" and "non-Newtonian movement" it is difficult not to describe their manifestations as being "interworld processes"."

These *natural self-luminous formations* (NSLF) are also known as plasma spheres, plasmoids, orbs, "balls of light" and vacuum domains, amongst many other names. Dmitriev et al. wrote the report, *Planetophysical Function of Vacuum Domains* to document the Russian scientific understanding of this plasma phenomena" [70].

These plasma spheres have been captured on photos, even though the eye cannot normally see them. Estimates of large scale NSLF give their average size as 1.5km across, see figure 2.12. But the size can vary from being usually 10m to 2-3km wide. In one instance at a field trip to the Altay mountains, one scientists observed a vacuum domain sphere that was 8 km in diameter (Dmitriev et al., 1992). They are thought to be the possible source of "small comets or atmospheric holes", which are "unknown" bodies that fall to the Earth from space, discovered on ultraviolet images of the Earth made at high altitudes. Dmitrev's Vacuum Domain report mentions 20 each minute, creating "black holes" in the upper ionosphere.

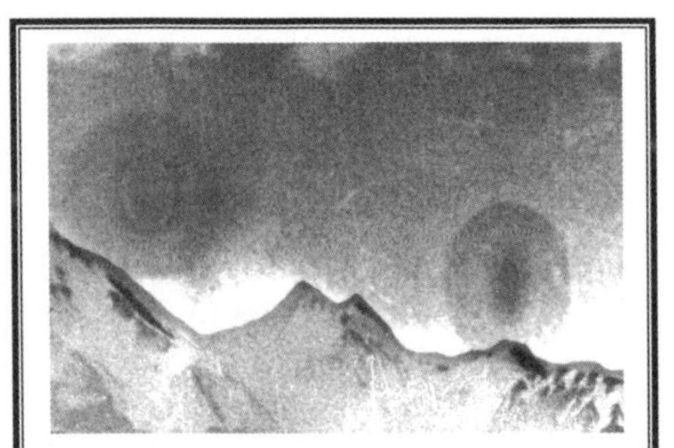

Figure 2.12. Largescale *natural self-luminous formations (*NSLF). Photo taken from a helicopter. Estimate of 1.5km width, above the Katun mountain ridge August 19, 1972 at 11local time. Credit: A. Dmitrev

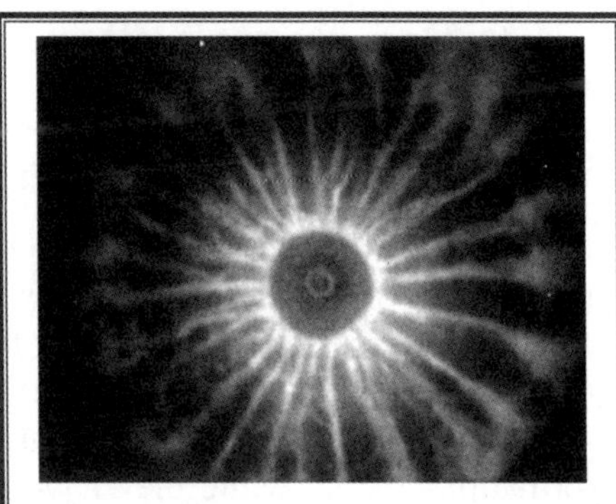

Figure 2.13 Plasma Discharge seen down a Plasma Focus Device, displaying the classic double layers of plasma. Courtesy: Anthony Peratt

As an aside, notice the similarity between these *natural self-luminous formations* (NSLF) photographs taken in Russia and the laboratory observed plasma discharge. Figure 2.13 shows what can be seen as one looks down the barrel of a plasma focus device! Also, see figure 2.14 and the small section, "How Does a Plasma Focus Device Work?" It is important to note that the Russian picture of a NSLF is taken in the ultraviolet, which is a slightly longer wavelength than X-rays in the electromagnetic spectrum, hence the X-rays are not seen. Dmitrev's Vacuum Domain report says, "Most often they appear near crust faults (in the energetically active zones of the Earth)". The Russians also say there has been an "exodus" of plasma spheres from mountainous regions and even an eye witness account of an event that took place in the eastern part of the Belokurikha massif, in an area of extensive geological faulting. It was reported:

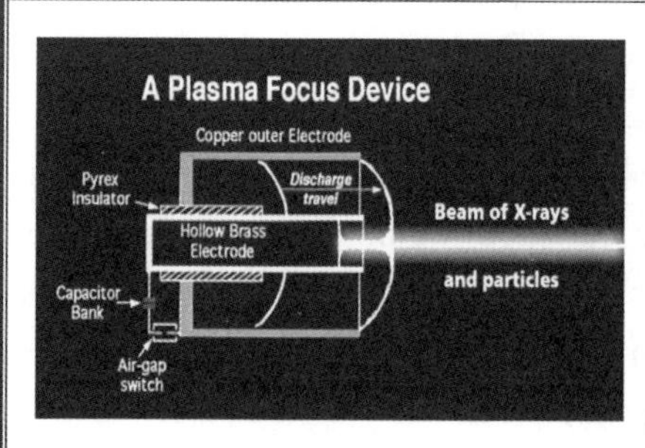

Figure 2.14 Plasma focus device Credit: Wal Thornhill

Who Does a Plasma Focus Device Work? Figure 2.14 In operation, the capacitors discharge in a several-microsecond pulse, the gas is ionized and a current sheath, consisting of pinched current filaments, forms and runs down the electrodes. When the sheath reaches the end of the inner electrode (the anode), the filaments pinch together, forming a dense, magnetically-confined, hot spot or plasmoid. The X-ray pinhole images show that plasmoids emit soft X-rays [21].

"The flame grew up from the Earth, then rolled itself into a bright ball, rapidly flew up and disappeared in the sky".

Figure 2.15 shows this event which was captured by photograph and is now referred to as the "Belokurikha flame". In 1992, Dmitriev et al. wrote a report called, *Plasma generation in energy-active zones* which describes the nature of these plasma entities that do not obey our laws of physics! [71] The existence of "atmospheric holes or small comets" that can be found in ultra-violet imaging is not disputed and research papers can be easily found [72]. Initially, these anomalous images were attributed to defective cameras, but when this was ruled out, the scientists involved had to come up with an answer. The theory of the Earth being hit 10 million times a year by a "rain" of ice, was devised, explaining how the Earth got its oceans [73]. As could be expected, this theory was not well received in the scientific community and papers from the principal scientist, Dr. Louis Frank were refused publication. He was told by one editor, "…if this was correct, we would have to burn half the contents of the libraries in the physical sciences."

Figure 2.15 The "Belokurikha flame". Photo captured in southeastern part of the Belokurikha massif. Photograph courtesy of Dr. Alexey Dmitriev

Eventually, Dr. Louis Frank told his story in the *book, The Big Splash*, (1990). In an interview with Laura Lee, Dr. Franks says, "What else could it be?" [74].

In 1991, Lee Carroll, a newcomer to the metaphysical community, started to give Kryon messages in Del Mar, California. The Kryon "channeling" was so well received that books comprised of these messages quickly spread around the world, they are now printed in nineteen languages. Carroll has been invited on numerous occasions to the United Nations in New York City, to give messages of love, to a United Nations chartered group, known as the Society for Enlightenment and Transformation (S.E.A.T.) [75]. According to Carroll, these plasma spheres are not UFOs, they are magnetic entities that are part of universal consciousness. He says, "This group has been part of the work of the Earth since it began. It's an energy that moves between two of the three grid structures on this planet and deals with them as they need adjusting." Carroll states the arrival of "The Kryon Group" in 1989, the year of "The Great Magnetic Storm", was to help reset the magnetic grids in response to our changing of the planet's goals and to enable our enlightenment. This adjustment finished at the end of 2002. Russians scientists validate claims by Carroll that there has been exodus of plasma spheres he calls, "place holder entities", the "ones who occupied the rocks", and the ones "in the cracks and crannies of your beautiful valleys" [75]. The metaphysical community, now have scientific backing to support claims that "old energy" has been leaving the planet. Yet, the resultant energy balance from the "changing of the guard", means humans need to take more responsibility.

Further proof of the existence of large plasma spheres is provided by NASA film footage of Discovery Missions from 1991 to 1996. *The Secret NASA Transmissions: The Raw Footage*, was produced by the Canadian ex-cable station manager Martyn Stubbs, who used sophisticated TV satellites, belonging to the cable station, to pick up unencrypted NASA film footage [76]. After scrutinizing 2500 hours of viewing, Stubbs put together a first class "special" to the delight of UFO enthusiasts!

As already mentioned, scientists describe celestial highways (cosmic string), that move around like "streams from a crazy garden sprinkler". So with this in mind, use your own judgement to assess "anomalies" that they have been captured by the SOHO satellite, whilst fixed on the Sun, see plates 15, 16 & 17. These images are totally amazing and there have been no satisfactory "official" explanations given. Maybe, we can also see "entities" riding the strings!

Finally, for more "official" acknowledgement of these plasma spheres, we can thank the United Kingdom (UK) Freedom of Information Act, which came into force, 1st January 2005. The UK Telegraph newspaper reported, 7th May

2006, that scientists at the Defence Intelligence Staff, part of the Ministry of Defence (MOD) on behalf of the British government, have been studying the "atmospheric phenomenon" of plasmas for four years [77]. The findings were published in a four-volume, 460-page report, titled *"Unidentified Aerial Phenomena in the U.K. Air Defence Region."* [78] This study was code-named Project Condign, and it was classified "Secret UK Eyes Only". It was so secret only 11 copies of the final report were produced, and they were only circulated to a restricted number of high-ranking Royal Air Force and defense ministry officials, not even the MOD UFO department were informed [79]. After years of denial, this ultra top-secret report came to light through the efforts of UFO author and university lecturer Dr. David Clarke and fellow ufologists Gary Anthony. The bulk of this report has now been published on the Internet by the MOD, with some censorship that appears to be largely related to the effect of plasma on radar performance. From the Condign Report, Executive Summary page 7, we find:

> "Considerable evidence exists to support the thesis that the events are almost certainly attributable to physical, electrical and magnetic phenomena in the atmosphere, mesosphere and ionosphere. They appear to originate due to weather and electrically-charged conditions. ...some of the events may be triggered by meteor re-entry, the meteors neither burning up completely nor impacting as meteorites, but forming buoyant plasmas."
>
> "Depending on an object's color temperatures and aerosol density, it may be seen visually, either by its self-generated plasma colour, by reflected light or in silouhette by light blockage and background contrast. As an electrically-charged but not ionised, gaseous mass, this may be either visible to the eye but not radar sensors, or fully ionised and visible to both." [80]

Interestingly, the report says the existence of UAPs is "undisputable" and refers to "the recent increase in UAP events". It even mentions Russian & U.S. interest into this particular plasma activity. Well, we know that 99.9% of the energy in the Universe exists in the fourth state of matter—plasma that can self-organize into various structures. Moreover, we have had "unprecedented" solar activity delivering vast quantities of plasma to Earth. Russian sources make it very clear that the frequency of this plasma phenomenon "grows several times in the years of active Sun" [81]. In the metaphysical community, it is understood that these "Messengers of Light" are busy working in order to create a new version of Earth. Maybe, we could even consider the increased presence of these plasma spheres, represents more heaven on Earth. As various scientific, military and government organizations watch this daily activity, they must realize that plasma "magnetic entities" exist, which are totally beyond human control.

Chapter Three

Earth's Changing Electromagnetic Environment

"I have grown to understand that the Galactic Alignment is the underlying reason for the unprecedented transformation currently sweeping the globe, and therefore the Maya win the best prize for prophecy"
John Major Jenkins

Earth's Alignment with the Heart of our Galaxy

Ancient cultures were aware that Earth makes a rare periodic alignment to the center of our Milky Way galaxy. As this is a significant event, there is a wealth of esoteric knowledge, embedded into art, architecture and literature, specifically left as a message for future generations. Wherever the heavens were mirrored and depicted, there is generally some subtle pointers to the Galactic Center. We know that every 25,920 years (normally approximated to 26,000), a great circular arc in the heavens known as precession is completed and the Earth aligns itself directly with the center of the galaxy. This is due to the Earth making a slow wobble on its axis and hence changing its orientation to the Galactic Center. It is understood that when these alignments occur, they offer spiritual renewal for humanity, a transformation or evolution of consciousness. The next galactic alignment is predicted to occur with the rising Sun on December 21, 2012 and this opens the way for the beginning of a New World Age.

The Galactic Center region is filled with relativistic electrons and magnetic fields, producing strong radio emission. The nucleus is marked by a bright radio source, Sagittarius A*, pronounced A star, which looks like an exploding bubble. The Galactic Center demonstrates abundant arcs, threads, and filaments which is a challenge to mainstream theories but is more confirmation of the Electromagnetic Universe. It is thought that a complete physical alignment would deliver a galactic size energy shift. Scholars who study galactic cosmology and cultural heritage, accept that Mayan Elders and priests maintain a highly creditable body of knowledge [1]. John Major Jenkins in his seminal work *Maya Cosmogenesis 2012,* writes:

> "If we imagine this field as being similar to the lines of force surrounding a magnet, we can understand that our changing orientation to this field has immediate consequences, and little to do with cause-and-effect transmission of energy between us and the Galactic Center. We are, instead in a relationship of *resonance* with our source, one that connects us deeply within to each other and, in fact, to all other beings in this galaxy. Based upon these considerations, I would like to emphasize that the Galactic equator-the precise edge of our spiraling galaxy-is the Zero Point location of the turn about moment in the cycle of precession. This World Age shift occurs when the solstice Sun crosses over the galactic equator, and thus the Galactic Alignment in 2012 is about a field-effect energy reversal."

Jenkins wrote a second book, *Galactic Alignment,* which gathered information from around the world, unveiling how other ancient civilizations knew of the same celestial alignment [2]. In that book, Jenkins suggests that there is electromagnetic entrainment between the Earth, the plane of our solar system, and the galactic plane taking place.

> **It is this entrainment which we are experiencing today, and the magnetic fields will be the strongest as we fully align with the Galactic Center, and hence influence our spiritual evolution.**

These ideas are not new and we find that Jenkins brought to light the work of Dr. Reiser who wrote the now out of print book *Cosmic Humanism* (1966). Reiser suggested that electromagnetic fields emanating from the Galactic Center, and their changing field dynamics, are linked to biological evolution. Reiser even states:

> "... the coil of life (DNA) which supplies the architectural pattern for the fabrication of all organisms has something to do with the earth's rotation and its magnetic polarities, and the cosmic ray showers which originate in our own spiral galaxy."

The Philosopher Dr. Reiser is not well known today, but he maintained a close relationship with Dr. Albert Einstein. In fact it was Einstein who made the suggestion that Dr. Reiser change his original title, "Scientific Humanism" to "Cosmic Humanism." Jenkins uses Reiser's arguments and studies to obtain the following model:

> "Precession changes our angular orientation to the larger magnetic field of the galaxy in which we are embedded. During regularly occurring eras in the precessional cycle, as indicated by the solstice-galaxy alignments (probably the equinox-galaxy alignments, too), the earth's protective magnetic shield becomes unstable and oscillates. Without a complete field reversal being required, this oscillation allows greater amounts of mutational rays to strike the surface of the earth. While this may result in mutations and a greater chance for "evolution", of greater significance is the possible transformative effect on human consciousness during alignment eras, when human beings are exposed to higher doses of high-frequency radiation."

The transformation process on human consciousness by the upcoming galactic alignment can be compared to a galactic sized kundalini awakening! At the human level, kundalini is associated with spiritual transformation and occurs when dormant energy held in the base of the spine is awakened. This energy then rises through the chakra system, until it finds it way out through the crown center at the top of the head. At this stage, the individual becomes a more evolved spiritual being. This process is not well understood even by the most spiritually advanced. For the galactic comparison, we can consider that the Galactic Center is the root, the Earth is compared to the heart and the Pleiades as the crown system. Jenkins identified the Pleiades star system as the Galactic Anti-center. Even though Orion and Gemini lie in the same direction, the choice of the Pleiades was made because it has always been associated with higher consciousness. For students of metaphysics and mysticism, this concept of a galactic size kundalini awakening that transforms consciousness is truly thought provoking! Kundalini is often described as a troublesome process, but this is not always the case, yet, the comparison with the coming 2012 galactic alignment is compelling. At this time, those with high consciousness are reminded that we are sufficiently empowered to create our own reality. We must remember our mastery and hold our intent firm that the coming evolutionary energy and changes will be bringing mankind and the Earth back into balance. This is the true meaning of the myth of the Phoenix rising from the ashes, symbolizing the death of the old and rebirth of the new. The pendulum has swung as far as possible into the descent of unconsciousness and now 2012 symbolizes the return to higher consciousness, metered with balance and harmony.

In support of Jenkins choice of the Galactic Center being the root, astronomers can now provide radio images taken of the galactic core, see plate 18. The dominance of the color red results from the fact that infra-red is the predominate wavelength of the light in that region – and also because the image was taken in the infra-red to eliminate the effect of cosmic dust. The long parallel rays slanting across the top of the above radio image, are known collectively as the Galactic Center Radio Arc and jut straight out from the galactic plane. The Radio Arc is connected to the Galactic Center by curving filaments known as the Arches. The rich imagery of doorways, portals and gateways leading to the heavenly realms, depicted in art and architecture around the world, seem to be validated by this image. The Radio Arc and the Arches have their geometry because they contain hot plasma flowing along lines of a constant magnetic field [3]. The Pleiades, also known as *The Seven Sisters,* identified by Jenkins as the Galactic Anti-center are young "hot blue" stars that have formed within the last 100 million years, see plate 19. The infra-red of the Galactic Center and the blue of the Pleiades also reflect the opposite poles of a magnetic body!

Galactic Core Explosions: The Evidence

Dr. Paul LaViolette is an astrophysicist and author of *Earth Under Fire* and *Beyond the Big Bang.* Among his many accolades, he is recognized in the Marquis Who's Who in Science and Engineering, and has published many original papers in physics, astronomy, climatology, systems theory, and psychology. The work of LaViolette gives credence to the theories that suggest the Earth is periodically disturbed by fierce emissions from the Galactic Center. Due to the serious implications, the research of LaViolette cannot be ignored. Since he proposed his theories in 1983, they have been increasingly borne out by scientific observation [4]. LaViolette was the first scientist to demonstrate that the Galactic Center periodically spews out cosmic rays, which could total an energy output equal to hundreds of thousands of supernova explosions. He coined the phrase G*alactic Superwave* to refer to this periodic seyfert-like galaxy activity. The term *Seyfert galaxy* is an astronomical term commonly used for galaxies with heightened illumination caused by eruptions at their cores. Astronomers believed these eruptions were very infrequent, occurring every 10 to 100 million years in our galaxy. They also believed that the interstellar magnetic fields, close to the Galactic Center would provide a mechanism to prevent emitted particles from reaching the Earth at relativistic speeds. For these reasons, many did not believe that galactic core explosions posed any immediate threat to the Earth. In 1983, LaViolette presented evidence to the scientific community indicating that firstly, galactic core explosions actually occur about every 13,000 - 26,000 years for outbursts and more frequently for minor events. Secondly, the emitted cosmic rays escape from the core virtually unimpeded. As they travel radially outward through the galaxy, they form a spherical shell that advances at a velocity approaching the speed of light. Once the shell hits our solar system, the effect of this cosmic blast is to push interstellar dust into the inner solar system (in normal circumstances cosmic dust is kept out by the pressure of the solar wind). The result of this dust has a major effect, in a number of different ways, including: (1) an increased flaring of the Sun, (2) downshift toward the infra-red in terms of the solar radiation reaching the Earth, (3) significant deviation from normal regarding the total solar energy reaching the ground

In the book *Earth Under Fire,* LaViolette suggests that catastrophes are the result of eruptions from the center of our Milky Way galaxy. He points to radio telescope observations showing that the galactic core (Sagittarius A*), has erupted 14 times in the past 6,000 years, with about 80% of these outbursts occurring within 500 years of each other. Citing the ice core beryllium-10 record as evidence, he argues that Earth has not experienced a large core "superwave" outburst for 11,000 years and, as it has been around 700 years since a minor event. He concludes by suggesting that a volley of galactic cosmic rays had bombarded the Earth and solar system toward the end of the last ice age, 14,000 years beyond present. This finding also implies that other such superwaves had passed us at earlier times and were responsible for triggering the initiation and termination of the ice ages and mass extinctions. Reviewing LaViolette's predictions from his 1980-1983 Ph.D. dissertation, we find that most have been verified, even though his ideas were initially greeted with stiff resistance from mainstream astronomers. A long list of predictions and verifications are documented on his website [4].

With regard to our discussion, the nature of galactic cosmic energy being evolutionary and the significance of rock and polar ice discoveries are important to consider. During the period of 1981-1982, LaViolette became the first to measure the extraterrestrial material content of prehistoric polar ice. Using the neutron activation analysis technique, he found high levels of iridium and nickel in 6 out of the 8 polar ice dust samples, an indication that they contain high levels of cosmic dust. This showed that galactic superwaves may have affected our solar system in the recent past. In addition, he discovered gold in one 50,000 year old sample, making this the first time gold had been discovered in polar ice. Recently, glaciologists have found concentrations of iridium and platinum (rare earth elements), in polar ice, two to three times higher than normal, during the last ice age. Scientists also have similar evidence from chemically analyzing rock strata [5]. From a series of sedimentary strata from Italy, one layer had 25 times the concentration of iridium residing in adjacent strata. The iridium-rich layer forms the boundary between the Cretaceous and Tertiary periods, 65 million years ago. The increase of iridium over normal levels is much higher in northern latitudes, which confirms the iridium came from a cosmic source. During that interval, 50% of the Earth's genera were wiped out, hence the correlation between an increase of iridium and mass extinction.

So, as evolutionary biologists believe we are now facing the sixth mass extinction, due to the highest rate of species extinction since the dinosaurs disappeared 65 million years ago, it does coincide with claims of "highly catalytic" energy being delivered to Earth. Iridium is actually part of the heavy platinum group in the middle of the periodic table. Iridium, gold and nickel are all ORMUS elements, which can exist in the recently discovered "high spin" state. Thanks to the work of David Hudson, who spent twenty years investigating these highly catalytic elements, we now know certain elements can exist in a state that make them invisible to normal detection methods. Furthermore, it can be shown that these elements from the platinum group and gold are indeed "evolutionary". In an interview in 2000, LaViolette revealed the following mystical experience:

> "After I made my discovery [about the galactic core explosion], I had a dream in which I met with people: I don't know if they were extraterrestrials or advanced spiritual beings. In this dream, I was given a medal; they were awarding me for making this discovery. On their level, this was a major event: Terrestrials had finally found proof of this cosmic event so important that it has decimated the civilization before...They were very wise. You just had extreme respect for them. They were extremely mature beings—old souls. I don't know if they were real or not, but when you're doing work like I do, where you're operating outside of the envelope, you need something to keep you going." [6]

Finally, LaViolette reveals that there is now some "official" monitoring of the Galactic Center. He is quoted as saying: "They're watching the center now every day. It's something they weren't doing 15 years ago. Now the radio telescopes schedule time every day to observe the center of the galaxy. That's what the Starburst Foundation was recommending back in 1984...at least daily observation of the galactic center…" Well, now that astronomers are regularly watching the galactic core, maybe it is pertinent to ask the question: does it have anything to do with the fast approaching galactic alignment in 2012?

A Galactic Leap of Consciousness

Energy driven evolution appears to be the way of Universal order, reaching up to ever increasing degrees of complexity. From the paper *Consciousness As A Self-Organizing Process: An Ecological Perspective,* the authors state:

> "We are now coming to understand the innate tendency of energy systems to evolve into structures that capture energy and use it to organize even more complex, flexible, and tenacious structures."
>
> "It turns out that systems which exist far from equilibrium are the natural product of the self-organizing tendencies of energy currents throughout the universe to move toward greater complexity."
>
> "Thus these systems are information intensive, capturing free but patterned energy from the environment and using it to enrich their own complex structures." *[End of excerpts]* [7]

As energetic systems, the Earth and human beings are both simultaneously undergoing transformation. Here, captured energy facilitates evolution and the first indication is a change in the electromagnetic field. The evolution of the human energy field is explained in chapter 8, *Strengthening our Energy Field Is Spiritual Evolution.* The science of "patterned energy" relates to the relatively unknown scalar and torsion fields, which distribute information around the universe and this is discussed in more detail in chapter 9, *Universal Energy.*

It is very difficult to discuss the evolution of human beings because there is so much "evidence" that is hotly disputed. However, anthropologists believe that the genus Homo appeared about 2 million years ago, a major expansion of the brain occurred about a half million years ago, and the appearance of anatomically modern humans appeared about 150,000 years ago. It is believed that there were three types of humans, Homo erectus, Homo neandertalis and Homo sapiens that came from a common ancestor, Homo sapiens (archaic). There is no strong evidence of archaic and anthropologists have no idea why erectus and neandertalis became extinct, even though there is apparently some evidence of all three living in the same place at the same time about 100,000 years ago [8]. It is agreed that 40,000 years ago, Homo sapiens underwent a transition to modern behavior but there is no consensus of opinion for how that occurred either. Yet, Greenland ice core data clearly shows there was a significant surge in cosmic radiation 40,000 years ago that lasted for about 3,000 years [9]. During this period, the Earth's magnetic field dropped in strength to about 10% of today's value, and so without the normal protective shield, cosmic radiation penetrated the Earth's atmosphere with ease. The facts reveal that the climate changed and there was a host of evolutionary changes, where numerous species in the Northern Hemisphere either underwent significant change or disappeared altogether. It is evident that the rare occurrence of a significant increase of cosmic radiation and the corresponding evolutionary changes are connected. We must conclude that evolution is not a slow progressive process, but rather it is marked by sudden external cosmic events, that directs the process.

"Human evolution could soon occur at a rate and with a set of rules that may be very different than what the Darwinian model has characterized so far."
Bruce Lahn, geneticist

Genetic research provides "overwhelming evidence" that human genes are still evolving and there is clear evidence of "accelerated evolution" in genes controlling brain size and complexity [10]. Thus evolution is deemed to be "fast", because genetic changes have been found to take place in a few thousand years, and not in millions of years as it was previously understood. After 50 years of research into DNA, geneticists now tell us that our genes (a subset of the DNA molecule), reinvent themselves to meet the challenge of changes to the electromagnetic environment. Studies show that even organisms as primitive as bacteria can actively modify their own genes. Hence, the view that humans and all other life forms were only products of random accumulated genetic accidents has to be discarded, (see important chapter notes here) [11]. Therefore, we can presume that a massive blast of electromagnetic energy from the Galactic Center, our Cosmic Mother, is quite capable of making dramatic updates to human DNA and consciousness. Therefore, when seers tell us that mankind has made the choice towards evolution and higher consciousness and that in previous evolutionary upgrades, "consciousness was delivered to the planet", described as "appropriate spiritual cosmic delivery... which continues to this day" [12]. The scientific perspective suggests that cosmic energy sources fulfill all the criteria to make these statements valid. The remainder of this chapter identifies the energetic impetus currently driving evolutionary change on Earth.

Cosmic Ray Homeopathy: Preventative Medicine for Earth

Amongst the electromagnetic onslaught that the Earth is currently experiencing, are galactic cosmic rays, moving in essentially straight paths, traveling close to the speed of light. Yet, the nature of this activity is such that scientists are starting to murmur that it looks like the Earth is being targeted!

"Some mysterious source from beyond the galaxy periodically zaps Earth with high-energy cosmic rays from all directions" [13].

When Japanese scientists registered cosmic rays coming from the same region of space at unexpectedly high energies, it was investigated and confirmed by the U.S. National Science Foundation's detectors in Utah. This lead to the discovery of, "a tightly clustered group of four ultra-high energy events from one segment of the sky". Professor Glennys R. Farrar, a physicist at New York University, is quoted as saying:

> "If, as widely supposed, tumultuous magnetic fields fill most of the cosmos, then charged particles such as these ought to be deflected when traveling to Earth and would not point back to their sources. The discovery of this bundle of cosmic rays seems to tell us that there is at least one direction in which the fields are sufficiently weak that the particles are not dispersed - just as one can sometimes see a patch of blue sky through a break in the clouds." [13].

> "By incredible luck, the source of this handful of ultra-high energy particles is in just the right direction to be seen clearly"

According to conventional theory, what was designated as "incredible luck" should not be happening! Cosmic rays are charged particles that constantly rain down on us from space. Scientists understand that most of those particles have solar origins or originate from exploding supernovae, but for the extremely energetic there is no scientific consensus about origins. Experts believe that the extreme cosmic rays, above 10^{19} eV, are rare and the arrival rate is only 1 particle per square kilometer per year, see figure 3.1. The especially interesting ones have energies above 10^{20} eV and have an estimated arrival rate of just one per square kilometer ($1/km^2$) per century! With this kind of hit rate, what is all the fuss about? Well apparently, the primary cosmic ray hits nuclei in the air, which creates secondary particles, which themselves hit further nuclei, and this sets up a cascade effect. An "extensive air shower", is created, which arrives at ground level with billions of energetic particles that can be detected over approximately 10 square kilometers.

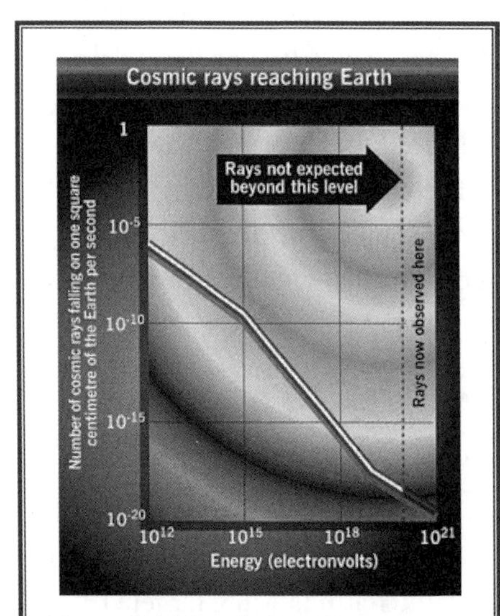

Figure 3.1 Cosmic Ray Energy Distribution Credit: Unknown

Like a doubled-edged sword, cosmic rays are believed to stimulate biological evolution by causing genetic mutation, but they are also regarded as being harmful to living organisms. So, with this in mind, it is instructive to know that in 2000, Polish scientists measured energetic particles in the range 10^{15} eV - 10^{17} eV and reported, "Lodz hodoscopic array has been registering extensive air showers (EAS) for most part of the year" [14]. It is not a coincidence that the Auger Experiment in Argentina is now tasked to investigate these extreme cosmic rays. A collaboration of more than 250 scientists from 16 nations, funded to the cost of 50 million dollars, will search for the source of cosmic rays [15]. Researchers will use the observatory, which consists of hundreds of small detectors spread over 1,200 square miles of farm and ranch land, to explore the universe. It was reported that the inauguration occurred in November 2005.

Barbara Marciniak is an internationally acclaimed trance channel, inspirational speaker, and best-selling author. In Marciniak's book, *Earth: Pleiadian Keys to the Living Library* (1995) we find the following:

> "When you encounter cosmic celestial events in your future, you will already have been exposed to the energy. So what you are being given now is like a homeopathic dose." [16]

The latest book by Marciniak, *Path of Empowerment: Pleiadian Wisdom for a World in Chaos* (2005), provides a formula for the dramatic increase in energy transmission rates [17]. Thus, from 1987 – 1996, the "energy of acceleration" will increase 10 times, year on year. From 1997 – 2006, the energies will increase 100 times, year on year. The last five years until 2012, 2007 – 2012, the increase will be 100,000 times, year on year. We are told in a rather matter-of-fact manner, this will have the effect of, "basically sending everybody soaring into orbit". There is no fudge factor here, we are told the energies are coming from the Galactic Center. In the discussion paper about Gamma Ray Bursts and CETI, the idea is put forward that the Sun would act as a gravitational lens. "Any beam of electromagnetic radiation (whether light, radio waves, or gamma rays) hitting the Sun from $\approx$ 540 Astronomical Units (AU) or farther out is focused by the Sun's gravitational field into a beam used for communication" [18]. This suggests that the Sun, in conjunction with "the network of tubes of light", provides a mechanism to explain how the Earth appears to be suffering from cosmic blasts. There is only a hint that this is being considered by NASA, who have recently started to refer to the "Superhighway" from the Sun in relation to space weather. Thus, bearing this in mind, dramatic reporting of cosmic ray phenomena can be found. From the story headlined, *"Unknown Energy Surges Continue to Hit Planet, Global Weather Systems in Chaos"*, we read:

> "An increasingly panicked global effort is now underway by the world's top scientists to understand an unprecedented series of "blasts", energy surges, which the planet has been taking from as an yet unknown source which has been bombarding Antarctica with cosmic rays and disrupting Northern Hemisphere weather systems on a global scale."
>
> "The first of these cosmic ray blasts occurred nearly 5 years ago and have been increasing in their frequency and intensity since the end of November. The once normally darkened skies of the Northern Hemispheres Arctic regions are now in twilight due to these blasts. Wayne Davidson, from the Canadian Government's weather station at Resolute Bay, located in the Arctic Circle, says about this mysterious lighting, 'The entire horizon is raised like magic, like the hand of God is bringing it up.'"
>
> "On December 1, 2004 the largest recorded blast sent not only shockwaves through the world scientific community but also through the Northern Hemisphere resulting in one of the largest weather events in recorded human history when 86,800 square miles of China was shrouded in fog, bringing transportation systems (especially air travel) to a virtual standstill throughout the country" [19].

Space Weather: Mayan Prophecy Fulfilled

As we attempt to understand the possible impact of Earth changes, there is a need to consult the "wisdom keepers" who have kept the memory of previous Earth changes alive. Also, known as the "Keepers of Time", Mayan Elders keep very precise calendars which describe and interpret the energies associated with the evolution of consciousness. History is seen as an evolutionary process that spirals, where similar events are favored at certain points in the cycle, yet, there is never an exact repeat, as each cycle is never identical. This process is nurtured by increasing levels of consciousness fostered by cosmic energies. The Mayan believe that there is one source of all energy which is divine consciousness, manifesting itself as an infinite number of possible creations, existing in all dimensions. Each creation has its own frequency and all matter is essentially interconnected. Hence, reality is based on energy, frequencies, and harmonic resonance. Time and space are not separate entities, space-time rather like Einstein's space-time, is a single quantity. It is a referred to as "najt", a spiral where history mostly repeats itself in a period of time. Understanding changing cosmic energies and how these influence human consciousness enable Mayan timekeepers to make precise predictions about the future. Thus, the importance of the Mayan belief that we are connected to the Galactic Center through a resonant circuit that transmits all evolutionary programs and memory patterns to each respective star system. In our solar system, the Sun focuses these vibrations down even further into the various planetary bodies. This idea can be understood through the Mayan concept of Kuxan Suum, literally "the Road to the Sky Leading to the Umbilical Chord of the Universe." This umbilical cord is a resonant pathway that connects the individual, through the Earth's core and the heart of the Sun, to the Galactic Center, our Cosmic Mother [20].

To integrate these Mayan beliefs, we must understand that the Maya describe a World Tree as well as a World Mountain. The World Tree is an axis that runs through the Earth projecting perpendicular planes (branches) unto the surface of the Earth, but it is anchored in the World Mountain in the center of the Earth [20]. We can interpret the trunk as the magnetic dipole of the Earth, the branches of the World Tree as being the electromagnetic grid of Earth and the World Mountain as the inner core of the Earth. The analogy of branches could also serve to encompass the "web" of electric currents and magnetic fields surrounding our planet in the ionosphere and magnetosphere. Most Mayan researchers agree that Mayan pyramids symbolize the World Mountain and speculate that the terrace-like pyramidal structures could actually reflect layers within the Earth's inner core. The scientific discovery of anisotropy in the Earth's inner core and the diamond (octahedral) crystalline structure, seem to support ancient knowledge. Human beings have the ability to tune into specific energies generated by the Earth and balancing these energies is required for optimal well being. Thus, the belief by many researchers not just Mayan Elders, that the electromagnetic grid of Earth has a strong influence on human consciousness. Any change in the electromagnetic grid of Earth will have a corresponding effect on the consciousness of mankind. This will be discussed in more detail in chapter 7, *Balancing in Chaos*.

Mayan Elders view the December 21, 2012 date as the start of a new era resulting from the solar meridian crossing the galactic equator, and the Earth aligning itself with the center of the galaxy. The Elders tell us that the Earth will experience a re-birth and a transition from the Fourth to the World of the Fifth Sun. The Mayan timekeepers reveal that previous epochs have been dominated by the four traditional elements of earth, air, fire and water, but now the fifth element to reckon with will be the aether or space. This is being borne out, as indeed life on Earth is becoming dominated by space weather. At sunrise on December 21, 2012 – for the first time in 26,000 years – the Sun rises to conjunct the intersection of the Milky Way and the plane of the ecliptic, describing in the sky a great cross of stars and planets. This is also referred to as the "Galactic Cross" in Gnostic tradition, or the Cosmic or Solar Cross [21].

It appears that astronomical observations do shed some light on this ancient knowledge. In 2004, European astronomers reported that not all the stars near the Sun travel in a near circular path around the Galactic Center [22]. In fact, the neighborhood of the Sun is a crossroads of many streams, made up of stars with different origins and chemical composition. Within 1000 light-years of the Sun, 20% of these stars move in peculiar directions, mostly towards the galactic centre or away from it, running like the spokes of a wheel. These stars are seen as 'rebels', which are forced together on their unusual trajectory by a 'kick' received from one of the Milky Way's spiral arms. European astronomers believe that an increased density of stars and "gas", referred to as a "density wave" within the spiral arms, can deflect stars in their motion, so even though the exact mechanism is unknown, the current variation in plasma and incoming dust in our solar system, measured by Russian and European Space Agency astronomers is highly significant. This all suggests that our current position in the galactic cycle is of great importance for the inhabitants of planet Earth. Whatever, this powerful alignment with the heart of the galaxy has already begun and we are told it will continue to accelerate.

The Mayan "Serpent Rope"

The Mayans also prophesied that a "Serpent Rope" would arrive by 2012 from the center of our Milky Way galaxy out of which will step a bearded god of enlightenment. Various researchers have concluded that this represented some kind of wormhole or stargate that links vastly different regions of space. Plasma physics and Birkeland currents, can help us now fully understand this prophecy. Indeed, a serpent rope has recently arrived and it is merrily dancing around our planet! It is called the Equatorial Electrojet! See figure 3.2.

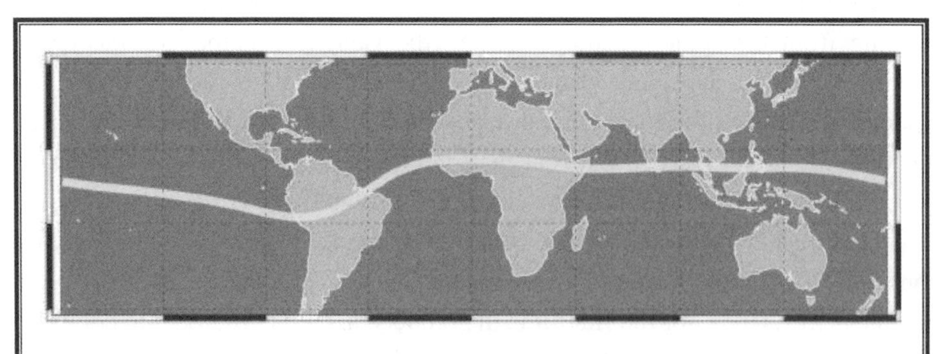

Figure 3.2 The Equatorial Electrojet as determined from CHAMP satellite observations. Copyright © Hermann Lühr, GFZ Potsdam

Here small sections denoted with ✧❖◆❖✧ provide slightly more technical details and can be skipped over by the less scientifically minded.)

Cosmic String Dancing Around Planet Earth 

It is important to realize that there is a web of electric currents and magnetic fields surrounding the Earth. Figure 3.3 shows us a schematic outline of the permanent terrestrial "Ring current" (Birkeland current), which is supplied by particles from the solar wind and the terrestrial ionosphere. It is part of the outer Van Allen belt, and is centered at the equatorial plane at altitudes of 10,000 – 60,000 km [23]. The Van Allen belts are part of the protective atmosphere surrounding Earth and consist of doughnut-shaped regions, containing high energy electrons and ions trapped in the Earth's magnetic field, see figure 2.1. A good analogy is that they should be considered as "comfort blankets" and the ionosphere would be the Earth's skin. The Van Allen Belts capture some of the charged particles whistling through the cosmos as the solar and galactic wind [24]. The ring current is also made up of the positive ions and negative electrons that drift in opposite directions creating an electric current that circulates clockwise around the Earth when viewed from north. These currents are not like electric currents on Earth that require a voltage potential or energy input. The ring current and other electric currents persist as long as its ions and electrons are trapped in the magnetic field. It is also important to note that the magnetic field produced by the ring current contributes to the magnetic field observed at the surface of the Earth. During a magnetic storm, the population of trapped particles is greatly reinforced and the ring current then becomes stronger. When this happens, the magnetic affects on Earth may grow 10-fold or more and there is a subsequent global decrease in the Earth's surface magnetic field [25].

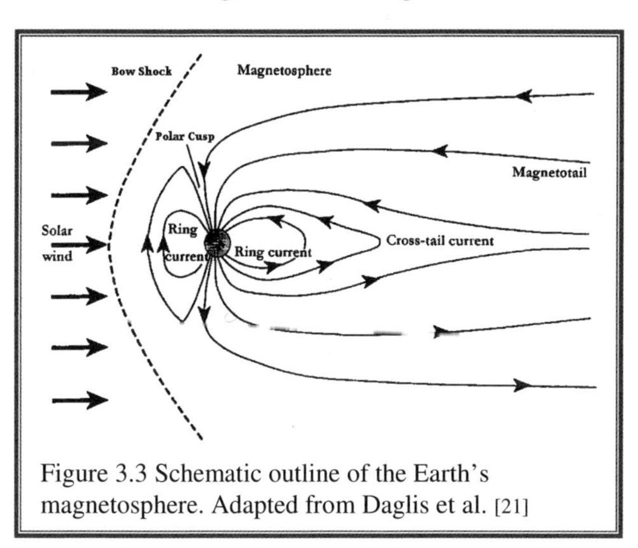

Figure 3.3 Schematic outline of the Earth's magnetosphere. Adapted from Daglis et al. [21]

Satellites are actually placed in a Geosynchronous Orbit (GEO), either very close to or actually in the main ring current around Earth. Problems occur when the outer boundary of the Van Allen Belt moves inward or outward. The Semi-synchronous orbit (SEO), which is used for GPS satellites, lies near the middle of the outer belt, directly in the "ring current" region. Both orbits are particularly vulnerable to high speed and highly charged particles that are generated during geomagnetic storms, where particle densities observed by satellite sensors, can increase by a factor of 10 to 1000 in less than half and hour.

Mythology and Plasma Phenomena

Figure 3.4 is an artist impression of the highly revered Australian aboriginal 'Sky Serpent' [26]. Despite interpretations that suggest a reference to the mystical kundalini, by applying the Ockham's Razor principle, the simplest explanation is that this is the basic structure of a feature seen in the sky. There is abundant mythology that refers to dragons and serpents. Maybe, they can now be now understood as how the knowledge of historical, often cataclysmic events are preserved. For example, there is the mythology of the Greek serpent-dragon Typhon, whose attack nearly destroyed the world before he was vanquished by Zeus [27]. Typhon is described as a flaming, bearded, feathered, or long-haired serpent, often embellished with multiple heads and mouths, whose writhing form appears in the sky as chaos and darkness overtake the world. The Greek sculpture of Typhon depicted in plate 20, shows three heads and the entwined serpent tails represent the braided nature of Birkeland currents.

Figure 3.4 Aboriginal Sky Serpent

The Equatorial Electrojet

Recently, scientists have been focusing on a new feature in the form of a thin electrical current, flowing in a very narrow band, dancing along the Earth's geomagnetic equator. This is a Birkeland current called "The Equatorial Electrojet" (EEJ) and it generates a "huge" electric current of "millions of amps". It is located approximately 100 – 115 km above sea level in the ionosphere, where it flows from dawn to dusk [28]. This narrow band of current looks like a snake across the globe, see figure 3.2, with very distinct signatures in satellite magnetic records, see figure 3.5. The electrojet has erratic behavior caused by the current reversing, and this is called the counter electrojet (CEJ). This electrical phenomena is being monitored by NASA, Goddard Space Flight Center and various other scientific establishments around the world.

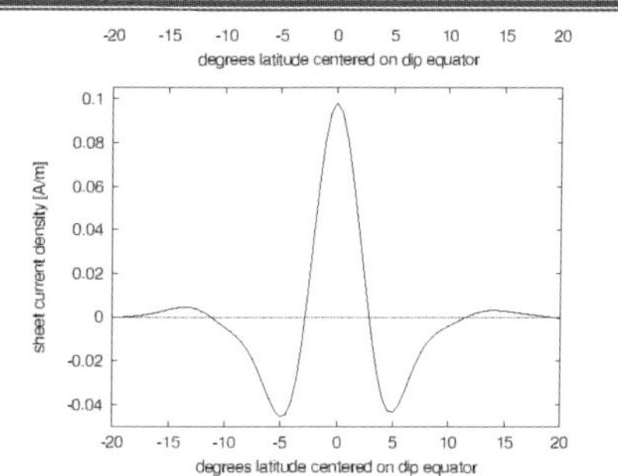

Figure 3.5 The Equatorial Electrojet (EEJ) magnetic signature. Common features of the EEJ are the return currents on both sides and the co-location of the electrojet peak with the dip equator. Copyright © Hermann Lühr, GFZ Potsdam

Historically, scientific papers have acknowledged that an equatorial electrojet existed. The discovery was first announced in 1922 and a little research followed over the years. However, it had not been considered a major phenomenon and all scientific attention has been given to the polar regions where there was an obvious electrical activity in the ionosphere in the form of the auroras. The electrojet first attracted the attention of NASA monitors between 1979 and 1980. A change was noted in the ionosphere in 1982, and because of the controversy, the Magnetic Field Satellite (MAGSAT) data sets were examined [29]. Even in 1993, a paper abstract stated, "It is shown that such fields, if any, at dawn are very weak and do not result in a persistent pattern from longitude to longitude or a pattern consistent with that expected from an electrojet current" [30]. However, this last paper is curiously out of step with action taken by the military, space agencies, and the geophysical community.

After the 1989 historic geomagnetic storm, scientific opinion changed dramatically and various initiatives were triggered. The electrojet suddenly attracted a lot of interest and the "International Equatorial Electrojet Year" (IEEY) was announced. An international task force was set up by the International Association of Geomagnetism and Aeronomy (IAGA) with the collaboration of member countries and support from various geophysical organizations, to contribute "to the basic understanding of electrodynamics in the Earth's environmental space" [31]. The French contribution to IEEY was ten magnetotelluric stations installed in Africa between November 1992 and November 1994 [32]. NASA launched a sounding rocket campaign in 1994 to study the ionosphere in cooperation with Brazil, with 33 weather rockets launched from Maranhao, Brazil. The purpose was to help scientists understand the "unique" properties of the Earth's ionosphere at the equator. This study involved 50 U.S. and Brazilian scientists supported by 300 engineers, technicians and staff [34]. In 1996, the Pacific Region Equatorial Anomaly Studies in Asia (PREASA) program, was set up to support the telecommunications network in the Pacific/Asian region. This organization consists of a wide variety of scientists from institutions in Russia, China, Japan, Taiwan, Korea, Thailand, Indonesia, Australia, Papua New Guinea and USA [35].

By 1998 the Equatorial Electrojet was firmly "part of the global circuit." *[36]*

In December 2002, Australia launched its first satellite in thirty years, called FEDSAT, with a multi-purpose mission that included monitoring the electrojet, the near Earth plasma environment and space weather forecasting. Researchers state that FEDSAT will orbit at 800 km and will pass through the region connecting currents and propagating wave energy to the ionosphere [37]. In review, geophysical authorities stated there had been an "explosive increase in the amount of data in geomagnetism and solar-terrestrial physics" [34]. What is described here is only a small part of the international effort to understand the Equatorial Electrojet and the near Earth electromagnetic environment that has drastically changed in recent times.

Finally, it has been placed on record that space weather forecasters monitor the Sun in relation to astrology, ancient text and the Mayan calendar to help anticipate the behavior of the Sun [38]. This confirmation was given in a live interview with Dr. Ernest Hildner, (recently retired), who was responsible for space weather forecasting as Director of the Space Environment Center at the US National Oceanic and Atmospheric Administration (NOAA). The live interview took place in October 2003, with Mitch Battros the owner of the Earthchangestv.com website and author of the *book, Solar Rain: The Earth Changes have Begun* (2005). Since Mayan Elders predicted the onset of a new era dominated by space weather, this is a fitting tribute to the accuracy of Mayan wisdom.

Extreme Physics Right Here on Earth

Now, to add to the perplexing mix of atmospheric changes, satellites are detecting flashes of gamma ray energy in Earth's upper atmosphere. One report suggested this amounted to "extreme physics right here on Earth". Yet, these scientists are linking this activity with electrical phenomena. First detected in 1994, by the Compton Gamma Ray Observatory satellite, blasts occur about fifty times a day, they last for about one millisecond and they launch into space from Earth's upper atmosphere, traveling at 99.99 percent of the speed of light [39]. A NASA press release stated:

"The energies we see are as high as those of gamma rays emitted from black holes and neutron stars."

The exact mechanism for how electron beams could accelerate fast enough to produce terrestrial gamma-ray flashes (TGFs) is not understood by the scientists observing this phenomenon. Terrestrial gamma-ray flashes have been associated with lightning strikes and may be related to red sprites and blue jets, side effects of thunderstorms that occur in the upper atmosphere and are typically only visible with high-altitude aircraft and satellites [40]. Scientists are puzzled because the favored theory of "runaway breakdown", caused by the interaction of cosmic rays and strong electric fields, does not match the size of the lightning discharge. Instead, the lightning is 50-500 times smaller than theory. Scientists suspect that "something else" could be happening, but they have no other theories. See the small section, "What is Runaway Breakdown?"

What is Runaway Breakdown?

"Runaway breakdown" begins with collisions between cosmic rays and the atmosphere, which generates a few very high-energy electrons. A sufficiently strong electric field can further accelerate these electrons, causing additional collisions, which produce more high energy electrons until "the whole process avalanches." Theory suggests that such an electron avalanche in the electrical field immediately following a strong lightning discharge could create a high energy electron beam at altitudes of between 30 and 50 kilometers. That beam would then produce gamma rays as it interacts with the atmosphere.

Plasma theory explains the "mysterious energy" seen emanating from Earth, as "incoming electrical energy", which is stored for a while and then suddenly released back out into space in bursts. This is described as a *relaxation oscillator circuit*, an explanation from plasma cosmology that can now be applied to Earth [41]. NASA have provided confirmation that Earth is now releasing excess electrical energy in the form of gamma rays back out into space. This scenario also suggests that our Earth could be moving through a denser and more electrically active environment.

In 2003, the European Space Agency press release was headlined, "*ESA sees stardust storms heading for Solar System*" [41]. Scientists reported that the weak configuration of the Sun's current magnetic field, which normally acts as a magnetic shield preventing cosmic dust entering into our solar system, is now allowing two to three times more stardust than at the end of the 1990s. It is believed that this influx could increase by as much as ten times until the end of the current solar cycle in 2012. Consequently, this and other reports suggest there has been a significant change in the electrical properties of our local region of space, providing another "huge surprise" for our atmospheric scientists. This phenomenon will be examined again in the light of further evidence of *New Energy* in chapter 9, *Universal Energy*.

The Current Chaos

Space weather induces electrical currents and this is providing much cause for concern. This is most apparent where the land is resistant to an electric current, and so any man-made conductor becomes an obvious target. A current flowing in a man-made conductor associated with geomagnetic flux is called a Geomagnetically Induced Current (GIC). When these currents are carried through oil and gas pipelines, they cause corrosion. This is a known problem, addressed in modern pipelines, where some protection from long-term current flows is achieved by applying a weak counter current of a few ampères. This is applied so that the pipeline has a net negative potential relative to ground [42]. Unfortunately, during geomagnetic storms the electrojet and auroral currents change polarity within minutes, rendering this "cathodic protection" useless, where during geomagnetic storms, ground currents as high as 1000 ampères have been detected [43]. Solar storms hasten pipeline corrosion and sometimes the consequences can be serious. When a corroded natural gas pipeline in the Urals sprung a leak and detonated in June 1989, 500 people died. In early March 2006, a major oil spillage from a corroded pipeline may have been caused by space weather. Various reports indicate that the leak was the second largest crude oil spill in Alaska, second only to the 1989 Exxon Valdez disaster. The media were quick to suggest that poor maintenance was to blame, yet vastly accelerated corrosion rates mean that space weather has to be considered as a factor. The following quote reported in the New York Times, from a BP Exploration Alaska company representative, states clearly that anticipated corrosion rates did not merit immediate concern. The newspaper report tells us:

> "When we inspected the line in September 2005, points of manageable corrosion were evident and all were within standards of operations integrity… Something happened to the corrosion rates in that line between September 2005 and the time of the spill that we don't yet fully understand." [44]

It is a fact, that September 2005 was the most active month on the Sun since March 1991 [45]. During this period of heightened solar activity, NASA news headlines read, "*Solar Minimum Explodes: Solar minimum is looking strangely like Solar Max*". The Sun was going berserk and it would seem that under these extreme conditions, aging pipelines have to be kept under constant surveillance [46].

The new electrical environment on Earth is also providing a headache for the power supply industry. The normal magnetizing current of a power station transformer is typically of the order of 1 ampère, so anomalous large GIC currents can lead to a saturation of a transformer. This can cause overloading, overheating, false relay tripping, and disturbances in the reactive power balance and harmonics. The nine-hour total blackout of the Canadian Hydro-Quebec power system was caused by the March, 1989 Great Magnetic Storm. The economical cost of the blackout, including power losses and replacing one damaged transformer in New Jersey (USA), has been estimated to be millions of dollars. The largest GIC associated with a geomagnetic storm was recorded at 150 ampères/phase at Newfoundland by Labrador Hydro Electric Utilities. Yet, for reference, the largest GIC ever observed was 201 ampères and occurred in March, 1991 in a Finnish transformer [47]. Obviously, this is a major worry for the power supply industry, so some preventative measures have been taken. In 1998, NASA launched the Advanced Composition Explorer (ACE) solar wind monitor and research satellite in order to provide real-time data for the U.S. Power Industry, thus providing early warning of potential trouble. In 2000, Powercast was launched as the world's first space weather prediction computer system. This system is used by national electric power grids to alert users to potentially hazardous current-inducing geomagnetic storms and it was first put into operation in the United Kingdom [48].

The Curious Sky Dancers

There are other electrical manifestations that have mysteriously appeared in recent times and this can only be described, in layman's terms, as weird! The *New Energy* has delivered a curious set of very strange electrical "entities" that manifest as now common luminous events in the stratosphere and mesosphere. In fact, eyewitness accounts of strange electrical phenomena have been reported and ignored for over a hundred years. Even when the reports came from credible witnesses such as airline pilots, and a scientific explanation was proposed by a Nobel Prize winning physicist, nobody paid attention and the phenomena were ignored—until recently, when the attitude of indifference changed in 1989 [49]. By accident, scientists testing a low-light camera system (LLTV) for an upcoming rocket flight, captured video evidence, which provided the hard evidence for what are now called sprites. From this single event, the scientific community woke up to find a new atmospheric, world-wide phenomena comprised of a host of *bizarre* electrical entities. In the early 1990s, worried NASA scientists searched tapes from the Space Shuttle LLTV camera archives and confirmed at least 17 apparent sprites above storm clouds. By 1993, NASA started to contemplate that this "newly discovered" cloud-to-space lightning might be fairly common and thus pose a potential threat to Space Shuttle missions, especially during launch or recovery [50]. The reason for concern becomes very clear when we understand that in July 1993, researchers managed to image 248 sprites over Kansas in just four hours. It becomes even clearer when we understand that these sprites are gigantic!

One description of a commonly seen sprite is like a gigantic red jellyfish (the ends of the tentacles are sometimes blue), that can extend vertically downwards between an altitude of 95km and 35km, see the central picture of the Sprite Gallery shown in plate 21 [51]. Telescopic investigations reveal that individual tendril elements may be in the order of 10m across and the envelope of the illuminated volume can exceed 104km^3. Scientists have given whimsical names such as sprites, blue jets, elves, sprite halos, gnomes and trolls. Collectively, they have been termed Transient Luminous Events (TLEs) and they only exist for thousandths of a second. In 2003, Japanese scientists reported a new description of mega lightning bolts called "gigantic jets" that reach an altitude of 90km [52].

This discovery of lightning discharges between the tops of clouds and the lower ionosphere has caused a serious rethink of our understanding of atmospheric electricity. Most atmospheric scientists readily admit their ignorance of this mysterious realm of rarefied air and charged electric particles and physicists jokingly referred to the lower reaches of the ionosphere as the "ignor(o)sphere" [53]. However, sprites and elves etc are just another natural manifestation of plasma discharge which looks like it is "alive". Laboratory experiments undertaken many decades ago, can mimic this phenomenon. There are a host of 19th century glow discharge tube spectroscopists, namely Rayleigh, Thomson, Wilson, and Langmuir, who all won Nobel prizes for their work [54].

In July 2005, NASA released a news item accompanied by an incredible image showing a red sprite, which looked like a "burning tree" situated above the National Cheng Kung University campus in Taiwan City, Taiwan, see plate 22 [55]. Actually, the photograph was taken in 2001, and the image is an illusion, as the sprite was in fact 300km away from the campus. Whatever, it appears to have been a totally awe-inspiring event and thoughts of the biblical burning bush come to mind! The explanation for this dramatic increase in electrical activity is that there is now more energy on the planet to balance. The Electric Universe model suggests that the "Earth plays a cathode role in the Sun's discharge and therefore is in the business of supplying negative electrons to space and receiving positive ions from the solar wind" [56]. According to plasma expert Wal Thornhill:

> "Thunderstorms are not electricity generators, they are passive elements in an interplanetary circuit, like a self-repairing leaky condenser. The energy stored in the cloud "condenser" is released as lightning when it short-

circuits. The short-circuits can occur either within the cloud or across the external resistive paths to Earth or the ionosphere. The charge across the cloud condenser gives rise to violent vertical electrical winds within the cloud, not vice versa. By creating a short-circuit to high altitudes in the storm the lightning effectively "throws the switch" connected to the glow discharge "tube" in the upper atmosphere." See the small section "What is a Capacitor?" [57]

What is a Capacitor?

A capacitor or condenser is a device for accumulating and storing electric charge. It is made of two conductors separated by an insulating medium. When charge is placed on one conductor it attracts charge of the opposite polarity on the other conductor. As a result, an electric field is set up between the conductors, producing a reservoir of electrical energy. As the charge on the capacitor increases, the electric field between the conductors will increase, placing a growing stress on the insulator. At some critical point, the insulator breaks down and the capacitor "short circuits", releasing the stored electrical energy suddenly. Such breakdowns may destroy a solid insulator and with it, the capacitor. However, if the charging rate is slow and the insulator is air or liquid, the damage may repair itself as fresh insulating material rushes in. That is a "self-repairing" capacitor. If the current is strong or the insulator weak, current will pass between the conducting plates, either steadily or in bursts, this then is a "leaky capacitor".

We have an interesting perspective from the world of Tibetan Buddhism. The Dakini is a female supernatural being or spirit, generally of volatile temperament, which is believed to act as a muse for spiritual practice. Dakinis are also known as "sky dancers", see plate 23 for some Dakini artwork. Similarly, scientists also describe red sprites and blue jets as if they are dancing [58]. Therefore, maybe this is the true origin of these supernatural beings and their re-discovery has been brought about by the dramatic increase of energy on our planet. If so, we have another example of mythology being linked to plasma phenomena. Whatever, the "life-like" property of plasma is being clearly seen.

The Schumann Resonance is dancing too!

Researchers have discovered that the Schumann Resonances are also being "excited" by the dramatic increase in *New Energy* phenomena. Firstly, the Equatorial Electrojet is acting as an amplifier to any input electromagnetic field – and that includes the Earth's natural Schumann Resonance – by a factor of 3-5 times [59]. Secondly, the Schumann Resonances are being excited by the same giant positive lightning ground flashes that cause sprites, boosting the amplitudes (intensity) of the Schumann Resonances, "several times greater than the background resonances" [60]. This supports claims by the Mystic Lee Carroll, who in January 1995, channelled that the magnetic grid lines or ley lines were repositioning and that local ley lines were "centering themselves" above "the great amplifier". Since this information was given in Hawaii, it is a clear reference to the Equatorial Electrojet, which "can be located up to 10°, or even 20°, latitude, or nearly to the latitude of Hawaii" [61]. The importance of these claims will be become clear when we discuss 'What the Egyptians Knew About Balance' in chapter 7, *Balancing in Chaos.* We will see that enlightened Egyptians truly understood the effect on the human energy field and consequent need for greater balance, in periods of heightened electromagnetic environmental conditions, caused by an erratic electrojet.

Hungarian scientists have come to the conclusion that it is not only the intensity of the Schumann waves that has changed, but the frequencies themselves that are also subject to substantial fluctuations [62]. They report that the lowest Schumann frequency is no longer 7.83 Hz, which was measured by Herbert König in the 1950s, but is closer to 8 Hz, sometimes even higher. The highest frequency values are occurring in the summer months (of the Northern Hemisphere), while they drop down again in winter. This trend is confirmed by investigations of the second and third Schumann Resonance frequencies. Here, the seasonal fluctuations are observed even more strongly and are measured to move between 13.8 and 14.1 Hz, and between 19.5 and 20.3 Hz respectively.

These observations substantiate metaphysical sources suggesting that the resonant frequency between the Earth and the top of the ionosphere has dramatically increased [63]. The Schumann Resonance measurement is normally taken between the Earth and the bottom of the ionosphere, which varies between 50km – 90km altitude. The top of the conventional ionosphere extends to 1000km altitude. However, the outer ionosphere reaches far out into space. In this ionospheric region, Alfvén waves (those magnetohydrodynamic waves discovered by Hannes Alfvén), exist in the ionosphere in the plasma state as resonant waves, sometimes described as oscillating or standing waves. These too should be considered when we try to measure the increase in resonant frequency from the earth to the top of the ionosphere [64].

Even though it is difficult to gauge parameter changes, due to lack of available historical data, we know that during high-energy particle storms, the region of the ionosphere, the upper boundary of the Earth's atmosphere, is being heavily ionized. Measurements taken at Arrival Heights, Antarctica, suggest this is leading to an increase of the resonance frequency and decrease damping of the first Schumann resonance. [65]. This observation is very interesting, especially when we consider the onslaught of cosmic rays hitting planet Earth. This indicates a dramatic boost in intensity of the energies that make up the electromagnetic spectrum that surround Earth. With respect to the Schumann Resonances, a suitable analogy is a pianist playing a piano chord. Previously, the notes were being played quietly, now, we now find that all the notes are being played much louder, so that even the higher Schumann Resonances are becoming much more pronounced, see figure 5.5.

The implications are that human beings can now tune into much stronger higher frequencies, accelerating human awareness to higher states of consciousness.

Finally, we have had over five decades of destructive programs to understand and control the upper atmosphere. This includes setting off nuclear bombs to study the impact on radio and radar communications [66]. This has been documented by Rosalie Bertell, the well-known Eco-warrior and Grey Nun of the Sacred Heart. In retrospect, deliberately making holes in the roof of the world seems rather foolish, as now we are being inundated with cosmic and solar rain.

The Magnetic Poles are Reversing *Fast*

Albert Einstein ranked the problem of explaining the origin of the Earth's magnetic field as one of the top three most important unsolved problems in physics. Until recently, scientists relied on very simple theories, but now that the Earth's magnetic field is fading at such a rapid rate, to the extent that there are satellite degradation issues, they are determined to find out what is going on! [67]

"It's quite surprising how little is understood about the Earth's magnetic field and how it's generated."
Jeremy Bloxham, Professor of geophysics

Historically, it was once thought that a solid layer within the Earth, made of iron or another magnetic material, formed a permanent magnet. This hypothesis was discredited because firstly, it could not explain how the magnetic field drifted and secondly, magnetic minerals only retain a permanent magnetism below their Curie temperature (e.g. 580°C for magnetite). Most of the Earth's interior is hotter than all known Curie temperatures, and cooler crustal rocks just don't contain enough magnetic content to account for the magnetic field.

The Geodynamo is the best known theory today, which postulates that the main part of the Earth's magnetic field is generated by a dynamo that operates in the Earth's fluid outer core, see figure 2.10. However, the details of how that dynamo works are still not totally understood. Paleomagnetic measurements of rocks indicate that the Earth has maintained a magnetic field for at least 3.5

billion years, so the dynamo theory has to explain how the magnetic field can be self-sustaining. Theory suggests that as iron is a conductor of electricity, electric currents flowing in molten iron would generate the requisite magnetic field (basic physics of electromagnetism). The molten outer core, more than six times the volume of the moon, convects as a means of releasing heat. This convective motion displaces flowing electric currents, thereby generating magnetic fields.

Geodynamo theory tends to gloss over the fact that the magnetic field is actually a composite, generated by electric currents that are deep within the Earth and high above the surface. The question arises: if the magnetic field generated by the Earth was so significant, then how do we explain the wild fluctuations in the direction of the magnetic field that occur in geomagnetic storms? Magnetic storms cause changes of 1%, to the total field strength of 50,000 gamma, the total geomagnetic field of earth's core (GMF), whereas typical diurnal changes are only 0.1% of the GMF. Yet, in one geomagnetic storm, the direction of magnetic North (measured at the Lerwick geomagnetic observatory in Scotland), changed by 5.1 degrees in only 25 minutes [68].

The dynamo today is operating more like a reverse dynamo or an anti-dynamo, actually destroying the dipole part of the field, which suggests a magnetic reversal is in progress.

Over the last 150 years or so, the main (axial dipole) component of the Earth's magnetic field has decayed by an estimated 10-15%. This is calculated as being a rate ten times faster than if the dynamo was simply switched off [69]. When geophysicists studied the evolution of the Earth's magnetic field over a 20 year period, by comparing measurements taken by the American satellite Magsat in 1980 and the Danish satellite Oersted in 2000, they noticed variations in the magnetic field in four main areas [70]. The first, under the Pacific Ocean in the Northern Hemisphere, is not a major concern because the rate of change here is only relatively minor. However, at the other three sites there are significant changes. These locations are at both poles and in the Southern Hemisphere, stretching from South America towards Southern Africa.

"The fact that it's dropping so rapidly gives you pause.
It looks like things we see in computer models of a reversal."
John Tarduno, Professor of geophysics [71]

The geographical area of most concern is called the South Atlantic Magnetic Anomaly, where the field at the Earth's surface is now about 35% weaker than would be expected. This "anomaly" over the South Atlantic, is cited as the cause of satellite failure as that region of Earth has now less protection from radiation due to the weakening of the magnetosphere. For instance, sensitive high-voltage instruments on the Hubble Space Telescope are powered down before the Hubble enters the South Atlantic Anomaly, an event that happens several times a day.

The European Space Agency (ESA) has recently approved a multimillion-euro space mission, called Swarm. As the name implies, Swarm is a constellation of satellites, and the mission scheduled for launch in 2009 will measure this anomaly. For scientists, the biggest benefit of Swarm is that high-quality magnetic measurements provide a new way of "x-raying" the hidden interior of Earth. Scientists are interested to learn more about this "anomalous field behavior", because it seems consistent with ESA computer simulations, identifying the "possible beginnings of a flip". Geophysicists think this all points to an "imminent reversal" in the Earth's North-South magnetic alignment. However, in geological terms, "imminent", could mean anytime between tomorrow and the next 3000 years, see plate 24a, plate 24b & 25 [72]. Yet, in reality, the South Atlantic Anomaly represents an area of Earth where the magnetic field has ALREADY flipped.

"There's really no question about whether the Earth's magnetic field will reverse again. The question is not, if that's going to happen, it's when that's going to happen."
Jeremy Bloxham, Professor of geophysics

If this process continues at the present pace, some researchers predict that the entire bipolar structure might actually disappear. We would then find on our planet "many north poles and many south poles scattered everywhere." If a reversal of the geomagnetic field does occur, it is more likely that it would not be a smooth transition, but marked by dramatic swings. This view is supported by evidence from geology that in past reversals, the decline was not always to zero. A lengthy reversal process can mean the magnetic poles can wander several times across the equator before stabilizing [73].

"It was hard for people to accept. They did not like the idea that the field reversed. It took about 50 years to convince people of this, but eventually that was established."
Mike Fuller, geologist

Steen's Mountain

The disorderly-flip theory is supported by evidence from geology that in past magnetic reversals the decline was not total. Lava flows that solidified at Steen's Mountain in southern Oregon (USA), during a lengthy reversal process, show that the magnetic poles wandered across the equator three times [74]. Though the strength of the field was reduced to about 20% of maximum, there is no record that it fell to zero gauss. Scientists regard Steen's Mountain as the best record of a magnetic reversal because the volcano spewed out 56 separate flows during that episode, each of these rock layers providing time-lapse snapshots of the reversal.

Within one particular flow, French geophysicists Prévot and Coe discovered that rock toward the top showed a different magnetic orientation than rock lower down. They interpreted this to mean that the field shifted about 3 degrees a day during the few days it took the single layer to cool. Such a rate of change is about *500 times* faster than that seen in direct measurements of the field today. Consequently, this scientific observation has been subject to much debate as it goes against conventional theory. As Prévot and Coe are considered "some of the best experimentalists in the world", their observations are difficult for skeptics to explain away [75]. Further analysis proved that the rate at which the orientation of the ancient magnetic field rotated, reached an astounding 6 degrees per day over an 8-day period. Coe et al. still maintain that these field changes recorded in the lava flows at Steens Mountain do reflect changes in the Earth's main magnetic field. Rob Coe, one of the two scientists who made the original Steens Mountain discovery, said the following:

> "And what we found was even harder to believe.....It was just as though, while the flow cooled, the field had moved sixty degrees, which if you calculate it out, that comes to about six degrees of movement per day. If we were observing this with a compass, you would be able almost to see the motion with your eye. It was truly astonishing and extraordinary." [73]

We know that it is quite possible for the Earth's magnetic field to move six degrees in a day because this is what happens when we have a geomagnetic storm, but usually the magnetic field returns quickly to normal. Obviously, what happened 16 million years ago at Steens Mountain, was that the lava erupted whilst the magnetic field was in the middle of a very fast flip and so a permanent record of events was recorded.

Now, the controversy here is that this discredits the dynamo theory and its time-scale of millions of years, so this part of the original research is conveniently ignored. However, it is cited here for one very good reason. We have to know, what could flip the poles *in a matter of days?* Well, Coe et al. gave a solar cause for the quick transition of the magnetic field. This conclusion was derived completely separately from the work of Paul LaViolette and acts as independent verification that the magnetic field of Earth can be reversed by solar activity. Paul LaViolette's seminal work in 1983, made the following proposal:

> "**Geomagnetic reversals are induced by solar cosmic ray storms**. He proposed that at times when invading cosmic dust causes the Sun to become very active and engage in continual flaring activity, major solar outbursts could occur that are a thousand times more intense than those currently observed. Further he proposed that solar cosmic rays from such a mega flare could impact the Earth's magnetosphere, become trapped there to form storm-time radiation belts, and generate an equatorial ring current producing a magnetic field opposed to the Earth's. If sufficiently intense, this ring current magnetic field could cancel out the Earth's own field and flip the residual magnetic field pole to an equatorial location. From this position it could later either recover or adopt a reversed polarity. He proposed that this geomagnetic excursion would be very rapid, occurring in a matter of days." *[Bold added for emphasis]* [76]

Well, everything that LaViolette proposed has been occurring with increasing intensity since 1989. We have scientific reports of cosmic dust engulfing the Sun and causing solar flares. The biggest flares have ratings that are virtually off the scale and NASA are predicting worse to come. There are geomagnetic storms that are so intense that new radiation belts are formed temporarily and we have a surprise new space weather feature, the Equatorial Electrojet, which is now acknowledged to be "huge". The magnetic field is quickly declining and in parts of the world the rate of decline is "alarming". The world-wide weather is increasingly bizarre and scientists are starting to see the connection with cosmic rays and space weather. Both poles are receiving blasts of energy and in one shocking report, the result was a record 60 percent loss of ozone in the upper stratosphere. Apparently, the ozone layer quickly recovered, or so we are told! [77]

LaViolette proposed a fireball aimed directly at Earth, an assertion supported by research related to evidence of "glazed" lunar rocks. The proposal made is that the Sun temporarily became a T Tauri-like star (a kind of variable star whose brightness varies irregularly) with solar flares of a far greater magnitude than normal, caused by the accretion of cosmic dust [78]. Interestingly, scientists who analyzed the glassy coating and crystalline interior of one lunar rock found that the coating is enriched in a number or rare earth elements and alkali metals including iridium and gold. The significance of these facts will be shown when we discuss ORMUS elements in chapter 9, *Universal Energy*. LaViolette's work has been ground breaking and it is not surprising he was given a medal, even if it was only in a dream!

New Magnetic Poles Promised?

In reviewing the writing of Barbara Marciniak, we are told that our current magnetic orientation does not serve us and so it has to be changed [79]. This was first published in 1995 and it is some acknowledgement as to what is happening to our planet, even if we do not like the consequences. Marciniak writes:

> "As the rays from the Sun change, activated by the consciousness of the inhabitants from Earth, and as the Sun releases solar bursts, the polar regions of the Earth are affected. The flares sent forth are like atomic explosions or jolts of electricity that go millions of miles deep into space. Earth's poles, which are magnets catch this energy. They grab energy that comes from space to the planet. Because of the magnetic force, they arc it either around the equator or inward to the core of Earth. Each pole grabs the solar energy, drives it in, and creates a huge cylinder of vibrational energy. As that vibrational energy jolts and jiggles to fit, it has to align with the energy gridwork of Earth that is connected from the poles. This gridwork is decreed by you, and to some extent, all energies merging or emerging through your version of Earth conform to this grid of beliefs."

> "Of course, many things are not in balance, which is why you are going to have a relocation of the poles so that the gridwork will be more able to catch the energy. Right now, the particular pole alignment cannot serve as the electrical ground or lightning rod that is required to avoid burnout. The poles create a lightning rod through Earth, though the current setup will short circuit everything. So, in order to avoid complete destruction, there will be a shift. The poles will move someplace else, as they have numerous times before when the balance of the Earth was at stake. There will be a minor shift from a space perspective. From your perspective, however, the shift will seem quite major."

The Plasma Core

> *"For decades, people thought of the Earth's interior as changing very slowly over millions of years. These results show that we live on a remarkably dynamic planet. They also underscore the fact that we know more about the moon than we know about what's beneath our feet. Now we need to understand what is driving this difference."*
>
> *Paul Richards, geologist*

Now, it is important to point out here that scientists still do not fully understand the origin of the Earth's magnetic field [80]. Some researchers have made the case that the Earth has a plasma core because the popular Dynamo theory does not match up with observations. Geophysicists have long wondered what gives rise to the geomagnetic field.

The heat of the solid inner and the liquid outer core is such that studies prove the heat would cook the magnetism out of magnets and liquefaction melt it away. Not surprising, these facts have been an obstacle to our understanding of how the magnetic field was created. One of the facts that is not well known is that if you connect the North and South Magnetic Poles with an imaginary line, the line would not pass *anywhere near* the actual center of the Earth. The Earth's main "dipole" magnetic field is not even symmetric with the body of the Earth! Actually, that is another misnomer, because there exists a number of additional, weaker magnetic poles that represent about 10% of the field strength. Even stranger, the movement and location of the two Magnetic Poles often seem to have no relationship with each other at all. Even though it is well known that the poles "wander around", they also sometimes "jerk" such as in 1962 and 1971.

What are the Polar Cusps?

Polar cusps are described as "magnetic funnels" but they could equally be described as vortices. There is one in each hemisphere between the Sunward magnetic field and the tailward magnetic field, focusing the solar wind particles. The solar wind particles enter the exterior cusp, which has a diameter of approximately 50 000 km, and then follow the converging magnetic field down to the ionosphere where the cusp size is around 500 km. NASA's Dynamics Explorer space probe determined that plasma wind streams in and out of the Earth via the poles and the polar cusps.

Researchers have demonstrated in a laboratory setting that a magnetic field can be created as a standing-wave of glowing aetheric plasma [81]. The main argument against this is that a plasma core would require a constant energy source. Of course, the obvious answer is that there *is* a steady supply of energy coming from the Sun. The Earth is bathed in a solar wind carrying plasma, **which is observed to spiral down into the poles of the Earth** via the polar cusps, this activity is being monitored by NASA's Dynamics Explorer space probe. See figure 3.3 and the small section, "What are the Polar Cusps?" [82] As part of the evidence for this, a solar eclipse provides us with a magnetic field that is weakened sufficiently to confuse migrating birds and effects the gravitational field [83].

An interesting alternative explanation for the origin of the Earth's magnetic field is provided by physicist C. Johnson from the University of Chicago [84]. Johnson addresses the failings of the Dynamo Theory with a neat suggestion of his own. From his mathematical analysis, he thinks that what we are actually observing is two fields almost canceling each other out! The fields are derived from convective cells that move opposite to each other, see figure 3.6. Johnson suggests the source of these cells would be enormous electric currents generated

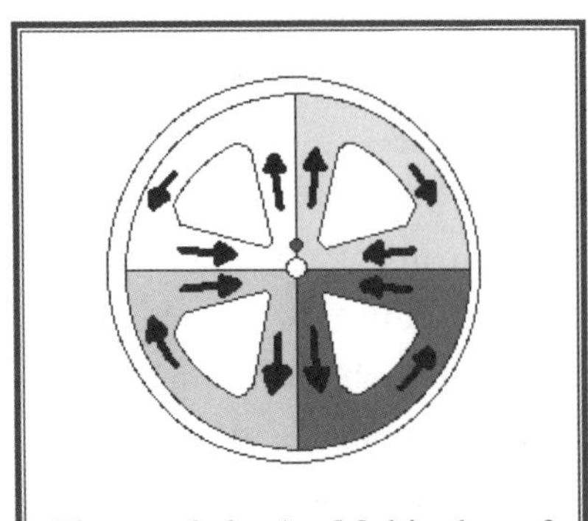

Figure 3.6 A Multitude of Convection Cells in the Earth's Core. Credit: C Johnson

from ionized iron as electrons are stripped off atoms in the heat and friction of the Earth's outer core. According to the "right hand rule" of electromagnetic theory, the direction of the magnetic fields thus created will be opposite, see figure 3.7. Of course the probability that they would be identical (due to various parameters such as size of the cells, velocities of flow rate, the proportion of ionized iron etc.) mean that the resultant of small differences would give an overall magnetic field measurement. Johnson's dissertation informs us:

> "Again applying symmetry arguments and the various conservation laws that we know should apply there, there is great statistical support for believing that they [convection cells] often exist in symmetric pairs, that have great similarity to each other, with opposite flow rotation, and where, as before, only the net effect of the difference between the pairs give any evidence of dipole magnetism. This also implies that, not counting eddy effects, there must be an even number of such active large convection cells at any moment."

This is not a plasma-based theory, but the principal is very similar. With plasma all we would need to create the opposing electric currents is a *separation of charge*. As Johnson points out, his model can be modified to reflect a multitude of cells that would help resolve the complex nature of the magnetic fields measured on Earth, still perplexing scientists. We can compare this to the known behavior of plasma that likes to self-organize into "double-layers". As it stands, this theory explains the quadrupole, octopole (and higher) components empirically measured in the Earth's magnetic field.

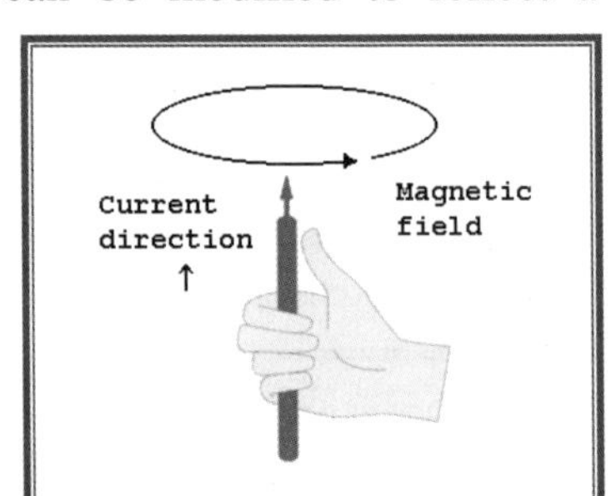

Figure 3.7 The right hand rule of electromagnetic theory applies to positive charge, where the fingers indicate the direction of the magnetic field and the thumb shows the direction of the current flow.

At this point, when discussing the Earth's field, we must remember that it also includes magnetic fields generated by electric currents in the ionosphere and magnetosphere. Maybe, there is a scenario that we could consider. Whilst the magnetic field that originates from the Earth is fluctuating and in parts of the world changing its polarity, we would still have a partial magnetic field derived from the electrojets and electric currents in the magnetosphere! However, these frequencies may not necessarily be the same as what we have been used to. This would explain why mystics and metaphysicians are encouraging us to re-tune to higher frequencies to maintain stability. This is discussed in more detail in chapter 7, *Balancing in Chaos.*

The Aztec Sun Stone

There are many accounts of catastrophic events on this planet, preserved through ancient texts and mythology, some are clearly evident from geological observation. It is considered most likely that some of these events were caused by asteroids or comets passing too close to the Earth. So, is it any wonder that many archaeological remains of astronomical observatories have been found. Even today organizations like the Vatican have their own astronomical observatories, the most recent was built in Arizona [85]. Yet, there are trips to Antarctica to watch the southern skies, thus allowing observation of the center of our galaxy at certain times of the year [86]. It has to be noted that we do not have to be hit directly by objects from space to cause disruption on Earth. The Sun will react to passing objects in a manner that is known as "action at a distance". This can be easily demonstrated to be factual, as massive Sun flares have been recorded by the SOHO satellite, in response to passing comets [87].

Maybe, the famous Aztec Sun Stone, depicting the Sun sticking it's tongue out, now takes on a more relevant meaning, see plate 26. Aztec legend has it that the squares represented the different manner by which the four previous Suns (or worlds) came to an end. Now, that we are *seeing* the Sun shooting out massive solar flares, maybe, we can consider that turbulent times could be ahead. The influx of *New Energy* permits an evolution of consciousness, but it must also interact with the mass consciousness of humanity. Since, the majority of humans exist with low levels of consciousness, signified by negativity, strife, war, etc, this energy with very high "potential" is *tuned* in such a way that the result is intense and extreme variations in weather, associated with rapid climate and Earth change. It is possible to steer the course of humanity and our destiny on Earth, but this can only be achieved when more people take responsibility and choose to raise their level of consciousness. This is discussed in more detail in chapter 8, *Strengthening Your Energy Field Is Spiritual Evolution.*

Chapter Four

Getting the facts straight: Electromagnetic Energy

"Electromagnetism — one of four basic forces in the universe — is neither quite particle nor wave, but displays properties of both simultaneously. Don't worry if this seems murky. Physicists tried for generations to solve EM mysteries — no one, not even Einstein, yet succeeded."

Dr. Robert Becker

Don't be Shocked: It's Electric

We are familiar with the properties of electricity and magnetism as they are commonly used in everyday life, we do not have to worry as we know that the fridge magnet will cling endlessly onto the fridge door due to magnetism. Moreover, when we plug in electrical appliances, we tend to think that electricity is flowing down the wires, which is scientifically incorrect, but for most people, as long as there is power, that is sufficient interest! The combination of these two distinct but related phenomena is known as electromagnetism, and the electromagnetic (EM) spectrum extends from radio and electric power to gamma radiation. The visible part of this spectrum that we call light, only represents a small part of the EM spectrum and the range covers wavelengths from thousands of kilometers down to a fraction of the size of an atom. An electromagnetic wave is considered to be a vibration of energy with two components, an electric field and a magnetic field, moving perpendicular to the direction of propagation and to each other. The electromagnetic wave is traditionally shown to be in a succession of cycles alternating "back and forth" and is characterized by two parameters; its frequency, (the number of cycles per second) and its wavelength.

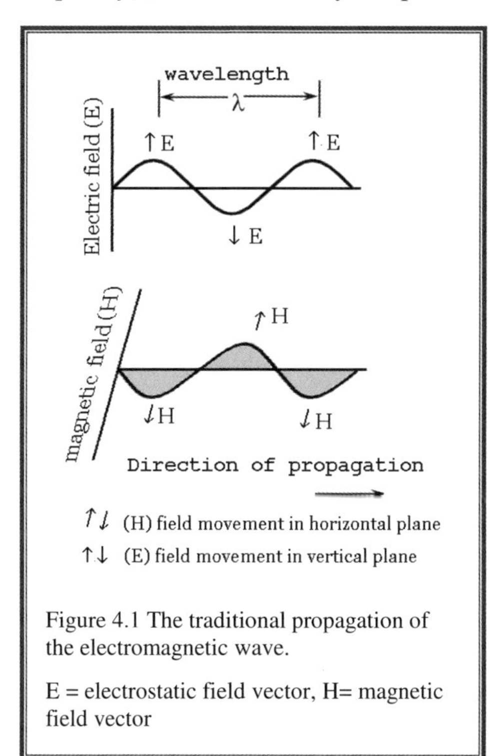

Figure 4.1 The traditional propagation of the electromagnetic wave.

E = electrostatic field vector, H= magnetic field vector

An important and perplexing aspect of the electromagnetic wave is that the two components do not move the same way at all, see figure 4.1 which depicts the distinct component parts of the electromagnetic wave. Michael Faraday was the first to determine that the magnetic field was continually rotating – hence, it is considered a dynamic field. The electric field exists at 90 degrees to the magnetic field and is carried along by the dynamic movement of the magnetic wave. The electric field is essentially motionless and provides a source of energy that is radiant, like heat from a fire. Therefore, Faraday named the electric field "electrostatic" energy. Yet, the standard model of EM wave propagation actually goes against all observations in electronics, where the current lags the magnetic field by 90 degrees out of phase. This means that the magnetic information must be present first before the electrostatic field.

The Power that causes galaxies to spiral by SuZar

"The power that causes galaxies to spiral, stars, planets and atoms to spin; that causes the double helix spiral of the DNA molecule; this same spiraling power causes spiraling hair – otherwise known as NAPPY, kinky, curly, crinkly, bushy, frizzy, wavy, WOOLLY hair! The words, SPIN, SPIRAL, and SPIRITUAL have common roots! The Supreme Power spins; spirals; it is spiritual. It moves or spirals the universe! The entire universe ever dances in spirals and rotations; everything in it reflects the "SPIRaling, SPIRitual" essence out of which it is made! Everything is alive with Spirit, the vital principle or animating lifeforce within all living beings. In many languages, the word for Spirit, Breath, and Air are identical: Sanskrit prana, Hebrew ruach, Greek pneuma, Latin spiritus. For breath and life are One. Latin spirare means to breathe; Latin spir and Greek speira mean coil. The Spiral Principle of the Universe is what makes nappy hair nappy-or spiraling." [1]

The Electromagnetic Wave and the Photon

The electromagnetic wave and the photon are two inseparable concepts – the same way that water and ripple are closely linked. The photon is observed as electromagnetic wave frequency and an energy transition when the electromagnetic wave is created or absorbed. However, when wanting to know what exactly the photon is, most definitions do not provide an adequate description. Most say the photon is a quantum of light, but the quantum, by the standard definition, is somewhat hazy. To know more, we have to follow the lead of the pioneers of new thought in physics. These new definitions are totally consistent with the information presented in this book. Four opinions are offered, which provide varying levels of clarity:

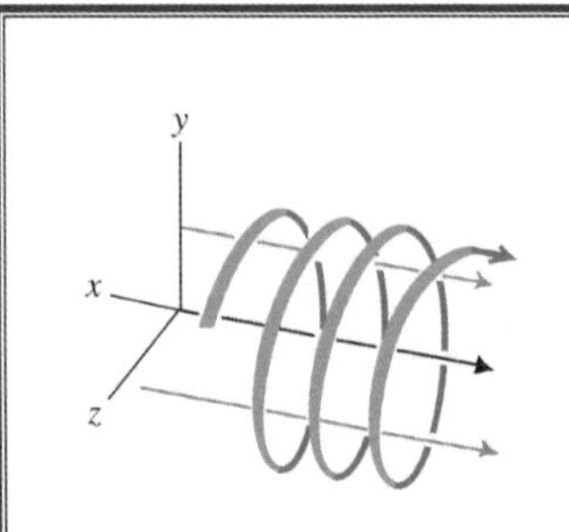

Figure 4.2 A Spiraling Wave. The EM wave is usually shown as alternating in two dimensions. This can be shown to be just a projection of the wave and the universal concept that energy spirals as it travels is lost [2].

1. "In my considered opinion I think that a photon is a manifestation of space-time curvature, the result of quantization of the electromagnetic field tensor in antisymmetrized general relativity." Dr. Myron Evans, Director, AIAS is the author of the 5-book series "The Enigmatic Photon", 18 January, 2003.

2. "A photon is a magnetic dipole. It is an elementary magnet. Evans' discovery of the photon's longitudinal magnetic field in 1992 is as significant, at the quantum level, as Einstein's discovery of relativity at the universal level. It helps to give a physical interpretation to string theory, wave mechanics, two-slit interference and the Faraday effect. A string is a harmonically moving photon that vibrates, oscillates, spins and twists." K. L. Rajpal

3. "The photon is a finite structure in empty space, made entirely of static magnetic field." Bibhas De

4. "Experiment presents the photon as an 'event' involving a quantum of energy transferring between aether and matter or vice versa and characterized by a frequency of electromagnetic field action." Dr. Harold Aspden

The photon (or biophoton from a living entity) is pure informational "static magnetic field".

The most appealing definition is no.3 and the reason is because we can compare theory to fifty years of research by the biophysicist Albert-Fritz Popp. His research group has experimentally verified that human and other animal cells, as well as plant cells, radiate light called "biophotons". This is pure "magnetic" light and it has the property that it exchanges information with other living cells, even over great distances. This light makes up the human energy field, commonly referred to as the aura. Biophotons carry information and the amount we emit can be defined in terms of our *Signal Power*.

Electricity — Electric Charge & Electric Energy

"I have struggled with this basic problem of electricity for more than twenty years and have become quite discouraged, though without being able to let go of it. I am convinced that a completely new and enlightening inspiration is needed."
Albert Einstein

Traditionally, electromagnetic forces have always held a level of mystique and these forces have never been fully understood. When Michael Faraday (1791-1867) first announced that he could generate an electric current merely by moving a magnet in a coil of wire, he was called a charlatan and a fraud! However, his discoveries helped to ignite the industrial revolution with electric generators. We have the ability to utilize these strange forces, but our scientists still do not fully understand them. In the book *The Nature of Physics* (1975) by Peter J. Brancazio, it is stated:

> "At the present time there is no real understanding of why charges are set in motion by a changing magnetic field. Thus electromagnetic induction must also be regarded as an unexplained law of nature." [3]

Experts assure us, that this lack of understanding still exists! Therefore, it is not surprising that there have always been fundamental differences in definition, even amongst expert sources. In scientific circles, there has been a shift away from using the term "electricity" and movement towards defining other related phenomena such as electric charge. This confusion is highlighted by electrical engineer William J. Beaty, who wrote the following amusing summary [4].

> "Electricity is a mysterious incomprehensible entity which is invisible and visible AT THE SAME TIME. It is both matter and energy. It's a type of low-frequency radio wave which is made of protons. It is a mysterious force which looks like blue-white fire and yet cannot be seen. It moves forward at the speed of light... yet it vibrates in the AC cord without flowing forwards. It's totally weightless, yet it has a small weight. When electricity flows

> through a light bulb's filament, it gets changed entirely into light. Yet no electricity is ever used up by the light bulb, and every bit of it flows out of the filament and back down the other wire. College textbooks are full of electricity, yet they have no electric charge. Electricity is a class of phenomena which can be stored in batteries! If you want to measure a quantity of electricity, what units should you use? Why Volts of course. And also Coulombs, Amperes, Watts, and Joules, all at the same time. Yet "electricity" is a class of phenomena; it's a type of event. Since we can't have an AMOUNT of an event, we can't really measure the quantity of electricity at all, right?"

The problem that Beaty has outlined is caused by many distinct phenomena being described under the umbrella term "electricity". So, to avoid confusion, his recommendation is to stop using the term electricity and instead use the correct term for the appropriate phenomenon. There are TWO main things that flow along wires:

- Electric Charge
- Electric Energy

Firstly ELECTRIC CHARGE flows through a light bulb and comes back out again through the other wire. Normally, no charge is lost during the operation of a circuit, and no charge is gained. Also, charge flows very slowly, and it can even stop flowing and just sit there inside the wires. In an AC circuit, charge does not flow forwards at all, instead it sits in one place and wiggles forwards and back.

Secondly, ELECTRICAL ENERGY or "electromagnetic energy" flows almost at the speed of light. It can be gained and lost from circuits, such as when a light bulb changes the flow of electrical energy into a flow of light and heat.

Electric charge and electrical energy have distinct properties, and understanding the difference is very necessary for electrical engineers and energy practitioners alike!

Strange Magnetism

"There are secrets and mysteries surrounding magnets and collapsing field energies, and only after exhaustive studies of these two phenomena, do these mysteries unravel themselves and emerge in their glory."
Robert Adams

We generally take for granted the never-ending supply of magnetic energy and physics theories have always used circular arguments to explain away "troubling" observations. Most agree that the energy source of magnetism is a complete mystery [6]. The following list briefly outlines known properties and recent discoveries, which utilize the rotating nature of magnetic fields [5].

- Lenz' Law (similar to Faraday's Law) states that by simply passing a wire over the north or south pole of any magnet, an electric current is generated within that wire. This discovery lead to the creation of both the electric motor and the generator.
- When you send electricity through a coil of wire, there will be a significantly higher amount of magnetic force generated than you would ever see from a single wire; the magnetic force will multiply as the coil grows larger.
- A non-magnetic iron bar can be easily magnetized if rubbed by a magnet in one direction only. A magnet can be used in this way as often as required with no loss of it's own magnetism.
- A rotating one-piece magnetic conductor (called a "N-Machine" by De Palma), can generate more electric current in output than required to make it spin. This is considered a *free energy* device and has recently startled scientists into investigating the implications [7]. It was tested in 1986 by Dr. Robert Kincheloe, Professor Emeritus of Electrical Engineering at Stanford University, who concluded that "De Palma may have been right in that there is indeed a situation here whereby energy is being obtained from a previously unknown and unexplained source." De Palma did not patent this process and it has been given as a gift to the world.
- The Aspden Effect: After a magnet has been rotated for at least five minutes and then brought to a complete stop, it will then take roughly ten times less energy to return it to the same speed. This occurs when the magnet is spun again in the same or opposite direction within less than about 60 seconds. In a sense the magnet now has a memory. This is a violation of the known laws of physics [8].
- "Magnetic Memory": Donald Roth has shown that once magnetism is flowing through a local area of space for a period of 5 days, it can continue at the same force even if the original source causing the magnetism is removed from the point of action [9].

Magnetic Pole Energies

Two pioneers in the realm of magnetism are Albert Roy Davis (deceased) and Walter C Rawls. These distinguished scientific researchers spent approximately 50 years each, investigating the effect of magnetism on living organisms. Davis, a scientist and professor of physics, was a recipient of a number of honorary doctorate degrees for his scientific investigations. He was an accepted authority and the founder of the Science of Biomagnetics. Rawls, a scientist and lawyer, but his sociological and scientific investigations have also took him to many countries of the world as a consultant to governments and world organizations. Davis & Rawls believed they were the first scientists to investigate and document the different energies associated with the north and south poles of a magnet. However, history tells us that in the nineteenth century Baron von Reichenbach also used "sensitives" to study the energies around magnets and people [10]. One of the observations they made was that there was blue energy at the north pole and red energy at the south pole. This information is of interest to energy practitioners as:

> **The natural energy in the hands is similar to the two different energies that exist in all magnets.**

The long held theory that the energies at both poles of a magnet are the same is totally incorrect. Specifically, north pole energies cause mass to contract and condense and have alkaline properties, they tend to collect fluids; north pole energies are considered to be negative. While south pole energies are expanding, dissipate fluids and are acid; south pole energies are considered positive. Rawls & Davis were able to support this discovery technically by the actual measurement of the direction of the electron spin that is transmitted from the two poles of all magnets. They found that the direction of the movement of the electron (magnetic energy) in the north and south poles was reversed in nature. So the energy coming from the south pole of a magnet traveled and took a spinning vortex of energy to the right, or clockwise, and the energy from the north pole of a magnet spun, moved and cycled to the left, or counter-clockwise. This was not confirmed until NASA measurements were taken from space. Furthermore, the ENERGY of a magnet does not simply leave one pole and travel around to the opposite pole. Space research shows us that the Earth, like a bar magnet, has magnetic energy leave one pole and travel only halfway around to the equator where is reverses the electron spin and then leaves the center of the magnet, or Earth to continue to the opposite pole. Figure 4.3 depicts the figure-8 loop patterns of the two distinct spiraling energies. This relates to the concept of a bar magnet and the area of zero magnetism called a Bloch wall. Within this zone the magnetic energy changes course by 180 ° forming a figure-8 pattern [11].

The energy emitted from the pole of a magnet can be photographed to show rotating small "cables" rather than lines of force as generally assumed.

With the help of a cathode ray oscilloscope, Rawls & Davis developed a method of photographing the spin of charged particles, hence revealing the invisible "lines of force" that are transmitted from the two poles of a magnet [12]. In modern physics, magnetic field lines are not considered to actually exist and are only used as a teaching aid. They can be compared to contour lines on a map, a convenient way of providing an indication that a force is being experienced by a charge at certain point. Yet, in reality there *must* be something there or a charged particle would not react by spinning. The rate of spin is called the cyclotron frequency and is determined by the magnetic field strength and the particle charge to mass ratio. Ultimately, this is why scientists believe that magnetism must originate in higher dimensional space. A cross-section of these photographed "ropes" of force, reveal triune points similar to tetrahedrons, see figure 4.4. This is understood as the balance of the three aetheric forces positive, negative and neutral. These forces relate to the images seen in meditation called mandalas.

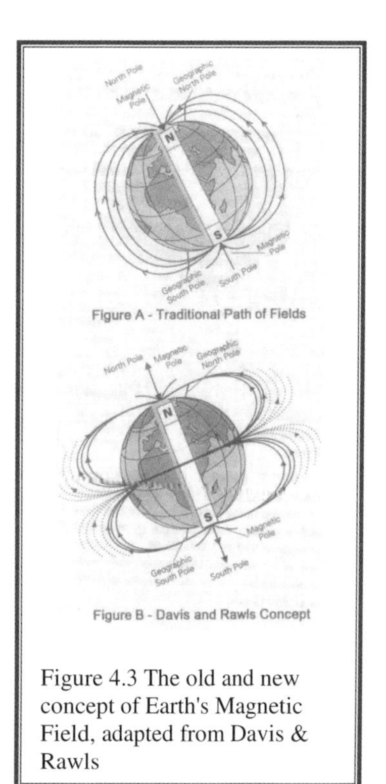

Figure 4.3 The old and new concept of Earth's Magnetic Field, adapted from Davis & Rawls

The triangle within the circle, introduces us to the concept of sacred geometry and the divine magnetic force [13].

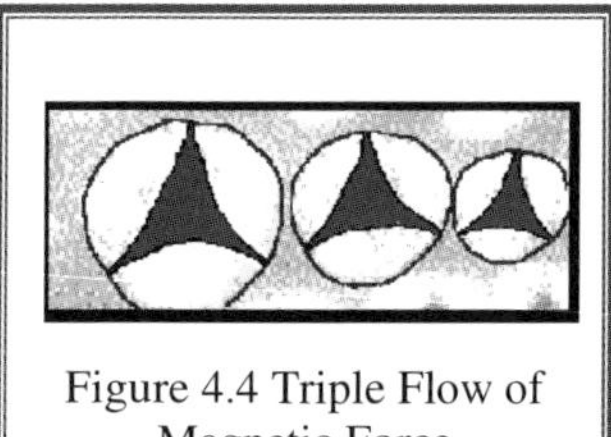

Figure 4.4 Triple Flow of Magnetic Force

The work of Rawls & Davis has been largely overlooked, yet their legacy will continue in the area of cleaning up toxic waste. The United Nations have endorsed Unipolar bioremediation as the method of choice [14]. It is now accepted that the use of only one magnetic pole can have substantially greater effects on living organisms. Hence, south pole magnetic energy produces big fat juicy worms, and they eat toxic waste with a ferocious appetite!

Levitating Frogs

It is also important to realize that **everything is weakly magnetic** – including water and living tissues. In April 1997, Dutch scientists, led by Andrey Geim of the University of Nijmegen in The Netherlands, announced that they had levitated a live frog using a powerful electromagnet [15]. These research findings were reported in various journals and publications. A popular UK tabloid newspaper picked it up the story and treated it like an April fool joke. Nevertheless, it caught the public attention and that of scientists too. Geim proved that all materials exhibit diamagnetism, which is a slight tendency to become magnetized in the direction opposite to an applied magnetic field. A diamagnetic object placed in an intense magnetic field, configured to diminish in strength with height, will experience an upward force, see figure 4.5. A sufficiently powerful electromagnet can balance the downward tug of gravity – at least over a small volume. News of this feat spread very quickly and when scientists realized it was not a joke, the experiment was copied for various other biological studies.

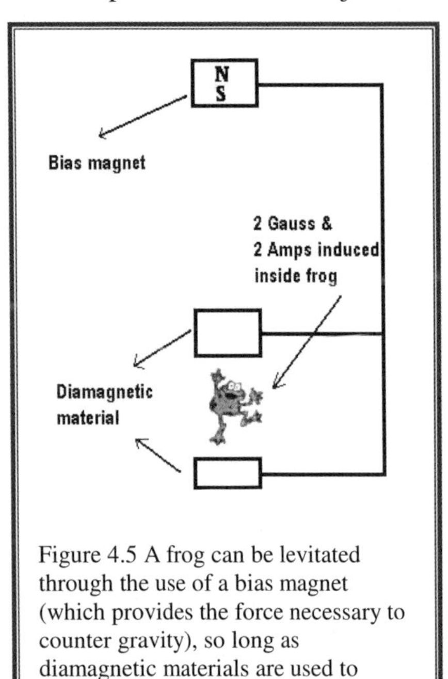

Figure 4.5 A frog can be levitated through the use of a bias magnet (which provides the force necessary to counter gravity), so long as diamagnetic materials are used to stabilize the levitation.

These experimental findings defied conventional thinking and broke down one of the most enduring prejudices in physics, that stable levitation of a magnet was impossible. Now this scientific discovery permits the use of frictionless magnetic bearings which, being passive and cheap, finding their way into high-tech devices. Geim states, “The Maxwell equations do not allow this. End of discussion.” We will soon see that there is considerable controversy in electromagnetism, especially surrounding Maxwell’s *original* equations.

Science Meets Mysticism

In the old Soviet Union, it was decided that maybe investigating and exploiting paranormal phenomena could be another way to gain tactical supremacy. To this end, studies came up with some startling conclusions about the origin of psychokinesis (PK) [16]. The most famous Russian psychic Ninel

Kulagina, originally known as Neyla Mikhailova in the west to protect her identity, was found to have a magnetic field that was only ten times less than the 0.6 gauss of the earth's magnetic field. Kulagina's brain was found to have fifty times the difference in voltage between the back of the brain than the front, whereas the average person only has three of four times a variation between the back and front. Furthermore, a magnetic pulse around her body occurred when she performed PK feats. The Soviets concluded that three things affect our force fields and our psi power:

1. Magnetic fields produced by machines
2. Natural magnetic fields by the sun, moon, and probably planets
3. Most importantly, **emotions** – including those of observers.

Kulagina was investigated by the most respected Soviet scientists and one professor commented: "Mikhailova's PK has nothing to do with mysticism. When a person thinks, he radiates energy and the energy is stronger in some people. PK is a physical-physiological fact." In experiments with Kulagina, both electricity and magnetism could be created and controlled by her ability to focus consciousness. The powerful fields around Kulagina's body were detected to *pulse,* and emanations could be detected 3.7m (12ft) away. The vibrations in the field around her body were thought to act like magnetic waves and magnetize nonmagnetic objects. This phenomenon is noted by psychics around the world who advise that if the *frequency of vibration* is stepped up, energy or information can come through from another dimension.

Our emotions have a major influence on our electromagnetic fields.

The relationship between emotions and the electromagnetic field is very important and so this theme continues throughout the book. Here, it is necessary to state that mystics and metaphysical sources are now encouraging us to build up our magnetic fields and this book gives the scientific reasons.

"We know today that man is essentially a being of light. And the modern science of photobiology ... is presently proving this. In terms of healing ... the implications are immense. We now know, for example, that ... light can initiate, or arrest, cascade-like reactions in the cells, and that genetic cellular damage can be virtually repaired, within hours, by faint beams of light. We are still on the threshold of fully understanding the complex relationship between light and life, but we can now say, emphatically that the function of our entire metabolism is dependent on light."

Dr. Fritz Albert Popp, Biophysicist

High Tech. Validation of Ancient "Know-How"

Leading-edge scientists and physicians around the world are exploring the science of the human energy fields and this is radically changing the way we view life and health. Back in the mid-eighties, Dr. Robert Becker wrote, "A knowledge of life's electrical dimension has yielded fundamental insights into pain, healing, growth, consciousness, the nature of life itself."[17] Now at the start of a new century, leading-edge scientists, physicians and alternative practitioners around the world are indeed having incredible success. Today's high tech exploration of human energy fields and understanding of our electromagnetic nature is uniting ancient wisdom with modern science.

The ancient Chinese theory of an invisible meridian system that runs deeply throughout the tissues of the body has been largely accepted in western medicine. These meridians pass life-force energy, known to the Chinese as Chi or Qi, see the small section "What is Chi?" [18]. As chi energy enters the body through the acupuncture points, it flows to deeper organ structures, bringing life-giving, subtle energetic nourishment. The Chinese also feel that when the flow of energy to the organs becomes blocked or imbalanced, dysfunction will occur. Modern scientific tests and measurements have validated this ancient knowledge. In fact, it was the Russian scientist Pankratov, who projected laser light on acupuncture points and found that this caused other points along the same meridian, to emit light. When he measured the light output, he concluded that the meridians are preferential pathways for the transmission of light in the body [19]. Robert Becker's research showed that the acupuncture meridians were conductors of current, the points being gateways to the body's electrical system. Incidentally, Becker tells us that the US Military were thinking of adopting acupuncture for use by medics

What is Chi?

This life-force energy, which exists everywhere, is know by many names in all cultures. The Chinese refer to it as "Vital Energy", "Primordial Breath", Cosmic Breath", or "Dragon's Breath". They believe that there are three sources of Qi energy (Eisenberg, 1995). The first of these is Nutritional Qi, which is obtained from the foods we eat and the liquids we drink. The second source whereby we 'absorb' Qi energy is through the air, and is called Air Qi (Yang, 1998). This Qi is also constantly replaced during every breath. Air Qi is understood to be the easiest source of Qi energy to manipulate, through meditation, martial arts, and other exercises. The final source of Qi energy is called Original Qi. This is that portion of Qi energy that is inherent to you, and was transmitted to you at conception from your parents.

in wartime as early as the 1960s. A colonel from the US Army Surgeon General's office informed him, "I can tell you for sure it does work". At that time, Becker was being consulted because the Military wanted to know *how* it worked [17].

Similarly, ancient texts of Indian yogic literature speak of special energy centers, referred to as chakras (from the Sanskrit, meaning wheels). They are also described like flowers with petals and act as vortices that extend slightly beyond the skin's surface. There are at least seven major chakras associated with the physical body. Anatomically, each major chakra is associated with a major nerve plexus and a major endocrine gland, see figure 4.6. There are also many minor chakras associated with the major joint structures of the body like the knees, ankles, elbows, etc. The chakras are, in turn, connected to each other and to portions of the physical-cellular structure via fine subtle-energetic channels or threads known as nadis. Various sources have described up to 72,000 nadis or etheric channels of energy in the subtle anatomy of human beings, which are interwoven with the physical nervous system.

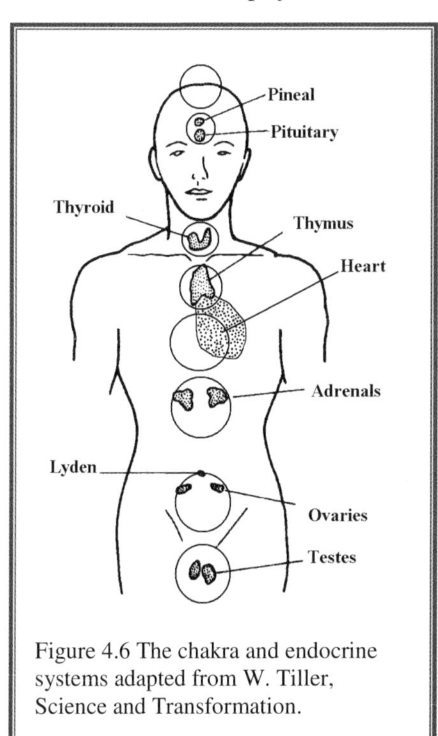

Figure 4.6 The chakra and endocrine systems adapted from W. Tiller, Science and Transformation.

This agrees with western research that suggests that there are at least two electrical systems, which provide pathways for the energies of the body [20]. The first is the central nervous system (CNS), where electrical charges cause nerve transmission, glandular secretion, sensation and muscle contraction. The other is an electromagnetic wave system, originating at the sub-atomic level, which manifests as vibrations at the level of atoms and molecules. In the scientific model, the acupuncture points and chakras are viewed as wave conversion locations, or EM antennas that can both radiate energy/information out and receive energy/information in and thus provide a mechanism for coupling the body to its external environment [21]. Now, we can validate the existence of the chakras with subtle-energy technologies that can measure their existence and function, scientists are starting to explore a new universe formally seen only by gifted mystics and sensitives.

Scientific Verification of the Chakra System

Dr. Valerie Hunt is one of the leading researchers in the Science of Human Energy Fields, Emeritus at the UCLA (University of California, Los Angeles) and was first to conclusively prove the existence of chakras. This was as a consequence of pioneering studies on the human energy anatomy and the effects of rolfing (a type of massage) on the body [22]. Hunt was quick to realize the potential of instruments that were developed to record the brain, heart, and muscle signals of astronauts whilst they were in space. These telemetry electromyographic instruments utilized a radio frequency system to send data back to Earth. In the 1960s, standard medical devices could not pick up frequencies over 150 Hz. This new device could measure frequencies from zero up to 250,000 Hz – a thousand times greater than anything ever used in medical science. Since that time – with the help of the manufacturers who developed the original telemetry device for NASA – Hunt is now the proud owner of a machine that measures up to 750,000 Hz.

During research, it was discovered that by amplifying the baseline bioelectric energy between muscle bursts and during rest, new dynamic signals were recorded, unlike any other signals from the body. These were continuous rather than intermittent patterns, ever changing with individual variations, which preceded rather than followed muscle depolarization or brain waves. It was found that it was possible to record the frequency of these low voltage signals from the body, during a series of rolfing sessions.

To make these recordings, Hunt used elementary electrodes made of silver/silver chloride which were placed on the skin. Simultaneously, with the recording of the electronic signals, the famous healer Rosalyn Bruyere of the Healing Light Center, Glendale, California, observed the auras of both the rolfer and the person being rolfed. Bruyere gave a running report of the color, size and energy movements of the chakras and auric emissions involved and her comments were recorded on the same tape recorder as the electronic data. Eight chakra areas were instrumented, based on the area of the body being rolfed. Next, Hunt mathematically analyzed the wave patterns recorded using Fourier and sonogram frequency analysis. Both revealed remarkable results. Consistent waveforms and frequencies correlated specifically with the colors reported. In other words, when the aura reader observed blue in the aura at any specific location, the electronic measurements would always show the characteristic blue waveform and frequency in the same locations. These experiments were repeated with seven other aura readers who all saw auric colors that correlated with the same frequency / wave patterns. Hunt concluded that:

> "These results were in direct correspondence with the aura reader's accounts of chakra and auric cloud colors. This constitutes the first objective electronic evidence of emissions by frequency, amplitude and time which validates the subjective observation of the human aura described by sensitives for centuries."

In these experiments, it was observed that the chakras frequently carried the colors often mentioned in the metaphysical literature, i.e., kundalini-red, hypogastric-orange, spleen-yellow, heart-green, throat-blue, third eye-violet and crown-white. It was also noted that certain chakras seemed to be coupled with other chakras. Hence, activity in one chakra would trigger increased activity in another. Yet, the heart chakra was consistently the most active. Subjects had many emotional experiences, images and memory recalls connected with the different body areas being worked on by rolfing. These findings also gave credence to the belief that memory of experiences is stored in body tissue.

Harry Oldfield and the Amazing PIP

Harry Oldfield is a British inventor, scientist, thinker and healer who has sent over 25 years conducting research into the human aura and energy fields, seeking to prove they have a strong scientific basis. Oldfield is interesting character because he originally discovered the chakra system by accident! [23] He found seven energy configuration points on the body, and to his amazement he was told that these energy centers coincided with the chakra system, which he knew nothing about at the time! [24] There are many devices now available to detect subtle energy, and the best known today, use variations on Kirlian photography. See the small section, "What is Kirlian Photography?" [25]

What Is Kirlian Photography?

Kirlian Photography was invented by a Russian electrical technician, Semyon Davidovich Kirlian and his wife, Valentina, in 1939. To produce a Kirlian photograph (also known as an electrograph), a high-frequency power source is connected to an electrode beneath a sheet of film, creating an electrical field of high potential that bathes the film. When a grounded object is placed on the film in complete darkness, the trails created by electrons flowing from the charged plate to the grounded object create an image, capturing luminous energy emanating from the physical body. Kirlian photography can be used to show the difference in the human energy field, (HEF), of someone harboring a disease that has not yet manifested in the physical body.

> Critics of Kirlian photography say in order to work with it, you have to introduce an energy field to enhance the radiation of the electromagnetic field. This means that what is being measured is a secondary response, not the primary one. There are also many things that can change the result, such as the moisture and one's emotional state. As the measurement comes in the form of a picture, it has to be interpreted, so this is considered to be quite subjective. New Kirlian devices overcome some of these issues, allowing much more of the electromagnetic field to be photographed.

Oldfield had a particular interest in cancer and became involved with Kirlian photography as a research tool in hospitals. He soon became very concerned when he detected severe energy field disturbances, in people undergoing the harsh treatment used in conventional medicine. Unable to keep his concerns to himself, he was soon told his services were no longer required. In response, Oldfield decided to develop his own system for working with energy fields.

It was originally noticed that subjects being photographed with a Kirlian camera were also transmitting "signals" when they were in contact with the device. Oldfield realized that if you disturb the very thing you are trying to monitor, your observations are invalid. Hence, by varying voltage and frequency he found that he could obtain a three-dimensional reference field around the body. Firstly, as the field was invisible, he used remote detectors (sensitive oscilloscope probes) to detect it. Later on, sound level devices were used to measure sound pressure waves and corresponding variations around the body. This new way of detecting the subtle energy field is called the Electro-Scanning Method, or ESM. Oldfield later invented a second device called the Polycontrast Interference Photography (PIP) Scanner, which was specifically developed to achieve a computerized visual energy-field scanning system. This is achieved by recording light interference patterns, created when ambient light interacts with the subtle energy fields. The PIP scanner shows up the energy counterpart, the etheric template on which our physical molecules are strung. Like other researchers, Oldfield recognizes the organizing nature of the human energetic counterpart. He says:

> "On average, every molecule in the human body is replaced every nine years. Therefore, I am a moving fountain of physical molecules and my molecules are constantly being destroyed and replaced. So what keeps me a coherent recognizable form? It could be an organizing template of energy: a morphogenetic field."

Innovatively, Oldfield used ancient knowledge about the chakras contained in ancient books from India, called the Upanishads. He found that each chakra is depicted as a flower with a specific number of petals. The number of petals represents the frequencies of each chakra. From this information he worked out, mathematically, the frequency patterns for the seven chakras from base to the crown. Due to the rigorous scientific methodology taken in the development of his devices, Oldfield has gained much respect amongst other biofield scientists.

The Signature Field

As a veteran of research in electromagnetism and the human energy field, with over 45 years of experience, Dr. Valerie Hunt says:

"All healing that takes place in alternative medicine is electromagnetic."

Hunt firmly states that all illness, disease and malfunction is caused by the disturbance in the pattern of electromagnetism in the body and the impact at the biochemical level is only secondary. As evidence Hunt points out that chemical reactions all require a catalyst in order to occur and that catalyst is electromagnetic energy [26]. Without electricity, power and charge there is no life, see the small section "What is a Spark?" and "How is Cloning Performed?" [27]

What is a Spark?

A spark is a volume of air which has been electrically converted from a gas into a plasma, the fourth state of matter. While plasma can be created by high temperatures, it can also be created electrically when a high voltage pulls loose the outer electrons of air molecules. Sparks are made of glowing air, and the color of the spark depends on the type of gases involved. Sparks in nitrogen/oxygen are bluish-violet, while sparks in Neon are red/orange. Also, sparks are conductive. Once formed, they can contain an electric current in much the same way that a wire can. In many ways a spark is like a bit of air which has been turned into an electrical wire. Scientists can only create life with a spark and this was clearly demonstrated in the scientific breakthrough of the cloning of dolly the sheep.

How is Cloning Performed?

The most likely method used is that an unfertilized human egg is taken from a woman's ovary and its nucleus/chromosomes are removed. Without the nucleus the egg now has no DNA. A cell is then removed from an adult and injected into the egg that has no nucleus. The adult cell contains a complete set of DNA and so the egg now has the same DNA as the adult who donated the cell. A small spark of electricity is passed through the two cells fusing them into one. The egg is "fooled" by the spark and thinks it has been fertilized by a sperm. It then begins to divide, in the same way as any normally fertilized new embryo. This provides an identical "twin" to the adult.

Hunt has discovered through many years of research that regardless of the type of alternative methodology employed, the healing takes place in the electromagnetic field. The whole spectrum of healing techniques, as well as a person's intent or spiritual state will effect and change the electromagnetic field. If the changes are maintained, the body can heal itself, and the body chemistry will reorganize. Traditional medicine is working at the level to encourage biochemical reorganization. Yet, this cannot be considered, as a way to create a cure, because ONLY if the electromagnetic field changes will there be a true cure. Hunt states emphatically:

> "For example, I can measure the energy field of a person who has had cancer but that cancer, according to chemistry, is in remission. I can tell you if the person still has a cancerous field, and until that cancerous field goes, I don't care if there is remission or not, biochemically, as long as the field does not change, it's going to recur."

In mapping bioenergy fields, each individual has a unique resting pattern, called the Signature Field [28]. A healthy human being has a signature field composed of balanced, coherent energy patterns across the full spectrum of frequencies. This coherency shows up on a graph as smooth, gentle, shallow waves evenly distributed throughout the frequency spectrum.

The signature fields of human beings who have (or are soon going to develop) diseases are of two kinds; deficiency patterns and hyperactive patterns. These show up on the graph as thick, jagged waves concentrated in the high or low-frequency bands. Deficiency diseases like cancer and fatigue syndrome have anti-coherent patterns in the high frequency ranges, with almost no energy at all in the lower frequencies. Hyperactive conditions like colitis, hypertension, and skin problems show up as anti-coherent patterns in the low frequencies, with absent vibrations in the high frequencies. Anti-coherent bioenergy fields cause all of our limitations, so when we balance these fields, we become fully functional human beings. Human potential can be described as health, energy, psychic abilities, creativity, mental genius, and physical prowess. By not working with our emotions properly and so creating anti-coherent energy patterns, this stops us from reaching our full potential.

The "Light Body"

Hunt proves that we have a "Light Body", a more powerful energy field than that of the physical body, which is detected *outside* of the body [29].

> **By testing different individuals, Hunt can now show the light body energy field has a range of different frequencies depending on the person and what they are thinking about.**

For average people who focus primarily on material and every day things, there are *no significant peaks* above the limit of 250 Hz, which is the same frequency as the heart and muscles. People with healing and psychic ability seem to have frequency peaks between 400 and 800Hz. People who connected with their 'higher self' seem to operate in the range of 800 to 900 Hz, but mystics operate at over 200,000 Hz! This could only be measured when the equipment was changed by the manufacturer to pick up the higher radio frequencies! The EM field does not even begin until 400 to 500 Hz, which is beyond the range of the nervous system of the human body. This means that what is being detected, is in the range of atomic and sub-atomic molecular activity of human cells, where transactions occur between the EM field of the body and subtle fields.

"We need a new model of the human being based on health, consciousness and evolution."
Dr. Valerie Hunt

In an interview, Hunt remarked that the current models that define our belief systems are incomplete and do not encompass all that we are. After decades of research into the human field and human consciousness, Hunt believes that we are designed to evolve, but rather curiously, she refers to a need for a new model of the human energy field. She says:

> "Currently, there are three models that define our belief systems. The first is the physiological model, which has to do with how we treat disease. We treat disease symptoms because we do not know what health is; we accept as fact that health is the absence of disease. Second is the biochemical model, which says that life started from a chemical soup and then progressed to protozoa and so forth. This isn't so. You can have all the chemistry in the world, but if there is no electricity, no power, and no charge, there is no life. In the medicine of the future, the emphasis on biochemistry will be phased out."
>
> "Then there is the behavioral model, which has to do with perception, experience, ego, personality, emotion, and brain hemispheres, and only addresses a very small part of human behavior, and only the memories and experiences of this current lifehood."
>
> "These models are not incorrect, but they are incomplete and cannot explain all of our choices, actions, and perceptions. **We need a new model rather than trying to fit ourselves into models that do not encompass all we are. This is the model of the human energy field or the mind of man, a field of energy that incorporates all behaviors, even to the highest level – the level of the soul.**" *[Bold added for emphasis]* [26]

Hunt claims that as we understand more of our electromagnetic nature and how to raise our frequency level, this will hasten spiritual enlightenment, which is our evolutionary goal. Hence as we acknowledge our electromagnetic field and learn how to enhance it, we can undergo an evolution of consciousness, creating health and healing in the process. Hunt has intuitively understood the need for a new model of the energy field that encompasses everything about us. Yet, there is a new energy field developing around humans at this time that allows us to balance ourselves, physically, emotionally, mentally and spiritually. The new energy field has been called the Universal Calibration Lattice and it is developing as part of the evolutionary change that is now underway on Earth, more details will be revealed in chapter 8, *Strengthening Your Energy Field Is Spiritual Evolution.*

Quantum Physics & The Biofield

Quantum physics tells us that material substances are composed not only of observable matter, but also more subtle field components with organized energy patterns, boundaries, and definitions. This means that the deeper one probes into physical existence, the more one encounters the underlying energy field. As physicists and biologists study the bioelectrodynamic qualities of living organisms, there is a need for some kind of theoretical model. The physicist Andrej Detela presents "The Biofield," to explain how biological living matter displays a variety of subtle phenomena, which cannot be explained by the biomolecular process. The informational and self-organizing processes inside living organisms can be understood as woven tiny threads of high frequency electric and magnetic fields. The Biofield describes the nadis system, described by Hindu mystics, as the complex electromagnetic structures found in the vicinity of biological forms [30]. Detela says in part:

> "It is assumed that the biofield is a three-dimensional web woven of vibrating electric and magnetic fields. Lines of these fields are like tiny threads in a three-dimensional textile. These electromagnetic fields display very complex internal organization. We find a peculiar variety of chiral solutions to Maxwell equations, which do not dissipate energy and lead to stable field structures."

> "The structure of biofield is in close correspondence with the molecular structure of living organisms. The discrete knots in the biofield web are in interaction with discrete atoms and molecules in living cells, therefore the biofield can regulate many processes in living cells. The most probable candidates for this kind of interaction are the chiral molecular structures of proteins and nucleotides, for example microtubules and DNA helices."

The knots in the biofield equate to the Cosmic Lattice at the molecular level and will be discussed further when we talk about DNA. Other studies reveal organizing bioelectric fields that demonstrate that living organisms are liquid crystalline in their composition, permeated with low-level, highly organized electrical activity.

Crystal Consciousness

Mae-Wan Ho Ph.D. is a biologist who has an original view of how biology may be linked to physics. Mae-Wan Ho suggests that the organism is, in the ideal, a quantum superimposition, of coherent activities, with instantaneous, non-local intercommunication throughout the system. She makes this claim based on empirical findings from her own laboratory work, as well as from established laboratories around the world.

All living organisms are liquid crystalline.

Mae-Wan Ho made the startlingly discovery that all living organisms are crystalline. This was achieved by using polarized light microscopy, a technique used by geologists to study mineral crystals and other materials with a high degree of molecular order. A slight modification of the optical system permitted Mae-Wan Ho and colleagues to look for crystalline molecular order in whole, living organisms such as the Drosophila larva, Daphnia, and brine shrimp. In this technique, color and its intensity indicate molecular structure and the degree to which the molecules are ordered. If there were no molecular order, no color would be generated in the images. Mae-Wan Ho describes the new view of the organism and the profound implications. She writes:

> "In the breathtaking color images we generated, one can see that the activities of the organism are fully coordinated in a continuum from the macroscopic to the molecular. The organism is coherent beyond our wildest dreams. Every part is in communication with every other part through a dynamic, tunable, responsive, liquid crystalline medium that pervades the whole body, from organs and tissues to the interior of every cell. Liquid crystallinity gives organisms their characteristic flexibility, exquisite sensitivity, and responsiveness, thus optimizing the rapid intercommunication that enables the organism to function as a coherent whole."

> "With our new view of the coherent organism, think of each organism as an entity that is not really confined within the solid body we see. The visible body just happens to be where the wave function of the organism is most dense. Invisible quantum waves are spreading out from each one of us and

permeating into all other organisms. At the same time, each of us has the waves of every other organism entangled within our own make-up."

"We are participants in the creation drama that is constantly unfolding. We are constantly co-creating and re-creating ourselves and other organisms in the universe, shaping our common futures, making our dreams come true, and realizing our potentials and our ideals." *[End of Excerpts]* [31]

This is still very much new scientific territory, but there is evidence that all the major constituents of living organisms are liquid crystalline [32]. Mae-Wae Ho humorously writes:

"Even now, most biologists still regard the idea of the liquid crystalline organism as "mysticism". But then, very few biologists know physics, and some have never even heard of liquid crystals. Such is the wonder of our over-specialized education system."

Mae-Wae Ho has come to the realization that, "The coherent electrodynamic field...underlies living organization" and this makes the organism a vibrant sensitive whole. Mae-Wae Ho has a particular fascination for the concept of coherence and remarks that this is foreign concept to Western trained scientists. Coherent excitations account for many of the most characteristic properties of living organisms, long range order and coordination; rapid and efficient energy transfer, as well as "extreme sensitivity to specific signals". She writes:

"How would coherent excitations make the system sensitive to specific weak signals? Such a weak signal will be received by the system only when the system is 'in tune'."

Signal Power

Here, we define the concept of our *Signal Power*. If we use the analogy of a light bulb, light emission is scattered in all directions which is OK if you want to light a room. In contrast, a laser is a highly coherent source of light, consisting of a narrow frequency that is in phase and extremely powerful, which can be used to cut metal or even diamonds, see the small section "What is a Laser?" [33]. The concept of coherence is important to understand as humanity is being requested to re-calibrate and evolve spiritually. We have vast amounts of unutilized potential, the basic ingredients are within us, but energy does not flow in a manner that creates empowerment. Our task is to transform energy stuck in old karmic patterns that do not serve us, into new energy patterns that are in line with our highest potential. A high level of calibration indicates a highly evolved human, which will calibrate others around them. This has been proven by the Heartmath Institute in relation to the heart!

What is a Laser?

Laser light is generated within a medium where a large number of atoms must be excited into an energetic state. Normally this is achieved by a beam of intense light which acts like a pump. Once the atoms are excited, some of them will spontaneously emit their stored energy in the form of a light wave, often at a different wavelength, or color, than the pump light used to excite the atoms initially. If this emitted light wave travels to another excited atom, it will trigger that atom to also emit its stored energy as an identical light wave. This is known as stimulated emission. Specially aligned mirrors force the light to pass back and forth through the laser medium to extract light from as many atoms as possible, and force the light waves into a highly directional beam. Only a small amount of light is allowed to escape in the form of a tightly focused laser beam; most of the rest of the light continues to reflect back and forth, extracting light from the atoms, which are continually excited by the pump light. In this way, a continuous beam of light is formed which is self-consistent, well ordered and coherent. It is this aspect of laser light that allows it to make high-precision distance measurements, create three-dimensional holograms, and beams energetic enough to cut through steel.

"The shift from incoherence to coherence can bring dramatic effects: a 60-watt light bulb whose light waves could be made coherent as a laser, would have the power to bore a hole through the sun—from 90 million miles away."
William A. Tiller, Professor Emeritus, Stanford University

Lock-and-Key Electromagnetic Balance

The world we live in is a complex electromagnetic environment and some people become highly sensitized to particular electromagnetic frequencies. The following case history illustrates the wonder of our electromagnetic nature. A 50-year-old woman suffers from multiple chemical sensitivity (MCS), chronic fatigue syndrome (CFS), and electro hypersensitivity (EHS). When this woman uses a mobile phone for 2 minutes, the phone gets hot and she develops aches and tingling sensations in the head. The more frequent the use of the phone, the sooner the effects occur and intensity increases. When reacting to chemicals, electromagnetic reactions also become more severe and when she enters the kitchen the microwave oven *automatically* switches ON! [34] Electromagnetic signals emitted during allergic reactions, usually trigger allergic reactions in other sensitive individuals nearby— not domestic appliances!

It is known that allergic reactions can be triggered by specific electromagnetic frequencies, but there is a paradox as similar electromagnetic fields can also halt the reaction [35]. Research shows that electrosensitive individuals usually have an individual "zero-frequency", where all allergic symptoms disappear. To find this frequency of balance, the patient is tested with an oscilloscope, an instrument used to generate electromagnetic fields of different frequencies. Once the offending frequencies are found, they can be used to treat the patient in the following manner [36]. An electronic device detects signals from the allergic patient, phase converts them and feeds them back into the body for therapeutic purposes. This is called *phase conjugation,* where a new signal is created 180 degrees out of phase with the old, see figure 9.1. When the signals combine, they cancel each other out. These methods work by connecting a sophisticated electronic circuit to the acupuncture meridians, associated with specific organs [37]. Utilizing a frequency matching system, some of these instruments can perform hundreds of tests for allergic responses, in only a few seconds and digital molecular signatures are used to check the body's response.

Pioneering research reveals that living systems transmit messages by electromagnetic signals between cells and organisms. When transmitting and receiving frequencies match, activation occurs and this is considered "cellular language". Research documented in mainstream scientific journals reveal the regulatory influence of electromagnetic fields on cell physiology. Pulsed electromagnetic fields have been shown to regulate virtually every cell function, including DNA synthesis, RNA synthesis, protein synthesis, cell division, cell differentiation, morphogenesis and neuroendocrine regulation. These findings are relevant because they indicate why biological behavior can be controlled by "invisible" energy forces, which include thought [38].

Experimental evidence shows how cells use electromagnetic waves to direct their own internal reactions as well as to communicate amongst themselves. For instance, French immunologist Jacques Benveniste proved that highly diluted compounds transfer information to cells via *electromagnetic resonance* [39]. In thousands of experiments repeated over many years, Benveniste proved that cell receptors respond to recordings of electromagnetic signatures. This means that the electromagnetic frequency that triggers a solution's biological activity, can be stored on a computer hard drive, sent over the Internet as an attached document and transferred to a water sample at the receiving end!

The role of electromagnetism in cellular function also invalidates the commonly held belief that DNA "controls" the structure and behavior of living organisms. DNA resides in the nucleus of a cell, so the old thinking was that if the nucleus was removed the cell would die, however this could not be proven. What scientists actually found is that cells can live for two months or more without a nucleus. Hence the question: where is the controlling brain of the cell? It is now understood that the cell membrane (also called plasmalemma) controls the messages going in and out of the cell. This provides the brain function and hence the reason why electromagnetic signals will direct the evolution of the cell. A simple analogy of the cell being an organic computer can be used to explain this new concept. The DNA and nucleus behaves like a hard disk (memory), the cell membrane is the "CPU" (Computer Processing Unit that processes information), and the cell receptors act like data entry points (a keyboard). This explains why DNA and genes (sections of DNA strand that carry the instruction for a specific function), can be re-coded or re-written. In the past, this type of DNA change was incorrectly viewed as a "mutation", when really this is simply how the cell adapts to outside stimulus and should really be understood as "evolution". This new understanding strongly challenges the belief that we are born with certain genes that cannot be changed, as leading edge science suggests electromagnetism plays a key role [38].

Dedifferentiation of cells and was rigorously shown by Becker with red blood cells. A specific unit like a cell and all its parts, including the genetics itself, can be moved back through previous stages of change, eliminating disease and damage!

In the 1960s, the groundbreaking experiments of Dr. Robert Becker, proved cells can be dedifferentiated and redifferentiated *electrically.* Becker demonstrated that the actual healing system in the body is the cellular regenerative system that restores the cells electromagnetically [40]. Becker was surprised to find when he studied fracture healing in frogs that it was their red blood cells, not bone marrow cells that dedifferentiated. Frog red blood cells have a nucleus with DNA, which can be reactivated to direct the cell to return to its primitive state. Human red blood cells, on the other hand, contain no nucleus and no DNA to re-program, therefore, our red blood cells will not serve as raw material to be dedifferentiated into primitive or embryonic cells to produce the blastema needed for regeneration. At the time, scientists refused to believe what they had been shown, but of course today, we have Stem Cell research, which appears to be the same studies under a new guise! Becker's experiments are strong indicators that cancer cells are capable of being reverted to a more primitive state by electromagnetic means and thus become normal healthy cells.

"Facts do not cease to exist because they are ignored."
Aldous Huxley

It is now time to face facts and understand that research has proven that cancer can be dealt with electromagnetically. The following information is largely based on the research and personal experience of Tom Bearden who is an undisputed, world-class, expert scientist in scalar electromagnetics and electromagnetic theory. Further details have been gleaned from a report by the *Office of Naval Research, (London) ~ Report R-5-78,* (August 16, 1978) and patent information [41]. Some readers may be shocked by what they are about to read. Get ready.

The Priore Affair

In the 1960s and 1970s, the French government funded to the equivalent of twenty million dollars, the experiments of Antoine Priore with electromagnetic healing machines.

> **Priore demonstrated that it was a very straight forward process, to cure all kinds of terminal cancer and leukemia. In thousands of rigorous laboratory tests with animals, Priore's electromagnetic machine had a nearly 100% cure rate.**

These results were shown to astonished medical scientists as early as 1960. Experiments were repeated successfully 'under lock and key' and under the eye of a bailiff appointed by the Commission de Contrôle, composed of university officials and local dignitaries. The Italian Antoine Priore built and tested his machine, which cured a wide variety of the most difficult kinds of terminal, fatal diseases known today. Prestigious members of the French Academy of Sciences carried out many of the experiments and tests. Robert Courrier, head of Biology and Secretaire Perpetuel, personally introduced Priore's astounding results to the French Academy. Incredibly, the success of the Priore machine, was viewed as incomprehensible and caused outrage in the medical community as it was thought that science had nothing to do with "black boxes". The French Academy wanted an explanation of how the machine worked, but the inventor explained that his invention was proprietary information! The negative reaction by the French medical community is extraordinary, because Priore was able to patent his invention, this is normally quite difficult to obtain, as the inventor needs to PROVE that it works. A United States of America Patent # 3,280,816 was granted in October 25, 1966 called *Method of Producing Radiations for Penetrating Living Cells*. In 1979, Priore was awarded French Patent # 2,408,357, *Treatment of a Patient with Negative Ions* and in the same year, this was accompanied by a report sent to the Nobel Committee by Professor Courrier. This was on behalf of Pautrizel a "reputable" physicist who had been assigned to work with Priore. He obviously thought he had some chance of winning this most prestigious prize.

This concept of healing just sounds too easy but Priore and Becker and other researchers have proven it! Healers prove it when they obtain miracles! In simplified terms, if an action in forward time induces a condition, then the time-reversal of that action will reverse the condition. Bearden says he believes the Priore machine was about phase conjugation and nobody in the world accept the Soviets knew of time-reversed waves. Curiously, Bearden informs us:

> **Russian scientists briefed Lawrence Livermore National Laboratory scientists in 1972, about a strange kind of electromagnetic wave that would suddenly appear in experiments and "restore order" in disordering processes.**

The Priore machine worked by using a tube containing a plasma of mercury and neon gas, with pulsed waves modulated upon a carrier frequency. These waves were produced by radio emitters and magnetrons in the presence of a 1,000 gauss magnetic field and experimental animals were exposed to this mixture during irradiation. The waves came from the plasma tube and modulating and riding the magnetic field, they passed through the animals' bodies during irradiation.

Each disease has it's own signature and so healing requires a reversal pattern. Normally the body works out what pattern is required for healing and initiates changes. It is well known that a cancer cell is just a normal human cell gone "wrong" and out of control of the body's master cellular control system. Bearden says:

> "The cancerous cells, viewed as a sort of separate, parasitic group of cells, form a special kind of organism having its own master cellular control system 'level', immersed in the host's biopotential."

For cancer/leukemia the reversal pattern of electromagnetic charge will either destroyed the cancer calls, or converted them back to normal cells as appropriate. Bearden believes, any disease with cellular, biochemical, or genetic basis can be cured in like fashion and the effect is universally applicable. Priore found that every cell of the body including hair had to be irradiated and treated, "charged up", with the signal because the disease pattern was in every cell. The master cellular control system is holographic and likewise every structural level of the body larger than the cell also has its own correlated pattern. In 1974, a change of local government lost Priore his government supporters and so he lost his funding. The tragedy was that Priore was just completing a 4-stories-tall apparatus capable of radiating and treating entire human bodies. It would have been capable of curing cancer and leukemia in humans rather than just in laboratory animals.

This story is fascinating because the reason why Priore caused such furore was because he was seen as 'unqualified'. He had only graduated from a small provincial school for electricity in Trieste, Italy and had became a radar technician and operator in the Italian Navy. Prioré had also worked as an electrical repairman and his preliminary research was on exposing plants, etc. to EM radiation. Priore continued research when he was introduced to Francis Berlureau, former Director of Studies at the School for Veterinary Medicine in Toulouise. He worked with Berlureau for some 10 years. Investigators testify to the fact that 'unofficially' Priore cured many people with terminal cancers, including malaria and also tuberculosis in humans, but apparently, he did not publish these results. Obviously, it was totally beyond the comprehension of the medical world, that electromagnetic beings could be cured by an electrician and this mindset still exists today! In their report, the UK Office of Naval Research, referred to the patent information as "pseudoscience," yet, Priore's machine worked and eliminated cancer! The reality is this: do we want to live in a world where cancer cures are ignored and people are allowed to die because scientists refuse to believe in the existence of laws of physics contrary to established dogma? It is a matter of historical record, that these same laws of physics have been discovered by many other researchers, over many decades, but they have been largely ignored, because they defy conventional explanations [42].

Strangely enough, we do have a practical application of these concepts on a grand scale. In the world of agriculture, diseased plants do not SELL. So we have a situation where these same EM techniques are being used successfully and this is called psychotronic farming! Large-scale experiments were conducted by the U.S. government in Pennsylvania, Arizona and California in the 1940s and 1950s and today, thousands of farmers in the U.S. and abroad are using these techniques. It is worth noting that this solution came from the U.S. military that were called in to help when US crop production was being threatened by locusts [43]. Dr. Galen Hieronymus, an electrical engineer, received a US patent for an instrument designed to detect and measure "emanations from materials" – this instrument remains the standard by which other American-made radionic instruments are now gauged. Agricultural pest species are successfully controlled over large areas by using radionic-type instrumentation designed by Hieronymus [44]. With simple organisms such as corn borers, the pattern corresponding to the organism is transposed electronically and then fed back, 180 degrees out of phase. Peter Kelly, an electronics engineer and the first president of the

Psychotronics Association, claims the "borers literally dissolve", leaving only "a wet smear" onto the ear of corn. Simple life forms such as bacteria and organisms in their larval stage, "go back to their native materials, like water and basic energy". In more complex forms, he suggests that one is more likely to have some remnants of the original structure. Thus, we see from the various applications outlined, that balancing energy fields by EM phase conjugation is a proven way to restore health and this applies to cancer cells too!

Playing Dice with Frequency

In the world of electronics, there are very important issues of Electromagnetic Interference (EMI) and Electromagnetic Compatibility (EMC) that have to be considered. All electronic technology operates at specific designed frequencies, but this also means they are prone to interference (EMI) by stray signals. We recognize this interference as static on the radio or phone or a distorted TV image such as 'snow', ghosting, horizontal or diagonal lines on the screen. Other examples of technical interference are as follows:

- Medical equipment malfunctioning due to interference from a mobile phone signal
- Radio control remote devices operating appliances and equipment other than that for which they had been programmed
- Pacemaker interference from nearby power cables or other strong ELF fields.
- A remote controlled ceiling fan/light operating erratically caused by interference from the remote control used to open a neighboring garage door
- Wheelchairs have become unexpectedly mobile due to interference from mobile phones.
- Motor vehicle accidents traced to interference from nearby TV or radio transmitters, affecting the electronic systems used in vehicles.

As you can see with these examples, some are more serious than others! It is now standard practice to request that aircraft passengers turn off all their electronic gadgets during take off and landing because of the concern that there maybe interference to navigational and other electronic devices. What's more, as customers want increasingly more sophisticated electronics, car manufacturers have also started to complain:

> "It is not so far wide of the mark to suggest, with increasing vehicle electronic complexity, military levels of radiated immunity are required for automotive systems that cost two orders of magnitude less than their military counterparts."

> "It is interesting to consider that vehicle manufacturers are expected to allow their customers to fit all sorts of transmitters to their vehicles yet no other manufacturer – e.g. aircraft, domestic appliance or computer manufacturer – would seriously allow such behavior." [45]

Now, in the *New Energy*, car manufacturers have to allow for stray cosmic rays, specifically neutrons from space, interfering with car electronics. As one report puts it, "Neutron-induced firm errors have progressed from being a nuisance to being a significant problem" [46]. So, with all these issues of Electromagnetic Interference and Compatibility to think about for manmade devices why must understand that as electromagnetic beings we can also be subject to EMF interference and compatibility issues too! Just like manmade electrical equipment, humans also operate within a specific range of frequencies, which occur as part of the natural electromagnetic radiation of the planet, but the frequencies that humans use to function are prone to interference. When this occurs, the human body responds by registering pain, allergy, abnormal behavior, or any other symptom that is listed under the title of electro-hypersensitivity (EHS) [47].

Maybe, we can also consider that these issues of EMI and EMC are highly relevant for energy practitioners. When frequencies are transmitted, they are exact! There is no such thing as an approximation. If an energy practitioner has been given particularly frequencies to work with in a process called an "initiation," then that means these particularly frequencies can be passed on correctly. If certain frequencies have NOT been received via an initiation from a suitably qualified person, then that means these particular frequencies cannot be passed on. This is particularly important for teacher initiations, where it is possible to conceive that certain frequencies of light can be encrypted to prevent abuse. This is pertinent to those people who think they can upgrade their status without merit. Thus, in this scenario, it is quite easy to see that it is not possible to "initiate" with an approximation! An analogy would be that of a bank robber trying to open a safe, which is state of the art and so has hundreds of numbers with millions of combinations. Trying to get into this ultra-secure safe by guesswork could be a long and frustrating experience. There is no such thing as nearly right!

If you try to pass off an inexact frequency range, then electromagnetic interference and compatibility issues will ensue. Barbara Marciniak puts it succinctly:

"YOU CAN'T FOOL FREQUENCY!"

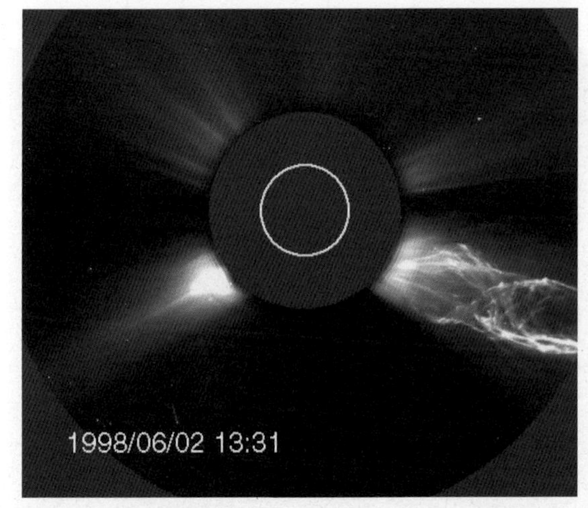

Plate 1a & 1b (left & below). False color images of an unusual and clearly helical Coronal Mass Ejection (CME). Observed by the LASCO C2 coronagraph on June 2, 1998.

Credit: SOHO/LASCO consortium; NASA/ESA.

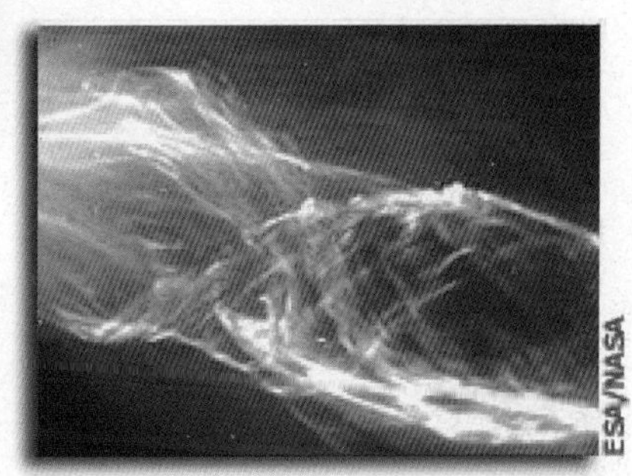

Plate 2 (below). Hubble Space Telescope image shows a tiny portion of the Cygnus Loop, a supernova remnant in the constellation of Cygnus, the Swan. The image taken by the Hubble space telescope illustrates the intricacy of the twisted Birkeland currents with characteristics that support an Electric Universe interpretation, including polarization of light, compression by magnetic fields, acceleration of relativistic electrons, and x-ray hotspots. Credit: ESA & Digitized Sky Survey (Caltech)

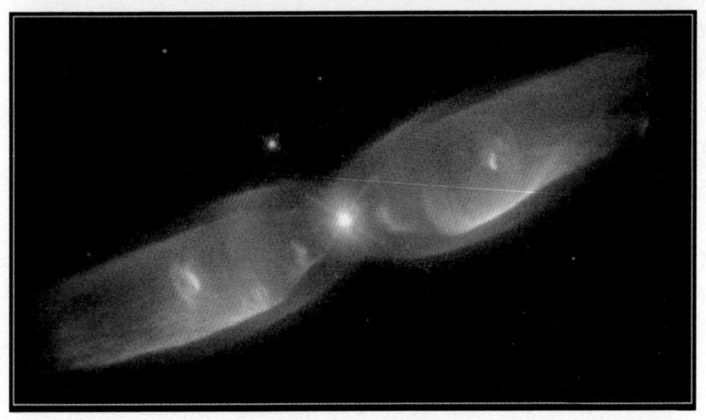

Plate 3 (left). "Butterfly Nebula" M2-9. Clear demonstration of double layers and compression caused by the "z-pinch effect" Credit: NASA/AURA/STSCI

Plate 4. Enigmatic features in space

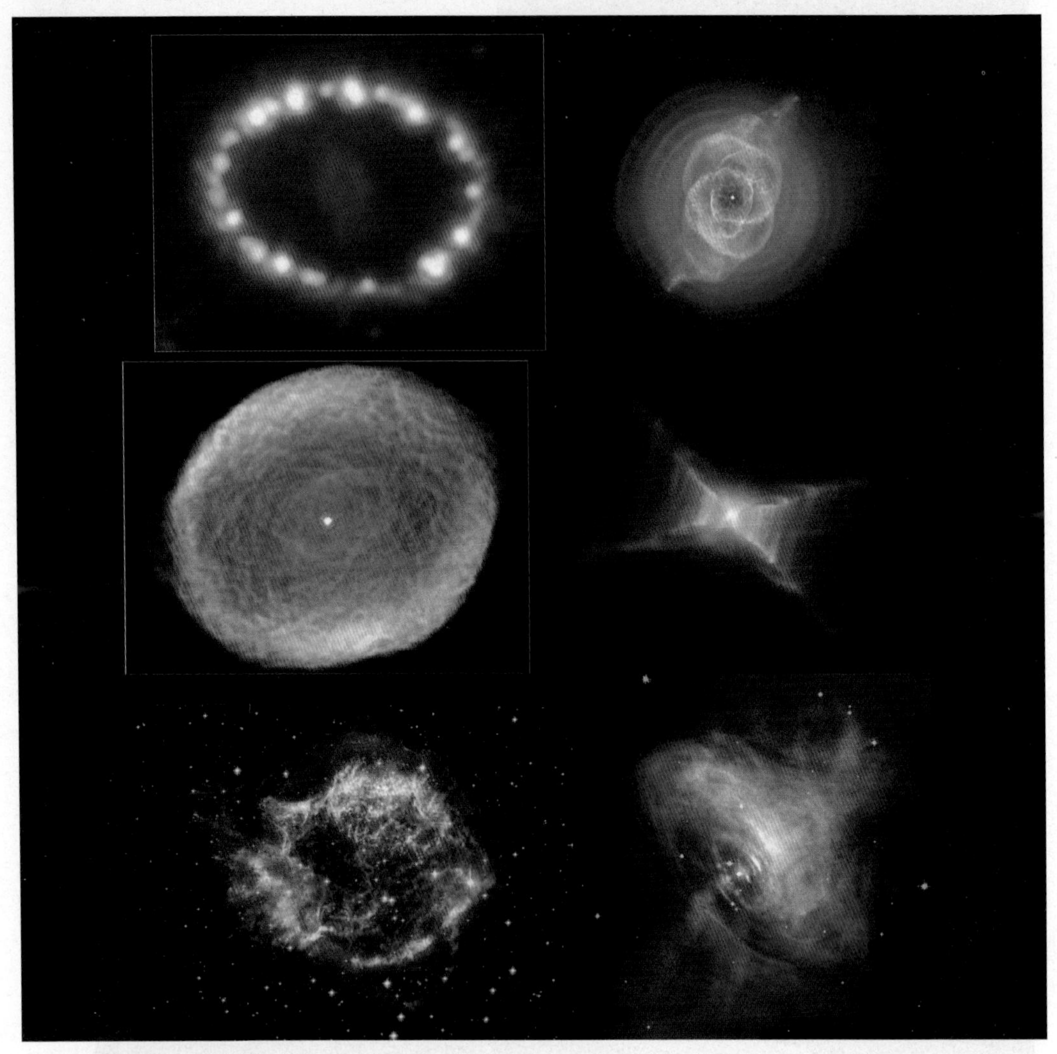

1. The "Cosmic pearls" of the enigmatic and beautiful Supernova SN1987A with its three axial rings, caused by the "z-pinch effect". Credit: NASA/STScI/CfA/P.Challis.

2. "Cat's eye" Nebula (NGC 6543) is one of the most complex planetary nebulae ever seen in space Credit: NASA/ESA Hubble Space Telescope

3. "Cosmic Egg" (planetary nebula IC 418), shell and "yolk" composed of plasma and displaying "double layers". Credit: NASA/Hubble Heritage Team (STScI/AURA)

4. The "Red Rectangle" Nebula HD44179, "the most unusual nebulae known in our Galaxy". Credit: NASA/ESA, Hans Van Winckel and Martin Cohen

5. Cassiopeia A supernova, a supposedly "dead" star that has shown recent signs of life! Credit: NASA/JPL

6. Crab Chandra showing the X-ray (blue), and optical (red) images superimposed, showing "jet" emission caused by plasma focus effect. Credits: X-ray: NASA/CXC/ASU/J. Hester et al.; Optical: NASA/HST/ASU/J. Hester et al.

Plate 5. M51 "Whirlpool" Galaxy with Spiral arms. Copyright: NASA

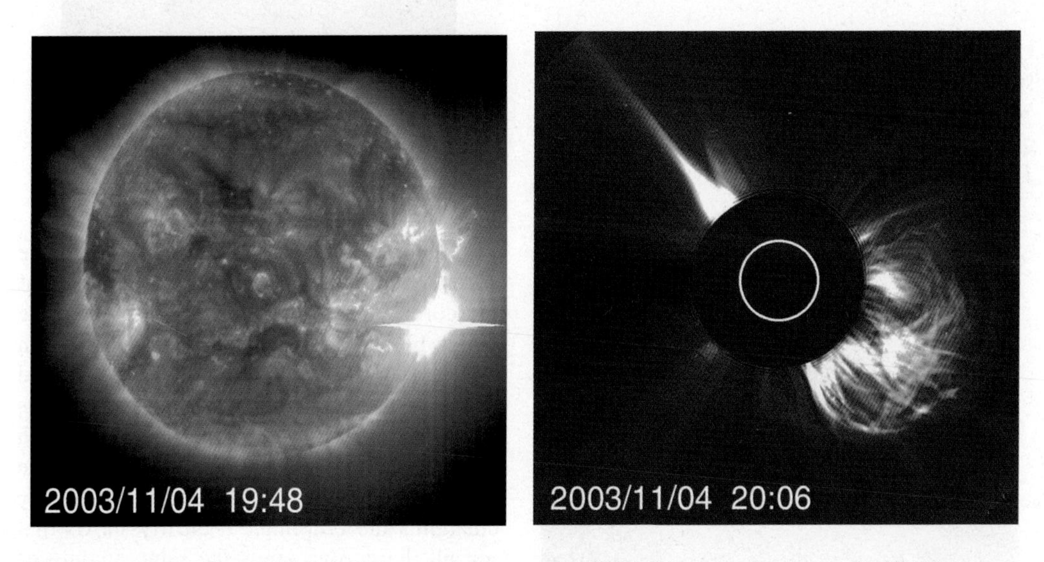

Plate 9. The massive X45 Solar Flare, 4th November 2003 (L) and subsequent CME (R). Credit: NASA-ESA

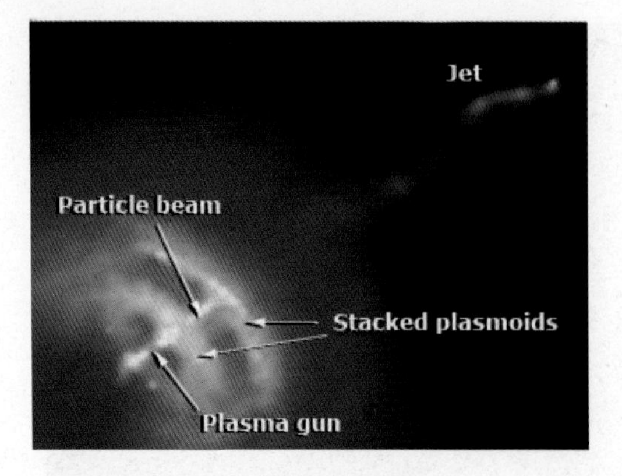

Plate 6. The Vela Pulsar Credit: NASA/PSU/G.Pavlov et al.

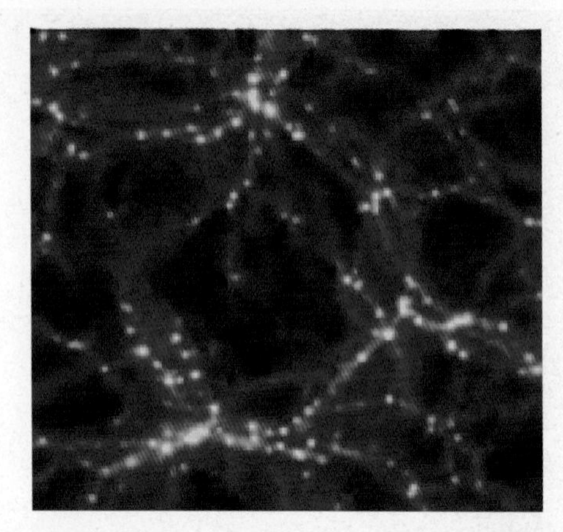

Plate 7. The Cosmic Web Credit: Uri Keshet et al., in "Gamma-Rays from Intergalactic Shocks

The Vela Pulsar is a "supernova remnant", which lies about 800 light-years from earth. It was first detected at gamma-ray energies and then it was modelled as a spinning magnet. Due to an immensely strong magnetic field and speed of rotation, it generates a powerful electric field. According to plasma physicists the "jets" are an electrical discharge of plasma at the center of an intense electric field.

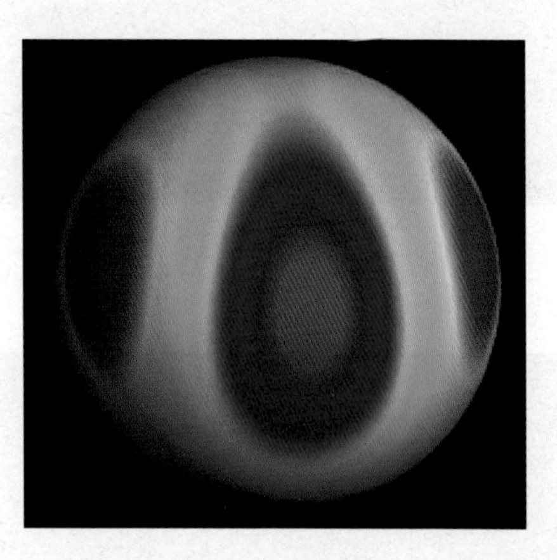

Plate 8 (right) Diamond superimposed on a sphere: displaying the symmetry of the Cosmic Microwave Background. This image shows the quadropole components only. Credit: Dr Max Tegmark, University of Pennsylvania, US

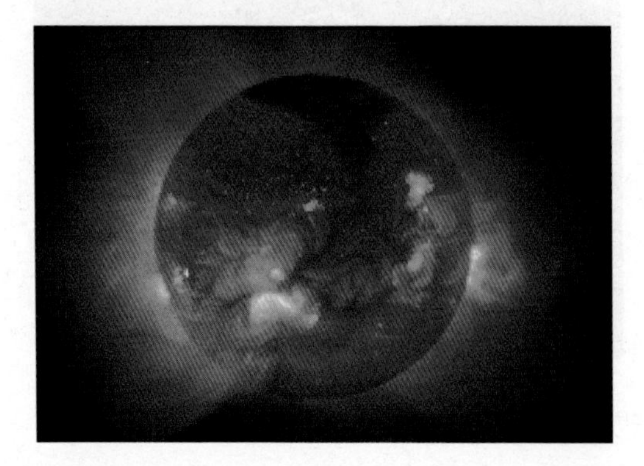

Plate 10. Sun Corona X-ray emission Credit: Yohkoh Science Team

The outermost layer of the Sun is called the corona or the crown. Pictures can be taken of the corona by using a coronagraph telescope which blocks the brightest light from the sun and captures the thin and faint energy emitted at the various wavelengths. This picture was taken by an X-ray telescope on the Yohkoh satellite currently orbiting the earth. The corona is a very stormy place, constantly changing and erupting. It clearly shows that not all the corona emits the same amount of X-rays. The most visible structures are the loops and arches around the active regions and "bright points." The large dark patch near the north pole is called a "coronal hole", a region of low brightness.

Plate 11. A coronal loop on the Sun that can break away and become a Coronal Mass Ejection (CME). The plasma is at a million-degrees and the loops are 300,000 miles high. Credit: TRACE

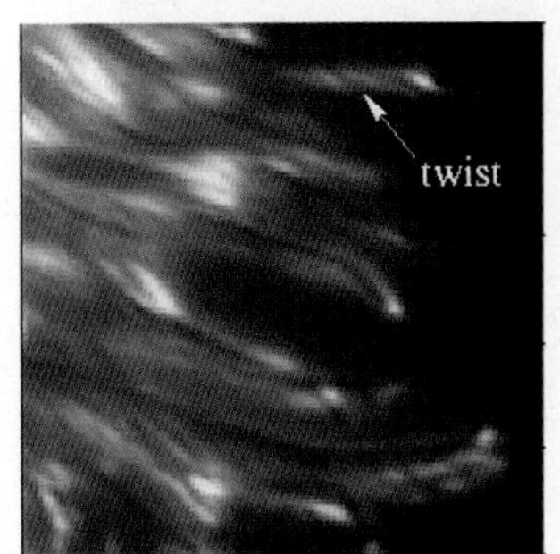

Plate 12. The Twisting Birkeland evident in a detailed image of the penumbral streamers. Credit: Royal Swedish Academy of Sciences, Institute for Solar Physics, Observer Göran Scharmer

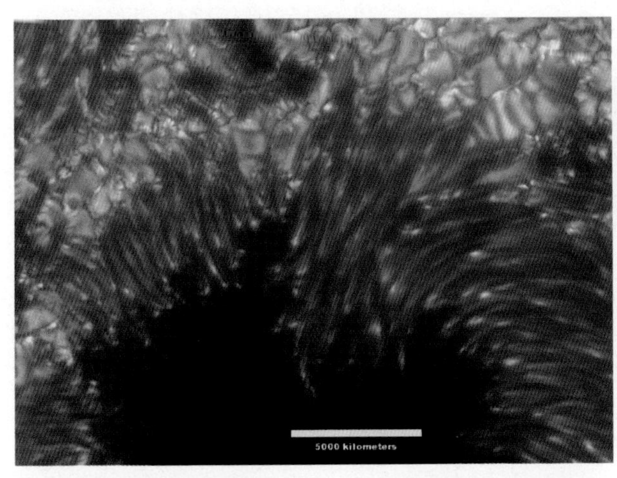

Plate 13. Close-up of a Sunspot The Penumbra Birkeland currents following the voltage drop from the photosphere down to the umbra. Credit: Royal Swedish Academy of Sciences, Institute for Solar Physics, Observer Göran Scharmer

Strong electric currents also flow in and above the Sun's surface at the edge of sunspot umbrae due to the voltage difference between nearby anode tufts and the central umbrae of the spots (where there are no tufts). This region is called a sunspot's penumbra. These currents of course produce magnetic fields. Since, in plasmas, twisting electrical (Birkeland) currents follow the direction of magnetic fields, the glowing plasma in these regions often shows the complicated shapes of these spot related looping magnetic fields. Note the twisting Birkeland currents!

Plate 14. Hurricane Frances occurred in September 2005. Credit: NASA

Plate 15. SOHO satellite image dated 2nd February 2005 possibly showing cosmic string. ref.: 1518Z

Plate 16. SOHO satellite image 14th January 1998 Ref: 0340Z Does this cosmic string look remind you of a "crazy garden sprinkler"? Plate 15, 16 & 17 Credit: NASA/SOHO

Plate 17. SOHO satellite image dated August 14 2005 ref.: 1442Z possibly showing entities riding cosmic string!

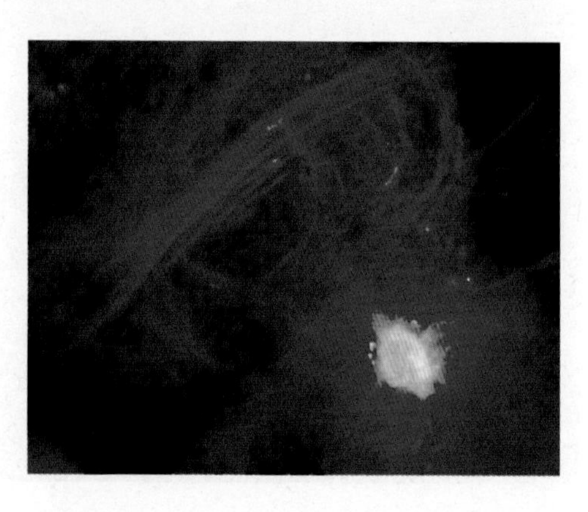

Plate 18 The Galactic Center Radio Arc. Credit: Farhad Yusef-Zadeh et al. NASA

Plate 19. The Pleiades. Credit: NASA

Plate 20. Typhon, the Greek three-headed serpent-dragon with entwined serpent tails.

Plate 21. Sprite Gallery - sprites showing tentacles

Plate 22. The Burning Tree in the Sky. Credit: ISUAL Project, NCKU/NSPO, Taiwan

Plate 23. Tibetan Buddhist Art. Dakini Fire Princess

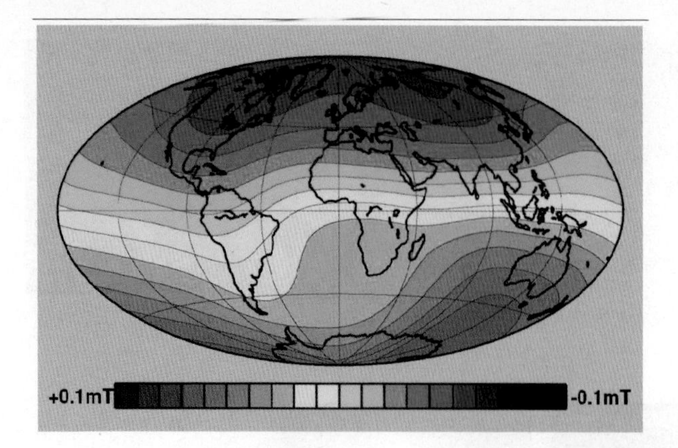

Plate 24a. The radial component at the Earth's surfaceas determined from Champ and Oersted satellite observations. The darker colours represent increasing intensity. Satellite measurements show that most of the magnetic flux is directed out from the core in the Southern Hemisphere and inward in the Northern Hemisphere. Credit & Copyright © Richard Holme, GFZ Potsdam

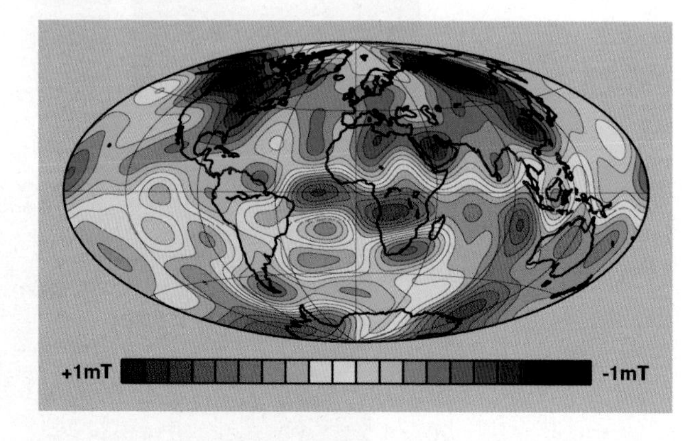

Plate 24b. The radial component of the magnetic field at the core-mantle boundary (CMB) 2900km below the Earth's surface determined from measurements taken by Champ and Oersted satellite. We can see that in some regions the direction of magnetic flux has reversed at the CMB, if they continue to grow and engulf both poles, a polarity reversal could ensue. Credit & Copyright © Richard Holme, GFZ Potsdam Credit & Copyright © Richard Holme, GFZ Potsdam

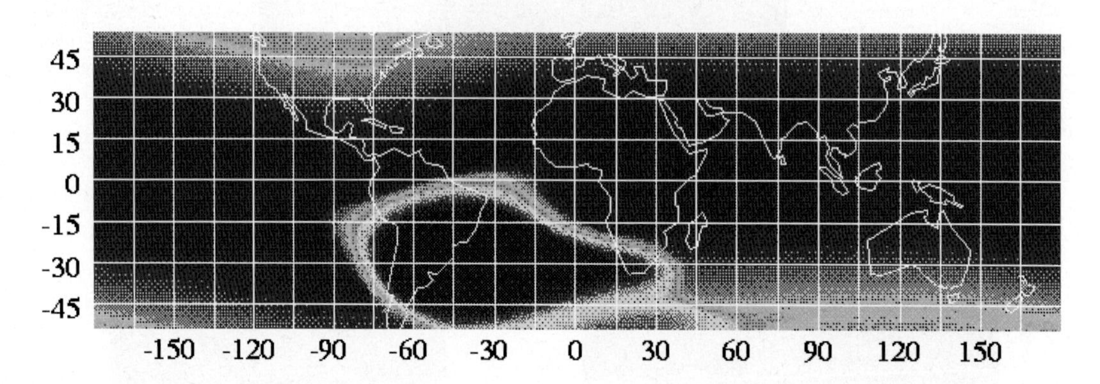

Plate 25. The South Atlantic Anomaly between South America and towards Southern Africa determined by South Atlantic Anomaly Detector (SAAD) aboard ROSAT.
Credit: NASA/ S. L. Snowden

Plate 26. Aztec Sun Stone. Courtesy of the National Museum of Anthropology, Mexico

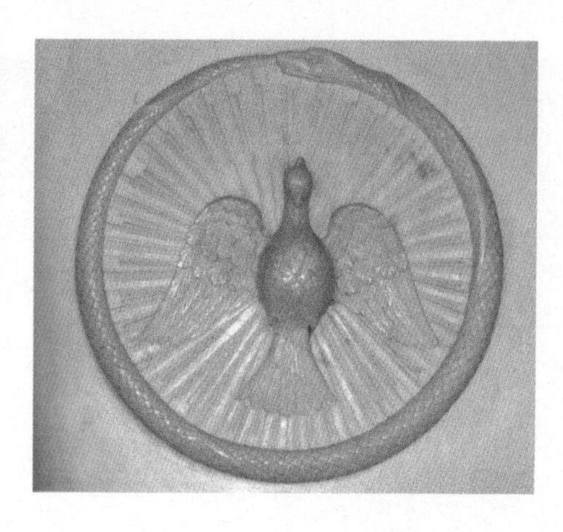

Plate 27. The Ouroboros encircling the Holy Spirit depicted as a dove. The illuminating rays of the Sun emerge from the Spirit. Lichfield Cathedral, Staffordshire, England.
Copyright © Philip Gardiner

Plate 29. Ormus glass (white) fused onto magnetite (dark ore).
Copyright © John Milewski

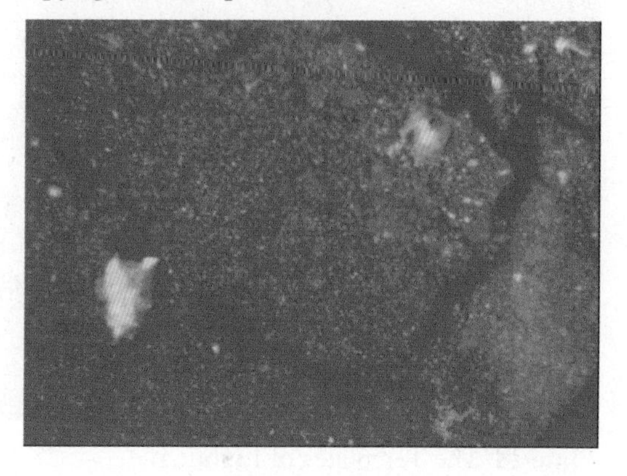

Plate 30. Large magnification of photograph showing projections of gold.
Copyright © John Milewski

Plate 31. Boulder showing white coating. As the coating is attracted to one side this indicates the rock is paramagnetic. Copyright © John Milewski

Plate 28. The Templates of Light.
Copyright © Energy Extension Inc

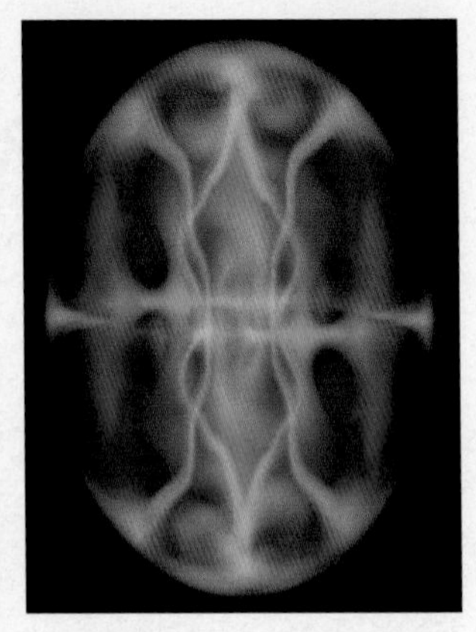

Plate 32 (above) Bose-Eintein Condensate (BEC).
Computer simulation showing tornado-like vortices forming within a spinning Bose-Einstein condensate, a new state of matter. We can see the diamond shapes of the overlapping vortex energy structures here! Credit: National Institute of Standards and Technology (NIST)

Plate 34 (below). The diamond within the torus. This image depicts the three-dimensional projection of a torus in four-space. Copyright © Thomas F. Banchoff

Bands on the torus have been removed to make it possible to "see through" it. This image is an interior view of a torus on a three-dimensional sphere in four-space projected stereographically from a point on the torus itself, leading to a third-order algebraic surface expressed as a union of circles (and four straight lines). This image is also featured on the cover of the Scientific American Library volume Beyond the Third Dimension.

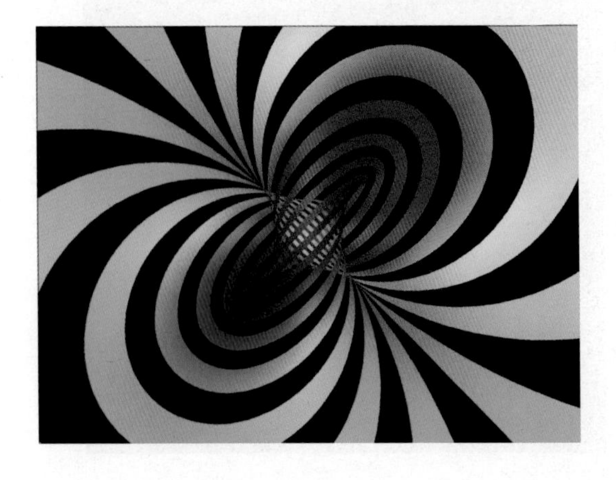

Plate 33. THEOLOGUE, painting by Alex Grey

1986 OIL ON LINEN 180×60 IN.

"During deep meditation, I entered a state where all energy systems in my body were completely aligned and flowing; it was in this state that I envisioned Theologue--The Union of Human and Divine Consciousness Weaving the Fabric of Space and Time in Which the Self and Its Surroundings Are Embedded."

"I was wearing a Mindfold which allowed me to stare into total darkness. I stared into an infinite regress of electric perspective grids that radiated from my brain/mind and led to the horizon. A mystic fire engulfed me. Across the horizon all I could see were perspective lines going into deep space."

"I was seeing both the perceptual grid of my mind on which space and time are woven, and the universal mind which was both the source and the weaving loom. At this moment, faintly, Himalayan mountains appeared. Transparent, but present, they formed a vast and beautiful panorama and then disappeared back into the grid." [alexgrey.com]

TUNiNG the DiAMONDS

ELECTROMAGNETiSM & SPiRiTUAL EVOLUTiON

Susan Joy Rennison

For more images, you can visit:
www.joyfirepublishing.com & www.susanrennison.com

Chapter Five

Mind & Body Electromagnetic Balance

How Emotion Rules

Our energy signature is directly related to our level of consciousness, which is also reflected in our mind and body. Since the 1970s, psychoneuroimmunology or PNI has studied this relationship as a new medical field of science. The name implies the links: psycho refers to the "mind", neuro for the neuroendocrine system (involving the nervous system and hormone systems) and immunology for the immune system. Psychoneuroimmunology (often termed mindbody medicine) has discovered a myriad of biological pathways that make the mind, body and emotions not separate but intimately entwined. Yet there is another aspect, the emotional mindbody seems to also behave nonlocally. Larry Dossey, M.D. writes:

> "The mind steadfastly refuses to behave locally, as contemporary scientific evidence is beginning to show. We now know, for example, that brain-like tissue is found throughout the body… So, even from the conservative perspective of modern neurochemistry, it is difficult if not impossible to follow a strictly local view of the brain." [1]

The following experiment under the direction of the United States Army Intelligence and Security Command (INSCOM) is phenomenal and demonstrates that our cells, even outside of our body, will still respond to our emotions [2].

In 1993, scientists conducted an experiment with white blood cells (leukocytes) that were scraped from the mouth of a volunteer, centrifuged and placed in a test tube. Next, a probe from a recording polygraph – a lie (or emotion) detector – was then inserted into the tube. The donor was separated from his donated cheek cells and placed in another room where they were shown a video with scenes of fighting and killing. The probe from the polygraph detected extreme excitation in the mouth cells even though the donor was in a room down the hall. Further experiments were carried out with donor and cells separated up to fifty miles and up to two days after donation, yet the results were the same. The donated cells remained energetically and non-locally connected with the donor and seemed to *remember* where they came from.

Doctors are now documenting stories of organ transplant patients who acquire the consciousness of the donor [3]. There is the unforgettable story of an eight-year-old girl who received the heart of a ten-year-old girl, who had been murdered. The heart recipient had such vivid dreams of the murder that she was able to describe the murderer to police. The murder scene details were so accurate, that the police were able to convict the man based solely on the testimony of the young girl. There is another story of a Croatia lumberjack who decided to sue his local health authority after receiving a kidney [4]. His complaint was that he had become a laughing stock since his operation that saved his life. Instead of heavy drinking with his male friends, he now preferred to do housework and had taken up knitting! He blames his new *female* kidney for his change of habit. There are so many stories of transplant patients altering their behavior after receiving donor organs, that this has now become a fresh area of research. Scientists are starting to realize that consciousness is transferable. Here, a basic scientific explanation requires that we know where our emotions actually originate and understand how emotions influence the mindbody.

Until the 1970s, it was thought that the brain and the central nervous system functioned like an electrical communication system. The "electrical" brain consisted of neurons or nerve cells that formed something like a telephone system with trillions of miles of wires that criss-crossed. For decades, scientists concentrated on neurotransmitters and the jump from one neuron to another across the synaptic gap to ignite another electrical discharge. All brain functions, even for the most complex levels of mental activity and behavior, were thought to be determined by the synaptic connection between billions of neurons. In the 1970s, scientists then discovered the "chemical" brain and the ligand-receptor system that represented a second nervous system that operated over a much longer time scale, over much greater distances. This chemical based system was far more ancient and far more basic to the organism of the human body, however it was difficult to switch focus to this new understanding of neuroscience.

The evidence showed that only 2 percent of neuronal communication actually occurred at the synapse and 98% by information molecules such as hormones and neuropeptides.

In 1984, a breakthrough found there was a bodywide network of information, which provided a biochemical basis for emotions. Receptors and their ligands (binding agents) came to be seen as "information molecules" – the basic units of a language used by cells to communicate across the endocrine, neurological, gastrointestinal and immune systems. A ligand is any molecule that binds to another, such as a hormone or neurotransmitter that links up with a receptor. A simple analogy to help us think of the relationship between cells, receptors and ligands is that the cell represents the house, the receptor is a doorway with a lock and the ligand is the key to unlock the door. See figure 5.1. Another description is that the ligand rings the doorbell, which allows entry at the doorway, representing the receptor. When this message is received, a signal is transmitted deep into the cell where profound changes are initiated. What occurs to a cell is very much dependent on what receptors are on the cell surface, resonating with outside signals. The language used to describe these biochemical functions, gives the impression of mechanical events, but what is actually occurring is a dance of

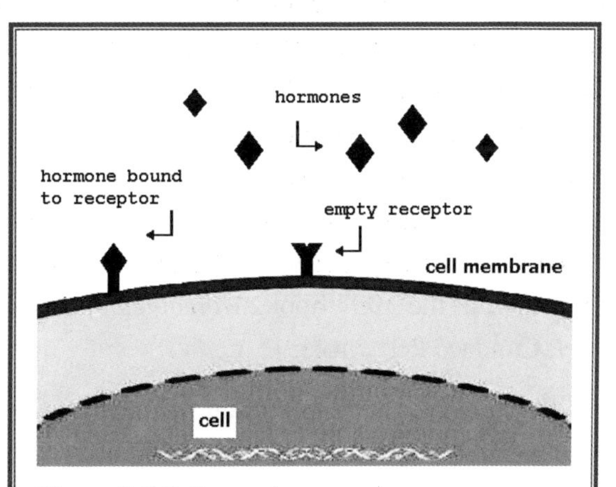

Figure 5.1 Cell membrane receptors.
Using neuropeptides our mindbody retrieves or represses emotions and behaviors. Nobel prize winner, Dr. Eric Kandel and his associates proved that biochemical change wrought at the receptor level is the molecular basis of memory. When a receptor is flooded with a ligand, it changes the cell membrane in such a way that the probability of an electrical impulse travelling across the membrane where the receptor resides is facilitated or inhibited, therefore affecting the choice of neuronal circuitry that can be used. This means that the decision of what becomes a thought arising to consciousness and what remains an undigested thought pattern buried at a deeper level in the body is mediated by the receptors [5].

energetic interactions. A molecule contains charged components and when these charges move, electromagnetic fields are set up. Each molecule has a specific frequency "signature" and this is how molecules recognize each other and interact.

Peptides, neuropeptides or "molecules of emotion" are a single family of molecular messengers, representing the universal biochemical language of emotion. They interlink and integrate mental, emotional and biological activities, altering behavior and mood states. Peptides are not only found in the limbic system (brain structures that associated with memory and emotion), but also the neo-cortex (outermost layer of the brain responsible for higher mental processing) and all over the body, and the entire intestine is lined with them. Wherever information is being relayed to the mindbody through the five senses – sight, smell, sound, taste and touch – there is a grouping of neuro-peptides. When there is a change in the physiological state, it is accompanied by an appropriate change in the emotional state and every change in the emotional state is accompanied by a change in the physiological state. Neuropeptides are the connecting factor between emotions and physiological processes. These molecules are only identified by their chemical make-up, but it is not too difficult to see that there are particular frequencies of vibration associated with different emotions. In the 1997 book, *Molecules of Emotion: Why You Feel the Way You Feel*, Candace Pert wrote:

> "I find I can't separate brain from body. Consciousness isn't just in the head. Nor is it a question of mind over body. If one takes into account the DNA directing the dance of the peptides, the body is the outward manifestation of the mind. The new science of psycho-neuro-immunology is redefining the connection between mind and body. We can no longer speak of body and mind as separate systems or entities" [5].

All our perceptions and thoughts are colored by emotions. There is no such thing as objective, rational thought. A chemical network of peptides integrates our mental, emotional and biological activities. So the question arises: where are the emotions? It used to be thought that mind and consciousness were located in the brain, but as the emotions are happening everywhere simultaneously we have to conclude that the definition of the mind has to change. Pert continues:

> "The neuro-peptides or 'molecules of emotion' are found not just in every system of the body but running every system of the body, connecting every system of the body to every other system. Wherever they are, they give rise to emotions. This means that our body is really our subconscious mind."

Theory states that we store our repressed emotions and memories as neuropeptide receptors on the surface of cells. We literally retain our history in the body, which explains why certain types of energy work, provide emotional relief, as they help to release this old information. This view of ourselves as an information network, departs radically from the old Newtonian mindset. In the old paradigm, electrical stimulation across the synapse ran the body in a more or less mechanical fashion. With information added to the process, we see an intelligence running all the systems, so another view would be to understand this as the body's **"innate wisdom".**

The biochemicals we call information molecules are not limited to space and time as quantum mechanics dictates, hence, the most intriguing aspect of the study of the mind and emotions, is where the body demonstrates non-local interactions. This implies there must be a way to interact with the body, outside of time and space, to make changes that will manifest instantaneously. This is how the Masters worked in the past and they called it working with karma. Yet how is this done? Our electromagnetic nature must provide the answer. Pert writes:

> "If information exists outside of the confines of space and time, matter and energy, then it must belong to a very different realm from the concrete, tangible realm we think of as "reality". And since information in the form of the biochemicals of emotion are running every system of the body, then our emotions must also come from some realm beyond the physical."

It is becoming increasingly accepted in neuropsychology that there is a significant emotional component to all personal decision-making. Researchers have found that people who have had strokes or brain tumors that caused injury to the prefrontal lobes of their brains, where the emotions are processed, have a very difficult time making even routine personal decisions, such as scheduling appointments. The work of respected neuroscientist and psychologist Vilayanur S. Ramachandra proves that bizarre neurological syndromes are caused by damage in parts of the brain that process emotions. Without the correct emotional guiding factors, certain decisions are impossible to make correctly, if at all [6]. Scientists say that our emotional reactions show up in brain activity before we even have time to think. We evaluate everything emotionally as we perceive it and think about it afterwards. So if emotional energy processes faster than the mind, how can we expect to manage our emotions with our thoughts? It appears that it takes more than the mind to manage emotions and so we find that we have to develop the power of the heart. When the head and heart are aligned it allows higher brain function, a direct link to higher intelligence or our higher self. The intelligence and power of the heart, if strong enough, can act as an override allowing us to bypasses mental analysis and gives us direct perception independent of any reasoning process.

The Power of the Heart: It's Electromagnetic!

There has always been a focus on the heart when it comes to assessing an individual's character and motivation. A 'large', 'warm' and 'open' heart signifies a person that will be motivated to go the extra mile and be loving, caring, empathic, emotional, courageous and wise etc. There is the opposite extreme where people are 'closed' or 'cold' hearted, and then there is a tendency to not trust, and to be wary of their true motives. We associate cold heartedness to being ruthless, unkind, unforgiving, selfish, unemotional, etc. Recently, scientists have started to explore the influence of the heart and they have made some surprising discoveries.

The physical heart is the most powerful generator of electromagnetic energy in the human body, producing the largest rhythmic electromagnetic field of any of the body's organs. The heart's electrical field is about 60 times greater in amplitude than the electrical activity generated by the brain. The field can be measured by an electrocardiogram (ECG), and can be detected anywhere on the surface of the body. Furthermore, the magnetic field produced by the heart is more than 5,000 times greater in strength than the field generated by the brain, and can be detected at 5ft (1.5m) away from the body, in all directions, using SQUID-based magnetometers. This means that when measurements are taken of the brain the frequencies from the heart have to be screened out to obtain an accurate measurement. Cardiologists have found that the electromagnetic field generated by the heart is modulated by different emotional states and studies suggest the possibility that this heart field may transmit information that can be received by others [7].

The heart has been shown to be the seat of emotions and health and not the brain. When a conventional EKG of the heart is converted into a frequency diagram, negative emotions such as frustration, unhappiness, anger, hatred, jealousy and the like can be clearly seen. These emotions generate chaotic, weak, high frequency heart-wave graphs, but on the other hand, positive emotions, such as love, appreciation and gratitude generate very orderly, low frequency, but very powerful waves on the graph. A model of the electromagnetic field of the heart shows a perfect, fractal, toroidal (donut) shape, see Figure 5.2. This shape is a subtle energy transducer, i.e. it converts one form of energy to another, because it generates an infinite number of harmonics allowing a step down or demodulation of higher energies. Energy travels through harmonics with no loss of power, so it can be thought as a transformer for 'higher' energies. Only when the heart is coherent, as in feelings of love and connected-ness, can this energy come through in force. Resonance and coherence in an orderly system are the apparent keys to tapping this supply of energy.

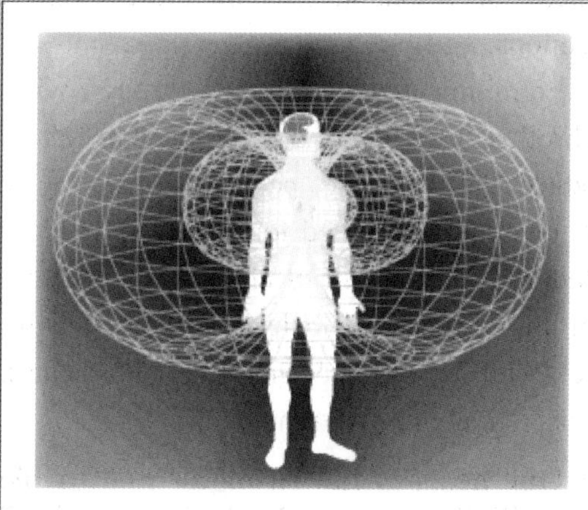

Figure 5.2 Electromagnetic field of the heart showing a perfect fractal, toroidal (donut) shape. Courtesy: Heartmath Institute

This has been proven by Dr. Rein who decided to conduct experiments with healers. It was thought that healers could change the absorption spectrum of DNA by either winding the coil tighter or unwinding it according to their intention. Healers were employed because they routinely work with subtle energies. They have the ability to work non-locally, so this experiment was even done from a mile away, when the spectrograph operator had no idea when the experiment was taking place. Most importantly, the ability to achieve this feat only took place when the healers changed their heart frequencies to a highly coherent state, in other words, when they were loving [8]. The theory of Heart Intelligence proposes that within living systems, the DNA molecule acts as an antenna and demodulator that is tuned to a non-local field that exists outside of space-time.

The DNA molecule functions as a conduit through which higher dimensional information can be downloaded to the level of the physical organism.

It was predicted that DNA would be particularly sensitive to this flow of information, and so would make a good model system to explore the effects of human intentionality. Thus, this highly successful study showed that individuals could completely separate the DNA strands! By using an *in vitro* DNA target, any potential neuronal or biochemical influence that could occur *in vivo* were eliminated, thus demonstrating a direct energetic interaction. The most intriguing aspect of this study was that heart coherence, generated through heart-focused positive emotions, appears to be necessary for this type of interaction to produce *significant* effects. While the DNA utilized in this experiment was derived from an exogenous source, it is likely that an individual's own DNA would be more "tuned" or resonant, and therefore even more responsive, to that person's intentions.

Entrainment is the process through which oscillators come into synch with each other. Oscillators can be mechanical or organic, and include anything that produces a rhythmic pattern of energy or movement. Mechanically, this phenomenon was noted long ago. In 1665, the inventor of the pendulum clock noted that a room full of clocks of a similar size would within a period of time "entrain", that is the clocks would begin swinging together synchronistically. The clock with the biggest pendulum (most energy field output), entrained the other clocks to match its rhythm.

Our heart is the strongest known biological oscillator. It will entrain oscillating systems in the body and will entrain other hearts, even over substantial distances.

Laboratory studies at The Institute of HeartMath® indicate that the heart's electromagnetic field can be detected by other individuals and can produce physiologically relevant effects in a person five feet away. Only emotions which occur in the frequency band of love (appreciation, wonder, joy, compassion) possess this unique, most powerful oscillating ability. Therefore a loving heart can and will entrain other hearts/minds and affect those in close proximity by virtue of the force of its energy output. This research highlights the power of being loving to affect our own well-being and it seems those around us.

The heart is also involved in intuitive perception. *The Concise Oxford Dictionary* (1964) defines intuition as "immediate apprehension by a sense, and immediate insight" and can be defined as a process by which information, normally outside the range of cognitive processes, is immediately sensed and perceived in the body and mind. Intuition comes with a certainty of knowledge or feeling of absolute certainty. The Hearthmath Institute reports:

- Both the heart and brain appears to receive and respond to intuitive information and that the heart appears to receive the information *first* before the brain.
- A significantly greater heart rate deceleration occurred prior to future emotional stimuli compared to calm stimuli.
- There were significant gender differences in the processing of prestimulus information and women seem more attuned to intuitive information from the heart.

Significantly, the electrophysiological evidence suggests that the heart is directly involved in the processing of information about a future emotional event *seconds* before the body actually experiences the stimulus. This intuitive information was also more forthcoming when the coherent mode was activated, i.e. intentional heart focus directing feelings of love, peace, joy, gratitude, bliss etc. which are all emotions and states associated with a higher calibration of consciousness.

The Harmony of the Head and Heart

The heart is far more than a simple pump, it is observed that **the heart acts as if it had a mind of its own** and profoundly influences the way we perceive and respond to the world, affecting intelligence and awareness. Pioneering research by a husband and wife team John and Beatrice Lacey, under grants from the National Institutes of Health, traced the neurological connections between the brain and the heart. Unfortunately, when they published their findings in 1978, their discovery was largely ignored [10]. In 1991, Dr. J. Andrew Armour of the University of Montreal, pioneered the concept of a functional heart brain and founded Neurocardiology as a new medical field of study [11]. Today, some neurocardiologists believe that 60 to 65% of the cells of the heart are actually neural cells, not muscle cells as was previously thought [12]. These heart cells are identical to the neural cells in the brain, operating through the same connecting links called ganglia, with the same axonal and dendritic connections that take place in the brain, as well as through the very same kinds of neurotransmitters found in the brain. The heart also communicates with the brain and body biochemically, by the hormones it produces. In 1983, some researchers reclassified the heart as an endocrine gland, but as usual, it has taken a very long time for this knowledge to filter through into the education system, see figure 4.6 and the small section "Endocrine Glands" [13]. The heart secretes the hormone Atrial Natriuretic Factor (ANF), which was quickly nicknamed the "balance" hormone because it has a major balancing effect in the body. Actually, the heart manufactures and secretes a number of other hormones and neurotransmitters that have a wide-ranging impact on the body as a whole. An excerpt from an Heartmath research paper entitled *The Coherent Heart: Heart-Brain Interactions* is provided in Appendix III, courtesy of the Rollin McCraty, Heartmath director of research.

Endocrine Glands

Any gland that produces hormonal secretions that pass directly into the bloodstream, these include the thymus, thyroid, parathyroids, anterior and posterior pituitary, pancreas, adrenals, pineal, and gonads.

Quite literally, there is a "brain" in the heart, whose ganglia are linked to every major organ in the body, and the entire muscle spindle system that uniquely enables humans to express their emotions. About half of the heart's neural cells are involved in translating information sent to it from all over the body so that it can keep the body working as one harmonious whole. The other half makes up a very large, unmediated neural connection with the emotional brain in our head, maintaining a twenty-four-hour-a-day dialogue between the heart and the brain. These influences profoundly affect brain function and most of the body's major organs, and ultimately determine the quality of life. What is interesting is that in human embryonic and fetal development, formation of a rudimentary heart comes first, followed by formation of the brain and finally the rest of the body. The electromagnetic field surrounds the embryo right from the beginning, which is then surrounded by the mothers more powerful heart.

> **The heart is a highly complex, self-organized information processing center with its own functional "brain" that communicates with and influences the cranial brain via the nervous system, hormonal system and other pathways.**

Paul Pearsall is a psychoneuroimmunologist with more than thirty years of scientific training. He is the founder and director of a large psychiatric clinic for seriously ill patients, many of whom had received heart and other organ transplants. From interviewing heart transplant recipients and their families, he says:

> "I have little doubt that the heart is not only the major energy center of the body, but that it also has its own intelligence, an intelligence superior to the brain's and that its cells hold memories that influence not only every other cell in our bodies but also every cell in the bodies of those close to us, and even those far away, in both space and time" [14].

In the old paradigm, any study of communication pathways between the "head" and heart had always been approached from the perspective of the heart's responses to the brain's commands. Now, we know better, the communication between the heart and brain is actually a dynamic, ongoing, two-way dialogue, with each organ continuously influencing the other's function. The brain's activity is significantly affected by various communication paths as the heart communicates with the brain in four major ways:

1. neurologically (through the transmission of nerve impulses).
2. biochemically (via hormones and neurotransmitters).
3. biophysically (through pressure waves).
4. energetically (through electromagnetic field interactions).

Taken together, the results of studies at the Institute of HeartMath demonstrate that **intentionally** altering one's emotional state through heart focus, modifies sensory neurological input from the heart to the brain. The data suggests that as people experience sincere positive feeling states, in which the heart's rhythms become more coherent, the changed information flow from the heart to the brain may act to modify cortical function and influence performance. Negative emotions lead to increased disorder in the heart's rhythms and in the autonomic nervous system, thereby adversely affecting the rest of the body. In contrast, positive emotions create increased harmony and coherence in heart rhythms and improve balance in the nervous system. The health implications are easy to understand. Disharmony in the nervous system leads to inefficiency and increased stress on the heart and other organs while harmonious rhythms are more efficient and less stressful to the body's systems. Dramatic positive changes occur when sophisticated techniques, developed by HeartMath, are applied that increase coherence in rhythmic patterns of heart rate variability. These include shifts in perception and the ability to reduce stress and deal more effectively with difficult situations.

In esoteric tradition, the heart is considered the gateway to higher consciousness. The philosopher Aristotle taught that the seat of human consciousness lies not in the brain, but in the heart. Recent translations of more than a hundred Vedas, Upanishads, Tantras and Puranas give us a fresh perspective on these Indian scriptures and a greater understanding of eastern knowledge [15]. The Vedas describe with great technical precision how the awakening of the spiritual heart brings about the opening of the "gate of heaven" [16]. The root of the word *veda* is vid, which means "to know" – thus *veda* is synonymous with *gnosis.* The Vedas describe the spiritual heart or heart chakra as a lotus flower hanging downward with its petals closed. When activated, the lotus lifts its head and opens its petals and consequently, a spontaneous expansion of consciousness that is potentially limitless occurs. Within the heart chakra, there lies an infinitesimal void. The heart space, or *hridaya,* is where we can experience "The whole", a place of unity, wholeness, oneness. This place has also been described as the Sacred heart of Jesus, the Tao and in Gnostic tradition, the all or Pleroma.

Interestingly, we find that the Tantras refer to two heart centers, an eight-petaled and a twelve-petaled lotus and there is disagreement between the saints and scriptures of India as to the precise locations. Maybe, this can be explained by their being two centers, as we know there is a chakra called the 'high heart' center, which is associated with the thymus, and it's activation is an important part of human evolution. Nevertheless, the scriptures agree on the importance of the heart center being open, as this permits energy pathways in the body to become active, accelerating spiritual evolution. Mystics from the east and west provide precise details of sacred anatomy and there are now many books detailing these energy pathways in relation to Kundalini, the hidden life force normally lying dormant at the base of the spine. The adept Da Love-Ananda (Da Free John) is quoted as saying:

> "Therefore, spiritual practice consists in constantly going beyond the wall of ego, in reaching out and embracing all life fearlessly, with an open heart. There must be complete clarity and integrity in one's feelings. Most people are "collapsed at the heart". They are in doubt of God, others and themselves. Their feeling being is stunted" [17].

Da Love-Ananda makes a point of directing spiritual seekers to what he calls, *The Way of the Heart*. He states:

> "The Heart is the key to the practice of real or spiritual life. It is at the heart, at the place of Infinity, the root of being, the feeling core of the body-mind."

Again, it seems that mystics and scientists now agree as to the importance of the heart center, spiritually, emotionally, mentally and physically. Mindbody medicine represents another paradigm shift to a new holistic and more spiritual understanding of how we function and create our reality. Yet, from an evolutionary perspective, the heart does appear to be the gateway to higher realms of consciousness.

There are always pioneers and forerunners who set the lead for others to follow. Joseph Chilton Pearce is an author and teacher who has given thousands of talks around the world on the head-heart connection. Over a twenty-five year period, he has also taught and written about the changing needs of children and the development of human society. In his book, *The Biology of Transcendence: A Blueprint of the Human Spirit,* he points out that we have five neural centers or brains [18]. The fourth and most recently developed brain is located in the head, while the fifth is located in the heart [19]. Pearce shares a spiritual revelation, an insight, highly relevant to the discussion in this book, which will help bring the message of this book down to a very personal level.

Siddha yoga meditations mainly center on the heart. On one occasion Pearce decided to use the pranayama, the "breath of fire," which is a rapid deep-breathing meditation. His aim was to gain a breakthrough understanding of the subtle sphere form of energy surrounding the body. As a disciple of Baba Muktananda he was taught that the vibrations or waveforms that surround the body were the same frequencies out of which the universe was formed. The subtle sphere surrounding us contains the whole universe within it in subtle or potential form. He makes it clear that this type of meditation is not recommended for people with weak hearts and older people, but this is what he wrote:

> "I did the breath of fire on and on into the early early-morning hours. When this breathing, which had become automatic, suddenly stopped of its own accord, leaving me in great stillness, I clearly perceived the subtle sphere of vibrations engulfing me. It was palpable I felt I could touch and embrace it. The word *plasma* came to mind for this sphere that was like a living presence, and I realized that this truly was a cocoon in which we are immersed all our lives. To me it was pure love—vibrant, alive totally nurturing."

On the global scale, the head-heart connection really matters. In the words of the Hopi Elders:

> "When the heart of man and the mind of man become so distant that they are no longer one, Earth heals itself through the catastrophic events of change". [20]

Blown a Fuse in the Brain? No Problem!

In the 1960s, Dr. Robert Becker, an early pioneer in electromedicine predicted that the flow of direct current in the brain would produce a magnetic field. He stated that it could be observed at a distance outside of the head, if a magnetometer of sufficient sensitivity was available. As usual, this forward thinking was met with laughter and derision. He was told that, "such a device would never be made, and that even if such a magnetic field could be measured, its strength would be so small that it would be of no physiological consequence whatsoever" [21]. Becker did not have too long to wait to be vindicated. Advances in solid-state physics and electronics permitted the development of this device, which was named the Superconducting Quantum Interference Detector, or SQUID. This device can easily read the brain's field, several feet away from the head and is the basis for the neuroimaging device known as the magnetoencephalogram, or MEG. The whole-head MEG sensor system is a method of measuring the tiny magnetic fields that are produced by the brain's 100 billion or so cells (neurons).

> **Electric currents in the brain produce magnetic fields that result from thought, sound, muscle movement, impulses and other types of brain activity.**

Historically, the magnetic alpha rhythm from the brain was first detected in 1968, and the MEG signal was first detected with a point contact SQUID in 1972. Currents circulating in the brain from electric dipole neuronal activity, produce tiny pulsating magnetic fields of the order of 10^{-9} gauss. As there are two hemispheres to the brain, sensory cortex currents will produce fields of symmetrical shape but with polarities opposing each other. An electroencephalograph (EEG) measures the electrical potential on the scalp and generates a record of the electrical activity of the brain.

For studies in Electroencephalography & Magnetoencephalography, the head is modeled as concentric spheres. When electrodes of an electric lead are placed on a spherical volume conductor (the head) and lie on the axis of symmetry of a magnetic lead, the electric and magnetic lead fields are normal to each other (i.e. horizontal and vertical) everywhere in the volume conductor [22]. See figure 5.3.

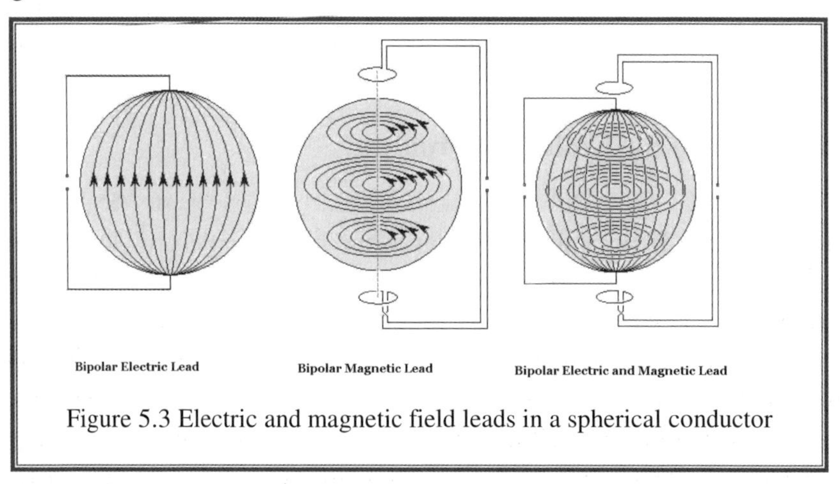

Figure 5.3 Electric and magnetic field leads in a spherical conductor

This research provides the theoretical explanation for electromagnetic rings of energy that circle a spherical conductor, but it also explains the horizontal and vertical multi-dimensional lines of energy seen around the head by sensitives.

Today, energy practitioners work directly with these invisible electromagnetic rings around the head, with the intent to "lock-in" changes made in the electromagnetic field of the body during energy balancing sessions. The ability to work directly with these rings and the findings of the latest medical research, gives us insight into how dramatic changes on the physical, mental, emotional and spiritual level can be attained.

The world famous healer/medium Betty Shine wrote 11 books about her life and work [23]. In the book, *Mind to Mind*, Betty describes the electromagnetic rings that encircle the head as follows:

"The healthy mind includes what looks like a series of separate goldish-yellow links which are not completely joined up but are attracted to each other, probably electromagnetically, to form a kind of chain around the head. In migraine-sufferers and epileptics there is always a break in these links, and it seems that when a link is broken it is *like a fuse has blown*." *[Bold added for emphasis]*

Betty also talks about depression and how negative energy can affect the electromagnetic field around the head.

"Everyone who is depressed has the same appearance. It always looks like as if the energy is being drawn down in a funnel shape, through the top of the head and down into the body. In every case I can see how depression and negative thinking come to create an unnatural pressure on the brain, literally depressing and compressing it. I see, too, how this affects the electro-magnetic field around the head and if that continues unchecked it eventually causes congestion in the energy counterpart and alters the body biochemistry."

This observation of irregularities in the electromagnetic field causing a subsequent biochemical change is very much in-line with the understanding that true healing occurs at the electromagnetic level. In another example, a young woman came to Betty for healing after 50 or 60 hospital tests revealed she was *allergic to everything*. After closely studying the energies around the head, the diagnosis was that this woman was 'completely unbalanced'. Betty also placed on record that ALL chemical drugs have the affect of pushing the energy counterpart out of place, so that the person is slightly out of body.

Scientists are starting to understand that there is a significant relationship between the interhemispheric electrical balance of the brain and depression. A Russian paper called *Interhemispheric Correlations of Electric Activity of the Brain in Late Depression*, stated in the abstract:

"It has been demonstrated that the development of depressive conditions gives rise not only to changes in the frequency and amplitude characteristics of the EEG but also in the ratios of interhemispheric asymmetry of the parameters of brain electric activity, attesting to a higher tone of the right hemisphere" [24].

Betty Shine's observation of the unbalanced state of the electromagnetic rings and an energy cure for depression, are linked by an "accidental" discovery that manic-depressives can be cured, virtually instantaneously, by strong magnetic fields.

In January 2004, the Harvard University Gazette reported that a small and preliminary study had been carried out to study people with bipolar disorder. Results suggested that the electromagnetic fields, produced by certain types of brain scans, can bring about mood improvement. This discovery was made by a psychiatric research team trying to determine how the brain chemistry of manic-depressives differs from those of people who are free of the problem. They realized that a significant change had taken place when severely depressed people left the MRI (Magnetic Resonance Imaging) scanner laughing and joking! It was immediately suspected that the electromagnetic fields generated by the scanner could nudge a depressed brain back toward normal [25]. Researchers were also intrigued that ALL of the manic-depressives NOT on medication responded favorably, yet this was reduced to only to two-thirds for those taking drugs. Unfortunately, rather than acknowledging that the drugs were in getting in the way of creating the cure, the diagnosis was, "medication may reduce the sensitivity of brain cells to the electromagnetic fields. If that turns out to be so, we may be able to raise the intensity of the fields."

The type of scan used is known as Echo-Planer Magnetic Resonance Spectroscopic Imaging, or EP-MRSI. The scientists speculate that the specific timing and amplitude of the magnetic pulses induce electric fields that may match the natural electrical firing rhythm of brain cells. Pulses travel from right to left through a thick cable of nerves (corpus callosum) that coordinate activity between the two halves of the brain. The two halves perform different tasks but still need to be in balance for good mental health. Hence the reasoning that:

> **"When the two halves of the brain get out of balance, the electromagnetic pulses may restore the balance."** [25]

Researchers at Harvard Medical School and elsewhere are experimenting with another technique that uses electromagnetic pulses to treat depression. Called Transcranial Magnetic Stimulation, or TMS. This involves holding a figure-of-eight-shaped wand near a person's head, see figure 5.4. Two coils of wire on the wand generate a strong magnetic field that induces electric currents in brain cells. It is thought that TMS works by normalizing disturbed levels of brain activity. Comparing the two methods, TMS uses electric fields that are more localized and much stronger than EP-MRSI. Some patients have reported feeling discomfort and there is a risk of seizures that does not occur with the other system. However, it speculated that the two methods use different techniques to achieve the same result. In 2003, a report by Scientific America revealed some TMS researchers were actually deliberately inducing temporary brain "lesions" in healthy subjects. The objective was to gain insight into fundamental brain functions with a magnetic pulse stream and then compare the "before" condition with the "after" [26]. It does make you wonder where they get the volunteers from!

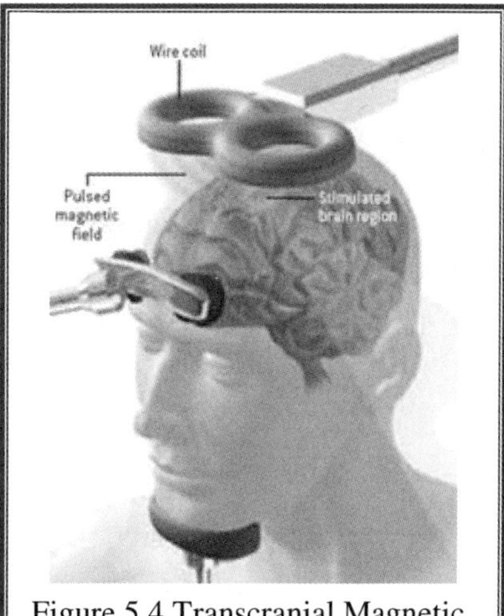

Figure 5.4 Transcranial Magnetic Stimulation. Copyright: © Bryan Christie Design

Results of hundreds of double-blind, placebo-controlled studies with magnets and pulsed electromagnetic fields reveal that a pulsed magnetic field to headache patients, will produce significant beneficial effects. This is disclosed by subjective patient reports, as well as EEG activity [27]. When using low-intensity and low-frequency magnetic fields, patients experienced a reduction in the frequency of epileptic seizures. One study found that two-thirds of the patients had a mean decrease in seizure frequency by 33 percent during the study [28].

Diamonds in the Brain: Tiny Crystal Antennas?

Those who danced where thought to be quite insane
by those who could not hear the music.
Angela Monèt

Our brains detect and use very low frequency signals from the Schumann Resonance, as a globally available, synchronization system that continuously stabilizes the brain. For reference, a cell phone next to the head, produces a signal around a billion times stronger than the Schumann Resonance, yet, without the Schumann Resonance signal, humans would quickly become disorientated. A brain EEG clearly shows that it shares the same frequency range with the Schumann Resonance spectrum, hence, the agreement amongst researchers that there must be some interaction with our consciousness, see figure 5.5 [29]. In this regard, we find that scientists exploring "unconventional" information pathways, connecting the human brain (consciousness) and the environment, give us a hint as to why the frequency range of the human EEG spectra shows a peak at 10 Hz. They say that the 10 Hz environmental signal is a sub-harmonic frequency that permits an "information-transfer medium that is independent of space and time". This is explored in more detail in relation to Healer Science, which can be found in chapter 9, *Universal Energy* [31].

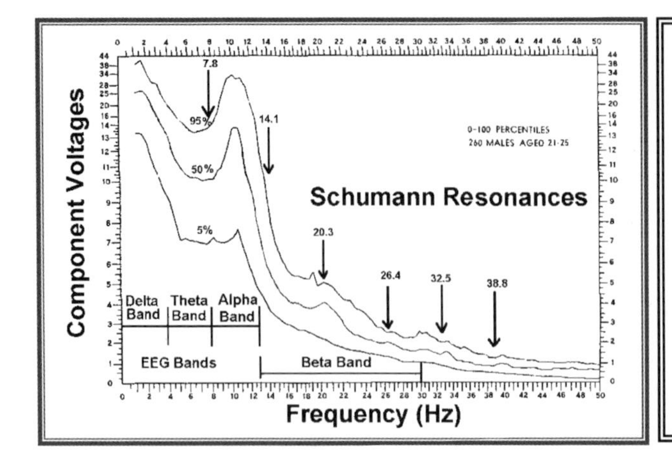

Figure 5.5 Comparison of the frequency spectra of the human EEG from 260 young males showing the 5%, 50% and 95%ile bands, adapted from Gibbs and Gibbs (1951), and Schumann Resonance peaks, from Polk (1982). Credit: Cherry, 2000 [30].

In addition to the Schumann Resonances, there are additional atmospheric signals. VLF-atmospherics or VLF-sferics occur when lightning generates a variety of signals in the very low (radio) frequency (VLF) range (1-100 kHz). Sferics are electromagnetic impulses that propagate at nearly the speed of light through the atmosphere. Most of these signals become dispersed with distances beyond 1000km, except a signal at about 10 kHz. They are characterized by very low amplitudes and short duration with an electric and magnetic field strength that does not exceed values of a few volts per meter and some microTesla, respectively. It does seem that these signals have not received the same level of attention as the Schumann Resonances, but they have biological effects too. Correlation studies show that weather sensitive individuals are prone to a whole host of induced symptoms. Briefly, patients report an increase in pain intensity from brain injuries, damaged tissue (operation wounds, scars), or internal illnesses (asthma, angina pectoris, migraine) and rheumatism. Spectral maxima at 6, 8, 10, 12, and 28 kHz are associated with the occurrence of epileptic seizures, sudden deafness, and myocardial infarctions (heart attacks) [30].

We know that every living thing is electromagnetic and all living organisms survive by harnessing energy from the Earth's external magnetic field. The question then arises: how exactly does this mechanism work? One answer is that the vicinity of the brain's pituitary and pineal glands contain cells with magnetite crystals homogeneously distributed. Specifically, magnetite crystals can be found in a cluster of nerves in front of the pituitary gland. The pineal gland also contains these tiny crystals of magnetite [32]. This has led to the proposal that these glands may use information from the earth's magnetic field to regulate the release of hormones in the human brain which directly control levels of conscious awareness [33].

So, are these crystals acting like tiny antennae, receiving and transmitting electromagnetic signals? The magnetite in the brain is slightly different to the geological magnetite crystals of this size, which are usually diamonds (octahedra), see figure 5.6. The crystal morphology was found to be cubo-octahedral, which is a prismatic particle shape and is thought to be a biological mechanism for maximizing the magnetic moment per particle. See the small section, "More about Magnetite" [34]. These little biological magnets made of the iron mineral magnetite, are the same as that found in homing pigeons, whales, salmon, honeybees and some shellfish and bacteria [35].

Magnetite

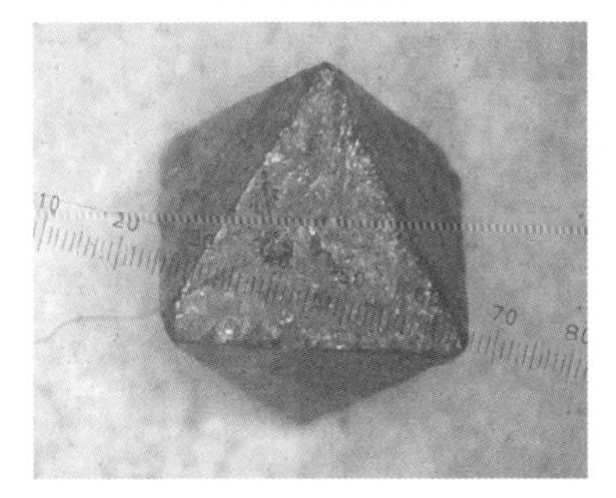

Figure 5.6 Magnetite (Fe_3O_4) or loadestone is mostly iron and is the only natural magnet found on Earth, besides plasma. It is most interesting that the only natural magnet that can be found as a solid, should be found as an octahedron (diamond) crystal.

More about Magnetite

Searches for biogenic magnetite in human tissues had not been conclusive until the beginning of the 1990s, when high-resolution transmission electron microscopy and electron diffraction on human brain tissue, identified magnetite-maghemite crystals. These magnetite crystals were found to be organized into linear, membrane-bound chains a few micrometers in length, with up to 80 crystals per chain. The Miller Index indicates crystal alignments. The faces of an octahedron make equal intercepts, positive and negative, on all three axes and therefore have Miller indices {111}. So these crystals have their {111} faces aligned along the length of the chain axes (the "easy" direction of magnetization). The {111} crystal alignment has been interpreted as a biological mechanism for maximizing the magnetic moment per particle, as the {111} direction yields approximately 3% higher saturation magnetization than do other directions. This prismatic particle shape is also uncommon in geological magnetite crystals of this size, which are usually octahedra. The crystal morphology was found to be cubo-octahedral with the {111} faces of adjacent crystals lying perpendicular to the chain axis.

Chapter Six

Making Sense of Consciousness

This (telepathy) has probably more to do
with physics than psychology.
Albert Einstein

Why our Special Agents use Good Sense

The New Scientist ran a front page that read, *Special Report — Power of the Paranormal: Why it won't surrender to science.* With a headline like that, it presupposes that eventually science will finally discredit paranormal phenomena. Nevertheless, it is apparent that as the evidence for Extra Sensory Perception (ESP) gets stronger, the harder the opponents dig in their heels. What is interesting is the results are often "more impressive for the reality of ESP than the outcome of clinical drug trials because they show a more pronounced effect and have greater statistical significance". From the New Scientist report:

> "What's more ESP experiments have been replicated and their results are as consistent as many medical trials — and even more so in some cases. In short, by all the normal rules for assessing scientific evidence, the case for ESP has been made. And yet most scientists still refuse to believe the findings." [1]

Paranormal powers are sub-divided into two parts. The first is extrasensory perception (ESP) which is the ability of two minds to communicate through an unknown channel. The other is telekinesis the ability to affect matter. Studies into the paranormal were galvanized when a book called *Psychic Discoveries Behind The Iron Curtain,* written by Canadians Sheila Ostrander & Lynn Schroeder, was published in 1971 [2]. This greatly upset the U.S. intelligence community as they found that the Soviets were training psychic spies! Instead of just doing the same old experiment time after time, they had actually created practical ESPionage! The U.S. intelligence services decided that something had to be done and so the CIA turned to two physicists, Russell Targ and Dr. Harold (Hal) Puthoff at Standford Research Institute in California, the country's second biggest think tank.

This was indeed a Paracelsus moment in history. Paracelsus (1493-1541) was one of the most important Renaissance naturalists who contributed substantially to the rise of modern medicine, including psychiatric treatment [3]. A German-Swiss physician and alchemist, Paracelsus established the role of chemistry in medicine. He rejected traditional education and medicine and believed that "Knowledge is experience". One of his more famous quotes can be seen to be appropriate here:

> "The universities do not teach all things…so a doctor must seek out old wives, gypsies, sorcerers, wandering tribes, old robbers, and such outlaws and take lessons from them."

Returning to Targ and Puthoff, they worked with skilled psychics and created a program called "Remote Viewing", with astonishing results, see the small section "What is Remote Viewing?" It can be noted that extensive, independent replication of remote viewing has been documented [4]. Furthermore, there are training courses available now for anybody to learn how to do this. Nowadays, there is even open acknowledgement of the usage of psychic methods in the United States military. A 2005 U.S. Air Force, *Teleportation Physics Study*, revealed that the Remote Viewing program was closed down in 1994 and declassified by Clinton in 1995, after it had lasted for 22

What is Remote Viewing?

Remote Viewing is the ability to obtain information by psychic means. This information manifests itself during a session as pictures, feelings or words that are recorded and drawn on (usually) white A4 paper. A session can last from 45 minutes to 1 hour and is very often monitored by a second person. This person acts as a guide who may only know the coordinates of the target (but not its name) and will steer the viewer (but not lead the viewer) to areas of interest in and around the target location. This is said to be remote viewing in double blind conditions. However for training purposes the monitor may know up front the name or location of the target in order to facilitate the learning process.

years [5]. It was highly funded and used by the highest echelons of the U.S. military. Remote viewing has been declared to be as high as 85% accurate, even though there have been attempts to downplay the success rates [6]. This is why commentators are highly skeptical that such a successful program would completely disappear. Rather, it seems more likely that remote viewing has just been buried under a deeper cloak of secrecy. From the *Teleportation Physics Study*, the report reveals:

> "The reader should note that very first US military-intelligence RD programs on psi, PK [Psychokinesis] and mind control were conducted by H. K. (Andrija) Puharich, M.D., L.L.D during his military service at the Army Chemical and Biological Warfare Center at Fort Detrick, Maryland in the 1940s-50s. Puharich has an interest in clairvoyance and PK, and dabbled in theories for electronically and pharmaceutically enhancing and synthesizing psychic abilities. While in Army, Puharich took part in a variety of parapsychology experiments and he lectured Army, Air Force and Navy groups on possibilities for mind warfare. He was a recognized expert in hypnotism and microelectronics." [5]

This military interest is not limited to a few isolated experiments, as there is plenty of documentation in the public domain, telling the story of military and government exploration into extrasensory perception, psi, telepathy and telekinesis. Success stories have also been released, such as being able to track the location of kidnap victims and crashed planes.

> **Psychic phenomena, is no longer the domain of gypsies, clairvoyants, and sensitives!**

For some readers, this may come as a bit of a shock that the military and government establishments are involved in such activities, but we can surmise that such organizations deal in reality not myth, and experimental observation and not just theory.

The Sixth Sense

Eastern philosophy has always maintained that everything starts with consciousness. However, in the West, this was deemed to be too mystical, so only a few philosophers and gnostics held this view. Hence, the western doctrine of "reductionism" prevailed, demanding that everything could be reduced down to matter. Hence, our reality was just viewed as interactions between elementary particles, the building blocks that make atoms, where increasing complexity allows for molecules and then cells etc. The problem with this viewpoint is that our will power, thoughts and beliefs cannot be taken into account, because they are not tangible – i.e. they are not made up of matter – so cannot exist, and this means that any seeming effect could only be described as an illusion. If you start with the premise that consciousness exists, then our free will, thoughts and beliefs can influence any creative process. Nowadays, scientists have started to concede that consciousness does indeed have an affect. Very strange experimental results have "spooked" scientists. Even though some scientists are uncomfortable with the findings, they cannot be disputed [7]. For example, Robert Becker revealed in his book, *The Body Electric* (1985), that weapon planners at the US Department of Defense were investigating the evidence that psychic intent could influence the flow of current in solid-state devices [8].

(Next, small sections denoted with ✧❖◆❖✧ provide slightly more technical details and can be skipped over by the less scientifically minded.)

The Aspect Experiment

Two properties of quantum systems that pose the greatest difficulties for the reductionist viewpoint are quantum superposition and quantum non-locality. Firstly, quantum superposition is usually presented as the paradox of Schrödingers cat and this well known concept basically defines a state of two realities existing at once, see small section, "What is Quantum Superposition?" [9]. Secondly, non-locality is represented as the Einstein Podlosky and Rosen paradox (the EPR paradox) and the human implications are of paramount interest here. At the beginning of quantum mechanics in 1900 and then when the equations of quantum mechanics were discovered in 1925, there were indications that there must be other levels of reality other than the material level. This started when objects in quantum physics began to be looked at as waves of possibility, waves that could not be in space and time. These waves became recognized as waves of possibility, or waves in potential that were somehow beyond matter.

Alain Aspect in France performed an experiment, which established conclusively that objects really do have connections outside of space and time and it was not just theory.

This was not properly understood for a long time until 1982 when quantum physicist Aspect and his research team, discovered that photons, light information sources going in opposite ways, somehow affect each other. This is done *without* exchanging any signals through space, but the affect is instantaneous. Aspect and his colleagues created two photons from the same quantum event and observed them as they speeded into opposite directions. After

What is Quantum Superposition?

Quantum superposition is usually presented as the paradox of Schrödinger's cat, a nice explanation given in a form of a parable. A cat is kept inside a box with an atom that has a probability to decay radioactively. When it does, it sends a signal that triggers poison gas to be released to kill the cat. According to quantum theory, unless and before the box is opened by someone (the observer), the cat is in a quantum superposition of being dead, being alive, and being both dead and alive simultaneously. This strange, indefinite quantum system can be described by a wave function of the quantum superposition of all the possibilities, and is real, in the sense that it can be experimentally created in many forms. However, once a macroscopic, classical instrument such as a person observes the indefinite quantum system, it suddenly collapses into a definite state. When the box containing Schrödinger's cat is opened, it ceases to be a quantum system, and the cat will be observed in one of two definite states: either dead or alive. This collapse of the wave function is generally thought to represent a transition between the quantum and the classical domains – the former is a domain of elementary particles and the latter of ordinary macroscopic systems, like organisms and matter.

travelling some distance with the speed of light, the researchers changed the polarization for only one of them. (Polarization is the orientation of the wave that corresponds to each photon.) As a result, the other photon adopted the opposite polarization, even though the two were far apart. The Special Theory of Relativity states that no information can travel faster than light. Einstein's theory had laid down the principle that two objects could never affect each other instantaneously, as he believed that everything must travel through space with a maximum speed limit, that of the speed of light. Therefore, any affect must take a finite amount of time to occur and this is known as "locality". What is interesting here, is that in 1935, Albert Einstein, with physicists Boris Podolsky, and Nathan Rosen criticized quantum mechanics, claiming that if it were a complete model of reality, then non-local interactions between objects *had* to exist [10]. Since that was deemed inconsistent with the theory of relativity, quantum mechanics had to be either wrong or at least incomplete. This critique is known as the Einstein-Podolosky-Rosen (EPR) paradox. Einstein described "non-locality" as "spooky action at a distance".

There is now a practical use for non-local interactions, Teleportation – but not quite in the same manner as the science fiction made famous by the TV series *Star Trek*. When physicists say "Teleportation", it means the transfer of key properties from one particle to another without a physical link. In 2004, scientists reported that they had transported the characteristics of one photon over 600 meters outside of laboratory conditions across the River Danube [11]. Quantum teleportation relies on an aspect of physics known as “entanglement”, whereby the properties of two particles can be tied together even when they are far apart, this is still seen as “spooky action at a distance”.

> **Aspect showed that somehow there must be another realm of reality that allows for instant communication between particles.**

Thus, non-locality is the principal that underlines all “absent” or “distance healing”.

The “Brain” Aspect Experiments

Amit Goswami, is a well known physicist who wrote *The Self Aware Universe: How consciousness Creates the Material World* [12]. Goswami discusses in the above-mentioned book, an experiment that provides evidence that EPR correlation, “non-locality” occurs between human brains. Goswami says in an interview that:

> “In 1984 or ‘85 at the American Physical Society meeting at which I was present, it is said that one physicist was heard saying to another physicist that, after Aspect’s experiment, anyone who does not believe that something is really strange about the world must have rocks in his head.”[13]

A Mexican neurophysiologist, Dr. Jacobo Grinberg-Zylberbaum at the National University of Mexico produced the most convincing experiments that electrical signals can be transmitted between humans, these results were first published in 1994 [14]. This is now thought of as the brain equivalent of the Aspect experiment and is still considered as “strange” by some.

It is well known that meditation produces increases in synchronization between both sides of the brain. In ordinary waking consciousness the two hemispheres – the language-oriented, linearly thinking, rational “left brain” and the perceiving, intuitive, “right brain” – exhibit uncoordinated, randomly diverging wave patterns in the electroencelograph (EEG). When a meditative state of consciousness is entered, these patterns become synchronized, and in deep meditation the two hemispheres fall into a nearly identical pattern.

In more than fifty experiments performed over five years, Grinberg-Zylberbaum paired his subjects inside sound-and electro-magnetic radiation-proof “Faraday cages”. He asked them to meditate together for twenty minutes and then he placed the subjects in separate Faraday cages up to 14.5 meters apart. When the primary subject felt a “direct connection” with their partner, a button was push, signaling this occurrence. Now the experiment could begin in earnest. The primary subject was given stimuli such as light, at random intervals in such a way that they, nor the experimenter, knew when they were applied. The non-stimulated subject remained relaxed, with eyes closed, and was instructed to *feel* the presence of the partner without knowing anything about his or her stimulation.

In general, a series of one hundred stimuli were applied, flashes of light, sounds, or short, intense but not painful electric shocks to the index and ring fingers of the right hand. The EEG of both subjects was then synchronized and examined for "normal" potentials evoked in the stimulated subject and "transferred" potentials in the non-stimulated subject. In experimental situations with stimulated subjects, the transferred potentials appeared consistently in some 25 percent of the cases. However, this did not happen in control experiments where interaction between subjects did not take place or when the interaction was not deemed successful (i.e. the subjects did not feel they had established direct communication with each other).

These experiments have been replicated by other researchers (and similar findings have been found with plants and trees). They provide significant evidence that identifiable and consistent electrical signals occur in the brain of one person when a second person (especially if he or she is closely related or emotionally linked), is "connected".

Human consciousness via the brain is capable of establishing relationships with other brains and can maintain such links even at a distance.

The above results cannot be explained as due to sensory communication or normal electromagnetic signals between subjects. In the experiments, the subjects were separated during the experiment and located in two semi-silent, electromagnetically isolated and distant chambers. Low frequency EEG correspondence was also ruled out. It is extremely significant that the occurrence of the successful brain coupling of EEG signatures is always associated with the participants' *feeling* that their interaction has been successfully completed. This emphasizes that consciousness is involved in the process. This interaction can be explained by the effect of quantum non-local interaction between correlated brains.

Next, we will examine why neurologists wonder what *exactly* is going on with the brain.

The Enigma of Brain and Consciousness

"The catalogue of our ignorance must also include the understanding of the human brain... nobody understands how decisions are made or how imagination is set free. What consciousness consists of (or how it should be defined) is equally a puzzle... we seem as far from understanding cognitive process as we were a century ago."
Sir John Maddox, former editor of Nature

Eminent neurologists have stated that in their opinion, the brain appears to be a complicated organism to register and channel consciousness rather than to produce it. This was summed up by Prof. J.C. Eccles who stated, "The brain is messenger to consciousness" [15]. However, one neurologist, went further by writing an article headlined: *"Is the brain really necessary?"* This enigma between the brain and consciousness can be encapsulated by the research of neurologist, Karl Pribram who actually proved that the memory of the human being is not actually stored in the brain at all! [16] His experiments seem to show that memory is not in the same space as the physical form of the brain, but somehow it is distributed in space, held in a holographic manner. See the small section "What is a Hologram?" [17].

This understanding was completely counter intuitive, at odds with the then prevailing views of consciousness, where memories had to reside at particular locations within the physical brain. Due to this belief, many experimenters tried to disprove Pribram's results with their own experiments on the brains of laboratory rats that had been trained to run through mazes. The idea was that if

What is a Hologram?

A hologram usually refers to a three-dimensional photograph made with the aid of a laser. To make a hologram, the object to be photographed is first bathed in the light of a laser beam. Then a second laser beam is bounced off the reflected light of the first and the resulting interference pattern (the area where the two laser beams commingle) is captured on film. If the film illuminated by another laser beam, a three-dimensional image of the original object appears. At this point, if the hologram is cut up and then illuminated by a laser, each piece will still be found to contain the entire image of the original apple. Holograms have an astounding capacity for information storage, simply by changing the angle at which the two lasers strike a piece of photographic film, it is possible to record many different images on the same surface. It has been demonstrated that one cubic centimeter of film can hold as many as 10 billion bits of information. This factor is why brain scientists believe that the brain functions according to holographic principles because we have the ability to quickly retrieve whatever information we need from the enormous store of our memories.

the experimenter could cut out the correct part of a rat's brain, then it would lose its ability to negotiate the maze. This would support the belief of localized memory. All attempts to disprove Pribram's hypothesis spectacularly failed.

For decades, researchers did things like take out rats' brains, and then return them placed sideways, upside-down and backwards, yet the rats never lost their ability to negotiate the maze. Another research team even removed the brain from a rat and put it through a blender and then poured the resulting liquid slurry back into the poor rat's skull. Yet, incredibly, when the rat awoke from the anaesthetic, it effortlessly ran the maze, and otherwise went on with normal business! After these findings, researchers became totally convinced that memories where part of another realm of reality. These results also imply that the memory of the human being is part of a holographic system, which does not reside in the same space as the brain. Pribram's clinically derived results support the concept of the holographic universe first proposed by quantum physicist, David Bohm in the mid-1960s. Curiously, Bohm's, illumination came when he was working with plasma. He noted that trillions of "independent" sub-atomic particles acted as though independent of each other, while all being interconnected and reacting in unison. Pribram believes that memories are encoded in patterns of nerve impulses, holographically, and so this explains how the brain can code and decode the avalanche of frequencies it receives.

So now scientists are searching for where *exactly* the hologram resides! One set of studies indicates that our consciousness has an electromagnetic basis. Important experiments were conducted with volunteer terminal patients, placed inside hermetically sealed chambers [18]. These chambers, and everything contained in the chambers, were weighed to an accuracy of one ten thousandth of a gram. Inevitably, when the individual inside the chamber passed on, the measured weight of the sealed chamber reduced by approximately 3 to 5 grams of mass. This mass discrepancy always coincided with the passing over of the volunteer in the chamber. The researchers came to believe that this might be due to some energetic component moving away from vicinity of the body. Subsequently, they placed very sensitive electromagnetic detection systems all over the outsides of the chambers. When a terminal patient died, they were able to observe that an electromagnetic impulse was picked up by the detection apparatus. Calculations reveal that three grams of mass is equal to about 17,000,000 kilowatt/hours of electricity. Consciousness has power! These findings also support the claims of mystics over the ages who declared that at the moment of death, a flash of light can be seen to leave the body.

These facts only represent a tiny fraction of the research that has swayed neurologists to believe that our consciousness has an electromagnetic basis. So amongst the many theories, there has been the inevitable proposal that our conscious mind could be an electromagnetic field [19]. Professor Johnjoe McFadden from the School of Biomedical and Life Sciences at the University of Surrey in the UK, believes that information is held in the electromagnetic field surrounding the brain. Every time a nerve fires, the electrical activity sends a signal to the brain's electromagnetic field, which is automatically bound together with all the other signals in the brain. The brain's electromagnetic field does the binding which is characteristic of consciousness, influencing our actions and manifesting our will. This helps to explain the perplexing brain condition called hyranencephaly, where an individual can have an amount, as little as 5%, of normal brain material within the skull cavity. The remaining space, 95% is just filled with fluid, yet people with this condition function normally. This implies that there *must* be somewhere else where brain functioning takes place. If the brain just serves as an interface between inter-dimensional realities then it is possible that the fluid can serve as a substitute brain. The higher dimensional consciousness and control mechanism takes care of the problem! [20] Professor McFadden and independently the New Zealand-based neurobiologist Sue Pockett, have proposed that the brain's electromagnetic field is consciousness [21]. Those that object to this theory, reason that external electromagnetic fields would render us unconscious, but this argument is not based on a multi-dimensional understanding of the brain's electromagnetic field.

Higher Dimensions: Theory and Evidence

To understand our true reality, we have to become Masters who understand that the physical world is *not* all there is. To co-create more effectively in our everyday world, we must learn ways of navigating in and out of higher worlds, in essence, we learn to operate as multi-dimensional beings. This has always been the teaching of mystics and philosophers, but it appears these notions are becoming popular with physicists, mathematicians and scientists. Due to experimental results and anomalous phenomena, explanations are not possible without some expansion into the unseen.

Today, a popular proponent of hyperspace is the physicist Michio Kaku, who wrote *Hyperspace: A Scientific Odyssey through the 10th Dimension* [22]. Yet, we find the idea of higher dimensions or hyperspace and the spiritual realm goes back, to nineteenth century. Edwin A. Abbott (1838-1926), is the author of the novel *Flatland: A Romance of Many Dimensions* [23]. Abbott was a minister who tried to make the spiritual realm more understandable and so he suggested that if we were two-dimensional beings, and something three-dimensional entered our world, we would consider it foreign, mysterious, or even a miracle! So, if we compare ourselves to a sheet of paper, then even if we could perceive a pencil, it would seem weird to us. Flatland helps us imagine that as three-dimensional beings we are really just a substructure of a higher dimensional realm in which all kinds of things are going on, which we cannot understand without some kind of mathematical or physical model. The principal here is that if we had the ability to somehow lift ourselves or objects out of this universe, rotate in the fourth spatial dimension and then revert back to our original dimension, then impossible tasks would become trivial. A good example would be entwined rings, it is normally impossible to separate them without some damage, but this is something that certain psychics and yogis would have no problem doing!

Entwined Rings

Chinese researchers report teleportation experiments conducted with psychic children and adults who had the ability to move objects, just by using their mind. When object were being teleported, high-speed photography/videotaping equipment recorded test specimens physically "melding" or blending with the walls of sealed containers. In one series of experiments, the test specimens would simply disappear from inside the container only to reappear at another location (after seconds to several minutes of time had transpired). Items that were being tracked by micro-transmitters to give their location, gave large fluctuations in the intensity (in both amplitude and frequency) of the monitored signal. When a radio micro-transmitter was being teleported, the weak or absent signal indicated that the specimen was "nonexistent" (or in an altered physical state) during teleportation [24].

An explanation given is that in a fourth spatial dimension (fifth dimension), there is an extra degree of freedom. Mathematicians believe that there has to be a dimension that is in a direction perpendicular to our normal three-dimensional space, where objects would not find any opposition. Hence, objects can move through solid three-dimensional obstacles without penetrating them. Obviously, this is just a convenient way of trying to add more levels of measurement to empty space. It is far easy to envisage that the *qualities of the energy in space* actually changes. In terms of making changes to our energy fields, the ability to move into a higher dimension would allow "impossible" changes to be achieved with minimum effort!

Moreover, it has been proposed that the ultimate components of our nervous system are actually higher dimensional, thus enabling the human mind/brain to imagine four-dimensional space [25]. If this is the case, then the three-dimensional nets of neurons that code thoughts in our brain may form four-dimensional patterns to achieve four-dimensional thought. This can be can be easily demonstrated if we look at a Necker Cube. As we gaze at this geometry, it spontaneously turns into its mirror image and back again, proving that we see into the 4th dimension and have four-dimensional thoughts, see figure 6.1. After a while the twinkling sort of motion from one state to the other begins to seem continuous, but this motion can only be continuous if it is a rotation in four-dimensional space. The mathematician August F. Möbius discovered in 1827 that it is in fact possible to turn a three-dimensional solid object into its mirror image by an appropriate rotation through four-dimensional space. As our minds can perform such a rotation, it therefore proves we can actually produce four-dimensional phenomena in our minds, and so our consciousness has to be fourth-dimensional.

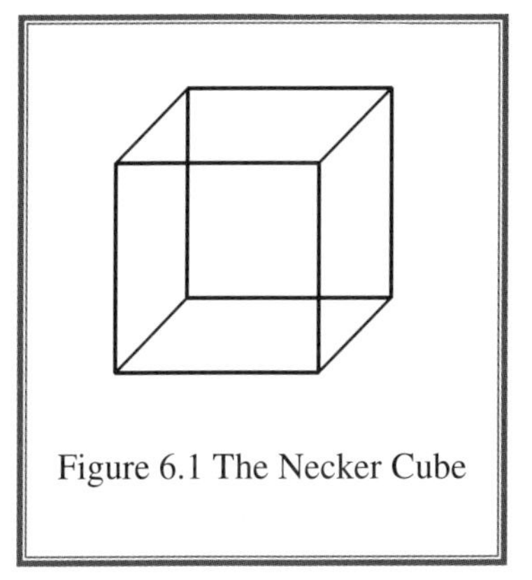
Figure 6.1 The Necker Cube

Next, we will examine western esoteric concepts associated with String theory, and how this relates to higher dimensions, but first, a mention of how this highly celebrated theory has surprising connections with old mystical traditions. The excitement surrounding String theory is surprising because it only allows scientists to get closer to what mystics have always held to be true. A few have noticed that one of the most sophisticated predictive models ever developed by modern science describes the processes of creation and annihilation as the poetic verses of an ancient Hindu poem! The Vedas is an ancient book of verses and represents metaphysical traditions of the ancient Hindu cultures of the East, dating back 5,500 hundred years. Quantum physicist Dr. John Hagelin, found a compelling coherence between String theory and the model of reality described by the Vedas [26]. Maybe, the fact that an ancient Hindu poem can be paralleled with the most sophisticated predictive model ever developed by modern science, proves the usefulness of the ability to operate in higher dimensions.

Historically, the concept of higher dimensions has gone in and out of fashion due to lack of any physical proof or application, but nevertheless it has recently had a revival. Once considered the province of eccentrics and mystics, higher dimensions are now in vogue for the simple reason that as a radical solution, scientists hope that it will unify forces and solve persistent problems.

String Theory

Einstein spent the last 30 years of his life trying to create one theory that could explain the four fundamental forces that govern the universe: gravity, electromagnetism, and the two nuclear forces (weak and strong). Ultimately, Einstein failed in his mission. The problem is that relativity and the quantum theory are precise opposites. General Relativity is a theory of the macrocosm, such as galaxies, quasars, black holes, and even the Big Bang. It is based on bending the four dimensional fabric of space and time. Quantum theory, by contrast, is a theory of the very small, i.e. the world of sub-atomic particles. Over the past 50 years, many attempts have been tried to unite these polar opposites, and have failed. In 1915, when Einstein said space-time was four dimensional and was warped and rippled, he used mathematics to show that this bending produced a "force" called gravity. Many physicists believe that light is created by ripples in five-dimensional space-time, and if more and more dimensions are added, then we can ripple and bend them in different ways, thereby creating more forces. It requires 10 dimensions to accommodate all four fundamental forces. These dimensions are tiny and physicists talk about them being curled up or in-folded.

String theory attempts to unify the General Theory of Relativity, (which is Einstein's Theory of Gravity) with quantum mechanics, thus achieving something that many physicists considered as impossible. The basic premise is that our multi-dimensional universe is inhabited by tiny energetic strings. Unlike an ordinary piece of string, which is itself composed of molecules and atoms, the strings of string theory are described as being deep within the heart of matter. These energetic strings are so small on average, that they are about as long the Planck length, 10^{-35} m, about a hundred billion billion (10^{20}) times smaller than an atomic nucleus, and they appear point-like even when examined with our most powerful equipment. These strings are tiny one-dimensional filaments somewhat like infinitely thin rubber bands, vibrating oscillating, dancing filaments and they create resonances or "notes" [27]. The melodies that these notes play is called "matter" and when these melodies create symphonies, that's called the "universe". When the string moves in space and time, it warps the space around, which connects this to theory to that predicted by Einstein. It was thought that this simple picture would help scientists unify gravity (as the bending of space caused by moving strings) with the other quantum forces, (now viewed as vibrations of the string). There are different versions of these theories that require ten, eleven or twenty-six extra space dimensions to unify and quantize gravity. The popularity of higher-dimensional theories re-emerged in the 1950s, when the number of sub-atomic particles discovered overwhelmed physicists. J.R. Oppenheimer, who helped build the atomic bomb, even said, out of sheer frustration, that the Nobel Prize should go to the physicist who did NOT discover a new particle that year! String theory explains why scientists were discovering so many sub-atomic particles, they were just notes on a string! String theory has evolved since about the 1970s and in 1995, Dr. Witten showed that what had been five different versions of string theory seemed to be related. He argued that they were all different manifestations of a shadowy, as-yet-undefined entity he called "M Theory" [28]. Membrane Theory (M-Theory), also know as "Mother-of-all Theories", is a recent extension of String theory in which the fundamental physical entities are considered as surfaces in a many-dimensional space (membranes) rather than as lines or loop elements (open or closed strings)

Theorists have tried to link String theory with the concept of nature as a kind of hologram. In the holographic images often seen on bankcards, the illusion of three dimensions is created on a two-dimensional surface. Likewise, String theory suggests that in nature all the information about what is happening inside some volume of space is somehow encoded on its outer boundary [29]. Just how and why a three-dimensional reality can spring from just two dimensions, or four dimensions can unfold from three, is not understood, Dr. Witten thinks that time and space are only illusions or approximations, emerging somehow from something fundamental about nature.

String Theory in Trouble

"Apart from the lack of agreement with reality,
it is a superb intellectual performance".
Albert Einstein

There are signs that String theory is running out of steam. The New Scientist editorial dated 10 December 2005 was headlined: *Physics' greatest endeavour is grinding to a halt: The hunt for a theory of everything is going nowhere fast.* This narrative reveals that a crisis in physics has been building for decades:

> "Physics' greatest endeavor has ground to a halt. We are in "a period of utter confusion", said Nobel laureate David Gross, summing up last week's prestigious Solvay conference on the quantum structure of space and time. That is worrying because the topic is central to finding a "theory of everything" that will describe every force and particle in nature."

"Einstein's relativity, which reigned supreme for a century, is a flawed basis for such a theory. Although it deals with gravity, it tells us nothing else about the nature and interactions of matter. Crucially, general relativity is incompatible with quantum theory. Since the 1960s, theorists have struggled to solve this problem, so far to no avail. And the trouble is we have nothing to put in relativity's place."

"The great hope, string theory, which views particles as emanating from minuscule strings, has generated myriad mathematical descriptions linked to the dance of particles. But these equations tell us nothing about where space and time come from and describe nothing we would recognize. At best, string theory depicts the way particles might interact in a collection of hypothetical universes."

"For decades, string theorists have been excused from testing their ideas against experimental results. When astronomers discovered the accelerating expansion of the universe, which string theory fails to account for, many string theorists took shelter in a remarkable excuse: that their equations describe all possible universes and should not be tied to matching data in just one of them."

"But when the theory does not match the one data set we have, is it science? There is a joke circulating on physics blogs: that we can, after all, call our universe unique. Why? Because it is the only one that string theory cannot describe. Should we laugh or cry?"

"There is a growing feeling that string theory has run into the sand. Gross thinks we are missing something fundamental. We need a leap in understanding, though where it will come from is not clear. Many of the greatest minds in physics were there at last week's conference, and none had an answer."

"We are approaching the end of Einstein's centennial year - a celebration of physics. While some lesser-known areas of the subject are flourishing, the search for a theory of everything is in a sorry state. Unless string theory gets a radical shake-up, gifted but frustrated minds will begin to drift into other areas of science." *[End or excerpts]* [30]

We can take it from this article, that all is not well in theoretical wonderland!

Aspden's Aether Lattice Model

"We all believe in the aether, but we call it space-time"
Dr. Dennis Sciama

A recognized comprehensive model of the aether was first proposed in 1958. Dr. Harold Aspden is an electrophysicist, inventor, engineer, chartered patent agent, and writer who has had a life long passion in determining the underlying nature of our reality with special regard to understanding the physics of the aether. See the small section "The Aspden Factor". The above quote comes from a conversation that occurred in 1954 when discussing Aspden's ideas of the aether. Both eminent scientists graduated with Ph.D.s from Cambridge and Aspden had a particular interest in Sciama's 1953-1954 dissertation, titled *On the Origin of Inertia.* The dissertation was:

> "...devoted to Einstein's work, which shows that inertia is connected with gravitation. However, as Einstein himself was the first to point out, general relativity does not fully account for inertia. Thus a new theory of gravitation is needed."

Aspden uses this excerpt to point out that the flaws in Einstein's theories have been well known and ignored for over fifty years and he explains why "a theory of everything is in a sorry state." In his acknowledgement of the work of Einstein, Aspden wrote the paper "Physics Without Einstein: A Centenary Review" [31]. This review dismisses the hero worship of Einstein and points out that physics has stagnated since Einstein's Theory of Relativity was accepted, because all contrary theories have been excluded. The weakness of quantum theory is exposed:

> "Quantum theory hides by its mathematics the physical picture of how fundamental particles, electrons, protons etc., are created, meaning their source and their acquisition of angular momentum when they form into atoms and there seems to be no way that Einstein's theory with its 'space-time' (or is it 'four-space'?) can get into that act. Therefore, I hold firm in saying that the truth is to be found by probing Earnshaw's vision of the aether based on a charge continuum permeated by the virtual particles, be they electrons, muons or taons that occasionally present themselves in a ghostly way in our particle experiments. Somehow also such aether particles are involved in the storage of energy and angular momentum in what we see as empty space, be it a vacuum between the plates of a charged electrical capacitor or a vacuum region within the solenoid of a magnetic inductor."

The Aether Lattice theory has been used to explain the "anomalous" energy found in plasma discharge research. In Canada, Dr. Paulo Correa and his wife Alexandra Correa, during laboratory research, made the breathtaking discovery that by discharge pulsing using a suitable circuit and a specially configured electrode system, it is actually possible to generate electrical power by tapping energy from the aether itself. This discovery was such, that it justified patent protection to continue their project. Patents are not easy to come by as a rule. Before a process or invention is patented, the inventors have to PROVE to the Patent Office that a process is real, unique and does exactly what the inventors says it does. The Correas maintain this energy is direct from the aether, and so this particular patent has taken us from "Aether theory" to proven scientific phenomena [32]. In the more practical experimental world of physics, there is some acknowledgement of the superiority of Aspden's work. In comparison with other authors it was declared, "It is shown that a Aether Lattice theory developed by Aspden gives the best overall agreement with experiment." The theoretical values for these important physics constants were derived years ahead of the experimental proof, see chapter notes for specific details [33].

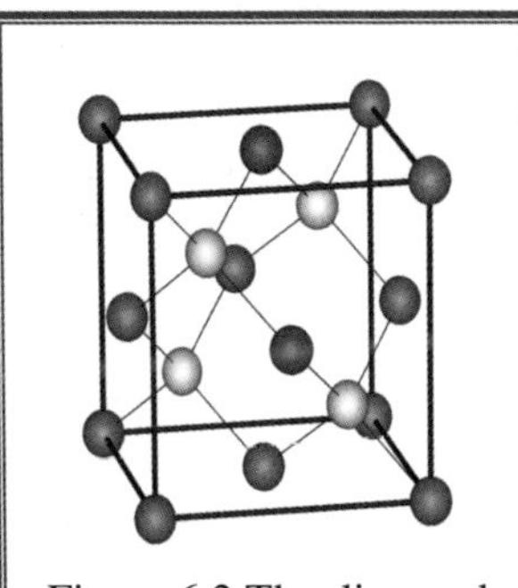

Figure 6.2 The diamond crystal habit

Theory is just theory, it should not be confused with reality. True science is where a theory can produce predictions, permit testing by experiment and be validated by data.

The Aether Lattice model requires a universe seething with energy that is held in a state of equilibrium, with only a very small proportion, involved as fluctuations in the vastness of space. (There is confusion generated here because many authors do not distinguish between the fluctuations in and out of the aether, and the aether itself. The fluctuations are strictly what is referred to as zero-point energy). The aether lattice is a charged array of aether particles, a subtle non-material medium that requires the property of a fluid-like crystalline lattice that is 'simple cubic' or hexagonal, see the small section "The Cubic Form and Diamonds" and figure 6.2 [34]. From a paper called *The Crystalline Vacuum*, Aspden writes:

> "The 'vacuum medium', otherwise known as the 'aether', is a cold neutral ionized plasma that has such a perfect crystalline form that it cannot be 'seen' or 'felt' as a medium resisting force. In fact it responds so easily in its reaction to invasion by matter that it dissolves its structure and reforms that structure in the wake of matter that does move through it."

The Cubic Form and Diamonds

In a diamond every carbon atom shares all 4 of its available electrons with adjacent carbon atoms, forming a tetrahedral unit. This shared electron-pair bonding forms the strongest known chemical linkage, the covalent bond, which is responsible for many of diamond's superlative properties. The repeating structural unit of diamond consists of 8 atoms arranged in a cube. Using this cubic form and its highly symmetrical arrangement of atoms, diamond crystals can develop in a variety of different shapes known as "crystal habits". The octahedron, or eight-sided shape that we associate with diamonds is its most common crystal habit.

The Aether Lattice "Unveiled"

This Aether Lattice model is based on the simplest arrangement of charge embedded in a uniform, background continuum of opposite charge. Surplus energy within the aether is the energy source accounting for the creation of matter in the form of protons and electrons. When scientists look out into space what they see is the aether constantly trying to produce electrons and protons. Fifty years after Aspden first announced his Aether lattice model he can now cite experimental validation. In January 1998, two articles in Science magazine reported the discovery that ions can form into crystal-like cubic array in a cold plasma [35]. Of utmost importance, was that the discovery that the crystal structure had the tendency to spin. These experiments were a validation of predictions made back in 1959!

In June 2005, a new state of matter was announced by scientists at the Massachusetts Institute of Technology, (MIT) [36]. A normal gas rotates like an ordinary object, but a superfluid can only rotate when it forms vortices similar to mini-tornadoes. The superfluid has the appearance of Swiss cheese, where the holes are the cores of the mini-tornadoes, a lattice-like structure, see figure 6.3. As scientists now model the aether as a superfluid, this equates to our understanding of Universal energy source some are calling the Cosmic Lattice [37]. Crystal lattice structures are comprised of combinations of interpenetrating lattices identified by the geometrical patterns made by octahedral or tetrahedra interstices, 'voids' or 'holes' at their center. The type of lattice is identified by the geometrical structure at the center, which can be positive of negative tetrahedra, octahedron or cuboctahedron, see figure 6.4.

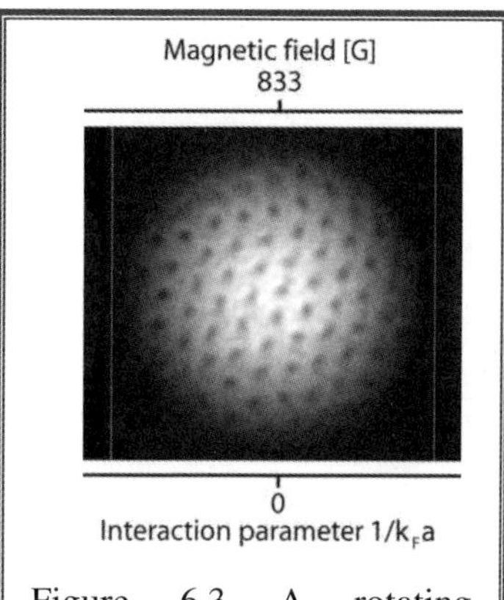

Figure 6.3 A rotating superfluid gas of fermions pierced with vortices. Image credit: MIT.

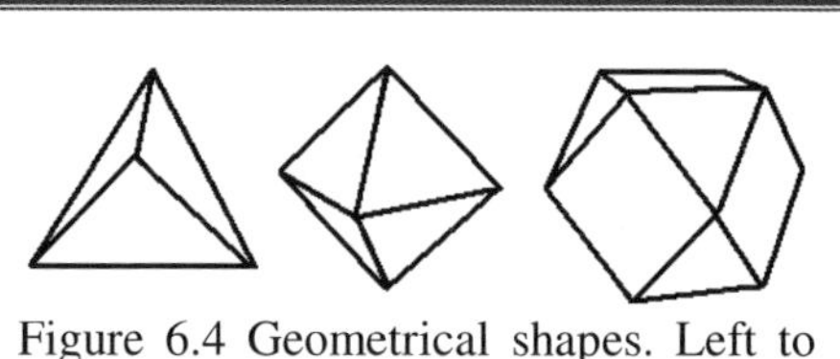

Figure 6.4 Geometrical shapes. Left to right, tetrahedral, octahedral and cuboctahedral

Further support was given to the Aether Lattice theory when the authoritative magazine, Nature, published an article regarding the distribution of stellar systems [38]. On January 9, 1997, an article pointed out that supernovae, stars that have exploded and become extremely luminous in the process, are arranged in the form of a crystalline lattice. The lattice structure appeared to be a rectangular cell with sides that are 360 million light-years long, like a three-dimensional chessboard. These results were confirmed by an international committee of scientists who had made vertical observations of a fairly limited region of space. Astronomers already knew that galaxies could form either disk-shaped or string-shaped supernovae, but these supernovae spun around space with no galaxies. These scientists were not anticipating any periodic structure, because according to the Big Bang Theory, supernovae should scatter randomly across the universe. If the observations are correct, it implies that scientists do not fully comprehend the factors that governed the formation of our universe in its early stages. Figure 6.5 demonstrates how a three dimensional arrangement of 'holes' creates a hexagonal effect.

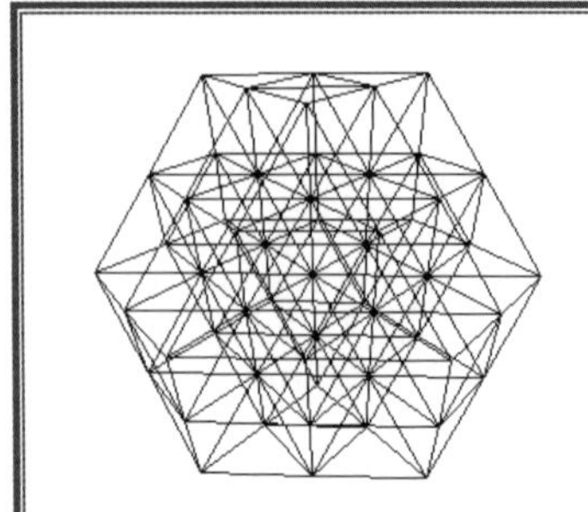

Figure 6.5 Lattice showing hexagonal pattern of holes at intersections.
Credit: R Chu [38]

Aspden has a 2020 vision where he believes that an alternative physics theory will eventually replace Einstein's Theories of Special and General Relativity. He suggests his Aether Lattice theory will go a long way in providing this replacement.

The Aspden Factor

Dr. Harold Aspden Ph.D., FIEE, FIMechE, C.Eng, C.Phys is physicist by professional qualification and vocation, with an academic research background in electrical engineering. Aspden has over 4 decades of extensive theoretical and experimental research work in magnetism, electrodynamics, thermodynamics and nuclear physics. From 1963 to 1983, Dr. Aspden served as European Director of IBM's Patent Operations in Europe, and was in charge of seven Patent Departments in Europe, staffed by 100 attorneys and supporting staff, concerned with inventions and patents dealing with technology rooted in electronics and magnetism. (This is why he compares himself to Einstein!) He served as Rapporteur in the Intellectual Property field within the International Chamber of Commerce and was, for a period, President of the Trademarks, Patents and Designs Federation, the voice of major industrial interests in the U.K. After taking early retirement from IBM, Dr. Aspden pursued his personal scientific research interests at the Electrical Engineering Department of Southampton University, with IBM sponsorship. Since 1994, and following his winning a U.K. Government SMART AWARD, Dr. Aspden has been pursuing research on a new magnetic reluctance motor project, which incorporates a novel and revolutionary design. Dr. Harold Aspden has written over a hundred papers, and is the author of several books, some of which are available online [39].

Born Again Theory

"Despite all difficulties, I think we shall eventually have to bring back the aether. Some difficulties are not that bad."
Caroline Thompson, physicist

The main challenge presented by theories that involve the aether and higher dimensions is that they prove very difficult to test. It is not possible by conventional methods to go directly into hyperspace and take a look! However, what is possible, is to predict how we believe energy transfer between these dimensions creates effects in our known 3 dimensions plus time. Richard Hoagland's Hyperdimensional model specifically relates to the massive planetary bodies in our solar system. Hoagland suspected that the standard astrophysical theories were wrong, when data collected over three decades revealed that the planets were "glowing". The planetary bodies were shining in the infrared, via internal energy sources, not just by reflected light. This discovery was first made in the mid-1960s, when data was gathered from Jupiter using ground-based telescopes. The other "giant planets", Saturn, Uranus and Neptune, without internal nuclear fusion, also manage to radiate more energy into space, than they receive directly from the Sun [40]. This was confirmed by the space probes Pioneer and Voyager fly-bys in the 1970s and 1980s. Based on this data, Hoagland decided that current astrophysical theories were drastically wrong and so proposed his own theory.

"These observations of other bodies in the solar system implied that the planets and moons were receiving energy from an outside source – higher dimensions."

In 1989, the first paper on what would later become known as "Hyperdimensional Physics" was published [41]. Basically, Hoagland had found a formula for predicting where the major energy spots of each planet in our solar system would be located. The ideas presented in that paper, were based on "tetrahedral physics" that relate to observations of planetary energy emissions and their preference to center near the "tetrahedral latitude" of 19.5°. The basic premise of this tetrahedron geometry, was that by spinning a tetrahedron inside a sphere (such as Earth), there will be a vorticular upwelling of energy at 19.5 degrees north or south of the equator, see figure 6.6. Planetary examples of this include the volcanoes in the Hawaiian Island, the Great Red Spot on Jupiter, Olympus Mons on Mars, the volcanoes on Venus and the peak sunspot activity on the sun. Hyperdimensional Physics provides an explanation for "anomalous

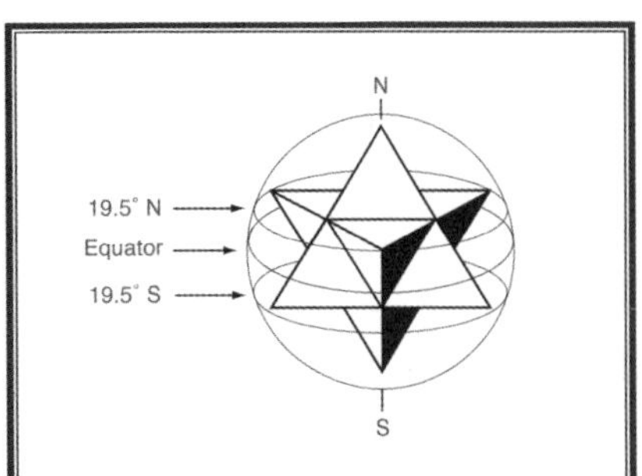

Figure 6.6 The Star Tetrahedron, a geometric form constructed by two tetrahedra centered 180° to each other. When mapped to a sphere, six corners touch points 19.5° above and below the equator.

energy" appearing in celestial bodies, demonstrating a "leakage" of energy from higher dimensions, associated with a specific geometry.

The hyperdimensional model is based on the original theories of the 19th century founders of modern mathematics and physics. Among these distinguished scientists include the German mathematician George Riemann, the Scottish physicist Sir William Thompson, the Scottish physicist James Clerk Maxwell; and British mathematician Sir William Rowan Hamilton. In 1873, Maxwell succeeded in uniting two hundred years of scientific observations of electrical and magnetic phenomena, into a comprehensive, overarching electromagnetic theory of light.

> **"The existence of unseen *hyper*spatial realities... through information transfer between dimensions, are the literal "foundation substrate" maintaining the reality of everything in *this* dimension."** [41]

Most importantly, as well as the reality of higher dimensions, Maxwell also incorporated the physics of Thompson, who proposed a radical new explanation for the most fundamental properties of solid objects, the existence of "the vortex atom". In 1867, William Thomson was inspire by smoke rings, as he realized that in an ideal fluid, a vortex line is always composed of the same particles, it remains unbroken, so it is ring-like, see figure 6.7. This disregarded the prevailing theory that atoms could be viewed as infinitesimal "small, hard bodies" endorsed by Newton. Thompson's "vortex atoms" were envisioned, instead, as tiny, self-sustaining "whirlpools in the aether". Thompson and his 19th Century contemporaries believed the aether existed throughout the Universe as an all-pervasive, "incompressible and highly stressed universal aetheric fluid" and that the basic elements of matter were composed of "knotted tubes" of ether [42]. Due to undeniable phenomena, the aether is experiencing

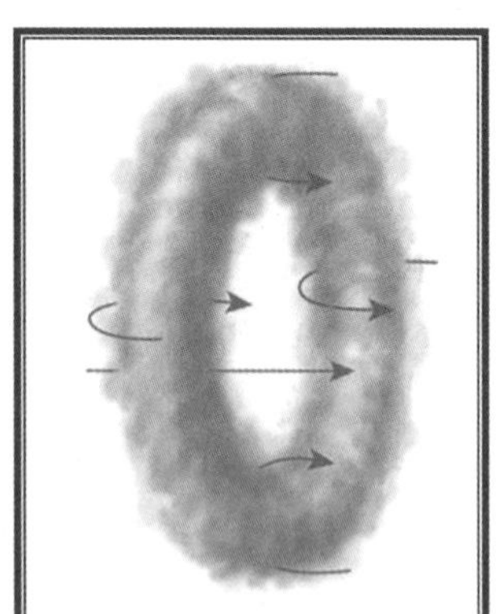

Figure 6.7 Smoke ring, arrows show direction direction of the vortex motion. Courtesy: American Scientist

a revival amongst scientists under different guises, the most obvious is zero-point energy. The vortex atom has new followers as the "closed string" of String theory and "Knot theory" is now one of the most active areas of mathematics. Yet, we find the physics of Einstein has always disguised the aether by calling it "space-time". It is difficult to comprehend how aether theories were discredited after only one high profile experiment and today scientists admit that this was "mistaken", see the small section, "What was the Michaelson-Morley Experiment?"

What was the Michaelson-Morley Experiment?

In the 19th century the aether was well accepted by science. However in 1881 Albert Michaelson and Edward Morley conducted an experiment to prove the existence of the aether. At that time, light was thought to be a compression wave that propagated just like sound waves through the motionless and stationary aether. So while the Earth itself is spinning, the Earth must have a relative motion with respect to the aether. It was reasoned that when the speed of light is measured on the surface of the Earth it should give different results when measured clockwise or counterclockwise with respect to the rotation of the Earth around its axis. However the Michelson-Morley experiment proved that the speed of light had the same constant value no matter in what direction the speed of light was measured. From this experiment it was concluded that the ether did not exist. This one flawed experiment caused physics to abandon the aether theory. Of course today, scientists now conceded that the results of the Michaelson-Morley experiment were "misinterpreted".

Today, we see that physics, which is over one hundred years old is being revived. Thompson's vortex atom is also being favored, as the standard model of the electron, which assumes a point-like particle, is also being shunned [43]. We find that the model presented by Niels Bohr where electrons fly in well-defined shells around the nucleus is unsatisfactory. Apparently, it has always been known that the electron continuously radiates energy, and it has been a problem explaining where the energy come from to keep it stable and prevent it from eventually collapsing into the nucleus. The respected physicist, Dr. Harold Puthoff, of the Advanced Studies in Austin, Texas, USA admits the existence of the aether, citing that the effects of the zero-point field have been proven [44]. He summarizes with the following comment:

> "In my paper it is shown that the electron in lowest energy or ground state of the hydrogen atom indeed does continually radiate away its energy, as predicted by classical theory, but it is also absorbs energy from the ever-present zero-point energy in which the atom is immersed, and an assumed

equilibrium between these two processes leads to the correct values for the parameters known to define the ground orbit."

"The bottom line is that the ground-state orbit is set by a dynamic equilibrium in which collapse of the state is prevented by the presence of zero-point energy. **The significance of this observation is the understanding that the very stability of matter itself depends upon, and verifies the presence of, an underlying sea of electromagnetic energy of almost inconceivable magnitude, a vast reservoir of random energy that is universally present throughout space**." *[Bold added for emphasis]*

String theory also proposes that a particle such as the electron is really a closed string, with fields flowing around it. Kanarev's 1990 paper shows this new version of the electron and analyzes its electromagnetic and physical nature on the basis of the laws of classical physics, see figure 6.8.

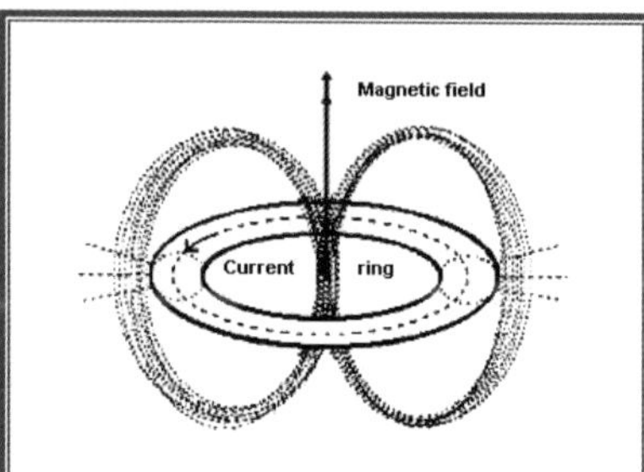

Figure 6.8 Model of the Electron. The electron has both magnetic and electric fields. The electron ring is a stable toroidal vortex made up of aether rotating at the speed of light. Adapted from Model of the Electron by Ph. M. Kanarev [44].

So now scientists are slowly conceding that the aether exists and that higher dimensions would solve a lot of problems in physics [45]. In addition, the Einstein legacy is in severe trouble. In January 2005, Reginald T Cahill of Flinders University, wrote a paper called *The Speed of Light and the Einstein Legacy: 1905-2005*, the Abstract reads;

"That the speed of light is always c=300,000km/s relative to any observer in non-accelerating motion is one of the foundational concepts of physics. Experimentally this was supposed to have been first revealed by the 1887 Michelson-Morley experiment, and was made one of Einstein's key postulates of Special Relativity in 1905. However in 2002, the actual 1887 fringe shift data was analysed for the first time with a theory for the Michelson interferometer that used both the Fitzgerald-Lorentz contraction effect, as well as the effect of the air in the interferometer on the speed of light. That analysis showed that the data gave an absolute motion speed in excess of 300km/s. So far six other experiments have been shown to give the same result. **This implies that the foundations of physics require significant revision.** As well data shows that both Newtonian gravity and General Relativity are also seriously flawed, and a new theory of gravity is shown to explain various so-called gravitational `anomalies', including the `dark matter' effect. Most importantly absolute motion is now understood to be the cause of the various relativistic effects, in accord with the earlier proposal by Lorentz." *[Bold added for emphasis]* [46].

"A beautiful theory is oft slayed by an ugly fact."
T.H. Huxley

Tapping the Enormous Invisible Energy All Around Us

In one cube centimeter of empty space the amount of energy is much greater than the total amount of energy of all matter in the known universe.
David Bohm, quantum physicist

The evidence is accumulating that humans can interact with an enormous invisible sea of energy. Scientists describe this as energy as the zero-point field that seems present at every point in the universe. Also called the electromagnetic quantum vacuum or the old fashioned aether referred to by mystics and mathematicians alike [47]. The name zero point was derived from the fact that even at absolute zero (minus 273.15° C) – the lowest possible energy state – energy remains as a background radiation source, hence the name zero-point energy. This name may have been chosen to disguise the fact that for years most scientists had debunked the idea that the aether existed. Now that empirical evidence has suggested there is no such thing as a perfect vacuum, rather than return to the notion of aether, we have something that 'sounds' modern. In this book we also discuss the Cosmic Lattice, which describes a structure within the old fashioned aether. The following is a non-technical introduction to zero point energy but it reveals a direct connection to mystical phenomena

For some decades now it has become increasingly understood that space was not an empty vacuum, but a vibrant mass of energy. Quantum mechanics describes this as particles that blink in and out of existence, with millions or even billions of fluctuations occurring in any given second. In an energy hungry world, it was calculated that if this source could be captured and controlled both on Earth and space, it offered an infinite and potentially limitless supply of energy [48]. We do know that the world of matter and this invisible sea of energy interact. Scientists tell us electrons utilize energy from the vacuum, zero-point energy to maintain an energy balance. Sub-atomic particles borrow energy (virtual photons) from the zero point field pushing them into a higher energy state. The give and take of virtual photons of energy is what shapes the zero point field [49].

There are attempts to harness this endless supply of power for spacecraft propulsion, but another more down to Earth use of this energy, would be to solve the world's energy crisis that is looming large on the horizon. In retrospect, it is amazing that in the 1940s, Wilhelm Reich was locked up in jail and all his books were burnt for his heretical ideas on the existence of the strange and invisible Orgone Energy! [50]

Anti-gravity or levitation is thought to be one side affect of perturbing the zero-point field. A Russian physicist and Nobel prize-winner Andrei Sakharov published a paper in 1967 suggesting that gravity and inertia might be linked by vacuum fluctuations in the zero point field. So it is interesting to find that scientists have discovered how to manipulate the aether to generate this effect. In 1996, the United Kingdom Sunday Telegraph, ran the headline, *Breakthrough As Scientists Beat Gravity*. Unfortunately, the report had used the heretical term "anti-gravity" instead of the more acceptable term "gravity shielding". As a consequence, Russian materials scientist, Dr. Evgeny Podkletnov's world was turned upside down. He was accused by his university in Finland that his work was not properly sanctioned and then punished. Eventually he was thrown out, and he had to seek refuge at the Moscow Chemical Scientific Research Center, where has gone on to conduct even more interesting gravity experiments. Meanwhile, NASA undeterred by the furore, approached Podkletnov to see if he could reproduce his findings. They were very interested that something odd was happening when gravity fields were influenced by superconductors and that a 2% weight loss was being consistently recorded. The Russian had discovered by accident that the gravity reduction would not diminish with distance and the effect would go on forever. This meant that there was a 2% weight reduction in *all* the air above, so a vehicle equipped with gravity shielding would be able to levitate, slightly buoyed up by the heavier air below. These reports will not go away, another report in July 2002, ran a headline that stated, *Boeing tries to defy gravity* [51]. The article reported:

> "The company is examining an experiment by Yevgeny Podkletnov, who claims to have developed a device which can shield objects from the Earth's pull....The project is being run by the top-secret Phantom Works in Seattle, the part of the company which handles Boeing's most sensitive programmes."

Scientists believe that the zero point field can be tapped into by anything that generates an electromagnetic field. Even though this kind of research is not very well disclosed to the public, we do find independent scientists who have received attention for their experiments. John Hutchison, is described as a "Tesla" like individual who is known for "The Hutchison Effect". In 1979, Hutchison stumbled across a collection of phenomena, during attempts to study the longitudinal waves discovered by Tesla back in 1979 [52]. The effects include levitation of heavy objects, fusion of dissimilar materials such as metal and wood (exactly as portrayed in the movie, "The Philadelphia Experiment"). Also Hutchison demonstrated the anomalous heating of metals without burning adjacent material, spontaneous fracturing of metals (which separate by sliding in a sideways fashion), and both temporary and permanent changes in the crystalline structure and physical properties of metals. It was believed that Hutchison was tapping into the zero point energy field.

Consequently, Hutchison drew the attention of the Pentagon who funded him in 1985 for a short time, to see if these affects could be replicated. The Department of Energy, and two aerospace companies, Boeing and McDonnell Douglas also felt it necessary to investigate the Hutchison Effect. Eventually, no funding was secured for research and so the anomalous energy effects were dismissed. Hutchison could not scientifically control the phenomena and there was suspicion that the most spectacular effects were caused by psychokinesis, i.e. Hutchison was 'tuning into' the machinery to create the anomalous effects. The Hutchison Effect also generated time-dilation, pockets of altered space-time within the target area. Moreover, the most extraordinary of all was the capacity of "The Effect" to turn metal ingots transparent. Momentarily, metal ingots were be made to phase-out, they were there but not there; visible in outline yet totally see-through. (Actually, that sounds rather like the biblical transfiguration!)

These reports of anti-gravity and anomalous experimental results are detailed because there are major points that need to be stressed. There are two kinds of science, the stuff they teach at academic institutions and the "weird" stuff scientists explore in top secret research! Electromagnetism is a major area of mystery and there are at least *34 major discrepancies presently existing in conventional electromagnetic theory* [53]. There are phenomena that can't be explained by current physics because our laws of physics are not complete.

In summary, even though there appears to be many different theories which seek to explain the fundamental make-up of our reality, they can all be linked together by the phenomena of plasma, a medium of electrically charged multi-dimensional aether particles. Thus, Hannes Alfvén must be counted amongst one of the greatest scientists that ever lived [54]. On the occasion of being presented with the prestigious Nobel prize in Physics, he stated at the end of his lecture:

"Because in the beginning was the plasma."

Seeing Miracles in a New Light

What is truly fascinating, is that human beings also have the ability to perturb the zero point field, as we too generate an electromagnetic field. What is being achieved in the laboratory – and may even be being used in top-secret aircraft – can be done naturally by humans, and there have been Masters who have spectacularly demonstrated their ability to interact with this enormous field of potential. Stories of yogis who can levitate, now have some kind of scientific explanation. There is an amazing modern account of Russian Orthodox monks who live on an isolated island near Kodiak, Alaska [55]. Local people report that these monks must be able to teleport, because they do not have any mode of transport, but they are regularly seen on the main island, picking up their mail and doing their shopping! The *Teleportation Physics Study* released in February 2005, informs us that the U.S. Air Force is investigating the viability of Teleportation [56]. In a related article it states:

> "The most surprising part of the Study comes when it examines the phenomenon of psychic or p-Teleportation which is defined as "the conveyance of persons or inanimate objects by psychic means" (p. 2). The Study reveals that p-Teleportation "has been scientifically investigated and separately documented by the Department of Defense" (p. 1). The Study concludes that there "is a wealth of factual scientific research data from around the world attesting to the physical reality of p-Teleportation" (p. 59). In short, psychic teleportation whereby individuals can move objects through space by teleportation is real and is actively being studies by elite research institutions of a number of countries."

This study, which was approved for released for public dissemination, implies that this information is not particularly sensitive. One could suggest that this report represents the tip of the proverbial iceberg, in studies and progress being made in more classified projects.

In Yogic tradition, these powers are categorized as greater or lesser siddhis. The greater siddhis are classified as levitation, teleportation and bi-location (being in two places at once). Lesser siddhis are things such as psychic abilities as clairvoyance (inner seeing), clairaudience (inner hearing), clairsentience (inner feeling) as well as clairgnosis (inner knowing), as in knowing something but not knowing how you know it. Healing and prophecy are also considered as lesser siddhis. These psychic powers can be seen as refinements of the physical senses and are considered a measure of spiritual attainment. At the same time, they are viewed as being glamorous and seductive and therefore can act as danger to the spiritual path [57].

As more and more scientists realize the deeper implications and the connection between "physics, consciousness and life". There is an inevitable merger between science and spirituality taking place. In one remarkable Art Bell radio show, the discussion included the belief that human beings are mini-stargates, and can harness the power of hyperdimensional energy to change the destiny of mankind [58]. This is a message of hope for the future, however, one that must primarily apply to those who understand the power of consciousness and intent. Here are some quotes from the guests, scientist Richard Hoagland and metaphysician David Wilcock.

- RH: "There is a unity between the Physics and consciousness … and life! That's what the bottom line of this research has proven now, to my satisfaction."
- DW: "So if the energy of the pyramid harnesses and focalizes this energy of consciousness, if the pyramid structure has sort of a funnel-like effect for this fluidlike energy … and can concentrate it …
- DW: "And if consciousness can move the energy the same way, then what **if each person is sort of like a little portable Stargate**, and the reason why we're having so much trouble has to do with people's inability to be honest with themselves, honest with each other. Then, their own internal shadow side gets projected out into the collective, so you get the shadow of each person being acted out in these occult politics. And when we get right with ourselves inside, the whole hologram changes."
- DW: "Now, if we get the disclosure of this technology, it can't but only add to the way that people are going to open up and change. And that will change the Physics. **So it's like you teach people the physics, and the physics … changes**."
- RH: "See, this is one reason I think why certain of these discoveries are suppressed. Not so much because of the technical or technological aspects of what they will make possible. But because of the incredible liberating effects on consciousness." *[End of excerpts, bold added for emphasis.]*

In agreement with Hoagland & Wilcock, we do have the ability to harness hyperdimensional energy and the solution to the issue of Earth change, is to teach people to change their consciousness.

"Teach people the physics, and the physics … changes."

Chapter Seven

Balancing in Chaos

"Space weather is now a fact of life."
Susan Joy Rennison

We Are All Astronauts Now! The Space Weather Impact

Earth is now experiencing regular blasts of space weather on an "unprecedented" scale and the effect on humans has not been extensively studied. Nevertheless, there has been some research related to the influence of sunspots and geomagnetic storms on human behavior and health. Astronauts are particularly vulnerable, as they travel outside the earth's protective atmosphere and magnetic field, so experiments have been conducted in conjunction with NASA Space Programs, measuring the effect of electromagnetic field distortions on the human energy field [1].

These experiments, utilized a specially shielded room, called a Mu Room (the name comes from the Greek letter, Mu), that was located in the Physics Department at the University of California (UCLA), Los Angeles. In a Mu room – which is about seven square feet square and high enough to stand up in – the natural electromagnetic energy of the air can be altered without changing the level of gravitational force or the oxygen content. Using instruments inside the room, physicists could alter the intensity, as well as the specific frequencies of the electromagnetic field. During the sessions, an aura reader read the auric field by penlight while physicists manipulated the environmental field. The reported findings were amazing.

> "If the electrical aspect of the room environment remained normal but the magnetism was decreased, gross in-coordination occurred. The entire neurological integrating mechanism was thrown off. Subjects could not balance their bodies; they had difficulty touching finger to nose or performing simple coordinated movements. They lost kinesthetic awareness. Contrariwise, when the magnetic field was increased beyond the normal state, subjects could stand easily on one foot, even on tiptoes, or lean to previously impossible angles without falling. Motor coordination had somehow improved."

When the electrical aspect of the atmosphere in the room was reduced, the auric fields became randomly disorganized, scattered and incoherent. Sensory feedback was so impaired that subjects were totally unaware of the location of their bodies in space [2]. When the electromagnetism in the air was depleted, subjects burst into tears and although not sad their bodies responded as though they were threatened. When the electrical field of the room was increased beyond the usual level, subjects could think clearly and reported an expansion of their consciousness. Dr. Valerie Hunt stated in summary the following points:

> "In a normal electromagnetic environment, the human field is nourished; physiological processes are carried out efficiently, and emotional experiences occur with clarity of thought. When the level of electromagnetism reached a critical saturation, there was evidence of improved motor performance, emotional well-being, excitement, and advanced states of consciousness. However, when the critical deficit was reached, motor, sensory and intellectual capabilities diminished with increased levels of anxiety and emotion."

The Mu room experiments reveal the impact of a fluctuating geomagnetic environment on emotional stability and why strengthening our energy fields will provide some protection from unhelpful external fields. In this regard, it is interesting to examine proposals to help astronauts venture into deep space.

Space consultants are now worrying whether it is even possible to send astronauts to Mars as they have found out that space is *highly* radioactive. The solution being proposed is to copy the Earth and to create a magnetic field to act as a shield in space, see figure 7.1. New research has recently begun to examine the use of superconducting magnet technology to protect astronauts from radiation during long-duration space flights, such as the interplanetary flights to Mars proposed in NASA's current *Vision for Space Exploration.* Superconducting magnets can generate strong fields to shield spacecraft from cosmic radiation, these intense magnetic fields can be created with little or no electrical power input, and with proper temperatures they can maintain a stable magnetic field for long periods of time.

We do not need to travel in space, to require a magnetic shield. Space is coming directly to us in the form of space weather!

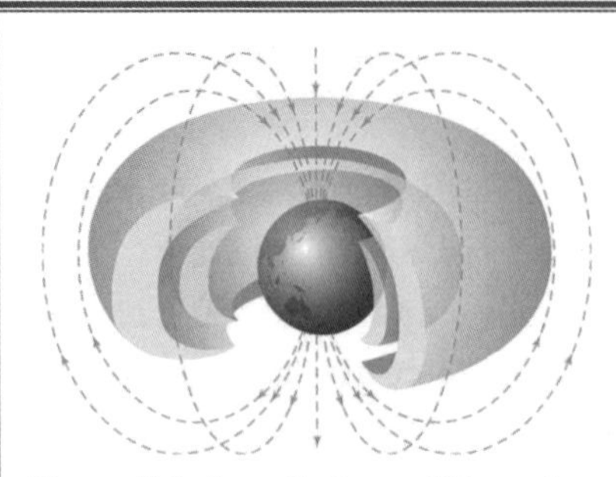

Figure 7.1 An artistic rendition of Earth's Van Allen Belts. The toroidal magnetic field are the dashed lines and the Van Allen belts can be thought of as the Earth's aura. Copyright © Stephen Francis

Figure 7.2 shows us the toroidal shaped electromagnetic shield, scientists believe will protect astronauts inside a prototype capsule. It parallels the evolving layer of light seen developing around humans, see figure 7.3. We will also see that the human energy field is also made up of superconducting electromagnetic units! Obviously, we have a clear solution available for humans in these times of evolutionary change. We are evolving and techniques are being developed, to help us strengthen our personal electromagnetic field even further.

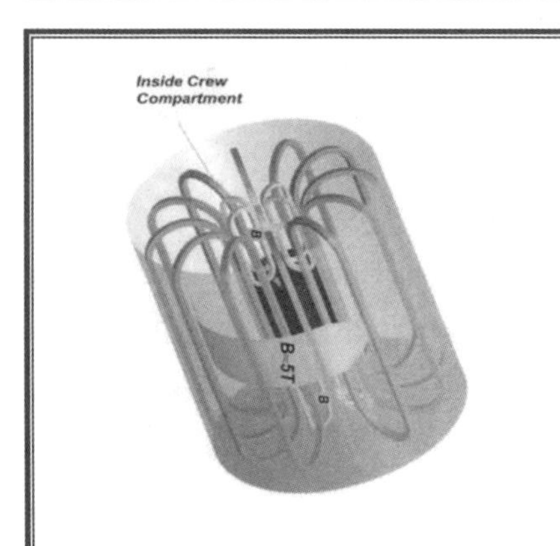

Figure 7.2 Concept of using superconducting magnets to shield electromagnetically charged particles from astronauts inside a prototype capsule. Credit: Massachusetts Institute of Technology (MIT)

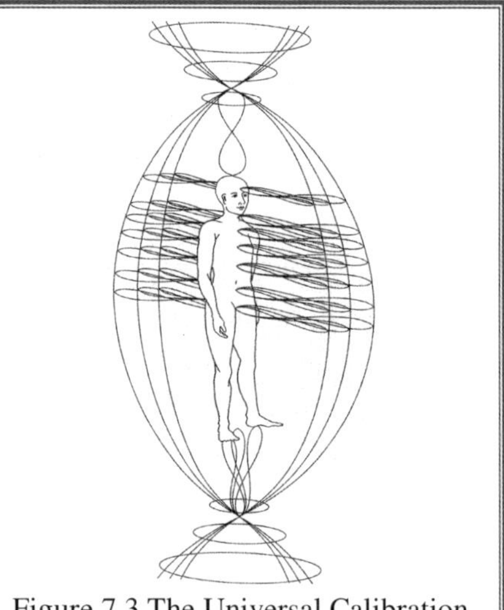

Figure 7.3 The Universal Calibration Lattice is the evolving layer of light in the human electromagnetic field. Copyright © Energy Extension Inc

As well as the lack of co-ordination and emotional instability brought about by fluctuating geomagnetic fields, there is evidence of other more serious effects on humans. Scientists report evidence of the association between geomagnetic disturbances and a host of effects on mental processing, leading to increases in work and traffic accidents [3]. An analysis of accidents caused by human factors in the biggest atomic station of the former USSR, "Urskaya" during 1985-1989, showed that approximately 70% of these accidents happened in the days of geomagnetic storms. It was found that work and traffic accidents in Germany were associated with disturbances in atmospheric electricity and the geomagnetic field. Russian scientists tell us that during geomagnetic storms, humans experience adrenaline rush and changes in blood flow, especially in the capillaries, and blood pressure becomes unsteady [4]. Young and healthy people are none the worse for it, but others may have problems. In one study linking geomagnetic storms and depression, British researchers found that male hospital admissions with a diagnosis of depression rose 36.2% during periods of geomagnetic activity, in comparison with normal periods. Again, Slovakian neurologists have found statistically significant links between strokes and related cerebral attacks to the 10.5 year peak of the solar flare cycle [5]. There is also another well-studied correlation between maximum sunspot counts and human behavior. A.L. Tchijevsky, a Russian professor, studied the social movements of 72 countries between 500 B.C. to 1922 A.D. and noted the correlation with social unrest in the histories of these countries, particularly wars, rebellions and riots. Tchijevsky's research established that 80% of the most significant historical events on earth occurred at the period of maximum sunspot activity [6].

Astronauts and cosmonauts face many hazards. Cosmonaut Shannon Lucid reports that on the Russian Mir space station, the typical radiation dosage was the equivalent of about eight daily chest X-rays, but during a solar storm at the end of 1990, Mir cosmonauts received a full year's dosage in a few days [7]. Astronauts even in the comparative safety of low-Earth orbit, report flashing lights inside their eyes. This is caused by energetic particles that pass straight through Space Station walls and their eyelids, striking their retinas and making their eyeballs glow inside. Some scientists suggest the possibility that exposure to cosmic rays may be passed on to children as a non-lethal mutation [8]. Other research states that cosmic ray exposure is more likely to produce temporary sterility. Whatever, compared to high-energy electromagnetic radiation, such as x-rays and gamma rays, cosmic rays may cause even more severe damage to cells and are more likely to result in gene mutations or cancer. Currently, scientists are using animals to model the health effects of cosmic-ray exposure on humans.

Nevertheless, cosmic rays do not just affect space dwellers. In January 2005, when we had a new type of solar storm, if there had been any astronauts on the surface of the moon, they would have got very sick. Proton storms cause all kinds of problems because of the extreme velocities that the particles can reach. Yet, we know that cosmic rays with even more extreme velocities are coming from galactic sources too. So even though we do have the natural protection of the Earth's atmosphere and magnetic field, it does not prevent all the cosmic and galactic rays getting through. We know this because cosmic ray detectors on Earth are registering *extensive* activity.

Re-tuning For Higher Frequencies

There is an interesting controversy amongst biomedical specialists regarding cardiac arrhythmia. There are so-called spiral or scroll waves that most scientists think could be responsible for many of the abnormal rhythms observed clinically. Electrical impulses regularly circulate through cardiac tissue and cause the heart's muscle fibers to contract. In a healthy heart, these electrical impulses travel smoothly and unobstructed, like a water wave that ripples gently in a pond. However, for reasons that have not been properly understood, these waves can sometimes develop into troublesome, whirlpool-like spirals of electrical activity that can circulate through the heart [9]. These electrical waves that re-circulate repeatedly throughout the tissue are thought to be at a higher frequency than the waves produced by the heart's natural pacemaker. Niels Otani, a senior researcher at Cornell University states on his website:

> "Computer experiments have raised the question of whether such waves can exist in diseased or even healthy hearts. If these waves are possible in the healthy heart, then all that may be required to kill you is the wrong electrical pattern, a scary possibility!" [10]

Cardiologists have found that the complicated structure of cardiac tissue, as well as the complex ionic currents in the cell, has made it extremely difficult to pinpoint the detailed mechanisms that cause life-threatening irregular heart rhythms. So it is fair to say that researchers still don't know what causes cardiac rhythm disorders, hence the controversy. Yet research has also found spiral waves with reentrant patterns that typically occur in the middle of cardiac muscle and have the tendency for the center of rotation to wander around, usually called meandering. Under some conditions the spiral tip does not travel in a circular or elliptical path around the core region but instead follows a more complicated, often "flower-shaped" trajectory. Scientists have tried to model simple versions of these waves, and in this process, compare the models, to that observed experimentally in cardiac tissue [11]. In figure 7.4 we see a variety of spiral-tip trajectories. At the end of each tip is shown a pattern that appears when parameters such as angular momentum are changed. Sometimes the patterns have inward petals, see figure 7.4 (B) and sometimes they have outward petals figure 7.4 (D). The predominant pattern in normal cardiac tissue are figures 7.4 (E) & (F). Figure 7.4 (D) is the unfinished trajectory of an eight outward-pointing petal spiral tip meander. Despite the lack of a general theory, scientists have some insight into which parameters can cause spiral tip trajectories to change amongst the different patterns of motion. The transition from circular to meandering motion originates when a second frequency is introduced and adds modulated waves. Within the meander patterns, the transition from epicycloidal (in-ward petals) to hypocycloidal (outward petals) occurs as the second frequency grows larger than the original, with cycloidal occurring in between both frequencies. From the literature, scientists can easily map spiral tip trajectories with 3, 5 and 8 petals, reflecting the fibonacci sequence, often seen in nature.

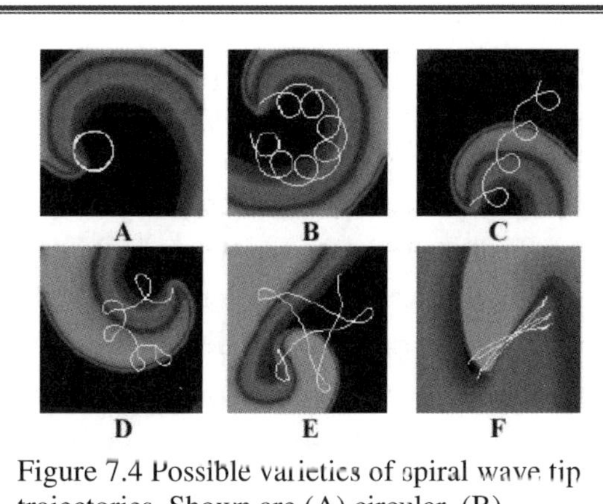

Figure 7.4 Possible varieties of spiral wave tip trajectories. Shown are (A) circular, (B) epicycloidal (also known as meander with inward petals), (C) cycloidal, (D) hypocycloidal (also known as meander with outward petals), (E) hypermeandering, and (F) linear trajectories. Credit: Hofstra University & The Heart Institute, Beth Israel Medical Center, New York. Copyright © 2005 Chaos, American Institute of Physics

For some energy balancing practitioners and clients, the eight petal outward meander pattern is known as the Orbital Sweep and the pattern is used as an effective way to attune to new higher frequencies. According to the founder of the EMF Balancing Technique® Peggy Phoenix Dubro, this pattern symbolizes the evolving human. Thus biomedical science does confirm how higher frequencies influence our evolution.

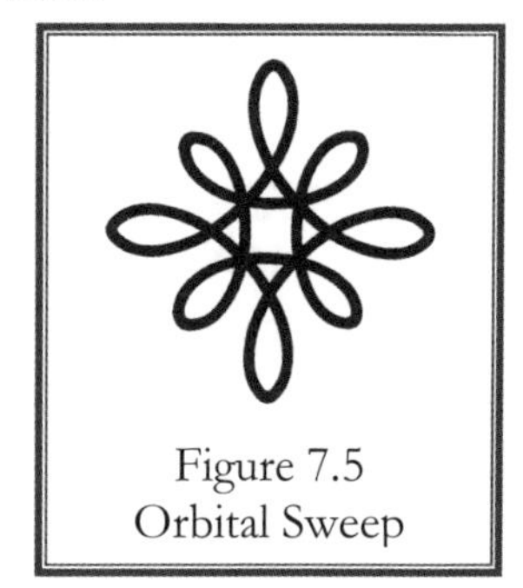

Figure 7.5
Orbital Sweep

Stabilizing Your Core Energy

During research, Dr. Wolfgang Ludwig came across the ancient Chinese teachings which state that man needs two environmental signals: the YANG (masculine) signal from above and the YIN (feminine) signal from below. This description fits the relatively strong signal of the Schumann wave surrounding our planet being YANG and the weaker geomagnetic waves coming from below, from within the planet, being the YIN signal [12]. These Chinese teachings state that to achieve perfect health, both signals must be in balance. Dr. Ludwig found that this is indeed the case and studies proved that the one sided use of Schumann (YANG) wave simulation without the geomagnetic (YIN) signal caused serious health problems.

On the other hand, the absence of Schumann waves also creates problems. This was also clearly demonstrated by Professor R. Wever when he built an underground bunker, which could completely screened out magnetic fields. Student volunteers lived for four weeks in this hermetically sealed environment. Wever noted that the student's circadian rhythms (biological cycles that repeat over 24 hours), diverged and that they suffered emotional distress and migraine headaches. As they were young and healthy, no serious health conditions arose, but this would not have been the case with older people or those with a compromised immune system. After only a brief exposure to 7.8 Hz (the very frequency which had been screened out), the volunteers health stabilized again [13]. The first astronauts and cosmonauts in space also reported the same complaints, as they were no longer exposed to Schumann waves. On the basis of the research work of Dr. Ludwig, NASA constructed "Schumann" frequency generators and now uses them in the manned space stations [14].

These environmental signals work by strengthening "Core Energy", which can be explained in terms of non-traditional electromagnetic fields called scalar waves. A very important constituent of our electromagnetic nature is the central tube of energy that exists and penetrates the human energy field. This column of light and energy is given many names in spiritual and metaphysical traditions and it is where we make fundamental connections to the Earth and cosmic spiritual energy, see figure 7.6. It has been the teachings of mystics and seers all down the ages that this core energy has to be strengthened and a sign of strong core energy is peacefulness. It is of great importance how much energy can be taken into this central tube of energy as it directly impacts how much energy is available to our organs and body systems. The central tube of energy

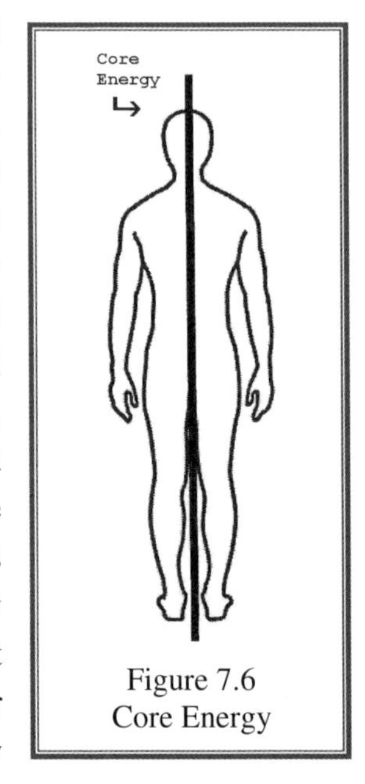

Figure 7.6
Core Energy

extends straight down through the center of our bodies from the crown (at the top of the head) down through the perineum (a mid-point between the genitals and the anus. The central tube of energy can actually extend deep into the Earth's core and out into the Universe depending on the development of consciousness. So if your consciousness is not very developed, the tube of *light will not extend much further than your body.* Strong core energy gives a size of energy tube that can be approximated as the circle made when you touch your thumb with your second finger. If this core energy is very weak, it is more like a thin piece of string than a rod. Scientifically, we can define core energy as the projection of two magnetic fields in the exact same place. As we have no metal core, there's no tendency to magnetize in either direction, the two magnetic fields can be made to propagate in exactly the same place at exactly the same strength, therefore canceling each other out. Scientists have found that these "cancelled" magnetic fields, can have dramatic effects [15].

"The scalar wave makes a coherent field to offset destructive electromagnetic fields."
Dr. Valerie Hunt

It is possible to direct electromagnetic frequencies to enter the body at opposite ends using the power of intent. According to Dr. Valerie Hunt:

> "Intent can direct electromagnetic frequencies to enter the body at opposite ends of a straight angle or line, i.e. front to back, up to down, right to left, placing scalar energy in the trunk, head or legs... In the same way each of us can create the powerful resting bioscalar energy and by thought we can direct it to bodily areas and give it instruction to: eliminate pain, heal traumatized tissue, destroy disease and eliminate tumor growths. Certainly this is not new thought to the healing arts, however the mechanism by which the mind creates and directs this energy is new and scientifically verifiable." [16]

We can create our own scalar field quite easily, and very simple energy balancing techniques suggest the use of the power of intent to direct energy up and down our central column of light.

Hunt says that scalar energy cannot be stored indefinitely, so it has to be recreated, as we need it. Hunt thinks that healers should increase and stabilize their own electromagnetic energy fields by first creating a scalar field for themselves before healing another person. However, she acknowledges that many healers create bioscalar energy automatically without awareness or realization that they have manipulated the structure of electromagnetic waves.

These powerful fields are not new, they have been known and understood in ages past. Core energy is a result of two electromagnetic waves that cancel each other out to leave a powerful "resting" energy that in theory should go on forever. Nikola Tesla in around 1900, experimented with two spiral coils (caduceus shaped, see figure 7.7). He found that when he fed the coils with opposing alternating currents, such that they would create electromagnetic fields that would self-cancel, he demonstrated that his Tesla coils were still able to transmit energy over long distances. This was a discovery of a new form of energy. Remarkably, Tesla's waves did not loose energy at the inverse square of the distance as normal electromagnetic energy does, even over long distances, there was no loss of energy to be noticed. During the course of his research with electricity, Tesla also observed a new type of electromagnetic energy that seemed to function as plasma. Because there was no theoretical basis for this observation in physics, Tesla examined and extended ideas originally developed by Thomas Maxwell. Tesla then called the unknown phenomena, radiant energy and he believed the energy represented a transfer of power from dimensions outside the visible universe.

In the course of his scientific endeavors, Tesla received two patents for radiant energy devices. He came to understand that a certain type of electromagnetic energy coming from the Sun carried the plasma he called radiant energy. This plasma is stored in the earth moving along magnetic grid lines. There was another form of this radiant energy that came direct from the Sun and cosmos. In ancient religious texts, a bird symbolizes radiant energy coming from the Sun and either a snake or a dragon symbolizes radiant energy that comes from the Earth. Nowadays, there are traces of this knowledge that remain. The medical profession adopted ancient symbolism, now called the Medical Caduceus, see figure 7.7. This insignia represents earth and cosmic forces which when they are in perfect balance bring health. A similar theme of life giving powers are portrayed by a wall plaque in a Cathedral see plate 27 [18]. The Ouroboros, meaning *tail devourer*, symbolizes the never-ending cycle of divine energy; birth, death and rebirth or creation, destruction and recreation. This particular wall plaque can be interpreted as the Holy Spirit being the source of divine illumination and inspiration, as the rays of the Sun provide life on Earth. Yet, the use of the Ouroboros and the radiant bird is universal symbolism

Figure 7.7 The Medical Caduceus

that can be traced back to ancient Egypt. Therefore, a deeper meaning passed on to initiates, would include the life giving powers of balanced earth and cosmic forces. For scientific validation, Dr. Friedemann Freund has proven in the laboratory that when igneous type rocks are stressed by tectonic movements, (in the laboratory this is simulated by squeezing these rocks only at one end), a standing wave is generated with currents flowing in both directions that occur without applying a voltage. Freund says that these currents flow prior to earthquakes and his research papers refer to this as "solid state" plasma. The other snake-like source of plasma, originating from the Sun and cosmic sources are the Earth's electrojets, thus proving that Tesla was right about the existence of these currents! [17]

What the Egyptians Knew About Balance

The concept of being in perfect balance with the fundamental forces of the Earth and cosmos was paramount in Egyptian culture. If you look at statues of the pharaohs, you will often see that they are clasping cylinder-like objects in their hands, whilst standing with one foot forward in a position, known as the "Master Position", see figure 7.8. The cylinder objects are called the Wands of Horus – metal cylinders filled with a variety of substances – were used by the Egyptians to maintain balance.

Figure 7.8 Red granite Statue of Senusret I located in the compound of the Mit Rahina Museum, Memphis, Egypt showing the "Master Position" stance and holding a Wand. Credit: R. Stadelmann

The initial discovery of the Wands can be traced back to World War II, where at a remote military facility, Soviet workers were puzzled to discover that when searchlights were switched off, they still remained dimly lit. After a thorough investigation, it was found that the phenomenon was related to the proportions of the searchlight tubes picking up radiation as vibrational standing waves – oscillatory mode frequencies from Earth. This initiated a long search that ultimately led to the Egyptian pharaohs and the Wands of Horus. In 1992, the Russian authorities started to take a more serious interest in the Wands and in 1999, the Russian Dr. Valery Uvarov authored the book, *The Wands of Horus*, presenting the first ever theory published regarding the use and construction of these cylinders [19]. Dr. Valery Uvarov is the head of the Department of UFO research, Paleosciences and Paleotechnology of the National Security Academy of Russia and he is also devoted to the study of the legacy of ancient civilizations. He gives his title as *Head of UFO association of highest officers of Russia.*

Geometrically, the Wands are attuned to the main resonance – the planet's own frequency of vibration and specifically electromagnetic energies coming from the core of the Earth. The external and internal dimensions of the Wands of Horus conform strictly to the proportions of the golden section. This is the ratio of length to width of approximately 1.618 found in nature, see figure 7.9.

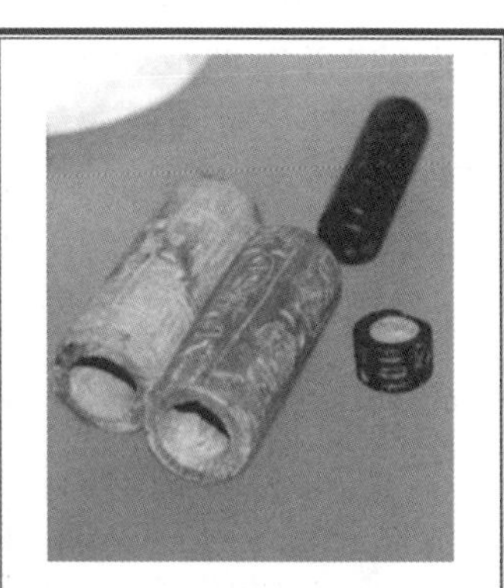

Figure 7.9 The Wands of Horus. This photograph, taken in the Metropolitan Museum, New York, in the autumn of 1999 shows the cylinders of Pharaoh Pepi II. Printed with kind permission. Copyright © Valery Uvarov.

According to Russian studies, The Wands have a harmonizing effect on the bodies Yin & Yang energy, synchronizing left and right hemispheres of the brain. In Egyptian terminology, this is referred to as the KA-BA principle [20]. The hierophant-priests knew that the KA and BA represented two energy flows, two principles, opposite and unified, different and homogenous at the same time. While they are interacting, the organism's vital functions are supported and a person exists without particular problems. The Russians have ascertained that the greater part of our illnesses begin with disharmony between these two fundamental flows of energy. Hence, the use of something that balances these flows leads to healing. Apparently, use of the Wands for as little as ten minutes, seems to have a prolonged effect on a person's energy field. The human energy field remembers, as it were, the rhythms that arose while the Wands were working and continues to maintain them for a period between 24 hours and several days. The Russians found that the filling in the cylinders consisted of minerals that were changed as the pharaoh made advances in the process of self-perfection. Evidently, there was a science associated with this method of the evolution of consciousness and so the Russians have consequently developed a range of Wands. The Russians believe the main reason the ancient Egyptians constructed the wands was prevention of cancer, yet they are not seen as a panacea and their main purpose is as an evolutionary tool.

The Wands are being used in Russian hospitals after extensive research. There have been very good results healing the cardiovascular system and in the treatment of cancer patients. The Wands have proven to offset the debilitating effects of some cancer treatments, such as chemotherapy and they allow the patient to recover faster following the treatments. It is well known that treatments such as chemotherapy have a significant negative impact on the bodies energy balance, so the Wands work to restore this balance, which not only leads to a faster feelings of well being, but also more rapid healing. In 2004, Dr. Uvarov published further research that was directed squarely at spiritual seekers and healers. He maintains that Egyptian text and images clearly warn of the dangers of not maintaining balance and the risk associated with the evolutionary process, see the small section, "The Egyptian god Apophis".

The Egyptian god Apophis

Apophis is the Greek name for the Egyptian serpent god Apep. The serpent is described as an immense snake and the great adversary of the Sun god, Re. Apophis embodied the powers of dissolution, darkness and non-being. There is no evidence of this god prior to the Middle Kingdom and Apophis seems to have come into existence in the Egyptian mindset during the troubled times just after the pyramid age. Various accounts of this malevolent force, say that as the Sun god made his nightly voyage through the underworld, each morning as the solar barque was about to emerge into the daylight, it was attacked by the great serpent whose terrifying roar echoed through the darkness. As we now realize today, important information was only written down in such a way that only the initiated would understand the true meaning. Hence, these descriptions give us a very strong hints that Apophis actually represented an electrojet. Today we can cite the example of the Equatorial Electrojet currently circling Earth, that also only operates from dawn to dusk! It would seem that references to chaos refer to the unbalancing of energies. This interpretation gives credence to the Russian interpretation of Egyptian texts, and why Apophis was associated with the need to maintain balance. These warnings to initiates emphasize the risk to the evolutionary process in disturbed electromagnetic environmental conditions [21].

Dr. Uvarov refers to the "Apophis" factor and warns:

"The core of the matter is that the beginning of the transformation processes that accompany the formation of a new energy system will always pass through a phase of spontaneous cell division in the organism. Medically this process is known as cancer."

"Indicative in this context is a statistical analysis of the consequences of the influence on the organism of those energies with which a person interacts when practicing as a healer. The results of an analysis carried out by specialists from the Russian Academy of National Security proved astonishing. Within 7 to 10 years of graduating from a school of healing, many diplomaed specialists actively engaged in healing practice died of oncological diseases. This applies not only to healers and psychics, but also to the ideological leaders of spiritual and esoteric schools. It was shocking to learn that such well known and acknowledged authorities as Sri Djuddu Krishnamurti, Romana Maharishi, Sri Ramakrishna, Sri Aurobindo, the Mother, Madame Blavatsky, Helena Roerich, Nisargadatta Maharaj, Vanga, Osho (Bhagwan Shree Rajneesh), Castaneda and many others also succumbed to cancer. Ignorance of the Law evidently does not free human beings from the requirement to observe it, be they even Ra himself!"

The Russian authorities have taken their findings very seriously and they have used their media to warn healers and spiritual seekers for the need to balance! Dr. Uvarov writes:

"Having read the warning left us by the priests of Ancient Egypt, the specialists of the Academy for the National Security of Russia consider it vital to pass on that knowledge to the broad masses of interested people."

The Russians are very specific, healers have to synchronize and balance their first, second and third energy bodies with the first, second and third energy bodies of the Earth and all at once! The Russians state emphatically that this is a Cosmic Law that must be obeyed! Dr. Uvarov continues:

"The conclusions drawn from the analysis of texts and images are obvious and call into doubt the reputation of the schools of "cosmoenergetics" and other trends throughout the world that do not recognize the danger that has entered the lives not only of the "adepts" of the doctrines listed above, but also the lives of those they instruct, people who have no idea of the ancient warning and not a thought for the threat hanging over them. That is the reason why the "Wands of Horus" and the energy of the pyramids were an inseparable part of life for priests and pharaohs, who were never parted from them. **They used them to correct the consequences of Sun storms and magnetic storms, stabilize energy processes and synchronize their own energy systems with that of the Earth**. With these tools the priests could pass through the "boundary of death" and develop exceptional abilities without damaging their health." [22]

This warning must be given due consideration by all healers and spiritual seekers. As we are moving into a New World Age dominated by space weather, the need for balance will be paramount. Metaphysical sources have been very clear that old energy practices will become less and less effective and so there will be an inevitable transfer to "New Energies" and methodologies. This message is especially pertinent for healers working directly with the powerful "New Energies" coming to Earth. Ignorance of Cosmic Law, does not prevent consequences. It would seem that the use of the Wands, combined with the cosmic energies harnessed and transmitted by pyramids, was developed and perfected by the Egyptians as an evolutionary tool. The Russians are attempting to replicate the Egyptians by the research and development of a range of Wands and the building of massive pyramids, which will be discussed later. The Russians are keen to point out that they wish to avoid the mistakes of previous civilizations, where spiritual evolution was restricted to a select few. Their solution is to make evolutionary tools available to the mass of humanity.

The Russian perspective is one that has been carried down through the ages in metaphysical literature. John Major Jenkins in his book *Galactic Alignment,* outlines the hidden symbolism in many esoteric traditions and cultures. He suggests the gateway to higher consciousness is guarded and that the wrong motivation can bring disastrous results. In support of this, Jenkins provides a curious quote from an obscure indirect source, dated 1927. It is given here because it is highly relevant to our discussion. One Edgar Conrow, whose original writings have been lost, is quoted as saying:

> "The Pineal Gland is the 'North Gate'. This in man, is the central spiritual creative center. Above in the heavens, it is found in the beginning of this sign Sagittarius and this is the point from which spiritual gifts are given. It is called 'Vision of God', and is the Light within, a gift to the pure in heart, who verily may 'see God', but to the impure or those who abuse this great gift the consequences are terrible."
>
> "This North Gate, the creative center in man, the most interior center in the body has become atrophied, and redemption or regeneration means its restoration to creative ability, by having **the electrical or positive and the magnetic or negative forces restored in balance in man or woman**." [23]

The seriousness of this message passed down through the ages means that any energy balancing technique must obey Cosmic Law.

Chapter Eight

Strengthening Your Energy Field *Is* Spiritual Evolution

Evolving Towards Bliss

Strengthening the human energy field means moving into greater levels of balance. To do this we have to re-calibrate, which means re-arranging how electromagnetic charge is distributed in our energy fields. Today the calibration process can be measured and spiritual progress, the evolution of consciousness, can be registered using scientific protocols. Pioneering studies using the scientific discipline of kinesiology and human reactions to truth and falsehood have made this possible. The science of kinesiology reveals the intimate connection between the mind and body and how the mind "thinks" with the body. *Applied kinesiology* clearly demonstrates that muscles instantly become weak when the body is exposed to harmful stimuli. So if you are allergic to a substance, it will make you test weak. In a similar manner, if a substance is introduced to the body that is therapeutic, the muscles instantly become strong [1]. In the late 1970s Dr. John Diamond pioneered a new discipline he called *behavioral kinesiology*. Diamond, made the startling discovery that indicator muscles would also strengthen or weaken in the presence of positive or negative *emotional and intellectual* stimuli. He also noted in passing that subjects listening to convincing sounding deceits tested weak, whilst people listening to true statements all tested strong. In 1975, the psychiatrist and physician Dr David

Hawkins decided to pioneer research on the kinesiological response to truth and falsehood.

Over a twenty-year period, research involved conducting millions of calibrations by testing tens of thousands of people from all ages, personality types, backgrounds, and varying states of health. Hawkins found a consistent response to the truth and so he devised a scale from 1-1,000 that calibrate the degree of power of all possible levels of awareness [2]. The result became known as the "Map of Consciousness", a calibrated scale, which coincides with levels of emotional and intellectual attainment identified in the disciplines of sociology, clinical psychology and traditional spirituality. Hawkins found that using chaos theory, the calibrated levels represent powerful *attractor fields* within the domain of consciousness, that serves to act as organizing energies for widespread patterns of behavior [3] *Attractor* is the name give to an identifiable pattern that emerges from data that just appears meaningless. This hidden coherence was first demonstrated in nature by Edward Lorenz who studied computer graphics derived from weather patterns over long periods of time. Known as "Lorenz's Butterfly", this attractor pattern is also the metaphysical infinity sign which represents balance and harmony! See figure 8.1.

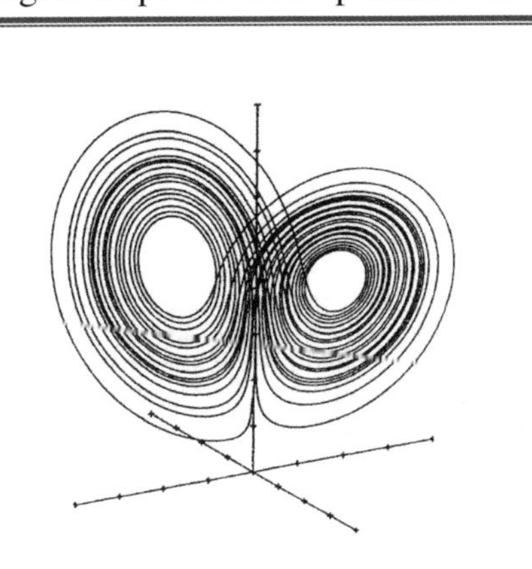

Figure 8.1 Lorentz's Butterfly reveals balance and harmony. Here a point cycles back and forth in the figure eight shape of infinity, but it never repeats its tracks. Even if the process were to go on to infinity, the lines would never cross over or repeat each other. There is always a new path to reach the other side. The Lorenz fractal is a geometric depiction of a spiral loop into infinity, the never ending cycle back and forth, yet forward and different.

The Path of Consciousness

The following list is a very brief description of the energy fields associated with evolution of consciousness, and for a full understanding it is recommended to purchase Dr. Hawkin's first book, *Power Vs Force: The Hidden Determinant of Human Behavior*. Along the path of consciousness, the level of 200, is a significant marker and it is associated with truth, integrity and courage. All attitudes, thoughts, and feelings etc below this level of calibration make a person go weak, but those that calibrate higher make a person go strong.

♦ **Shame** at **20**	Has the most destructive effect on emotional and psychological health, and the consequence in low self-esteem, makes one susceptible to physical illness. Guilt is the next most weakening emotion.
♦ **Apathy** at **50**	This is a state of despair, hopelessness and helplessness. As people evolve, they move out of apathy and grief to overcome fear as away of life.
♦ **Fear** at **100**	Represents fear of the world and limiting beliefs. Fear is used by dictatorial regimes to control the populace and it is exploited in consumer societies to sell more products. The next level leads to desire with excessive greed.
♦ **Anger** at **150**	When desires are not met, frustration generates anger due to the inability to control situations and events.
♦ **Pride** at **175**	Taking pride in appearance and social status is socially encouraged, but pride is divisive and has a downside of arrogance and denial.
♦ **Courage** at **200**	This is the first level of empowerment where one is able to face life with courage and make a difference to the world. At this level we start to **gain** energy.
♦ **Neutrality** at **250**	An attitude of being relatively unattached to particular outcomes, trusting that life will work out overall. Neutral people are easy to get along with as they don't need to control people or situations and in turn they are difficult to control.
♦ **Acceptance** at **350**	Is where we take responsibility and we understand ourselves to be creators of our life's experiences. At this level we take back our power and demonstrate balance, this is a clear sign of spiritual evolution.
♦ **Love** at **500**	Is unconditional, forgiving, understanding and nurturing. This kind of love emanates from the heart and is the level of true happiness.
♦ **Joy** at **540**	Becomes a constant in life and is experienced, as inner joy not specifically associated with any particular external events or sources. This is the level of healing and levels higher than this are associated with saints and advanced spiritual teachers and healers. Near-death experiences normally transform people to experience levels between joy and peace [4].
♦ **Peace at 600**	It is surmised that the level of **peace** and **bliss** is relatively rare and it is associated with transcendence, self-realization and God-consciousness. Yet it is important for as many as possible to acquire these levels to help raise mass consciousness.
♦ **Enlightenment 700 – 1000**	At this level people set in place attractor energy fields that influence all of mankind. The greatest spiritual leaders calibrate here, with great teaching to uplift the mass of humanity. Great avatars like Krishna, Buddha and Jesus Christ.

The energy fields of consciousness are always mixed and so a person may operate at varying levels of consciousness in different areas of their life, so our overall calibration is defined as the sum total effect. The most important thing to know is that this scale is not arithmetic but a logarithmic progression. So 400 is not twice the power of 200, it is 10 to the power 400 (10^{400}) and 200 corresponds to 10 to the power 200, (10^{200}). Therefore, an increase in a few points represent a major advance in power. When we spiritually evolve we increase our levels of power to affect others around us; our *Signal Power* is greatly enhanced. Hawkins stated in an interview:

> "The evolution of consciousness is inevitable and it occurs because of its own nature, just as water always runs downhill. The consciousness level of Mankind is advancing inexorably. When we calibrated evolution and society, it's verifiably progressive." [5]

Dr. Hawkins has received many accolades for his work. After 50 years clinical experience, he is outlined in Who's Who in America, and Who's Who in the World. He has a knighthood and is honored in the East with the title "Tae Ryoung Sun Kak Tosa" (Foremost Teacher of the Way to Enlightenment). Hawkins has found a way to measure the evolution of consciousness. If we choose, we can work directly with our consciousness to hasten spiritual evolution.

Unsticking the Pendulum: Clearing Old Emotions

Our emotions are very important. Many studies indicate a clear relationship between our mental and emotional state and our health. It has been proven that our emotions program our DNA and influence the coherence of the immune system. Emotions like – anger, guilt, anxiety, fear, depression, cynicism and impatience, are toxic – affecting the immune system, the digestive system, the circulatory system and the hormonal system because these all interact with each other instantaneously. The relationship between heart attacks and other adverse health effects is well documented. Studies show that individuals who are unable to express anger and 'get things off their chest' are at the greatest risk [6]. If you think of an old fashion clock with a pendulum it only functions properly if the pendulum is swinging freely. If for any reason the pendulum is stuck then the clock cannot keep time. We can compare our emotions to a pendulum. If for any reason our emotions swing into an anti-coherent mode and get stuck, then we start to suffer physically, emotionally, mentally and spiritually. Sometimes, we are very unconscious that certain emotional states are stuck and need to be dealt with. The pendulum of our emotions was designed to swing but always come back to balance. If our emotions swing and get stuck for one reason or another, then we become "unbalanced." Spiritual evolution will only occur when we progressively remove the blockages caused by unresolved emotion, past and present, when we do, we strengthen our energy fields, and create empowerment.

Here we need to create some clarity by determining what we mean by emotions. Our feelings are physical sensations that we experience, relating to our outer sensory world and our inner or subtle worlds, but emotions are feelings, with thoughts about those feelings. We evolve our consciousness, when we learn to develop our feeling nature without using judgement, so our feelings just become neutral reports of our awareness. To be a living vibrant human who is completely in touch with their greater reality, then that means being as conscious as possible. High consciousness means our feeling nature is operating at the highest levels of human capability. In reality, there are increasing levels of consciousness and so this is a continuos upward spiral.

Scientists tell us that the body operates as a series of antennas, receiving and transmitting electromagnetic messages. If parts of the body are "frozen" caused by unresolved emotion, then the body cannot function properly at the optimum level. The situation then arises that areas of the body become "dead zones," messages cannot be sent or received. That is why alternative medicine such as acupuncture enables healing, as blockages to the flow of chi energy are removed. Sometimes, negative emotions are stored in parts of the body so that deeper work is needed to bring about resolution and many therapies have been developed to deal with these trap memories, thus helping people to evolve. What's more, various spiritual practices also help to remove the dead zones caused by excess emotion and trauma. Very often, when people take up meditation or start to pray, what comes to mind is all the painful issues that have been left unresolved, but dealing with these painful memories, by acts of forgiveness, will resolve these thoughts and memories, elevating consciousness and at the same time promoting health. Good spiritual practices also help us to take in greater amounts of spiritual energy that enable us to evolve our consciousness, as a direct result, studies show that this enables people to live longer [7]. When we work specifically with our emotional nature, we are also working with our electromagnetic nature, more specifically, the magnetic field emitted by the physical body.

Humans are made up of many layers of light and energy. As well as a physical body we have subtle bodies that can be considered to be our consciousness that exists at specific quantized levels of higher frequency. The subtle emotional body is a field of energy that surrounds and interpenetrates our physical body and our feeling nature is just an attribute. Medical intuitives tell us that they can often see disease in the subtle bodies, up to two years before they manifest at the physical level and once disease appears at the physical level, then it can be harder to deal with. When we work with our consciousness at the higher levels, unresolved issues do not have to manifest at the physical level, hence revealing our state of consciousness and areas where we have issues to deal with.

Learning how to move energy through our physical and emotional bodies will help us to evolve graciously, hence the need to cultivate the feeling nature. Some of the most therapeutic emotions to feel are those of unconditional acceptance or unconditional love. When we experience these emotions, an intercellular resonance is set up, that promotes coherence. This positively affects our DNA; making it stronger and helping it to code more precisely, as revealed in studies conducted by the Institute of HeartMath. Allowing the feeling of unconditional love and acceptance to move through the emotional body activates a process of profound healing and balance.

It is generally accepted that most people lose the awareness of their feelings and emotions through childhood training and cultural conditioning. As we are unaware of our feelings it means that we tend to get stuck in the mental body and hence deprive ourselves of additional sources of information. Again the mental body can be considered to be a frequency domain associated with our consciousness and one that is highly regarded in the western world. Yet, if we ignore our feelings we can be depriving ourselves of an additional system of judgement and decision making, as proposed by the "feelings-as-information" hypothesis [8]. It is perfectly natural to receive information from the subtle realms of consciousness and we call this intuition. However, this can only be achieved when we utilize the feeling nature and thereafter, it is translated into thoughts and language. This implies we cannot rely on our mental body completely, as we can be driven by unknown feelings. In this situation, we are "unconscious", which is the antithesis of spiritual evolution. If we have negative emotions without knowing their source, then we often allow these emotions to affect decisions on unrelated issues [9].

Feelings and emotions are reactions to situation based upon the *interpretation* of the events. They are mirrors that allow you energetically to respond to and become aware of your own calibration to an event or experience.

Very often, when we start to label our feelings, the process can cause us to close down, preventing progress as we experience emotional events. This is anti-evolutionary and so energy does not flow in the area of the body where the emotion was held and eventually a problem will surface in that part of the physical body. Yet, it is not realistic to deny our negative emotions and negative experiences because these are part of our fundamental perception of reality. Emotions cannot be surgically removed and thrown away, so the simple solution is that we need to transmute our emotion by re-balancing. As e-motion is energy–in–motion, we need to address an energy issue with more energy with the intent to balance. If you like, fight fire with fire.

It is understandable with certain types of trauma, especially when it comes to matters of the heart, to feel very vulnerable and feel the need for protection. However, for our own emotional health we need to open up, so how exactly do we do this when we are afraid? Well, the process of being open does not mean being vulnerable and so we can discriminate and choose whom to open up to. The goal is to be able to open up at will, rather than not having any choice in the matter. Once we start to develop the feeling nature, it is possible to detect the chakras as they open-up and become more active, as they respond to different types of emotions. Where our thoughts go, energy soon follows.

The chakra that is quite a challenge for most people to open completely is the heart chakra. However, in the right conditions the heart chakra will open, and the sensation in the body is like a flower with many petals opening up into full bloom. The opposite can occur when the heart chakra can be felt as a throbbing 'stump', tightly closed after a heart-felt upset. For the heart chakra, we can help ourselves by imagining the heart opening up like a flower, in doing so, we literally create an electromagnetic opening. Humans are emotional beings and working with our emotions and will help us to recalibrate to higher levels of consciousness and reach new evolutionary heights. Mastery is about total flexibility, this means we can experience emotional highs and lows but quickly stabilize and still move on to higher states of consciousness. The emotional body is not suppressed, but stabilized at will.

Our Evolving Layer of Light

"We are layers upon layers of light and energy
and we are just discovering new layers."
Peggy Phoenix Dubro

In the western mystical tradition, initiates were instructed to know him or herself as energy system like the Earth, hence the study of the planetary grid was considered an integral part of a person's education. The "Key of Life" sciences were considered to include physics, astronomy, chemistry, biology, mathematics, geometry, genetics, meteorology, astrology and anthropology. Now the Earth is in "ascension", i.e. the vibratory rate is increasing and there is scientific support for this notion, new teaching, encouraging us to upgrade our energy fields, is truly in line with mystical tradition.

There have been many books written that detail subtle energy bodies that exist around the physical body. Yet, there is a new multi-dimensional organizing field evolving around the human being at this time. This is viewed as the human energy field "re-wiring" to carry *New Energy.* This electromagnetic field has been called the Universal Calibration Lattice (UCL), and it is described as an energy pattern of self-empowerment. Being aware and understanding this energy pattern is an important part of accelerating up the evolutionary process.

In 1988, Peggy Phoenix Dubro states that she experienced herself as pure light, in the patterns of "The Lattice" and "Templates of Light". After this profound mystical experience, Dubro spent six years interpreting and mapping these energy fields and developing the first four phases of the Electromagnetic (EMF) Balancing Technique®. Dubro had spent several years of study with a wise Native American Lokata Pipe carrier where she was appropriately given the name "Phoenix", see the small section, "The Phoenix Tells the Secrets of Light".

In 1995, Sonalysts, a group of Navy scientists, sought collaboration with Dubro. Their aim was a NASA grant to study The EMF Balancing Technique®, which meant making a Small Business Innovation Research (SBIR) proposal. With Dubro's help, the proposed study would test the effect of electromagnetic field energy awareness on improving team performance and strengthening the human health maintenance process for astronauts. The outcome was that NASA received a 23-page report, but eventually no grant was awarded.

The Phoenix Tells
The Secrets of Light

According to investigative mythologist William Henry the Egyptian hieroglyph of the heron/phoenix, ♉ the 'bird of light' *(ak*h), closely matches the stylized fish glyph of Jesus, though it predates him by millennia. In addition, these two symbols are structurally identical to, the mathematical ∝ sign sometimes used for infinity, which spells *O*C. According to Webster's dictionary 'Oc' is the root for 'octo' or 8 and the ocular eye. A related Egyptian word *Ak*, means 'light'. The French Cathars believed the Language of *Oc* (Language of Light) gave enlightenment and that is why the named their home *Languedoc*. These symbols suggest a continuous transmission of knowledge, relating to the secrets of light [10]. So in the same tradition, a person who is known as a "Phoenix", is a teller of the secrets of light.

However, Dubro considered gaining this attention from scientists to be highly encouraging. As a testament to the effectiveness of the EMF Balancing Technique® there is now a growing network practitioners across the world. The following concepts represent some of the core teaching of Dubro, see figure 8.2 as a reference for the following UCL descriptions. Peggy Phoenix Dubro writes:

❖ "The UCL functions similarly to an electrical transformer, transferring energy from one circuit to another. This is why we refer to this process as the "rewiring for the new energy." It allows us to receive and use the energy we are learning to release from the Cosmic Lattice through our intent."

❖ "Though the basic pattern of the UCL is the same for all of us, the calibration (meaning to gauge or strengthen) is uniquely personal. It is determined by the mathematical relationship between each person's vibrational frequency and the Cosmic Lattice. The calibration of the fibers of the energy anatomy is quite complex, and this is where the role of INTENT is so important. The basic intent of an EMF Balancing Technique® energy session is to balance the human electromagnetic field, allowing the individual's energy to open as many circuits as possible to the Cosmic Lattice."

❖ "Note in the illustration the column of pure light that runs straight down through the center of the body. Here, in your center, is found the unification of the chakra system in progress. This is the core energy, the open circuit of the UCL that connects us to Unlimited Source. The greater the flow of energy here, the greater the release of spiritual knowledge within. The more present you are in the now, the greater the electrical charge you carry. The electrical charge of your history and the charge of your future potential all feed into the now."

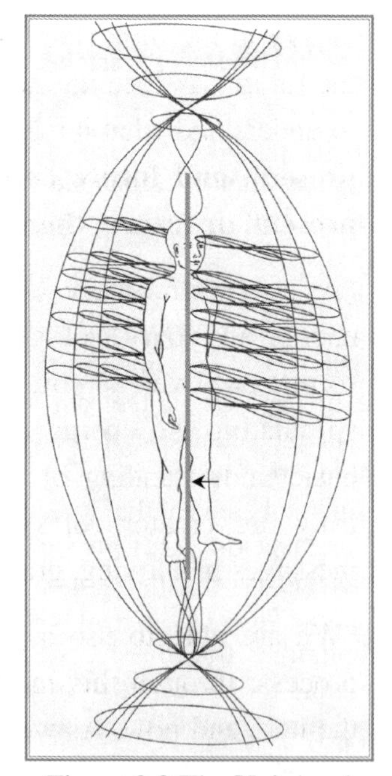

Figure 8.2 The Universal Calibration Lattice

❖ "Fibers of light and energy radiate horizontally from the chakras. These fibers form figure eight shaped loops that feed into long vertical fibers of energy that surround and permeate our energy anatomy. This is the framework that forms the UCL. The figure-eight fibers radiate from the chakras and connect us to Core energy. These are the self-balancing loops of the UCL. They form the infinity symbol, representing the infinite connection between you and Creator."

- "As an EMF session progresses, a rewiring of the individual's energy field occurs, and a new order is created within the field, producing a stronger structure to receive energy from the Unlimited Source (the Cosmic Lattice). After the connections have been made, we often see a dramatic increase in the co-creating process of life. The determining factor is soul's growth. The process of balancing the electromagnetic field can lead to spontaneous release, even without insight. With this strong foundation, we raise our own vibrational level, which in turn raises the Earth's vibrational level. This is how we can personally achieve what many think of as Ascension."

- "As I work with the energy patterns over and over, I realize that I have the awesome privilege of occupying a front row seat to view the evolution of the light body. The information presented here about the UCL results from working with thousands of people, individually and in groups."

- "As you study the illustration of the UCL once again, notice how the energy from behind (the past) connects and feeds information to the energy in the center (the present). This core energy connects and feeds information to the energy in the front (the future). The channels are open in both directions, so the future can feed into the present and even back to the past. Here, we begin to understand what it means to live in circular time. **This connection of past, present, and future creates the eternal NOW. There really is no past, present, or future; there is only the NOW.** This information is not new."

- "As you exercise the UCL, you strengthen your capacity to hold the new energy in your Biology. This in turn helps the UCL to reach its full formation. Even as you read these words and study the illustration; you are stimulating the energy of the Lattice within your being. When we gain a basic understanding of how this "message system" works, we realize we truly are creators of our own reality. By sending out stronger, clearer messages in a loving, gracious way, we create a stronger, clearer reality."

- "We are able to use a horizontal energy pattern to power the co-creative process; through this mechanism, we have brought co-creating energy into the here and now. As we reach our full potential, physiological changes will occur. Our hormones will secrete differently. This will have a chemical reaction upon our brains and bodies, which, in turn, will prepare us for

Ascension and to live in a new age and a new reality. Once the energy is coursing through our whole field - through the energy body - it will affect the physical body through these hormonal and chemical changes. Eventually, the body will be able to heal and regenerate itself over and over again with astonishing speed. Moreover, our learning processes will change as we learn in dramatic new ways by knowing how to connect to the collective consciousness to obtain information." [End of excerpts] [11]

Scientific validation of the existence of the human energy field has been proven by many scientists over decades of research. However, scientific trials specific to *Energy Balancing* have also been carried out. Researchers from the Kennedy Krieger Institute say they are the first in the United States of America to scientifically study the efficacy of energy therapy on children with developmental disabilities [12]. These trials were conducted with the famous U.S. healer Rosalyn Bruyere, who is noted for participating in studies with scientists over decades. Since this announcement in June 2003, positive results led nurses, therapists and doctors at the Kennedy Krieger Institute, to undergo training with Bruyere on how to energy balance.

The Diamonds in Your Energy Field

We have diamond-shaped energy structures in our energy field and they exist as one of the many layers of light. These diamond energy field looks like two four-sided pyramids joined at the base, forming the geometric shape known as an octahedron. They display the same fractal geometry seen at the macro scale in the universe, hence existing as diamonds within diamonds. The mystic Peggy Dubro describes the diamonds as "Templates of Light" and states, "Everyone has his or own sacred templates of light and energy. In seeking to know ourselves, we begin to activate or give life to these templates, causing them to vibrate in a unique way". Plate 28 shows four diamonds activated within one large diamond, but there are many more. The founder of the Diamond Light Grid Activation, Julie Umpleby states:

- "The vehicle for connecting with and accessing the Universal Grid is your Diamond Light Grid, which is a lattice-work of etheric energy fibres that provide the transport mechanism for electrical energy transfer between you and the universal web. The Diamond Light Grid is so called, because in it's perfect state it has a three dimensional octahedron shape, one of the sacred geometries understood by mystics."

- ♦ "The Diamond Light Grid is part of our development to accommodate much higher frequencies of energy, activating new energy templates and helping to restore inter-dimensional communication."
- ♦ "The Diamond Light Grid is a holographic projection directly from your DNA, which carries the blueprint of your divine nature and purpose in your inherent state of perfection. When we work with the grid, we are therefore working directly with our DNA."

The spiritual alchemy inherent in The Diamond Light Grid Activation means it is the most advanced, scientifically verifiable and most in-line procedure with older esoteric knowledge. The Diamond Light Grid Activation converts the diamond light body into a tunable electric circuit board, directly linked to our DNA. A fully activated diamond light grid is essential to permit the reception of new light codes that will ensure that we successfully evolve according to universal design. For the esoterically astute, this means we now have full access to the game board of life. This new understanding gives us deeper metaphysical insight into why we must fully activate the diamond light energy field at this critical time in the evolution of mankind. Here are some quotes from Barbara Marciniak's book, *Path of Empowerment – Pleiadian Wisdom For A World In Chaos:*

- ⌘ "The codes and patterns offer instructions that the cells can use to maintain the body at a higher level of awareness, so that you can adapt to the great social and environmental changes that characterize these times."
- ⌘ "Your genes are programmed to respond to stimuli, and with the new codes streaming through the body, the DNA can be played like an electronic circuit board, with the various signals decoded and translated on a subatomic level."
- ⌘ "The checkerboard is a symbol that has captured the ultimate complexity of the field of existence in a design that is layered with symbolic meaning."
- ⌘ "The sixty-four squares ...form an eight-sided design on a two-dimensional surface in third-dimensional reality, a metaphor for revealing the essence of cosmic law and the basic instructions for building energy in any reality ...The alternating pattern of black-and-white symbols triggered the mind to remember the higher cosmic and spiritual laws for working with energy."
- ⌘ "Perhaps you are wondering how you can learn to play on the game board, working your way up to multi-dimensional chess. The game is about managing energy in every aspect of the cosmos. It is a game of awareness,

and the board represents the field of existence ...it's presence announces and reminds you, on very deep levels of consciousness, that you are playing the field." [End of excerpts] [13]

There are now many metaphysical messages encouraging those who are interested in their evolutionary progression. The following is an excerpt from the internationally respected channel Ronna Herman.

> "The Earth and humanity are becoming multidimensional Bearers of Light as the radiance from the Supreme Creator and our Mother/Father God permeate the solar system and the Earth via the Great Central Sun of the Milky Way Galaxy. The Crystalline Grid system bears the encodings and the Divine Schematic for your return to multi-dimensionality, as well as the Divine Blueprint for the future of the Earth and humanity."

> "During these swiftly changing times, you will find the energy patterns of your new multi-dimensional nature fluctuating at a wide range of frequencics, for the Crystalline Grid system is programmed with the highest vibrational patterns that people in each area can incorporate and anchor to the Earth and themselves. It is a two-fold process: the Grid system will affect humanity through its advanced encodings for the future, and humanity will affect the Grid System as each person anchors the Living Light from the Celestial Cities of Light." [14]

The internationally respected channel Celia Fenn has also provided important messages with regard to our relationship to the updated Earth Grid.

> "At this time, dearest Lightworkers, many will choose to activate their Infinity Codes, and will step fully into their Diamond Solar Light Bodies. At this time, they will know themselves to be "Diamond Light", Infinite and Eternal and yet existing within Human form as Divine Human or Human Angel. And, dear Lightworkers, as you make this physical transition, you will activate a radiant burst of cosmic light in every cell in your body that will transform your very being on a deep level. And, you will be the way showers who will point the way forward to the next step in the evolution of Humanity." [15]

The diamond geometry is the perfect receiver and transmitter of electromagnetic signals, thus in this time of electromagnetic chaos, it is imperative that we only pick up the most beneficial electromagnetic signals to re-code our DNA. So, as our DNA alters rapidly, we now have the energetic tools to help us radically transmute ourselves at the subatomic level and fully embody our divine and multidimensional nature.

The existence of diamond shaped energetic structures in our energy fields was part of the "underground stream" of knowledge held in esoteric organizations and passed on to initiates. Thus, we find that the Irish poet William Butler Yeats (1865-1939), with his wife George, devised an esoteric system, which he expounded upon in various books. This teaching was based on the adventures of fictional characters and in his books, most notably *A Vision* (1925) that was completely revised in 1937, Yeats described the "spiritual constituents of the human being" as being composed of gyres (or vortices) and geometry [16]. The large diamond surrounding the body represented "the original Principle of the Celestial Body, within which the Spirit moves as a single gyre". The spiritual evolution of the soul was outlined as "Principals" and the geometry of gyres or vortices attempted to represent a four-dimensional system, in constant movement.

Elsewhere, these energetic structures have been called Holons [17]. The Hungarian author and philosopher Arthur Koestler proposed the word "Holon" to describe a basic unit of organization in biological and social systems [18]. Another description, defines a holon as 'one part within a larger whole that is itself also a whole containing smaller parts', a self-organizing phenomenon observed in all areas of life.

These diamonds are part of human consciousness and so they can be used in the mind or imagination to compel energy to flow in specific ways. This is particularly important with the volatile nature of Earth changes and the subsequent effects on our psyche. Therefore, in a simple process, we can imagine ourselves inside a diamond to help stabilize internal energy, especially our emotions. This is a two step process, as outlined below:

1. Imagine yourself inside a huge octahedron (2 pyramids base to base) with the center at your pelvic region.
2. Imagine feelings of safety and comfort.

This is a short and simple meditation to practice so that eventually, it would just take thinking of the diamond to create the feelings of peace. The diamond will compel subtle energies within to create a state of balance. This method is considered NOT the best way to spiritually evolve, but it is still an effective energetic tool to help us through difficult times ahead.

Today, there are powerful new ways to work with consciousness. Yet, there are metaphysical teachings that have been around for decades, given to us by the highly regarded mystic Jane Roberts that now can be more fully understood. The understanding of electromagnetic energy units (EEs) and consciousness units (CUs) which create our reality, can now being applied in a practical manner.

Creating Your Reality, It's Electromagnetic: Seth Revisited

Between 1963 and 1984, the mystic Jane Roberts, delivered discourses which have appeared in the twenty-three volumes that comprise *The Seth Material.* The Seth books have sold over 8 million copies and are the only metaphysical literature to be archived in the prestigious Yale University Sterling Memorial Library in New Haven, Connecticut. When Jane Roberts died in 1984, her papers where donated to Yale and they became the second most visited collection, which attests to the quality and significance [19]. Numerous scholars and lay folk alike, refer to *The Seth Material* as one of the top sources of metaphysical information and scientists have found parallels to the Seth view of reality, after extensive study of both paranormal phenomena and quantum physics [20]. The Seth philosophy is said to echo aspects of eastern mysticism, modern physics, and New Age concepts, though it is structured in a format that is unique to Jane Roberts. The metaphysical term 'You Create Your Own Reality' is the most famous Seth quote.

Our focus here is that *The Seth Material* reveals the existence of electromagnetic energy units (EEs), which we use to create reality. On some analysis, we will learn that the EE units are indeed the same as the disks of light described by Peggy Phoenix Dubro. The Seth teaching provides exact detail of the nature of this particular energetic charge, that makes-up the layer of light called the Universal Calibration Lattice and it's importance to creating our reality. Here are details about the disks of light from Dubro:

- ❖ "Your history – your hereditary patterns, past-life records, and all the events you have experienced in this lifetime – are recorded within the long informational fibers located behind you. **These records look like tiny disks of light; they hold the information in place electromagnetically. When an excess energy charge surrounds one of these disks, it will often manifest as a reality that repeats over and over in what we call present time**. If that reality is one we desire, that's good. But too often our "energy history" creates a repetitive pattern that becomes an anchor of negativity that holds us back from forward growth. As we balance the energy charges within the long fibers behind us, our intent is to transmute the "energy history", or the "past", into a column of golden wisdom and support. We gently release the excess "negative" energy, now freed to be used in more beneficial ways as we co-create our reality in the NOW."
- ❖ "The ability to **rearrange these energy charges** creates an opportunity for release, often known as karmic release, from restrictions of the past."

- "In effect we reclaim the energy we have overly devoted to our history, particularly **to highly charged emotional attachments to past events**."
- "In some cases **we are able to neutralize the electrical charges** of genetic, physical and psychological patterns that are no longer helpful to us. As you strengthen and balance your Personal Empowerment Prism, you may spontaneously release a condition if you no longer need to experience that pattern as part of your evolution."
- "The light strands in front of the human energy field comprise the field of potential possibilities. In linear time, we call this the future. Here, we place our hopes and dreams and wishes. We also place our fear-filled and worry-filled events in this portion of the UCL. **The light disks contained in these long informational fibers function like transmitters, attracting "like" energy."**
- "Many traditional therapeutic approaches do not reach deep enough into our energetic anatomy to bring about a balancing and **releasing of old unwanted energy patterns**. Some therapies do bring about beneficial changes, but only after lengthy processes**. It is far more beneficial to work directly with this energy….**"
- "The figure-eight fibers that radiate from the chakras and connect us to Core energy. These are the self-balancing loops of the UCL. They form the infinity symbol, representing the infinite connection between you and Creator. **I observed these light fibers feeding information back into the human biology from the universe.** When I saw the biology sending information back out through the figure-eight loops, I realized we had taken a sizable evolutionary leap with the activation of this part of the energy anatomy. Here is the means of bringing co-creation into the here and now. **The returning wave of energy from the universe brings with it experiences that shape your future reality."** *[Bold added for emphasis, end of excerpts]* [21]

The Seth Material on EE Units

Electromagnetic energy units (EEs) were first introduced in the book *The Seth Material* (1970), which was the first of the Seth books to be published. Jane Roberts attributed all the information to a personality called Seth and this is how the material is structured and referred to for ease of understanding. The information on EEs was given in response to a question by Jane's partner. Rob

Butts queried the statement "that all ESP perceptions have an electromagnetic basis". Jane wrote:

> "The sessions on the electromagnetic units that lie just beneath the range of matter have begun just now as I finish this book. Scientists have long wondered what physical matter "disappeared into", and Seth's EE units may well be the answer."

There were references to EE units in the first four Seth books, so they were rather important to the Seth philosophy. *The Seth Material* stresses the connection of EE units to emotional energy and scientific research provides support to these claims. David Wilcock writes:

> "The Seth Material basically helps us to understand how the basic spherical units of energy in the Cosmos interact with each other. It took us several years to actually match up all of this information with scientific data, but now as we conclude the three volumes of the series [The Convergence Series], we have found some degree of proof for almost every point that Seth had made back in 1969."

The following quotes, mostly from the book, *The Seth Material,* detail the importance of the EE units/disks of light are to how we create our reality.

SESSION 504, SEPTEMBER 29, 1969, 9:17 P.M. MONDAY

❑ **SETH:** There are electromagnetic structures, so to speak, that are presently beyond your (scientific) instruments, units that are the basic carriers of perception. They have a very brief "life" in your terms. Their size varies. Several units may combine, for example; many units may combine. To put this as simply as possible, it is not so much that they move through space, as that they use space to move through. There is a difference. [504.1]

❑ In a manner of speaking, thermal qualities are involved, and also laws of attraction and repulsion. The units charge the air through which they pass, and draw to them other units. The units are not stationary in the way that, say, a cell is stationary within the body. Even a cell only appears stationary. These units have no "home". They are built up in response to emotional intensity. [504.2]

❑ They are one form that emotional energy takes. They follow their own rules of attraction and repulsion. As a magnet, you see, will attract with its filaments, so these units attract their own kind and form patterns, which then appear to you as perception. [504.3]

- ❑ Now: the foetus utilizes these units. So does any consciousness, including that of a plant. Cells are not just responsive to light because this is the order of things, but because an emotional desire to perceive light is present. [504.4]
- ❑ The desire appears on this other level in the form of these electromagnetic units, which then cause a light sensitivity. These units are freewheeling. They can be used in normal perception or what you call extrasensory perception. I will discuss their basic nature at a later session, and I would like to tie this in with the foetus, since the foetus is highly involved with perceptive mechanisms. [504.5]
- ❑ It is not that you cannot devise instruments to perceive these units. Your scientists are simply asking the wrong questions, and do not think in terms of such freewheeling structures. [504.6]

Comments on Section 504

- ⌘ [504.1] This hints at the property of light behaving like a wave, but a wave would requires a medium to propagate through e.g. sound waves require air. In 1969, the prevailing view was that light traveled through a true vacuum but, now we realize that the so-called vacuum is a plenum of electromagnetic energy, thus, Seth was correct in talking about electromagnetic structures *using* space to move through [21].
- ⌘ [504.2] Seth says that thermal qualities are involved. The author can personally testify to the thermal properties of these units. As an energy practitioner with high sensitivity, energy can be detected in the form of heat associated with the centers above the head and below the feet. With people with strong energetic connections, this sensation can be described as 'a ball of fire'.
- ⌘ [504.3] Seth is saying that everything we perceive is some form of pattern built up from these electromagnetic units.
- ⌘ [504.4] The idea of an "emotional desire to perceive light" relates to the work of Garaiev and Poponin and the "DNA Phantom Effect". They found that a DNA molecule can be inserted in a cylinder with light passing through it, and the DNA will actually attract the light and cause it to spiral along with it! Furthermore, when the DNA is removed, the light continues to spiral as if the DNA were still there. This has puzzled scientists but Seth's views helps us to

understand it; the DNA has an "emotional desire to perceive light," as it naturally attracts light into itself. This might not seem feasible until we realize that all life and matter has some degree of consciousness, since it is made of "intelligent energy" [21].

⌘ [504.6] Seth stated that we could design instruments that would be able to perceive these units. There are now many torsion-field detectors (to be discussed in the next chapter) which can detect these not ordinary electromagnetic type fields. So, the latest research shows that since the time when Seth gave these readings in 1969, some scientists are now asking the "right questions."

SESSION 505, OCTOBER 13, 1969, 9:34 P.M. MONDAY

❑ **SETH:** These units of which we spoke earlier are basically animations rising from consciousness. I am speaking now of the consciousness within each physical particle regardless of its size; of molecular consciousness, cellular consciousness, as well as the larger gestalts of consciousness with which you are usually familiar. [505.1]

❑ These emanations rise as naturally as breath, and there are other comparisons that can be made, in that there is a coming in and a going out, and transformation within the unit, as what is taken into the lungs, for example, is not the same thing that leaves on the exhale stroke. You could compare these units, simply for an analogy, to the invisible breath of consciousness. This analogy will not carry us far, but it will be enough initially to get the idea across. Breath is, of course, also a pulsation, and these units operate in a pulsating manner. They are emitted by the cells, for example, in plants, animals, rocks, and so forth. They would have color if you were able to perceive them physically. [505.2]

❑ They are electromagnetic, in your terms, following their own patterns of positive and negative charge, and following also certain laws of magnetism. In this instance, like definitely attracts like. The emanations are actually emotional tones. The varieties of tones, for all intents and purposes, are infinite. [505..3]

❑ The units are just beneath the range of physical matter. None are identical. However, there is a structure to them. This structure is beyond the range of electromagnetic qualities as your scientists think of them. Consciousness actually produces these emanations, and they are the basis for any kind of perception, both sensory in usual terms and extrasensory. [505.4]

- These emanations can also appear as sounds, and you will be able to translate them into sounds long before your scientists discover their basic meaning. One of the reasons why they have not been discovered is precisely because they are so cleverly camouflaged within all structures. Being just beyond the range of matter, having a structure but a nonphysical one, and being of a pulsating nature, they can expand or contract. They can completely envelop, for example, a small cell, or retreat to the nucleus within. They combine qualities of a unit and a field, in other words. [505.5]

- There is another reason why they remain a secret from Western scientists. Intensity governs not only their activity and size, but the relative strength of their magnetic nature. They will draw other such units to them, for example, according to the intensity of the emotional tone of the particular consciousness at any given "point". [505.6]

- These units then obviously change constantly. If we must speak in terms of size, then they change in size constantly as they expand and contract. Theoretically there is no limit, you see, to their rate of contraction or expansion. They are also absorbent. They do give off thermal qualities, and these are the only hint that your scientists have received of them so far. [505.7]

- Their characteristics draw them toward constant interchange. Clumps of them (Jane gestured – her delivery was quite emphatic and animated) will be drawn together, literally sealed, only to drop away and disperse once more. They form – and their nature is behind – what is commonly known as air, and they use this to move through. The air, in other words, can be said to be formed by animations of these units. [505.8]

Comments on Section 505

⌘ [505.4] Russian research into torsion fields has validated Seth's statements here, as these fields are indeed non-electromagnetic in a conventional sense.

⌘ [505.5] It is interesting that Seth says that these emanations can also appear as sounds. Some energy practitioners and clients say they can 'hear' energy adjustments taking place in the electromagnetic field during energy sessions.

SESSION 506, OCTOBER 27, 1969, 9:40 P.M. MONDAY

- **SETH:** The units about which I have been speaking do not have any specific, regular, preordained "life". They will not seem to follow many scientific principles. Since **they are the intuitive force just beyond the range of matter**, upon which matter is formed, they will not follow the laws of matter, although at times they may mimic the laws of matter. [506.1]

- **It is almost impossible to detect an individual unit**, for in its dance of activity it constantly becomes a part of other such units, expanding and contracting, pulsating and changing in intensity, in force, and *changing* polarity. This last is extremely important. [506.2]

- This is rather difficult to explain, but it would be as if the positions of your north and south poles changed constantly while maintaining the same relative distance from each other, and by their change in polarity upsetting the stability (pause) of the planet – except that because of the greater comparative strength at the poles of the units (gestures, attempts to draw diagrams in the air), a newer stability is almost immediately achieved after each shifting. [506.3]

- **The shifting of polarity occurs in rhythm with changing emotional intensities, or emotional energies**, if you prefer. **The "initial" originating emotional energy that sets any given unit into motion, and forms it, then causes the unit to become a highly charged electromagnetic field** with those characteristics of changing polarities just mentioned. The changing polarities are also caused by attraction and repulsion from other like units which may be attached or detached. There is a rhythm that underlies all of this changing polarity and changing intensities that occur constantly. But the rhythms have to do with the nature of emotional energy itself, and not with the laws of matter. [506.4]

- **Without an understanding of these rhythms, the activity of the units would appear haphazard, chaotic**, and there would seem to be nothing to hold the units together. Indeed, they seem to be flying apart at tremendous speeds. The "nucleus" – now using a cell analogy – if these units were cells, which they are not, then it would be as if the nucleus were constantly changing position, flying off in all directions, dragging the rest of the cell along with it. [506.5]

- The units obviously are *within* the reality of all cells. Now: the initiation point is the basic part of the unit, as the nucleus is the important part of the cell. Now: The initiation point is the originating, unique, individual, and **specific emotional energy that forms any given unit**. It becomes the entryway into physical matter. [506.6]

- Now these intensities of emotional energy, forming the units, end up by transforming all available space into what they are. Certain intensities and certain positions of polarity between and among the units and great groupings of the units compress energy into solid form (resulting in matter). The emotional energy within the units is obviously the motivating factor, and you can see, then, why emotional energy can indeed shatter a physical object. [506.7]
- Now the intensity of the original emotional energy controls the activity, strength, stability, and relative size of the unit; the rate of its pulsation, and its power to attract and repel other units, as well as its ability to combine with other units. [506.8]
- The behavior of these units changes in the following manner. When a unit is in the act of combining with another, it aligns its components in a characteristic way. When it is separating itself from other units, it will align its components in a different way. The polarities change in each case, within the units. The unit will alter its polarities within itself, adapting the polarity-design of the unit to which it is being attracted; and it will change its polarity away from that design on breaking contact. [506.9]
- Its **intensity, however, can vary to amazing degrees**, so that it could, relatively speaking, be too weak or fall back, not strong enough to form the basis for matter, but to project into another system, perhaps, where less intensity is required for "materialization". [506.10]
- The units so charged with intensive emotional energy formed patterns for matter that retained their strength. Now these units, while appearing within your system, may also have a reality outside it, propelling the emotional energy units through the world of matter entirely. **These units, as I told you, are indestructible. They can, however, lose or gain power**, fall back into intensities beneath matter, or go through matter, appearing as matter as they do so and projecting through your system. [506.11]

Comments on Session 506

⌘ [506.1] Neuroscientist Candace Pert has made this observation after decades of scientific investigation and Seth has provided the exact mechanism for how emotional information moves into the physical realm and creates matter.

⌘ [506.6] Seth discusses "The initiation point" and how emotional intensity forms any given unit and becomes the entryway into physical matter. This agrees with research that attempts to explain the importance of emotion and intent. Scientific research now identifies the interrelation of consciousness and emotion, and attempts to recast the distinction between rational and emotional people in the light of neurodynamics [23].

⌘ [506.7] Seth suggests an understanding of the phenomenon of telekinesis, and the origin of psychokinesis. The documented cases of people with enormous emotional stress causing a change in matter or the movement of objects is an example of the instant manifestation of these electromagnetic energy units. Russian research with the famous psychic Ninel Kulagina also confirms the importance of emotional intensity [21]. Again, we will also discuss in the next chapter, Russian research on how psychics use torsion fields to change matter.

⌘ [506.8] Here Seth is emphasizing again how powerful emotions influence the build up of these units.

⌘ [506.10] Seth points out that the large variation in intensity occurs and this is a very important focus of energy balancing. We know that excess electromagnetic charge is associated with traumatic experiences and this can be significantly changed with energy balancing techniques that disperse the charge and prevent old memories having enough energy to keep affecting the NOW.

⌘ [506.5], [506.11] Dubro says that the electromagnetic charges move in circular patterns within the infinity loops and that the charges are not removed they are just redistributed to create balance.

SESSION 509, NOVEMBER 24, 1969, 9:10 P.M. MONDAY

❑ Today Jane had been reading Experimental Psychology by C. G. Jung, first American edition, published by Jung's heirs in 1968. [509.1]

❑ **SETH:** There is one large point, underestimated by all of your psychologists when they list the attributes or characteristics of consciousness. I am going to tie in this material with our discussion on our electromagnetic energy units, as there is a connection. [509.2]

- Let us start with Jung. He presumes that consciousness must be organized about an ego structure. And what he calls the unconsciousness not so egotistically organized, he, therefore, considers without consciousness–without consciousness of self. He makes a good point, saying that the normal ego cannot know unconscious material directly. He does not realize, however, nor your other psychologists, what I told you often–that there is an inner ego it is this inner ego that organizes what Jung would call unconscious material. [509.3]

- Now: the inner ego is the organizer of experience that Jung called unconscious. The inner ego is another term for the inner self. As the outer ego manipulates within the physical environment, so the inner ego or self organizes and manipulates with an inner reality. The inner ego creates that physical environment, with which the outer ego then deals. [509.4]

- It is this inner self, out of massive knowledge and the unlimited scope of its consciousness, that forms the physical world and provides stimuli to keep the outer ego constantly at the job of awareness. It is the inner self, here termed the inner ego, that organizes, initiates, projects, and controls the EE (electromagnetic energy) units of which we have been speaking, transforming energy into objects, into matter. [509.5]

- The energy of this inner self is used by it to form from itself – from inner experience – a material counterpart in which the outer ego then can act out its role. The outer ego then acts out a play that the inner self has written. This is not to say that the outer ego is a puppet. It is to say that the outer ego is far less conscious than the inner ego, that its perception is less, that it is far less stable though it makes great pretense of stability, that it springs from the inner self and is therefore less, rather than more, aware. [509.6]

- The outer ego is spoon-fed, being given only those feelings and emotions, only that data, that it can handle. This data is presented to it in a highly specialized manner, usually in terms of information picked up by the physical senses. [509.7]

- The inner self or ego is not only conscious, but conscious of itself, both as an individuality apart from others and as an individuality that is a part of all other consciousness. In your terms, it is continually aware, both of this apartness and unity-with. The outer ego is not continuously aware of anything. It frequently forgets itself. When it becomes swept up in a strong emotion it seems to lose itself; there is unity, then, but no sense of apartness. When it most vigorously maintains its sense of individuality, it is no longer aware of unity-with. [509.8]

- The inner ego is always aware of both aspects and is organized about its primary aspect, which is creativity. It constantly translates the components of its gestalt into reality – either physical reality through the EE units I have mentioned, or into other realities equally as valid. [509.9]

- Now: the EE (electromagnetic energy) units are the forms that basic experience takes when directed by this inner self. These, then, form physical objects, physical matter. Matter, in other words, is the shape that basic experience takes when it intrudes into three-dimensional systems. Matter is the shape of your dreams. Your dreams, thoughts, and emotions are literally transformed into physical matter purposefully by this inner self. [509.10]

- The individual inner self, then, through constant massive effort of great creative intensity, co-operates with all other inner selves to form and maintain the physical reality that you know, so that physical reality is an offshoot or by-product of the highly conscious inner self. [509.11]

- The powers of consciousness are clearly not understood, then. Each individual has his part to play in projecting these EE units into physical actuality. Therefore, physical matter can be legitimately described as an extension of the self, as much as the physical body is a projection of the inner self. [509.12]

- It is obvious that the body grows up about the inner self, and that trees grow out of the ground, whereas buildings do not spring up like flowers of their own accord; so the inner self has various methods of creation and uses the EE units in different ways, as you shall see as we continue with the discussion. [509.13]

- Having determined upon physical reality as a dimension in which it will express itself, the inner self, first of all, takes care to form and maintain the physical basis upon which all else must depend; the properties of earth that can be called natural ones. The inner self has a vast and infinite reservoir from which to draw knowledge and experience. All kinds of choices are available, and the diversity of physical matter is a reflection of this deep source of variety. [509.14]

- ❑ We will shortly end the session. Suffice it to say, however, that in the future what I am telling you will be more generally known. Men will become familiar to some extent with their own inner identity, with other forms of their own consciousness. [509.15]

- ❑ Throughout the ages, some have recognized the fact that there is self-consciousness and purpose in certain dream and sleep states, and have maintained, even in waking life, the sense of continuity of this inner self. To such people it is no longer possible to identify completely with the ego consciousness. They are too obviously aware of themselves as more. When such knowledge is gained, the ego can accept it, for it finds to its surprise that it is not less conscious, but more, that its limitations are dissipated. [509.16]

- ❑ Now: it is not true – and I emphasize this strongly – that so-called unconscious material, given any freedom, will draw energy away from the egotistically organized self in a normal personality. Quite the contrary, the ego is replenished and rather directly. It is the fear that the "unconscious" is chaotic that causes psychologists to make such statements. There is also something in the nature of those who practice psychology: a fascination, in many cases, already predisposed to fear the "unconscious" in direct proportion to its attraction for them. [509.17]

- ❑ The ego maintains its stability, its seeming stability, and its health, from the constant subconscious and unconscious nourishment which it receives. Too much nourishment will not kill it. Do you follow me here? [509.18]

- ❑ Only when such nourishment is for some reason cut off to a considerable degree is the ego threatened by starvation. We will have more to say concerning the ego's relationship with the "unconscious." In a healthy personality, the inner self easily projects all experience into EE units, where they are translated into actuality. Physical matter, therefore, acts as a feedback. [509.19]

Comments on Session 509

⌘ [509.1] Seth goes into a discussion about Jung's definitions of the different levels of consciousness, compared to his own definitions. Jung did not ascribe the degree of significance to the subconscious that Seth does here.

- ⌘ [509.11] Here is a reference to the "holographic universe" theory before it became well known and accepted in scientific circles [19].

- ⌘ [509.12] Wilcock writes, "It is also easy to see here that the more densely populated an area is, the greater amount of torsion-field charge there can be on the physical objects built there. This is one reason why cities can be extremely damaging to the psychic work process. They will often have a great deal of stored energy, which can be predominantly chaotic and negative due to the hardships and crowding faced by many people. These chaotic emotions translate directly into energy that enters into the structures" [21].

- ⌘ [509.15] This comment by Seth is intriguing. Could this be a reference to the fact that we now have access to other forms of our own consciousness, including what we identify as the Universal Calibration Lattice?

- ⌘ [509.17] Interestingly, Seth directly addresses psychologists by pointing out the fear of the unconscious and providing the reassurance that working with electromagnetic units will strengthen and not weaken the outer ego.

- ⌘ [509.19] This has been the teaching by spiritual teachers over the ages. Our physical world acts as a feedback mechanism.

After the introduction of electromagnetic energy units, Seth introduces the term consciousness units (CUs), which he then starts to use interchangeably in the next three Seth books [25]. Session 789, from the book *The Nature of the Psyche: The Human Expression*, will put to rest any doubt that the disks of light and the EEs are the same.

SESSION 789, SEPTEMBER 27, 1976, 9:30 P.M. MONDAY

- ❑ The EE units which I have mentioned in other materials are important because they exist in an electromagnetic sphere of activity, and they trigger certain responses in the brain and nervous system. Events themselves involve a steady condition of highly related fields of activity, however, that exist between the EE units, so to speak. [789.1]

- ❑ These fields involve psychological reactions, not physically perceivable, and yet as explosive in their way as a nuclear detonation. That is, these psychological activities "explode" in physical events by virtue of a transformation and a charge that allows purely mental acts to "break the time-space barrier" and emerge as realities in a physical world. In a way, the EE units occur on the furthest reaches of this activity. If an event were a physical craft such as a spaceship the EE units would allow it to land in your world, but would not be the original propellants. Those propellants are psychic fields of interrelationship. [789.2]

- Let us use an analogy. Pretend that you are a planet, as indeed in certain terms you are. You exist in a highly complicated and sophisticated universe. You know that space is filled with all kinds of inhabitants, and we compare these space inhabitants to probable events. As a planet you have certain characteristics. Some space inhabitants would not be able to land under those conditions at all. The conditions represent your own psychological individuality. You send out messages to the stars because you are lonely, and events or visitors are one of your main methods of gaining experience and knowledge. To land their own rocket ships, space travellers must enter your atmosphere and use its conditions while maintaining their own integrity. They must also have their own reasons for such a visit. [789.3]

- Now any physical event is something like the impact of a rocket ship entering your world from "somewhere else." Thoughts often seem to swim in and out of your system of consciousness and you barely notice. Events often appear and disappear in the same manner, yet they have impressed your reality. You have attracted them to one extent or another, and they have been attracted to you. Momentarily a field of relatedness is set up that is highly charged, one that provides an inner path by which probable events can flow into your area of recognized events. [789.4]

- This path exists on psychological levels, and triggers your perceptive mechanisms, which then of course react and dutifully perceive. **Your intent and purpose or belief is one of the main attractions. These serve as beams searching the universe,** but the conditions of manifestation also exist. There must be a proper fit. [789.5]

Comments on Section 789

⌘ Understanding the Seth teaching about the Electromagnetic Energy units acting as 'beams searching the universe' is crucial if we want to consciously create our reality, as it directly relates to the concept of *Signal Power*. We have the ability to send out stronger signals, when we work to balance our energy fields and then specifically empower certain intents at will. In closing, energy balancing will enable us to work specifically with these EE units as identified by Seth over 35 years ago. There is now clear teaching and procedures available that allow us to work with this energetic charge, providing us with an effective way to deal with karma and create our reality.

Resolving our Karma in the Way of the Masters

The Seth Material states that the electromagnetic energy units are the "breath of consciousness" and this has to be understood, as the aetheric energy that underlies the whole of our reality, as scientists now admit. We have compared Seth's EE units with "disks of light", but traditionally, this has been the realm of the Masters, where Yogis and adepts have worked at the level of karma and consciousness to help souls evolve. Hence, we can continue to compare the descriptions of consciousness with that given by Masters in the past. Here is a selection of the more traditional view of consciousness.

♦ *Lifetrons*

In the book, *Autobiography of a Yogi*, the famous Hindu author Paramahansa Yogananda explains how the yogi, Gandha Baba, was able to manifest objects out of thin air [26]. Yogananda writes that he understood by inner realizations how this was achieved and he makes the following explanation:

> "The different sensory stimuli to which man reacts tactual, visual, gustatory, auditory, and olfactory—are produced by vibratory variations in electrons and protons. **The vibrations in turn are regulated by *prana* "lifetrons," subtle life forces or finer-than-atomic energies intelligently charged with five distinct sensory idea-substance."**
>
> "Gandha Baba, attuning himself with the pranic force by certain yoga practices, was able to guide the lifetrons to rearrange their vibratory structure and to objectify the desired result. His perfume, fruit, and other miracles were actual materializations of mundane vibrations, and were not the inner sensations hypnotically produced."

Yogananda provides further details about these lifetrons, which were passed on to him as the teachings of his Master Sri Yukteswar .

> "You have read in the scriptures that God encased the human soul in successively in three bodies—the idea, or causal, body; the subtle astral body, seat of man's mental and emotional natures; and the gross physical body. On earth a man is equipped with his physical senses. **An astral being works with his consciousness and feelings and a body made of lifetrons."**

Yogananda in the page notes, then tells us:

> "The Hindu scriptures refer not only to the *anu*, "atom" and to the *paramanu*, "beyond the atom", finer electronic energies, but also to prana,

> "creative lifetronic force". Atoms and electrons are blind forces; prana is inherently intelligent. **The pranic lifetrons in the spermatoza and ova, for instance, guide the development of the embryo according to Karmic design."** *[Bold added for emphasis]*

♦ ***Anu***

Two extraordinary personalities Annie Besant and Charles W. Leadbeater conducted research over the course of 38 years from 1895 until 1933. They were trained by Indian Yogi teachers to "see" the microstructure of matter using extra-sensory perception [27]. Besant and Leadbeater described the "Anu", as a kind of a sophisticated vortex of "string-like" streams of energy-matter from a subtler realm than the physical. The Anu or the "ultimate physical atom" as named by Besant and Leadbeater, exists in two forms, positive and negative or clockwise and counterclockwise vortexes, see figure 8.3. These heart shaped building blocks are aether vortices. In Eastern tradition, they are thought to make up all matter. Anu combine with each other in different combinations to create more sophisticated structures, which then become "subatomic particles" which add up to make basic atomic particles. Increasing complexity make up the atoms of the Periodic Table of Elements which in turn, make up all the molecules and substances of the physical world including those that make up our bodies. Today, String theory advocates tell us that "elementary particles" such as the proton and the electron are ultimately made up of string and that sub-atomic particles are made-up of quarks, leptons and omegons, which eastern mystics collectively called anu! [28]

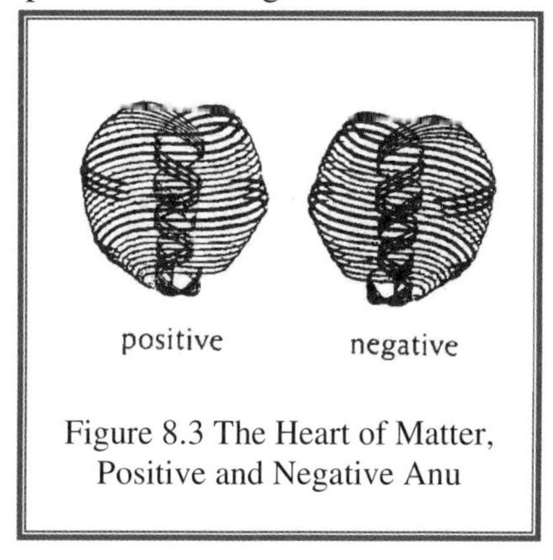

Figure 8.3 The Heart of Matter, Positive and Negative Anu

♦ **Microvita**

The Ananda Marga spiritual organization was founded in India in 1955 by Shrii Shrii Anandamurti (Prabhat Rainjan Sarkar). Devotees say that their Master dealt with his followers karma, by working with their positive and negative microvita [29]. From one of his discourses, Sarkar said:

> "There are entities which come within the realm of both physicality and psychic expressions which are smaller or subtler than atoms, electrons or protons, and in the psychic realm may be subtler than ectoplasm. For such objects or for such entities I use the term "microvitum". This microvitum, or

in plural microvita, are not of protoplasmic order, and as such they have got little to do with carbon molecules or carbon atoms, which are treated as the initial points or initial stage of life in this universe."

♦ Life Units

A reputable English medium Geraldine Cummins (1890-1969), channeled information about the invisible subtle realm.

> "Mind does not work directly on the brain. There is an etheric body, which is the link between mind and the cells of the brain. Far more minute corpuscular particles than scientists are yet aware of travel along threads from the etheric body, or double, to certain regions of the body and to the brain. They whirl with a very great intensity. I might call them life units."
>
> "The threads I speak of are connected with the glands. Medical men have been impressed by the alteration in character caused by certain deficiencies in one particular gland. They will find perhaps in time – when they discover the etheric body – that this deficiency is partly caused by some weakening of the thread or wire which carries the life current from the etheric body to these glands. I know I am uttering heresies. But I want you to realize that this invisible body – called by me the double or unifying mechanism – is the only channel through which mind and life may communicate with the physical shape. Should a thread snap between the two, there is immediately a failure in control." [30]

This is an incredible description by a medium that talks about threads and "life units" that whirl with great intensity. We cannot assume the role of the threads here, but since she talks about the relationship with vital organs it could indeed be the nadi system – translated as "conduits", "nerves", "veins", "vessels" or "arteries" – which constitute the composition of the subtle or yogic body described in the Tantras (indian scripture). Like the Chinese meridians, the nadis constitute channels of flow for the subtle life force (chi, prana) and have been described as the biofield by physicist Andrej Detela. These examples demonstrate that Masters and adepts in the past were able to perceive the world of consciousness and manipulate energy, sometimes directly into matter at will.

Shamanism

The ability to communicate with consciousness is also the domain of shamans. The anthropologist Jeremy Narby, provides a fascinating scientific perspective on shamanism. In the highly recommended book, *The Cosmic Serpent: DNA and the origins of knowledge,* Narby describes his utter amazement, when he realized that Amazonian shamans have the ability to take their consciousness down to the molecular level and communicate with the consciousness of DNA [31]. The shamans described how they, "sing to the spirits" and the spirits are "beings of light". Shamans also compare this consciousness to "radio waves" and state, "once you turn on the radio, you can pick them up". Narby realized after his consultation with shamans and subsequent research, that the light was in fact biophotons emitted from DNA [32]. Narby writes:

> "This is how they learn to combine brain hormones with monoamine oxidase inhibitors, or how they discover forty different sources of muscle paralyzers whereas science has only been able to imitate their molecules. When they say the recipe for curare was given to them by the beings who created life, they are talking literally. When they say their knowledge comes from beings they see in their hallucinations, their words mean exactly what they say."

In 1992, Narby attended the world conference on development and environment, the "Earth Summit" in Rio. There he was surprised to find wide acceptance of the ecological knowledge of the indigenous people, by world governments and pharmaceutical companies who were eager to exploit this Amazonian botanical knowledge [30]. Narby in his quest for truth, turned to the German biophysicist Fritz-Albert Popp, who is a leading pioneer in detecting ultraweak photon emissions from living systems. Popp and many others since, have found that all organisms emit 'biophotons', at ultraweak intensities, yet they are highly coherent and laser-like. This light is often called the aura, see the small section, "What Are Biophotons?" [34]. Narby decided to correspond with Popp and asked him to consider the relationship between DNA's photon emission and consciousness. This was his cautious response:

What Are Biophotons?

In the early 1980s, a team of scientists demonstrated that the cells of all living things emit photons at a rate of up to approximately 100 units per second and per square centimeter of surface. DNA was found to be the source of this photon emission at wavelengths, which correlate to the narrow band of visible light: The spectral distribution ranges at least from infrared (at about 900 nanometers) up to ultravioletwith (up to about 200 nanometers). According to researchers, the photon emission though weak is such that it corresponds "to the intensity of a candle at a distance of about 10 kilometers", but it has "a surprising high degree of coherence, as compared to that of technical fields (laser)". This can be explained as follows: "A coherent source of light, like a laser gives the sensation of bright colors, a luminescence, an impression of holographic depth" [31].

> **"Consciousness could be the electromagnetic field constituted by the sum of these emissions. But as you know, our understanding of the neurological basis of consciousness is very limited."**

We note that Yogananda like Seth, talks about the development of the foetus requiring an organizing field for development, according to karmic design [35]. This view is supported by scientific studies which show that any living entity exhibits an electromagnetic field. In the 1970s, biologist Bruce Lipton, took part in embryonic research that revealed minute electromagnetic fields forming around embryonic forms, whether seeds or embryos within eggs, as soon as conception or germination occurred. This means, for example, that if we place two electrodes at the two ends of a chicken egg, a tiny voltage of 2.4 mV will register, indicating a current running between the two ends of the egg. The electromagnetic field around the seed, whether plant or animal, then becomes the organizing field of life. So, in the case of a chicken, the embryo's spine develops along the line of this current, and the growing organism follows a pre-existing electromagnetic hologram, or morphogenetic energy field.

Yet, it was actually Harold Saxon Burr, a distinguished neuro-anatomist of the Yale School of Medicine in the 1940s, who pioneered the study of the organizing fields of life [36]. His research with animals and living plants revealed what he termed "L-fields" or "Life Fields". With plant seedlings, for example, he found that the surrounding electrical field was that of the adult plant, indicating that any developing organism is destined to follow a prescribed pattern of growth generated by its individual EM field. Moreover, in relation to human behavior Burr writes:

> "The behavior of living systems is a consequence of the pattern and organization provided by the L-field and abnormalities in the L-field can give advance warning of future symptoms before they are physically evident. L-fields reflect also mental and emotional states, which evoke energy in the nervous system. The L-field regulates and controls the creature whatever it may be, and its aims are wholeness, organization and continuity."

The Akashic Record

It is out of Akasha that every form comes,
and it is in Akasha that every form lives.
Tattvic Philosophy

In 1986, an historic discovery was announced by a scientific team at Sydney University [37]. The discovery was of a low energy vortical or spiraling EM field that seems to be an effect of the Universal field. This field is able to transmit energy patterns from one natural source to another and is the responsible agent for form, growth, development and behavioral patterns in nature (morphogenesis). Eminent biophysicist, Dr. Sergei Barsamian, has over thirty years experience in the study of polymers and bio-polymers and their dielectric nature [38]. Explaining the nature of the formative 'morphic' field, he says:

> "The field is of low-energy; it is dynamic or active. It is a receiver and transmitter of all energy patterns existing in our physical universe. It recycles information according to a specific energy pattern existing at the physical level when the conditions are conducive. It is the responsible agent for form, growth and development in living biomatter. It is an expression of dynamic nature herself and is an attribute and expression of one formative, background field of potential energy."

The findings were later successfully replicated by the Max Plank Institute's Department of Biophysics in Berlin, Germany [42]. The international photo-journalist and researcher Mark Balfour from his interviews with Dr. Barsamian, describes in layman's terms the importance and implications of this research, especially in regard to the electromagnetic cause and control of cancer [39]. Balfour writes the following:

> "The nature of the formative field can in one way be imagined to exhibit the function of a magnetic video recording tape upon which is impressed the energetic patterns of all physical, moral and psychic emissions occurring throughout time. The individual pattern or blueprint for form and growth has its origin at this source and is radiated when the pattern of an embryo or seed at the physical level attracts that sympathetic vibration, and when the conditions for its manifestation are conducive – in terms of physics, when a state of 'coherence' or pattern recognition exists."

Barsamian and his team conducted research with crystals, yeast cells, thymus cells and mouse cells in relation to transmissions of patterns over a distance, which led to some amazing discoveries. In his book, *The Sign of the Serpent*, Balfour cites a typical example, as follows:

> "A glass slide coated in a solution of poylstyrene and benzol gave the slide a polymer coating. (Polymers are macro molecules, important in living systems.) A carbon particle or 'charge' placed on the slide, upon examination revealed a spiral appearing on the polymer and surrounding the charge. Acting as a sensitive film emulsion, the polymer recorded a phenomenon which must involve factors outside the normal concept of space/time dimensions."

It seems from this description that the charged carbon particle (diamond) acted as an inter-dimensional doorway! [41] (Diamond and carbon are the same

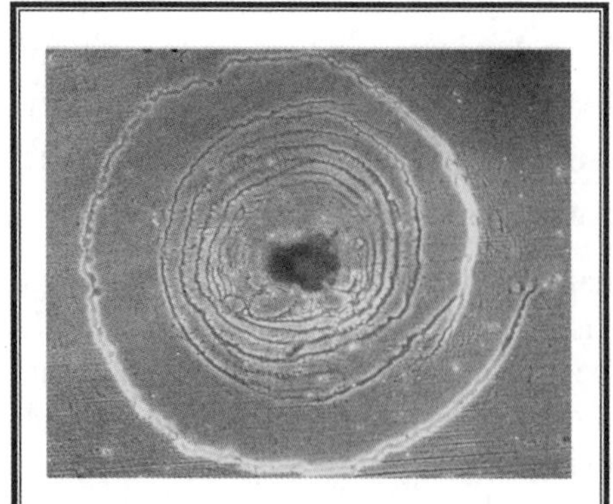

Figure 8.4 A low energy spiral EM field. Historic photograph believed to be delivering information stored in the Universal Field or akashic record. Credit and Copyright © Dr. Sergei Barsamian

This photograph was taken in a Sydney University Laboratory in late 1986, marking an historic event. It shows the low-energy spiral field that surrounds a carbon particle. The particle was placed on a polymer-coated slide. Polymers are used by scientists as a substitute for human cells. They can act as sensitive film emulsions and thus record an impression of a physical event — in this case, that of a previously undetected field pattern surrounding the carbon particle. Energy is believed to flow in spirals. This photo is considered to be evidence in support of the Unified Field Theory, which Einstein amongst others, believed to be the basis of the physical universe.

element, but diamond is the high-energy crystalline form). Balfour gives us another astounding insight into the discovery of this field, see figure 8.4. Balfour writes:

> "A photograph taken of the vortex field shows a speck of carbon, a charged particle in the center of the vortex. The energy frequency of the particle attracts a sympathetic or cohering frequency existing in the field. This situation creates an unfolding of the field's potential energy towards the particle, in a spiral or vortex pattern, which is electro-magnetic in nature. The result is a stimulation of the energy of the particle or host."

Balfour writes that the energy enters the particle, via a vacuum point in the charge, where the vortex field will not be deformed in any manner. In the ancient Indian Vedic understanding, the information stored in the universal field is identified as the 'akashic record' – 'akasha' being the Sanskrit term for 'space'. It appears that these scientists have provided hard evidence for the role of inter-dimensional disks of light! According to Dubro, the akashic record is "downloaded" into the Universal Calibration lattice onto constructs she calls the disks of light. Here is a description:

❖ "Your history – your hereditary patterns, past-life records, and all the events you have experienced in this lifetime – are recorded within the long informational fibers located behind you. These records look like tiny disks of light; they hold the information in place electromagnetically."

Balfour writes that the charged particle attracts the field's "potential energy" in a spiral or vortex pattern. Dubro says:

❖ "The light strands in front of the human energy field comprise the field of potential possibilities... The light disks contained in these long informational fibers function like transmitters, attracting "like" energy."

In Kashmir Shaivism, based on the Vedas, matter is composed of "tattvas" which are units of consciousness. The "Tattvas" are "three-dimensional geometric energy vibrations" which are "modifications of Svara, or the spiraling current" [42]. The relationship between the spherical and geometrical property of consciousness relates to the dimension in which the energy is being perceived. This is discussed again in the chapter 10, in respect to sacred geometry. Nevertheless, once again ancient knowledge is verified, in relation to the discovery of this spiraling EM field!

Many ancient teachings used the symbol of the spiraling serpent to represent "universal wisdom", this symbolism has now been scientifically validated.

The main conclusion of the Sydney research, is that biological EM field disturbances, rather than biochemical factors, are primarily the cause of disease. Thomas Bearden writes about the work of Dr. Barsamian on the dielectric behavior of biosystems and the related work of Dr. Bevan Reid on his website [43]. Lamenting the fact that this research is relatively unknown, Bearden gives the following cause: "it is difficult to find a referee who sincerely understands the related experiments and their underlying theory. This presents a nearly impenetrable barrier to publication in leading scientific journals". Regardless of the lack of recognition, these researchers have gone on to new endeavors, both related to the early detection of cancer [44]. Barsamian developed the Diagnostic Analyser (DDA) which is capable of providing early warning of cancer even before clinical or physical appearance. Reid became a co-founder of a Sydney based company, Polartechnics, that was set up to develop and commercialize a revolutionary new cervical cancer detection test.

Dr. Valerie Hunt, has also discovered the influence of the akashic records and our energy "history" that can directly impact the NOW. She explains her understanding of this influence in terms of "lifehoods".

"The word "lifehoods" is not just a term I coined for the old ideas about past lives. Past lives emphasize the physical existence of a life, a time-space construct. Lifehoods emphasize the soul itself, which is part of the field, exists now, and has no time reference. As Stephen Hawking as pointed out, laws of science do not distinguish between past, present, and future. Neither do higher states of consciousness. There is neither soul-time nor soul-space, and since the soul is never destroyed, information from lifehoods is always a part of each new life, or incarnation."

"As a hardcore scientist, this was the hardest thing for me to understand, until my own lifehood started coming through with information that I had no way of ever knowing otherwise. Of course, some people say, "Well, I don't believe in that," but whether or you believe in it or not, it's a fact, and more and more information is coming out that verifies that the soul has existed before this lifetime. And each time the soul comes into this life, it brings through its experiences. Lifehood information can either help or hinder our evolution, but in each new life this information powerfully influences the development of our selfhood and behaviors. In addition, these memories are the true psychological source and deepest director of human life. It is as if the soul is saying, I've got to solve this and therefore I'm going to have these experiences."

"When a person re-experiences a lifehood, the past and the present are now, and it is not a historical event. Likewise, as people go up in consciousness and vibration to the levels in the field where recalls occur, there is no time but the present time. **I believe that as man evolves rapidly in the future, the concept of lifehoods will become a dominant, new philosophical idea, one which is important because it views human emotions, spirituality, and the body in a way that focuses holistically on human empowerment.** My work in this regard focuses primarily upon the spiritual aspects of lifehoods, which I find to be the ultimate source of a person's problems in this lifehood, especially the emotions connected with other lifehoods which are the barriers to progress. **When I open people's fields there is a dramatic increase in the frequency and quantity of the field, and not only do they get better, they evolve**."

"This is different from what is known as past life regression, which based upon the person regressing backwards in time. The person doesn't have to regress at all. In their field the memory is right there. All you have to do is expand their consciousness, which can be done by the use of energy frequencies, and it's there. Once their conscious expands, they can take the information and they can put it consciously in the human mind so that they can do something with it. This is one of the great frontiers of human consciousness. I think it's probably one of the most important, although it's beyond where most people are ready to go." *[Bold added for emphasis, end of excerpts]* [45]

The work of Dr. Valerie Hunt work is remarkably in tune with the teaching of the "Practical Mystic", Peggy Phoenix Dubro. So even though these specialists in their respective fields have used a different approach, the conclusions have been the same!

The New Energy

It is very important that Energy practitioners understand that *everything* has consciousness. It is quite clear that the "New Energy" arriving on our planet Earth has a "new" and "different" consciousness to the "old" energies used in the past. Therefore, it is absolutely essential that procedures are derived, that work effectively with these new energies. If this is not understood, energy practitioners working with the new energies will soon find themselves in uncharted waters with consequences not envisaged. It is not enough to *assume* that the New Energy will automatically create balance, it cannot be emphasized enough that the human being is evolving. This situation can be likened to the biblical idea of pouring NEW WINE into OLD WINESKINS!

Chapter Nine

Universal Energy

Energy Fields That You Can Tune

When two equal and opposite electromagnetic fields are balanced, we have established that rather than the result being zero, we are left with a powerful resting energy. Nikola Tesla, at the beginning of the last century, described this as powerful non-hertzian energy (without frequencies) which he referred to as "radiant energy" or "cosmic waves". Yet, even today most modern physics journals and university textbooks do not mention these powerful energies, but these mysterious fields are filtering into mainstream scientific thinking to explain experiments that demonstrate "impossible" phenomena.

These fields are most often described as "Scalar" in the Western scientific literature and "Torsion" in Russian studies. However, there are other names in circulation, such as quantum fields, tachyon fields, gravity fields, neutrino fields, Tesla waves, non-hertzian waves or longitudinal waves. In general, these fields still require to be incorporated into electromagnetic theory [1]. As the literature gives slightly different properties for Scalar and Torsion fields, here the definitions are kept separate.

(Small sections denoted with ✧❖◆❖✧ provide slightly more technical details and can be skipped over by the less scientifically minded.)

Scalar Power

The scalar field is considered as a component of the electromagnetic field, which is always there, but as it is masked by the electromagnetic field, thus it has been undetected in the past. So, even though it is considered to be much weaker in amplitude, this does not matter, because this is where all the information is carried. Hence, experimentally, you can actually cancel out electromagnetic fields, eliminating the strong outer shell and leaving behind the underlying scalar information field. See figure 9.1.

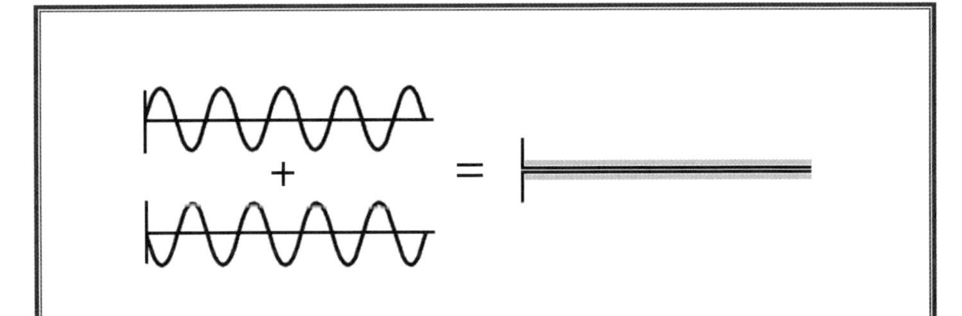

Figure 9.1 Phase conjugation. When two EM waves that are 180 degrees out of phase combine, the energy of the strong outer shell is removed leaving behind a strong resting 'scalar' energy that is normally hidden.

Today, the science of bioelectromagnetism is discovering how to use these scalar fields and devices are being produced to modulate and it is claimed, to heal biological systems. Yet, as human beings have tremendous potential, healers have always worked with mysterious forces and energies, so the practical application has been known and used in the past, but generally only understood by a few.

Scalar is a terminology that's been popularized by the work of Thomas Bearden. It is described as having zero frequencies, to be static, a stationary energy, one that does not move either in time or space so it cannot be evaluated by most electromagnetic instruments. The primary purpose is to hold information as vibrational energy patterns. In scientific vocabulary, scalar is used to denote the opposite of vector. A vector is something that has both velocity and direction. A scalar is something that has neither velocity nor direction. A simple analogy is to compare wind and air. Wind is a vector phenomenon, because it has velocity and a direction, but air is a scalar phenomenon, as it has neither. So air would be analogous to scalar energy.

The space the scalar occupies is not a vacuum.
It is alive with checked and balanced energies.

Scalar waves are waves with such a huge wavelength that no gradient can be measured in space, but are only a fluctuating "potential" in time. We do have common examples, such as radio waves in the Extremely Low Frequency (ELF) range, like the Schumann Resonance (7.8 Hz) which encircles the entire Earth with one wavelength. The oscillation takes place between the Earth's surface and the bottom side of the ionosphere. There are also scalar waves generated by a Tesla coil with their electric and magnetic field, oriented in the same plane, but are out of phase with each other in time by 90°,where a second Tesla coil can receive this wave. In summary, any EM field is just two dynamic scalar potentials with dynamic functions imposed. A good analogy is a whirlpool in a river, it may appear completely static, but inside it is highly dynamic, with water constantly flowing through it, so it is defined as a "static" potential or field.

Morphogenetic Fields

Rupert Sheldrake's "Morphogenetic Fields" is a popular theory of a scalar type field [2]. This theory can be summarized by the idea that all living creatures have an organizing and guidance system, which is a field of information, related to their particular species that helps them to manage their activities from birth. Morphic fields can be thought of as fields of habit and as new challenges and environmental changes occur, the field is "updated".

> "Through morphic resonance, each member of the species both draws upon and contributes to a collective memory of the species." [3]

The saying "The Hundredth Monkey" comes from a source other than Rupert Sheldrake, although the idea is related to the concept of morphic resonance. Apparently, the saying originated in Lyall Watson's book *Lifetide* (1979) and was also featured in the book, *The Hundredth Monkey* (1982) *by* Ken Keyes. Due to the uproar in academic circles caused by the publication of his book, Watson maintains the following story was intended only as a metaphor and may not have been a documented incident. However, the concept caught on and became accepted as true. The story goes that there was an experiment that took place on an isolated island with monkeys. After the monkeys mastered a new task, it appeared that monkeys on other islands had "magically" learned how to do the same thing with no instruction [4]. This story can be used to explain the concept of critical mass and how information is relayed to others of the same species, via the morphogenetic field. Scientists still hotly dispute this idea, but somehow this law resonates as true. Basically, biologists have no reasonable explanation for a whole host of behavior related to living organisms, hence Rupert Sheldrake may just be stating the obvious. The Asia Tsunami disaster that struck 12 countries on December 26, 2004 had many in the media asking the perplexing question: how did the so-called "primitive" stone age tribes and the animals survive? Here, we have a well-documented incident, that clearly demonstrates it is possible to receive information directly from the environment, albeit, an ability most humans do not commonly use [5]. The following is a summary of the most important properties of scalar energy.

Scalar Properties:

- They transmit information, not energy.
- Energetic changes can be produced in a distant system at a distant place without transmitting energy "through" space in the normal sense, i.e. transmission is directly in time or through a higher dimension.
- Propagation is at 10^9 times faster-than-light speed (hence scalars have also been called "tachyons"), except when transmitting scalar information on electromagnetic carrier waves.
- Can be shown to have effects 3-5 times stronger than electromagnetic fields.
- More fundamental than electromagnetic fields.
- Detection cannot be made by conventional instruments, where normally electric and magnetic fields are measured by interaction with electron flow and energy transmission.
- They pervade all matter and cannot be shielded against by Faraday cages.

Torsion Fields – The Magic of Spin

Torsion and scalar fields are similar in some ways but there is one fundamental difference and that is related to the concept of angular momentum and spin. After nearly a century of research, Russian scientists are now no longer puzzled by strange experimentally observed phenomena. Research has found that torsion fields are subtle energy fields which can be detected by Kirlian photography. They also report that the torsion fields of various objects, commonly reported as the aura, can be visually seen by "sensitives" (psychics). Even more astounding, is the effect of a certain type of torsion generator, (mechanically rotating magnets), which is able to alter the inner structure of ANY substance (it's spin structure) and this can only be duplicated by sensitives and NO other known technology [6].

The concept of torsion fields is truly exciting, but the application of these mysterious forces is not new. Mystics, yogis, shamans and healers have clearly demonstrated proficiency in the use of these forces over millennia and documented cases prove that humans have the ability to manipulate these forces at will. Scientific research only seeks to de-mystify and in the process encourage us to realize that we can harness these forces if we are seeking higher consciousness and empowerment. Curiously, in our review of research in this area, we will learn why some Russian and Ukranian scientists have recently persuaded their governments to harness these forces for the benefit of mankind.

Over the last century, various scientific endeavors around the world repeatedly reported the discovery of unusual phenomena that could not be explained in the framework of existing theories [7]. These scientists realized that the phenomena was caused by unknown fields, emanations and energies and so gave their own names and descriptions of what they observed [8]. Eventually, this collection of phenomena was pinned down and related to the unknown Torsion Field Theory, which first originated from physicists Albert Einstein and Elie Cartan in 1913.

Theory states that torsion fields are some 30 orders of magnitude weaker than gravitation, and gravity is already known to be 40 orders of magnitude weaker than the electromagnetic force!

This miniscule level of influence was thought to be basically irrelevant and so was dismissed. Torsion fields carry information, so nowadays we would compare this to computer software. Nobody now would think it odd if a massive industrial complex ground to a halt because of a computer software failure. Where energy carries information only, size comparisons cannot be made!

In the 1950s, Soviet astrophysicist Nikolai Kozyrev conducted a large series of experiments with gyroscopes. He was the first to show that variations existed in a gyroscope's weight, depending on the angular velocity and the direction of rotation. Eventually, in 1991, Gennady Shipov showed that the violation of Newton's Laws by gyroscopic systems was caused by the appearance of torsion fields generated by spinning mass [9]. Now, it is important to know that torsion fields come in two flavors "static" and "dynamic". Static torsion fields are created from spinning sources that do not radiate any energy. However, if the spinning source releases energy in any form, such as the Sun or the center of the Galaxy and/or has more than one form of movement occurring at the same time, such as a planet that is rotating on its axis and revolving around the Sun at the same time, then dynamic torsion fields are automatically produced [10]. Torsion waves propagate through space and this is of great importance as we try to understand how "information" is distributed around the universe.

Historically, Einstein showed mathematically the existence of a close connection between gravitation and the curvature of space-time and at the same time Cartan was the first to point to the possibility of the existence of fields generated by the spin angular momentum density. These ideas became known as Einstein-Cartan theory or ECT. When these ideas gained momentum, thousands of papers were written, devoted to the idea of gravitation with torsion. However, as already stated, it took over eighty years for the theories to match up with experimental observation! By 1996, there was 10,000 papers written on the subject, but over 5,000 had Russian authors, so we can conclude that the Russians are fairly familiar with this subject. Here is a summary of torsion field characteristics:

Torsion Properties:

- Torsion fields are generated by spin or by spin angular momentum density on a macroscopic level. Torsion fields have axial symmetry so there exists both right and left torsion fields.
- They are not the same as conventional electromagnetic and gravitational fields.
- A mechanically rotated object like a gyroscope, if spinning uniformly about its central axis will generate a "static" torsion field. If the gyroscope wobbles then "dynamic" torsion waves are created.
- Like scalar fields, torsion fields transmit information without transmitting energy.
- They appear to travel through space affecting spin states of the physical media only, but that allows them to be detected.
- Torsion signal velocity is a minimum of 10^9 times the speed of light.
- Torsion fields can only be shielded by certain materials with particular spin-structures.
- Any physical object possesses it's own torsion field and can be affected by the torsion field of a permanent magnet.
- Strong torsion fields are generated by high electrical potentials and by devices that have circular or spiral electromagnetic processes.
- Torsion fields can be generated, detected, switched on and off (such as for communication purposes).
- Russian research tells us that "torsion waves," or waves in the aether, are always spiraling in their form.
- Torsion fields are shown to produce cosmic strings!

There are several types of torsion generators; permanent magnets, the torsion component of an electromagnetic or electrostatic fields, rotating magnetic fields, the effect caused by distortion of geometry and combinations of the above. In the 1980s, the Russian scientist Akimov, experimentally established that objects having geometrical sizes obey the rule of the "golden section" (ratios of 1:0.618) and can be considered as passive torsion generators. Torsion field detectors confirm the unusual effects of pyramids, cones, flat triangles etc. that generate physical, chemical and biological effects.

Power Field Effects

Western research into scalar fields dates back to 1950. The Max Planck Institute in Germany, found that when an artificially generated scalar wave was introduced to living cells in a petri dish, the cells separated, lost their clumping and became more active within the fluid medium. This is a significant finding, as all disease, injury or degeneration is accompanied by swelling and stasis in blood and lymphatic circulation, immobilizing the body's healing processes. By applying a scalar, an improvement in circulation is generated by removing the pressures. Andrija Puharich, was one of the world's leading innovative scientists and researchers. His research found improvement in the immune and endocrine systems from in vitro study of scalars. Dr. Eldon Byrd who worked at the US Naval Surface Weapons Centre, Maryland, U.S., showed scalar energy increased the strength of low-level EEG frequencies. His work was highly controversial and included understanding the psychoactive properties of low frequency electromagnetic fields.

It was thought long ago, that healers could magnetize water and Franz Mesmer in the 1700s, became famous for his cures with 'magnetized water'. As with anything new, the establishment ridiculed Mesmer and it took until the 1960s for his discovery to be confirmed by Dr. Bernard Grad who replicated Mesmer's findings. They both reasoned that the phenomena, was caused by subtle energy fields, but today we know that water is effected by torsion fields. Dr. Masaru Emoto has proven conclusively that water has the ability to capture information that reflects the level of our consciousness [11]. This is achieved when ice crystals catch the imprint of human intention, emotion and thoughts, thus sometimes resulting in crystals that form beautiful patterns. Torsion fields have been know to affect; gravity, laser beams so that they change frequency, biological processes, quartz crystals, some electronic components and some beverages can be favorably changed. In addition, melting or solidifying some materials generates torsion fields.

The Cavernous Structures Effect (CSE)

An important discovery was made by a Russian naturalist who stumbled across the torsion generator affect of geometry when he had an encounter with bees! Viktor Stepanovich Grebennikov is known as the discoverer of the Cavernous Structures Effect (CSE). In the 1980s, Grebennikov found that the empty honeycomb of certain bees could influence biological systems from microorganisms to human beings. This discovery was made after several experiences, but the most famous account was when he came across a "bee city" in the steppes of the Kamyshlovo valley [12]. Fascinated, he spent too long studying and so decided to spend the night in the open with the bees. When he tried to fall asleep, he had terrible and strange experiences; sensations of expansion and contracting, falling, flashes in front of his eyes, metallic taste in the mouth, ears ringing, head spinning, feeling light and then heavy nausea. A few years later when Grebennikov returned, the "bee city" had died. When he picked up a handful of old clay lumps with multiple chamber cells, which were then old fragments of the nests, he experienced unknown "jerks". The old nests were cold to the touch but the energy surrounding them was warm. Curiously, he then re-experienced all the same strange sensations from the "dead" bee chambers!

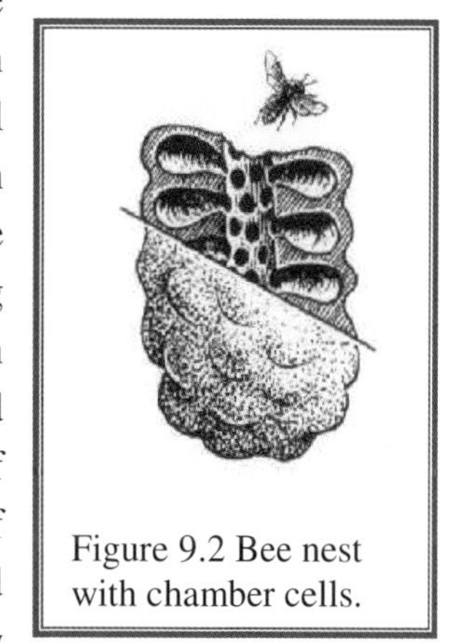

Figure 9.2 Bee nest with chamber cells.

During his research, Grebennikov discovered a list of biological effects. Although, the most interesting effect, in terms of quantum physics, was that clocks-both mechanical and electronic, placed in a strong CSE field started running inaccurately. He also invented a few devices, the most unusual was called, 'The Always-Active Honeycomb Painkiller!' It was simply a chair with an overhead section packed with trays of dry honeycombs. According to Grebennikov it only took a few minutes to cure headaches!

It must be explained that some of Grebennikov's experiences are the same as some of those reported by people undergoing excessive Kundalini energies. In metaphysical language the "jerks" are known as "kriyas", and this strongly suggests that torsion fields are the cause of adverse spiritual experiences. Could it be that people who suffer from excessive Kundalini energies, are somehow being more affected by torsion fields in their surroundings? Kundalini is considered an evolutionary process of spiritual transformation and the process can be accompanied with an assortment of symptoms, that can be sometimes quite disturbing [13]. It has always been the aim in Eastern mystical tradition to awaken

Kundalini energy through various spiritual practices like meditation and yoga. However, in the West, Kundalini is rarely explained as a possible consequence, so it often comes as a surprise when powerful energy is triggered in the body. Gopi Krishna was an Indian government official who wrote many books on kundalini. His personal experiences with kundalini energy were such that he became rather scathing of gurus who professed enlightenment, who he felt should understand the Kundalini process [14]. Gopi Krishna may have been far too critical, as there have been many documented cases of mystics who have reached enlightenment without any kundalini difficulties. It would seem that Kundalini problems are caused by unbalanced and disturbed energy fields, aggravated by torsion fields in the local environment. Therefore, if Kundalini sufferers were monitored in different passive torsion fields, it would make a very interesting study. In everyday life, cavities large and small, rooms, corridors, halls, roofing, furniture and buildings surround us. Grebennikov points out that even our own cells are torsion generators. Maybe, Kundalini sufferers for reasons unknown struggle to integrate certain types of energy within their personal energy fields and require some help. Research is important, as many kundalini sufferers have very little support for their condition and possibly with the increase of aetheric energy on the planet, this may become more of an issue.

Traditionally, the shape of a building plays an important role in the process of meditation. Thus, we see the "information transmitters", the passive torsion generators of spires and domes on top of churches and temples. The torsion fields of a meditating person can be significantly magnified if the meditation takes place in a building having these particular geometric proportions. A large pyramid shaped building was opened on November 1, 2002 in Pune, India for the sole purpose of meditation. This beautifully designed modern pyramid holds over 5000 people and it was designed by the Indian mystic and spiritual teacher, Osho just before he died [15]. Osho specified that the building would only be used for meditation purposes.

Why Balancing Is More Powerful Than "Zapping"

Dr. Valerie Hunt reports on her website "clinical evidence for bioscalar healing", that includes cancer patients reporting improved tolerance to chemotheraphy and patients who learned to create their own scalar energy and break a long drug addiction without withdrawal symptoms. Hunt believes it is the combination of ordinary electromagnetic fields with scalar energy that causes the most complete healing and so she provides meditations to harness this power [16]. Hunt was awarded a $US 4 million grant to investigate the scalar waves used by psychic surgeons. She believes that they do not emanate strong electromagnetic fields like most healers, rather, they have developed more passive and strong inner core energy. Hunt describes their energy fields as being like "inert posts".

"The bioscalar energy adds the unique qualities of strength and sustaining power for enduring changes."
Dr. Valerie Hunt

The famous Russian healer, Dr. Barbara Ivanova reached the same conclusion, when she realized that normal healing only treated symptoms on the physical level. Ivanova came to believe, "Body, mind, and soul must be brought into the process" and that a second level of healing called "harmonizing" was necessary to allow people to live in harmony with themselves and the world. She believed that when people are in harmony, the healer can connect in resonance with them and bring lasting cures [17].

Ground-breaking research was undertaken by Glen Rein Ph.D. who is leading pioneer of bioelectromagnetics and psychoneuroimmunology [18]. Rein conducted various experiments to detect subtle electromagnetic fields and scalar fields, using biological systems that would be sensitive to these subtle quantum fields. He decided to work with healers because he hypothesized that healers had the ability to heal regardless of distance and time. His research partner, an engineer called Ted Gagnon, designed a special modified "caduceus" coil, which cancelled out electromagnetic fields. In addition, Rein conducted experiments with the Teslar watch originally designed by Andrija Puharich. The Teslar watch generates a scalar field at the critical 8Hz Earth frequency which stabilizes the biosystem. Rein knew that these three sources of subtle energy would produce different frequencies and healers would generate the most complex frequencies. Logic dictated that different frequencies would produce varying affects on biological systems, but he also decided that varying states of consciousness would create different affects. Rein states that:

> "Conceptually, the work that I have been doing is the first application of these kind of quantum non-hertzian fields to biological systems… I've been able to show the same set of frequencies are more biologically effective in non-electromagnetic fields. In comparing a signal delivered through a conventional electromagnetic field using a Helmholtz coil, for example, versus the same sort of frequencies where the electromagnetic field is canceled out and you have the non-hertzian or scalar left behind, **even using the exact same set of frequencies and keeping all other variables constant, the scalar fields turned out to be anywhere between three and five times more biologically active.**" *[Bold added for emphasis]*

Rein suggests that "these scalar fields are much more biologically active and could be what's causing the actual healing process, or activating the physiological changes" [19]. Rein proved that it was not just the "right" set of frequencies that generating this effect. The validation came when he used the same frequency information placed in a regular Helmholtz coil—which does not generate a scalar, but a regular electromagnetic field. In that case, the biological response of the cells was very strong, but again three to five times less than the response to the scalar field. So he concluded that the electromagnetic field by itself will do some good, but when you add the scalar component, the biological system really takes off!

The Scalar Controversy

The most intriguing aspect of scalar theory is that it supported by some very elaborate mathematics with physical descriptions of scalar fields and their properties. Thomas E. Bearden is a retired army officer and physicist, who has carried out a one-man 20 year crusade to get physicists to understand that the first successful unified field theory in the history of science existed over a hundred years ago, developed by James Clerk Maxwell [20]. Today we find that his legacy of a fully-fledged mathematical theory was crudely "butchered" and passed down. In his writings, Maxwell made it clear that his choice of quaternions (mathematical operators that are ordered pairs of complex numbers), were based on his belief that three-dimensional physical phenomena – including quite possibly human consciousness – was dependent upon higher dimensional realities. The author realizes that the some of the following explanations maybe difficult to comprehend, but it is comforting to know that physicists have not understood these principles either! In fact, the felony to simplify the original Maxwell equations was committed by his successors, Oliver Heaviside and Josiah Willard Gibbs, who according to Scientific American (September 1950), actually felt that Maxwell's use of quaternions and their description of the "potentials" of space was "...mystical, and should be murdered from the theory". Bearden's states his opinion on this situation as follows:

- " ... In discarding the scalar component of the quaternion, Heaviside and Gibbs unwittingly discarded the unified EM/G [electromagnetic/ gravitational] portion of Maxwell's theory that arises when the translation/directional components of two interacting quaternions reduce to zero, but the scalar resultant remains and infolds a deterministic, dynamic structure that is a function of oppositive directional/translational components. In the infolding of electromagnetic field energy inside a scalar potential, a structured scalar potential results, almost precisely as later shown by

Whittaker but unnoticed by the scientific community. The simple vector equations produced by Heaviside and Gibbs captured only that subset of Maxwell's theory where electromagnetic field and gravitation are mutually exclusive. In that subset, electromagnetic circuits and equipment will not ever, and cannot ever, produce gravitational or inertial effects in materials and equipment."

- "As a result of this artificial restriction of Maxwell's theory, Einstein also inadvertently restricted his theory of general relativity, forever preventing the unification of electromagnetics and relativity. He also essentially prevented the present restricted general relativity from ever becoming an experimental, engineerable science on the laboratory bench, since a hidden internalized electromagnetics causing a deterministically structured local space-time curvature was excluded."

- "Quantum mechanics used only the Heaviside/Gibbs externalized electromagnetics and completely missed Maxwell's internalized and ordered electromagnetics enfolded inside a structured scalar potential. Accordingly, QM [quantum mechanics] maintained its Gibbs statistics of quantum change, which is nonchaotic a priori. Quantum physicists by and large excluded Bohm's hidden variable theory, which conceivably could have offered the potential of engineering quantum change – engineering physical reality itself."

- "Each of these major scientific disciplines missed and excluded a subset of their disciplinary area, because they did not have the scalar component of the quaternion to incorporate. Further, they completely missed the significance of the Whittaker approach, which already shows how to apply and engineer the very subsets they had excluded."

- "What now exists in these areas are three separate, inconsistent disciplines. Each of them unwittingly excluded a vital part of its discipline, which was the unified field part. Ironically, then, present physicists continue to exert great effort to find the missing key to unification of the three disciplines, but find it hopeless, because these special subsets are already contradictory to one another, as is quite well-known to foundations physicists."

- "Obviously, if one wishes to unify physics, one must add back the unintentionally excluded, unifying subsets to each discipline. Interestingly, all three needed subsets turn out to be one and the same ..." *[End of excerpts]* [21]

The scalar components of Maxwell's original quaternions, which were removed, are a "hidden" set of electromagnetic waves traveling in two simultaneous directions in the scalar potential of the vacuum.

Scalar Fleas and Elephants – Non Tech description

Now, for the non-scientifically minded, a Tom Bearden explanation is given to show why these internal forces are so important and the effect caused, by excluding the internal electromagnetic field energy had on physics.

The Balance of Power!

In the physical world, scalar quantities are very often a combination of zero vector systems, where the "scalar" or motionless system is actually filled with hosts of smaller "vector" things in violent motion. We have to be very careful, therefore, when we apply mathematics (which does not decompose fundamental scalars into vectors, or identify them as vector zeros) to a physical situation. To use an extreme example, two elephants pushing strongly head-on against each other may produce a "two-elephant" system of opposing forces (vectors), where the resultant system is stationary. Thus, representing a zero vector system, whose motion is represented by a vector zero. The same would be true for two fleas pushing against each other and not moving as a system. However, it is clear that the mathematics does not portray the real situation and so betrays us. In vector analysis, all vector zeros are identical, which means that the effect of the flea system and the elephant system are considered to be the same. In mathematical terms that's true, but there's a big difference in the two systems that must be accounted for physically. If you don't believe that, then imagine being in between two pushing elephants. It is not difficult to comprehend that this is not the same as being between two pushing fleas! This analogy is very useful in helping us to understand that in the process of a balanced electromagnetic field, the resultant effect is not *no-thing*, in terms of scalar energies there could be a tremendous amount going on [22]. This is very important to consider when we understand that our "core energy" is the result of two equal and balanced vector forces.

When the internal order and internal structure of the local space-time is discarded, then any hidden factors, controlling variables that could be manipulated to create and control quantum change itself, are also removed. It is possible to offer evidence in the form of "impossible" phenomena that proves conclusively that the current laws of physics are not complete and that "hidden potential" exists. The Aharonov-Bohm Effect, discovered in 1959, was the first major indication that not all was well with the current theory of electromagnetism, see the small section, "What is The Aharonov-Bohm Effect?"

"What is The Aharonov-Bohm Effect?"

The Aharonov-Bohm Effect demonstrates that potentials represent a physical reality and exert measurable physical effects. Physicists, Yakir Aharonov and David Bohm, conducted a seminal electrodynamics laboratory experiment, where they succeeded in actually measuring the "hidden potential" of free space described in Maxwell's original scalar quaternion equations [23]. To do so, they had to cool the experiment to a mere 9 degrees above Absolute Zero, thus creating a total shielding around a superconducting magnetic ring. This is considered to be a non-trivial laboratory set up, but their efforts were rewarded by observing the something never seen before. Totally screened, by all measurements, from the magnetic influence of the ring itself, a test beam of electrons fired by Aharonov and Bohm at the superconducting "doughnut", nonetheless, changed their electronic state (wave functions) as they passed through the observably "field-free" region of the hole – indicating they were sensing "something" even though it could NOT be the ring's magnetic field. Confirmed now by decades of other physicists' experiments as a true phenomenon (and not merely improper shielding of the magnet), the "Aharonov-Bohm Effect" provides compelling proof of a deeper "spatial strain" – a "scalar potential" – the underlying existence of a magnetic "force-field" itself. (Later experiments revealed a similar effect with shielded electrostatic fields.) This provides compelling proof of "something else", underlying all reality, capable of transmitting energy and information across space and time ... even in the complete absence of an electromagnetically detectable 3-D spatial field [24].

So, according to theory, the reason that the scalars are so powerful in their biological effects is because they can affect the nucleus. If this is true, bioscalar energy is deeper than cells, molecules, genes, and DNA. Human thought and intent can make major changes by programming scalar energy at the most microscopic level – the nucleus of the atom. Bearden talks about 're-engineering the nucleus'. He says about using scalar technology:

> "Literally, eventually anything at all can be materialized and brought into physical reality, or dematerialized so as to disappear from physical reality. And we shall be able to engineer and change the local laws of nature" [22].

Electromagnetic fields predominantly affect the electrons, the nucleus is not really altered. There may be some slight effect when electromagnetic fields are absorbed and radiated in an interaction between energy and matter, but generally speaking, the nucleus is not altered in any way. If it is possible that we can actually modify the nucleus, then we can potentially cause very profound biological effects. Powerful effects have already been observed, but this suggests transmutation of matter, being able to make very profound manifestations in our three-dimensional world.

Now, we can see why the Pentagon investigated a maverick scientist called John Hutchison who in his backroom laboratory, on a shoestring budget, managed to make things levitate and metal objects to become translucent!

As we have examined these new concepts in electromagnetism, we can now appreciate how harnessing this power can make profound changes to our reality by using the power of human intent and consciousness. When we give intent for balance, we invoke scalar energy, facilitating a much more powerful way to connect with the body's innate wisdom and promoting a stronger connection to the Universe.

The Mystery of Healing Energy is Solved!

"The heavenly, celestial forces...actually have a reality as particles."
Tom Kenyon, Shaman

There has been a great deal of research undertaken to understand the science associated with healers and the mechanisms involved [25]. This book focuses on the concept of *New Energy* and the delivery of that energy onto this planet in the form of space weather. Hence, a case has to be made that the energy is "different" and that this energy is now available for use. It is already established that human beings are sensitive to variations in the magnetic field and that we all require an environment signal to maintain balance. We will briefly examine this relationship and the phenomena of "spiritual healing", the forerunner to the more modern concept of "energy work" that aims to encourage balance within the human energy field and body. Here are some quotes about spiritual healing from some good old-fashioned healers, Olga and Ambrose Worrall who were performing thousands of miracles in the 1960s and 1970s in the United States.

- "Spiritual healing is the channelling of energy into a recipient from the universal field of energy which is common to all creation and which stems from the universal source of all intelligence and power, called God. Emanations surround each individual, caused by electrical currents flowing in the physical body. There are sound waves from the various physical organs and thought waves from the mind as well as vibrations from the spiritual body. Energy from the universal field of energy becomes available to the healer through the act of tuning his personal energy field to a harmonial relationship with the universal field of energy so that he acts in this way as a conductor between the universal field of energy and the patient." Olga Worrall
- "Spiritual healing is a rearrangement of the microparticles of which all things are composed. The body is not what it seems to be with the naked eye. It is not a solid mass. It is actually a system of little particles or points of energy separated from each other by space and held in place through an electrically balanced field. When these particles are not in their proper place, then disease is manifested in that body. Spiritual healing is one way of bringing

the particles back into a harmonious relationship – which means good health." Ambrose Worrall [27].

This husband and wife team understood the principle of electromagnetic balance and that a healer was only a conduit to carry electromagnetic energy from the universal field. Today, we have famous healers who profess complete ignorance of how this works, but get results anyway! The following is a very short introduction to Healer Science, but the aim is to outline the main principles that identify our electromagnetic nature and how we interact with the Earth's magnetic field.

♦ *Healer Science: Healers synchronize their brains with Earth frequencies*

In 1969, Dr. Robert Beck, a nuclear physicist, started a decade of research when he travelled the world measuring the brain waves of healers. He measured their electrical brain waves with an electroencephalograph (EEG). In the brain activity of healers he found that they all exhibit the same brain-wave pattern of 7.8-8 Hz during the times they were giving healing, no matter what their belief system or customs. Beck tested charismatic Christian faith healers, Hawaiian kahunas, practitioners of wicca, santeria, radesthesia, and radionics, as well as seers, ESP readers and psychics. Most of these healers entered an altered state of consciousness and produced nearly identical EEG signatures, which lasted from 1 to several seconds [28]. Investigation revealed that during the healing moments, the healer's brain waves became both frequency and phase-synchronized with Schumann waves.

♦ *Healer Science: Healers link up their client's brains with Earth frequencies*

Dr. John Zimmermann, founder and president of the Bio-Electro-Magnetics Institute of Reno, Nevada then realised that what all healers call grounding into the earth is the action of linking up with the magnetic field of the earth, both in frequency and in phase [29]. He found that once healers have linked up with the Schumann waves, the right and left hemispheres of the brain become balanced with each other and show 7.8-8 Hz alpha rhythm. After a healer has connected with the client for some time, it has been shown that the brain waves of the recipient also goes into alpha and is phased-synchronized with the brain of the healer as well as right-left balanced. The healer has, in effect linked the client with the earth's magnetic field pulses and has thereby tapped into a tremendous energy source for healing. The Schumann Resonance is thought to act as a wave carrier. This means that when the healer tunes into the Schumann wave frequency, it allows other types of energetic and frequency information to be passed on to the clients.

♦ *Healer Science: Scientists discover the similarity of healer energy and magnetic fields*

Dr. Robert Miller of Atlanta, Georgia, is a research chemist who has studied the biological effects of healers. Miller confirmed previous research by Dr. Bernard Grad that there was a significant similarity between the energetic affects of magnetic fields and field-effects noted with healers [30]. At the same time that Grad's work became public, a number of studies were published which demonstrated the ability of high-intensity magnetic fields to accelerate enzyme kinetics.

♦ *Healer Science: Healing energy is "intelligent"*

Dr. Justa Smith, a biochemist, found that healers were able to increase the enzyme reaction rate over time, and that the longer the healer held a test tube of enzymes, the more rapid the reaction rate [31]. Enzymes direct the building of cell structures, allowing our bodies to get energy from the food we eat, amongst many other functions. Similar effects on enzymes had been noted with *high intensity magnetic fields,* yet the strength of the magnetic fields utilized were approximately *13,000 gauss, 26,000 times the intensity of the earth's magnetic field.* The type of change in enzyme activity noted after exposure to healers was always in a direction of greater health of the cells, and thus of the organism.

> **Whatever enzyme was used, the healers always caused changes in activity, which would result in a push to greater health and energy balance of the sick organism. This healing energy appeared to have an almost *innate intelligence* in the way it could therapeutically distinguish between test tubes of enzymes.**

Magnetic fields could only produce a non-specific increase in the activity of enzymes, whereas, the energy fields of the healers could cause enzymes to either increase or decrease their activity, dependent on what was required for greater health. The measurable increase in enzyme activity by human hands is important because it is believed that any disease or illness can develop from the lack of activity or malfunctioning of enzymes. It would appear that any change in the cellular structure of disease or illness would require a change in enzyme catalysts, which healers are able to achieve. By speeding up different enzymatic reactions, healers assist the body to heal itself [28].

We have an important concept here, the consciousness of the healer is paramount, to tune into and mediate with the universal energy source so that the appropriate transactions can be generated. An artificial magnetic field on it's own, is not intelligent enough to balance a system as complex as the human body!

Healer energies demonstrate similarities to magnetic fields, yet are almost undetectable with conventional EM recording equipment. This obstacle was overcome when Zimmermann used the highly sensitive detector known as a SQUID (Superconducting Quantum Interference Device), that can measure infinitesimally weak magnetic fields. He measured increased magnetic field emission from the hands of psychic healers during healing, in the order of hundreds of times stronger than normal body activity. Dr. Justa smith's research suggests that healers have the ability to selectively affect different enzyme systems in the direction toward greater organization and energy balance.

- ***Healer Science: Healers generate a "unique" brain pattern***

In the United Kingdom, distinguished British psychobiologist and biophysicist Maxwell Cade reported biorhythm entrainment between healers and patients [31]. He utilised a EEG device known as a Mind Mirror, that differs from the traditional EEG in that it used spectral analysis to simultaneously measure eleven different frequencies in each hemisphere of the brain. This device was specifically developed to measure states of consciousness. Cade discovered a new brain wave pattern that had never been found in human beings before. He called it a State 5 pattern (waves are usually Alpha, Beta, Gamma and Delta) and only occurs when human beings are in healing meditation. It wasn't just one peak of brain wave, but three peaks, not only in the Alpha Theta range, but one in the very slow Delta range and one in the rapid Beta range. This triple curve has to date only been found to be dominant in master yogis and those who are more continuously in deep meditation. Yet, this unique complex brainwave pattern became prominent in the brainwaves of patients during the healing process and could be measured when the healer was both in direct contact as well as at a distance from the patient. This state of mind is clearer, sharper, quicker, and more flexible than ordinary states. Thinking feels fluid rather than rigid. Emotions become more available and understandable, easier to work with and transform. Information flows more easily between the conscious, subconscious, and unconscious levels. Intuition, insight, and empathy increase and become more integrated into normal consciousness [31].

Evolutionary Energy: The Discovery of "Stealth" Atoms

The revelation of inter-dimensional elements described as "stealth" atoms, hidden from normal chemical analysis, has finally given us the "missing link" for the makeup and delivery of universal energy.
Susan Joy Rennison

ORMES comes from the acronym Orbitally Rearranged Monoatomic Elements. These elements were discovered in the late 1970s by David Hudson, an Arizona farmer who discovered strange substances mixed in the soil on his land, whilst mining for gold. During the next decade, Hudson spent 8.7 million dollars trying to identify this substance and understand how to work with it [32]. ORMES are literally, precious metal elements in a new form, a new state of matter. They are also referred to as "ORMUS elements" in the monatomic-state (m-state). These peculiar elements belong to the platinum group (platinum, palladium, rhodium, iridium, ruthenium and osmium) and to transition elements (gold, silver, copper, mercury, cobalt and nickel). Hudson had to employ some of the best chemists in the world, using the most sophisticated equipment available and using Russian spectroscopy techniques to unravel this mystery. Eventually, he was able to file 22 US and worldwide patents, 11 ORMUS elements and 11 S-ORMES (ORMES in the superconducting state). These include the above listed elements except for mercury [33].

These elements have very strange properties. It is suspected that they are able to hide in our atmosphere, where they can be easily mistaken for other gases such as argon, nitrogen and carbon dioxide, which might have similar weight and vapor pressure [34]. In addition to existing as a gas and because of their small size and chemical inertness, they easily diffuse into matter, both liquids and solids. It has been suggested that they are captured in water and in most crystal structures such as quartz, magnetite and marble, just to name a few. During physical and chemical activity, ORMUS elements would remain invisible to ordinary detection methods and that is why they are known as "stealth" atoms. In this state, they don't assay or analyse as precious metal elements. They can be produced as a white powder instead of like a metal and can even show up as oil. Moreover, it is possible to extract ORMUS elements from air, rocks, and water, including the water of the body. ORMUS elements can be found in plants and the highest concentration can be found in the gel of the "miracle plant," Aloe Vera! Alchemists believe David Hudson has discovered the fabled white powder of gold!

Inter-dimensional Atoms

Ormus elements are inter-dimensional atoms. In conventional chemistry it is believed that all chemical reactions between elements take place because of the action of their outer electrons. However, transition elements which exist in a monatomic state NEVER share or swapping their electrons with their near neighbours. Instead, the outer electrons of these elements form cooper pairs (or photons) and become whirlwinds of light rotating at super speeds around the atom. A flow of light has now been permanently set up, believed by Andrei Sakharov and Hal Puthoff to be universal energy coming direct from the zero point energy field or the aether and the atoms now behave as if they are a single atom. Another aspect of this energetic state, is that these whirling electrons that have become light, set up a Meissner diamagnetic field. This is a special magnetic field that is unique with no north or south polarity. Once activated, it acts as a protective barrier and resists any further entry of applied magnetic field into the sample, at this stage, it has become perfectly diamagnetic, i.e., it will expel all magnetic fields. Magnetic fields are no longer absorbed, but are forced to go around the sample. So, as the sample is unaffected, it keeps its unique superconductive qualities. This can be observed in the atoms of metals at extremely cold temperatures (2-3 degrees Kelvin). Before Hudson's work, they had never been seen at room temperature. Once the transition group elements in the monatomic state obtain a Meissner field, they will only respond to certain specific outside frequency stimulus, even if the external field is withdrawn. This means the only way to get energy into the sample is to 'tune' the vibrational frequency of the incoming electrons that have become light, to match the vibrational frequency of the superconductor.

> *ORMES and Diamonds*
>
> All the elements that can become ORMES are good conductors, and they are amongst the 82% of all good conductors that form or can be cleaved into octahedron crystals when grown in perfect conditions! There are only three ORMUS elements that don't grow to octahedron crystals by themselves, instead they combine with another element which will become an octahedron crystal when grown in ideal conditions and these are cobalt, rutherium and it is presumed osmium (which in the literature behaves very similarly to rutherium) [35].

Hudson with the help of Hal Puthoff, a well-known and respected physicist, discovered that these elements could exist in two dimensions at once. This occurred when the substance was heated and so with sophisticated equipment he could measure a 5/9ths or 56% weight loss that matched mathematical predictions. The strange thing is that this matter will actually disappear when heated and become visible when it cools down. Yet, it still weighs something even when invisible! Strange stuff indeed! This is the superconductor S-ORMES state and there are many implications both scientific and metaphysical. Hudson says that over 5% of our brains by dry matter weight are made from rhodium and iridium in this high spin state. There is an effect on DNA, and experiments help to verify Hudson's claims that, "It perfects the cells of our body", (DNA discussion to follow). The aura is the Meissner diamagnetic field generated by superconducting ORMES held in our physical body and DNA! David Hudson has presented various lectures on his discoveries and backed up his research findings with parallel research being done in the conventional science world [36].

Ormus in the Air

Vast quantities of these ORMUS elements are being delivered by Space Weather.

Next, we will examine the work of Dr. John Milewski, an internationally recognized leader and consultant in his field of Advanced Materials. He is a professional engineer, scientist, inventor, entrepreneur, writer, publisher, editor and lecturer. Dr. Milewski is a retired staff member of Los Alamos National Labs and has worked previously as a scientific staff member at Exxon Research Center and at Thiokol Chemical Rocket Engine Division [37].

Milewski believes that ORMUS elements are present in our atmosphere and are easily extracted out to form gold beads and white powder. (From this point we will refer to ORMUS elements as just Ormus.) In his investigations into Ormus, he deliberately fused a sample of Ormus glass onto a piece of magnetite and stored it away in a polythene bag, see plate 29. Four years later, in 2003, he was surprised to find beads of gold growing on the opposite side of the magnetite. He believes that the surface structure is such, that the gold is growing. The gold surface is not smooth as would be the case in melted gold, but it has projections that appear **to be reaching out and collecting material from the air**, see plate 30 [38]. Milewski writes:

> "This is not basal growth but tip growth**. It is theorized that the gold comes from the surrounding air**."
>
> "The sample was stored in a sealed plastic bag. Apparently the small gold atoms diffuse through the bag and then were attracted to the magnetite substrate by the energy field set up by the Ormus at the base to react to form metallic gold. For some reason not fully understood the Ormus gold is converted to metallic gold as the atoms touch the surface of the magnetite."

> "It could be the increased magnetic field surrounding the magnetite or the ability that magnetite has to either give up or receive electrons, alone or in combination with the special energy field sent up from the Ormus gold below in the glass." *[Bold added for emphasis]*

This may also give us further clues for the purpose of magnetite in the brain! Milewski gives further examples of old ore samples that had been left over from experiments that he had just left outside exposed to the elements of wind and rain. He found that over time, they became coated with a heavy white powder deposit. He believes that most gold or platinum group metal ores not only contain the ore element as a metal but an even a greater amount of the ore element in the Ormus form. The Ormus material in the glass is the force that is attracting additional material out of the air and water to form the white powder.

Milewski lives in Albuquerque, New Mexico, near the Sandia Mountains. He has been hiking up the mountain trails near his home for ten years and he has noticed in the last few years *significant* amounts of white coating on many of the rocks along and beside the trail. Many call this substance "Caliche" a presumed calcium carbonated material. Prior to living in Albuquerque, he lived in a town call White Rock, near Los Alamos National Laboratories. The town was called White Rock because many of the rocks around the town were covered with this same mysterious, ill-defined, white coating. The town of White Rock is built on a large lava flow. Milewski believes that the lava contains significant amounts of Ormus glass in its structure and is also very strongly paramagnetic. These properties help attract the white powder to form the heavy white coating on the rocks and lava beds at White Rock. Milewski says that he is now paying more attention, and that he has noticed this white coating can be seen on many rocks in many places in town, around the state and in Colorado. His conclusion is that the atmosphere has to be the source of the white powder, which is being attracted by some force within the rocks. He presumes that this force comes from the Ormus glass in the lava rocks to cause such heavy coatings and that the other variety of rocks like the granites, sandstone's, etc. must have a paramagnetic like nature that causes the attraction. The rain captures the Ormes on the way down and deposits them on the rocks where some of it is attracted to stay. If there is not too much or too heavy rain, it does not wash away and after drying up, it hardens into a permanent coating of white powder, see plate 31, showing only one-sided attraction! He has started to devise a series of experiments to investigate this mysterious white powder!

The "Golden" Age is the period of time when vast amounts of high potential energy, in the form of Ormus elements, is delivered to Earth.

Ormus and Gamma Rays 

The dramatic increase in lightning discharge may also be symptomatic of the vast amounts of inter-dimensional m-state elements in our atmosphere. In the previous analysis of gamma ray emission in our atmosphere, there was one significant fact that had been left out. In our atmosphere, "these strong gamma outbursts also seem to *precede* associated lightning discharges by a split second" [39]. This observation can be compared to experiments that produced nuclear level gamma emission from Ormus.

In 1982, Hudson attempted to force a sample of Ormus powder to the low spin-state by the application of extremely high energy in order to make metal [40]. Using an arc furnace, a water-cooled copper crucible with a tungsten electrode mounted above it and atmosphere controlled with argon as the plasma gas, Hudson struck an arc on the sample and within one second, totally destroyed the tungsten electrode. The energy created far exceeded any chemical energy reaction possible and Hudson was so concerned for the safety of his staff that he never attempted to reproduce the procedure. He suspected a nuclear level energy release to be causing the phenomena. In 1991, Hudson's suspicious were confirmed when he found an article in Scientific American [41]. Berkeley Brookhaven had observed that superdeformed high spin atoms, when subjected to external magnetic fields sufficient to affect the nuclear quadripole moment, would cause the nucleus to emit gamma radiation without fissioning. (Energy is released in the fissioning process caused by the splitting an atomic nucleus into two or more lighter nuclei.) The research physicists doing the testing at Berkeley Brookhaven were amazed at their findings, and they confirmed Hudson's suspicions about Ormus elements.

In our atmosphere, it is possible to find all the ingredients of a natural arc discharge, with space weather delivering Ormus elements and extreme high-energy cosmic rays entering the mixture. These extreme cosmic rays are electrically charged and so generate magnetic fields. As already mentioned, some scientists suspect that these extreme cosmic rays are really superconducting cosmic string, misinterpreted as ordinary but very energetic particles [42]. If this is the case, then we have a situation where a meissner field is also generated which will not allow energies of a different resonance to enter and so this will result in a voltage difference and an electrical discharge. However, it is not the electrical discharge from the cosmic string that ignites the Ormus to produce gamma rays, it is the magnetic field! This explanation helps us to understand the sequence of events being observed as nuclear level gamma emission from ORMEs in the atmosphere which precede lightning and as already stated, fits the observation in electronics that the magnetic field always leads the electrostatic field. This scenario would also apply to any highly "magnetic entity" falling to Earth. More simply, an analogy would be like a room full of balloons filled with hydrogen. A small spark would cause the extremely combustible hydrogen to ignite. Our atmosphere is now highly charged and stray magnetic fields are causing ignition in the form of gamma rays!

Ormus and Cosmic Lattice Goo?

We have mentioned that Ormus can show up as different substances and recently, it was found in a very unusual place! There is a very curious story about a potentially dangerous situation for astronauts on the International Space Station, undertaking a long five and a half-hour space walk to do repairs [43]. In January 2005, the media reported that the space station's stabilizing gyroscopes repeatedly became overloaded with a mysterious torque, and they had to be relieved periodically by firing rocket thrusters located on the Russian half of the station. On at least one occasion, and contrary to mission control procedures, these thrusters appear to have been activated when the two crew members were working dangerously close to them. Back down on Earth, this caused a row between Russian and American scientists in mission control, due to the breach of protocol. Now, what is mysterious, is that during their 225-mile-high excursion, the astronauts also inspected the station's vents and found a large patch of dark, oily residue and a white, honeycombed substance. Reports say that it was not immediately known what the "strange goo" was, but it was called "an important discovery".

Even though there is no scientific explanation to be found in the public domain, it is possible to do our own analysis. The discovery of the white powder and an oily substance has all the hallmarks of being Ormus. Incredibly, it was also demonstrating the structure of the Cosmic Lattice, which is described as "honeycombed energy cells", just like the geometry found on the Sun! [44] There is no question of *how* Ormus got onto the side of the International Space Station. Since 1989, frequent blasts of space weather have been delivering this energy, which scientists have acknowledged as being "different". Our understanding of the properties of Ormus elements provides valuable insight into new electrical phenomena occurring in the atmosphere of Earth. The changes taking place are complex, but an understanding of the behavior of plasma, and theories that can be tested by laboratory experiment, help us to understand the massive electrical changes taking place on Earth.

Yet, the question arises: why is space weather delivering highly *catalytic* energy? Well, the Earth is a complex energetic system, being driven into a higher evolutionary state. Studies show that if an energetic transition occurs too slowly and reaches a critical tipping point, the system may collapse completely and the original state of the system becomes very hard to restore. Therefore, catalytic energy speeds the whole process up and ensures that the system reaches the next level without total catastrophe [45].

Furthermore, new studies show how these inter-dimensional elements have highly beneficial effects on our biological internet—human DNA!

Superconducting Your DNA

"To live and survive, a living system must have access to other functional levels and other mechanisms beyond those contained in our present physics, electromagnetics, and biochemistry."
Tom Bearden

The term "junk" DNA (deoxyribonucleic acid) was first coined to hide the fact that molecular biologists had absolutely no idea of the purpose of 90% of our DNA, so what they did not understand became the "junk". Nowadays, scientists understand that 10% of our DNA is being used for building proteins but the other 90% is responsible for building the body, data storage and communication [46]. Now, there is a radical new concept of how DNA works. Russian researchers working with linguists and geneticists have now discovered that the genetic code follows the same rules as our human languages. This means that words and intent can program our DNA. Consequently, the correct light frequencies can also be used to repair genetic defects, removing the need to cut and splice!

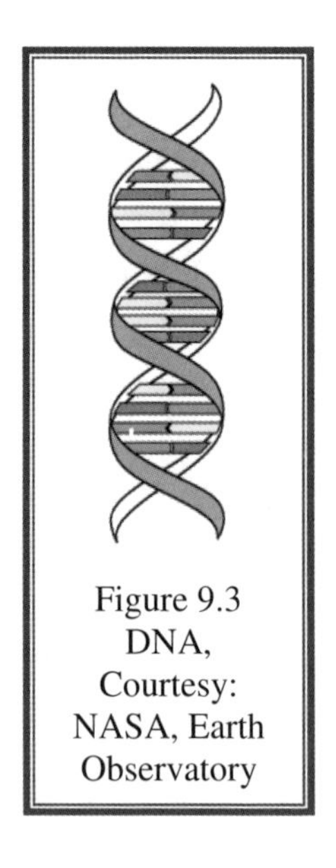

Figure 9.3
DNA,
Courtesy:
NASA, Earth
Observatory

To prove this, Russian biophysicist Peter Garjajev and colleagues carried out experiments that captured and transmitted information patterns of DNA, thus reprogramming cells to another genome. [47] From the paper called *The DNA-wave Biocomputer,* we find the following description:

> "The *quantum holographic* DNA-wave biocomputer model describes the morphology and dynamics of DNA, as a self-calibrating antenna working by phase conjugate adaptive resonance capable of both receiving and transmitting quantum holographic information stored in the form of

diffraction patterns (which in MRI can be shown to be *quantum holograms*)."[48]

The DNA helical structure of DNA appears to act as a holographical "projector" of the DNA code. We know that complex signals can be encoded in electromagnetic (EM) fields, because this is how television and radio signals are coded and decoded, but even more complex information can be encoded into holographic images. DNA is also an organic superconductor that can work at normal body temperature, (as opposed to the artificial variety that only works at extremely low temperatures between minus 200 and 140°C). As one of the properties of a superconductor is the ability to store light, this also helps to explain the ability of DNA to store vast amounts of information. Hence, in the nuclei of each cell of the human body, the DNA carries the blueprint of the structure of our whole body and also the code of how to process this information. Yet, the most interesting aspect of the latest research by Garjajev et al. was that they found out that our DNA can generate magnetized wormholes and hence attract information from outside of time and space [49]. Normally, these super-small wormholes are highly unstable and are maintained only for the tiniest fractions of a second. However, under certain conditions, stable wormholes can develop.

DNA can retrieve information held outside of time and space.

These concepts are supported by experiments that are undisputed. In the mid-1980s, the physicist Peter Gariaev at the Institute of Physics in the Academy of Sciences of the USSR first noted an unexpected DNA phantom phenomena effect in his experiments when researching the vibration modes of DNA. When DNA was bombarded with laser light and then removed from the scattering chamber, a ghost holographic image remained. This could be measured by the scattered light coming from the phantom DNA field. As long as the chamber is not disturbed, the effect is measurable for long periods of time. Researchers insist that this effect is NOT the electron emission captured by Kirlian photography but something more fundamental. Gariaev and co-reseacher Vladimir Poponin claim to have demonstrated subtle fields emerging from the underlying "sea of infinite potential", or "zero-point energy", or aether! [50]. There is evidence that Ormus elements work to help DNA communicate with a non-physical information field that surrounds and interpenetrates the body. From Hudson's 1995 Dallas lecture, he stated:

"Now what does it do in the body? It literally corrects the DNA, by a process the equivalent of a denaturing solution, the DNA relaxes and recombines corrected. So all diseases that originate with a problem with the DNA can be corrected".

Hudson's claims were supported, the same year by an article in Scientific America called *Electric Genes,* revealed a surprising effect when DNA was given a little help [48].

"The researchers examined the electrical properties of short lengths of double-helix DNA in which there was a ruthenium atom at each end of one of the strands. Meade and Kayyem estimated from earlier studies that a short single strand of DNA ought to conduct up to 100 electrons a second. Imagine their astonishment when they measured the rate of flow along the ruthenium-doped double helix: the current was up by a factor of more than 10,000 times-over a million electrons a second. It was as if the double helix was behaving like a piece of molecular wire."

This experiment confirmed what chemists had suspected for some time, that the double helix might create a highly conductive path along the axis of the molecule, a route that does not exist in the single strand. Again, in 1997, a scientific report on DNA reported announced:

"A DNA molecule with a chemical group artificially tethered to one end appears to mediate a chemical change far down the helix, causing a patch of damaged DNA to be mended." [51]

Iridium is now being used in a revolutionary new type of cancer treatment that is yielding encouraging results [52]. As reported by The Platinum Metals Review, the new treatment involves the use of Iridium as a radiation device, and markedly cuts down the amount of time spent by patients at hospital. Other research has also studied the treatment of cancers using platinum and ruthenium. Apparently, the application of a platinum compound to an altered DNA state (as in the case of a cancer) will cause the DNA to relax and become corrected. It is known that both iridium and rhodium have anti-aging properties, that ruthenium and platinum compounds interact with DNA, and that gold and the precious metals can activate the endocrine glandular system in a way that heightens awareness and aptitude to extraordinary levels. This is relevant because the gold and platinum frequencies of light are associated with *New Energy* and are specifically available for our evolution, see the small section "Gold and Platinum Catalytic Energy".

It would seem that ORMUS works by opening up the inter-dimensional doorways of DNA and keeping them stable. In the superconducting state and at a

Gold and Platinum Catalytic Energy

Gold and platinum are part of a group of elements found in the middle of the periodic table known as "transition group elements". They are in an uncertain state as regards their positive or negative electro-charge behavior, hence the name "transition". For these elements, the electrons in the outer shells are always half filled or half empty. Elements with fewer electrons in the outer shells tend to be electro-positive, and those with more electrons in the outer shells tend to be electro-negative. These transition elements possess a unique property in that the electrons in the partially filled outer orbitals can interchange under the right conditions with electrons in the partially filled inner orbitals. This is the underlying basis of catalytic reactions. A catalytic reaction is a chemical reaction that occurs much more rapidly than normal without the catalyst itself participating in the reaction.

certain threshold, a meissner magnetic field is set up that expels all frequencies except for a particular "resonance" frequency. This means only the "correct" frequency of light is accepted, allowing DNA to code correctly, which improves communication between the DNA in individual cells and quantum coherent communication with non-physical information realms. ORMUS researcher Barry Carter gives the analogy of a cell phone in each cell.

> "With the ORMUS elements I think we can demonstrate a system of instantaneous communication that takes place between all living things and, perhaps, even with spirit."
>
> "It helps me to think of the ORMUS materials as tiny cell phones in every living cell. When the ORMUS elements are depleted, by modern chemical agriculture and food preparation technology, these cell phones behave as if their batteries are weak and their antennas are broken. This means that they can only reach to the cell next door but cannot maintain continuous coherent communication with the cells in your big toe, for example."
>
> "When we eat foods grown in soil where there are ORMUS elements it is like they go into these cell phones; recharging their batteries and repairing their antennas so that coherent communication can take place between all of the cells of the body. It is like the small signal power of each cell phone is reinforced by resonance with the signal of every other cell phone so that instead of a single five-watt phone you have a trillion watt transmitter capable of communicating with the farthest reaches of the universe instantaneously." *[End of excerpts]*

Energy workers can entrain to particularly frequencies of light and are capable of directing healing energies using their consciousness. In doing so, they deliver inter-dimensional "spirit" particles, which help to "perfect" and "balance".

Chapter Ten

The Master Diamond Template

"Know thyself"

An ancient injunction inscribed over the temple of Apollo at Delphi. The teachings held that to know another, we must first know ourselves

The Science of Sacred Geometry

In the book, 'Cracking the Da Vinci Code' by Simon Cox, sacred geometry is defined as "The art of passing on divine wisdom through the use of geometric forms such as symbols" [1]. This definition relates to the tradition of sacred geometry being a cypher that exists between initiates. Certain knowledge was considered so divine that it was thought necessary to erect barriers to prevent this information being learned by the "uninitiated". In fact, this has been going on for thousands of years and so sacred geometry was blended with mystical beliefs and esoteric traditions. Even today, many books and films are veiled, containing hidden meanings for the initiated. Well known examples are; the *Wizard of Oz, Alice in Wonderland, Star Wars, The Matrix Trilogy, The Lord of the Rings* trilogy etc. In recent times, there is a much wider audience, becoming aware of knowledge that has been embedded, literally, into ancient and modern culture.

The popularity of Dan Brown's, *The Da Vinci Code,* which has sold over 40 million copies, is evidence of this growing awareness [2]. The factual aspects of this particular book, were largely gleaned from several other books, which are also bestsellers. The question arises: is it really possible that knowledge can be hidden for such long periods of time and communicated from one generation to the next with symbols only known to a few? The answer has to be yes! Today we have the example of François Mitterand, (1919-1989) who was the President of France for fourteen years. In his time in office, he took the opportunity to spend public money and transform the heart of Paris with many architectural works and monuments. Mitterand was not known to belong to any esoteric secret societies, but he is remembered for his pronounced taste for hermeticism and sacred geometry and so he was accused of transforming "Paris into a journey for initiates" [3]. The most obvious of these constructions are the *Grande Arche of La Deféense,* completed in 1989. Interestingly, the architect Dane Otto van Spreckelsen who designed the Grande Arche called it a 'porte cosmique' – a 'stargate'. The other famous structure is the glass pyramid, a feature of the *New Louvre*, built in exactly the same proportions as the Great Pyramid of Giza. Mitterand even built a 'temple', it was set in the Parc du Champs-de-Mars, fronted by the elaborate *Monument to the Rights of Man and the Citizen.* He is also known to have paid nocturnal visits on a private basis, which were kept secret until after his death [4]. What can be said, is that as we approach a New World Age, a continued rise of human consciousness and the destruction of old paradigms, scientific and spiritual endeavors are making certain truths more accessible to anyone seeking enlightenment. We will examine the basics of sacred geometry and universal laws, which will then lead us to lesser known aspects that are relevant to how we can facilitate our enlightenment today.

It can be shown that everything that exists in the Universe, obeys certain mathematical laws. When we seek to understand these laws, then the signature of the divine becomes obvious and will result in our enlightenment. It is well known that certain numbers and ratios constantly come up in nature as well as in architecture and art. An example is the "golden ratio", known by the Greek letter phi (ϕ), also known as the "divine proportion", the "golden mean" or the "golden section". This is the ratio of length to width of approximately 1.618 and it is deemed as visually pleasing. The DNA spiral, the program for life, is based on the golden section. It measures 34 angstroms long by 21 angstroms wide for each full cycle of its double helix spiral, where 34 and 21, are numbers in the Fibonacci series and their ratio, 1.6190476 closely approximates phi, 1.6180339 [5]. The Fibonacci Sequence is an infinite sequence of numbers beginning 1, 1, 2, 3, 5, 8, 13, 21, 34 where each number is the sum of the two numbers preceding it. Thus1+1=2, 1+2=3, 2+3=5, 3+5=8, 5+8=13, and so on. For any value larger than three, the ratio between any two consecutive numbers is 1:1.618, or the golden ratio. This fibonacci sequence is often seen in nature, like the number of petals on a flower, the spirals on a pinecone and the spiral of the snail shell. These are examples of how nature uses this sequence for self-organization. The ancient Greeks believed that understanding the number would help one to get closer to the divine, moreover God was *in* the number.

"Let no one destitute of geometry enter my doors."
Plato (c. 427-347 B.C.E.)

Sacred geometry has been the cornerstone of esoteric teaching regarding the hidden order of the Universe. Traditionally, we are taught that the Pythagoreans, Greek philosophical mathematicians, first discovered "Platonic solids" and their regularities, so they were first called the "Pythagorean solids" [6]. When the ancient Greek philosopher Plato discovered them, he wrote about them in great detail in his book, *Timaeus*, and so the Platonic solids were later renamed after him. There are 5 Platonic solids and these are essentially the basis for all other solid geometry [7]. The Ancient Greeks, in their love for geometry, called these five solids, the "atoms of the universe" and they were also sometimes referred to as "cosmic figures". It was believed that all physical matter is made up of Platonic solids atoms with mystical attributes represented by their connection with earth, air, fire, water and aether. These philosophers felt that the figures also had a spherical property, where one Platonic solid fits in a sphere, which alternately fits inside another Platonic solid, again fitting in another sphere. The Platonic solids have certain characteristics:

- All faces are the same size.
- All the edges are all the same length.
- They have only one size of interior angles between faces e.g. the cube has 90% angle.
- If a Platonic solid is placed in a sphere, all points will touch the surface of the sphere.

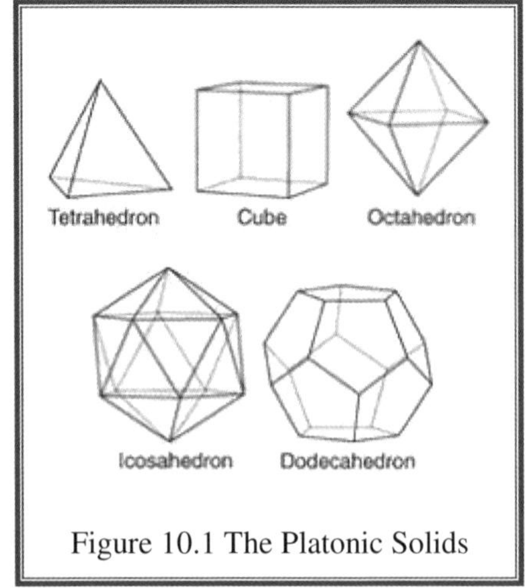

Figure 10.1 The Platonic Solids

In the 1980s, Professor Robert Moon at the University of Chicago demonstrated that the entire Periodic Table of Elements – literally everything in the physical world is based on these same five forms! [5]

In metaphysical tradition, this geometry also represents the shape of energy fields.

Toroidal Geometry

Isn't it astonishing that all the secrets have been preserved for so many years just so that we could discover them!
Orville Write

The torus is used to describe a special form in our physical material world, as well as the invisible "subtle" worlds. The toroidal form describes the area and volume of a torus or the so-called doughnut shape, see figure 10.2. There is a wide range of use in science for the toroidal shape. It has been discovered to be the most efficient way to wind an electrical transformer, as a coil wound in this configuration produces very clean, highly accurate, precise and reliable power. Hence, toroidal transformers are employed by engineers in high-end audio equipment and other electronics to lower distortion and increase power at the same time. They are used for particle accelerators, and space energy storage magnets, which result in small external magnetic fields.

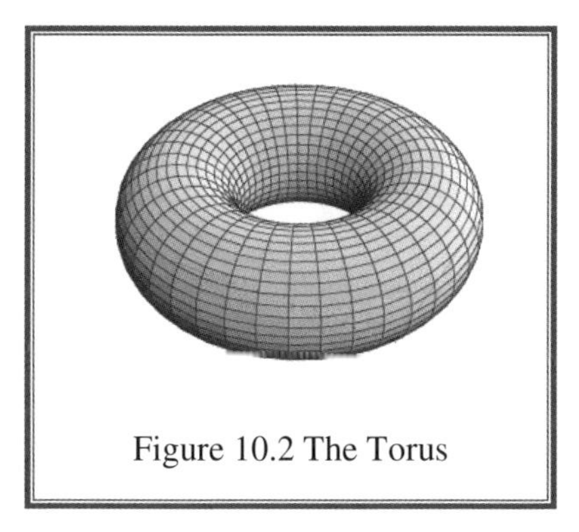

Figure 10.2 The Torus

The torus is an important part of sacred geometry. Since ancient times, seers have confirmed that the human aura appears as a series of nested spherical torus formations. As we have already understood, The Universal Calibration lattice is in the shape of an elongated torus with the energy flowing around the body and looping around to connect above the head and below the feet in the central core energy. The energy center known as a chakra is shaped like a two-ended trumpet, which is the shape of a spherical torus on its axis.

The vortex concept appears in many different cultures, most often as the mythology of the World Tree, with the tree roots, branches and tree trunk creating the vortex shape. The connection here, is that the vortex can be thought of as the inside of the torus. Moreover, the geometric shape of the torus describes the self-reflexive nature of consciousness.

The torus allows a vortex of energy to form, which bends back along itself and re-enters itself. It 'inside-outs', continuously flowing back into itself, continually refreshing and influencing itself.

A major branch of geometry is the study of geometrical structures on manifolds [8]. A manifold is a curved space of some dimension. For example, the surface of a sphere, and the torus (the surface of a doughnut), are both 2-dimensional manifolds. Here, the manifold only acts as a background for some mathematical object defined upon it, as a canvas is the background for an oil painting. This geometry was how Einstein's theory of General Relativity describes the Universe – the whole of space and time – as a 4-dimensional manifold. Manifolds are used to understand the large-scale structure of the Universe in cosmology and since the mathematics of higher dimensions, string theory hypothesizes that the universe is at least a ten or eleven dimensional manifold.

We have already discussed that science is starting to model the electron as toroidal vortex and new theories suggest that all particles are really rotating objects in the aether, hereby returning to old discarded ideas. John Ernst Worrel Keely (1827-1898) was an eccentric scientist and has the accolade of being the first sub-atomic physicist in the study of alternative physics and science. His toroidal atomic structure was derived from his development of the science of vibratory physics. The Keely atom is depicted in a stylized format in figure 10.3 and even though it is closer to a spherical shell, it is still considered toroidal. He discovered that the substructure of the proton was a vortex particle made up of three sub-nuclear particles, also vortices [9]. Further research led him to believe think that this three particle substructure continued to smaller and smaller levels of particles, as a fractal, 27 levels down from the basic proton. In mainstream physics, it took until 1958 for the physicist Richard Feynman to eventually identify the first level of the substructure of an atom. Feynman called the three particles making up the proton "quarks", over 60 years after Keely's work! He was later awarded a Nobel Prize in 1965 for his work in quantum electrodynamics.

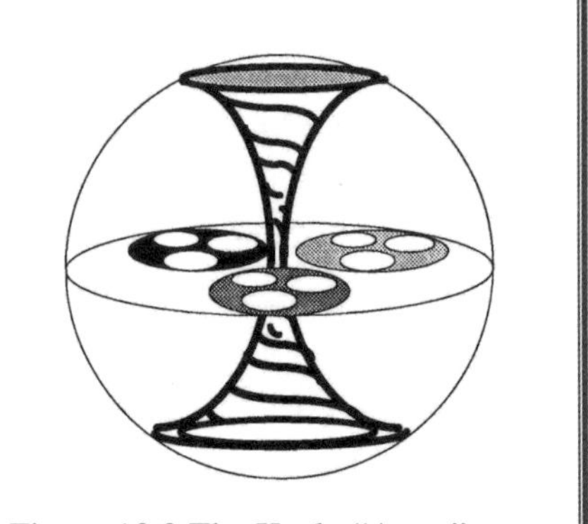

Figure 10.3 The Keely "Atom" Proton Showing Toroidal Structure. Courtesy: Dan A. Davidson

Nowadays, we can use computer simulation to help us understand atoms. BEC's are a new state of matter in which a collection of about 1 million atoms, all at exactly the same energy level, behave exactly alike one uniform "superatom" [10]. Plate 32 shows a computer simulation displaying tornado-like vortices forming within a spinning Bose-Einstein condensate (BEC). These BEC atoms can be compared to cloud of atoms in the same way as a laser is compared to a light bulb. Since BECs were first observed in 1995, physicists worldwide have devised experiments to probe their unique properties. This simulation helped confirm that BEC's are superfluids— the conventional explanation is a kind of liquid/gas that flows without friction. If the BEC had behaved as a classic fluid (such as water), it would form a single vortex in the center of the trap as it spins (like water going down a plug hole). However, if it were a superfluid (such as liquid helium), it would resist rotating completely until the angles forced on it by the elliptical trap gave rise to an even number of well-organized quantum vortices. As the aether is also modeled as a superfluid we must compare the behavior of BECs with plasma and specifically aether particles and so this discovery should serve to give us a greater understanding of the underlying fabric of our reality.

The Diamond Lattice and Universal Consciousness 

In String theory, the torus is known as the "perfect" shape and there are mathematical models that describe how the entire universe may be shaped like a torus. String theory postulates that all matter in the universe is connected by an infinite number of miniscule, energetic vibrating strings that pulsate back and forth in spirals from one single point in space [12]. All these strings vibrate out the exact same distance (forming a perfect sphere), and then vibrate back to the point of origin. There are so many strings that some cross over at certain node points, and all strings that form nodes do so in the exact same place relative to the length of the string. At these node points, the energy would be stronger, because they contain the energy of two strings working together rather than just one. Farther out on the string, other node points also form where the strings intersect, all in the same relative position on the length of the string. If you connected all these nodes, you would find yourself drawing 3D geometrical objects, but not just any 3D geometrical objects. All lines have to be the same length, with sides the same shape, and each angle the same, all fitting perfectly into a sphere. There are only five known geometrical patterns that fit these criteria—the Platonic or sacred solids! These basic structures form the core foundation for each dimensional universe. The higher dimensions as postulated by String theory, are not mysterious and random. They have a very definite structure and are

> Itzak Bentov in his final book called "A Brief Tour of Higher Consciousness", published just after his passing is dedicated to the idea that all reality including consciousness itself can be modeled with the toroidal manifold. His diagrams show galaxies as being toroidal forms with "white holes" putting out energy while "black holes" on the opposite side taking it back in [9+].

considered to be crystalline. According to theoretical physicist Saul-Paul Sirag, who explores the relationship between consciousness and physics, crystallographic structures form hexagonal lattices that give a honeycomb effect. We recognize the importance of the hexagonal because it is really a two-dimensional representation of an octahedron, figure 10.4 and figure 10.5 show the octahedron as we look down perpendicular to one of it's sides. Simply explained, each point, each vertex within the lattice is actually an active point that can act on the space that it is sitting in. The entire lattice acts on space and creates a new space and that new space is toroidal space. Membrane theory suggests that there is a master seven dimensional lattice. This is known as the E7

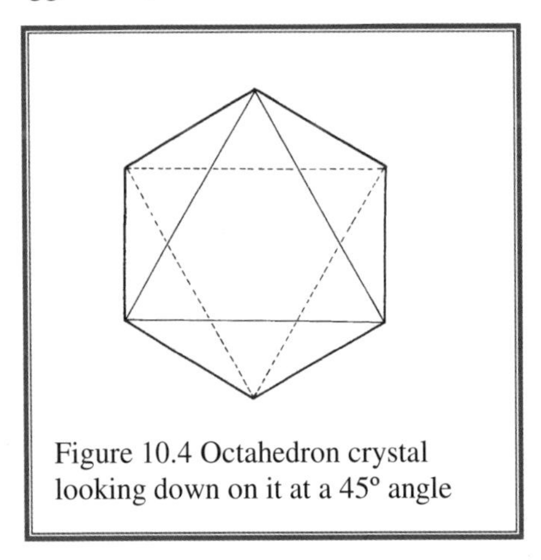
Figure 10.4 Octahedron crystal looking down on it at a 45° angle

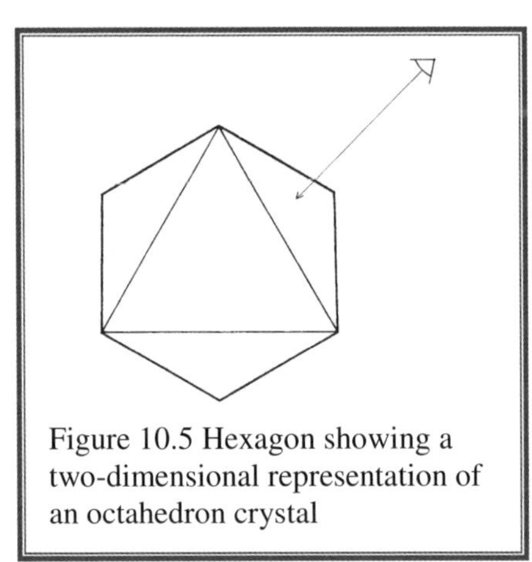
Figure 10.5 Hexagon showing a two-dimensional representation of an octahedron crystal

Lattice that creates the seven hidden dimensions of eleven-dimensional space-time. There are an infinite number of lattices defined "A" and "D" type but only 3 "E" type lattices which correspond directly to Platonic solids. We find that E-6 corresponds to the tetrahedron; E-7 corresponds to the octahedron and the cube, which are considered dual to each, (meaning that one can be created by connecting the midpoints of the faces of the other); and the E-8 which corresponds to the icosahedron and dodecahedron, which are also dual to each other. That accounts for the five Platonic solids. Interestingly, Sirag says he identifies the E7 lattice with universal consciousness [13].

Diamond Consciousness

Merkabah teachings describe a layer of light in the human energy field that consists of two interlaced tetrahedron energy fields, one with the tip pointing upwards and another with the tip pointing down, denoted by the "Star of David", see figure 6.6. Some consider this geometry to represent a separation of our consciousness into two parts, thus enabling us to experience life in the depths of the 3rd dimension. Yet, physics theory suggests that the tetrahedron and octahedron energy fields are in fact counter-rotating within each other, where the tetrahedron and octahedron represent two primary levels of aether density that must exist in the Universe [14]. So, as we move into a new era dominated by space weather and presumably an aetheric density that we have not experienced in such quantity before, the octahedron energy can be activated and empowered with *New Energy.* The strengthening of the octahedron energy field promotes a flow of energy between the mental and emotional aspects of our light body, facilitating greater balance. This is especially important as our sense of balance is tested. This will occur, as we are confronted by challenging situations and world events that impact us more, while our feelings of connectiveness with humanity and the Earth continue to increase.

With the restructuring of the Earth's electromagnetic grid, completed at the end of 2002, we are now moving into a time of greater awareness of universal consciousness. Curiously, this is the exact same time that D. Swarovski & Co., the world-famous Austrian crystal manufacturer, built the world's biggest octahedron, a magnificent one ton crystal piece designed to resemble the shape of a natural diamond. This was presented as a gift to GIA, the Gemological Institute of America (GIA) and now takes pride of place in the GIA "Tower of Brilliance". The symbolism is immense and maybe this can be taken as a sign that a major energy shift has taken place [15].

Art is another way to convey the concept of the diamond lattice and universal consciousness and we can cite the visionary experiences of the highly regarded artist Alex Grey. The picture "Theologue" was inspired by a deep meditation where he found himself staring into an infinite electric grid that radiated from his mind [16]. This perceptual grid or lattice was where time and space were woven – representing universal mind – both the source and weaving loom, see plate 33.

"Know Thyself"

The concept of geometry ordering our reality is becoming more widely known. Dan Brown's book *The Da Vinci Code,* revealed that the planet Venus traces out a perfect pentagram every 8 years. Actually, according to detail from James Ferguson's, *Astronomy Explained Upon Sir Isaac Newton's Principles*, published in 1799, these are the facts. The pentagram occurs by plotting the recurrence of Venus' westward elongation from the Sun, over five consecutive synodic periods, and this will create the points of a pentagram. This period is approximately 584 days long, each period determining a different point of the observed pentagram—taking approximately eight years, five days to complete the geometrical figure. Simply, one would get a pentagram by picking any sunrise date on which the morning star is prominent and then repeating the observation at 584-day intervals following that date [17].

According to sky watchers, if you took a picture of the Sun at the same time each day, it would NOT stay in the same position. In fact the shape traced out by the Sun over the course of a year is called an Analemma, see figure 10.6. This is the infinity sign — the metaphysical symbol for balance and harmony! The Sun's apparent shift is caused by the Earth's motion around the Sun when combined with the tilt of the Earth's rotation axis. The Sun will appear at its highest point of the Analemma during summer and at its lowest during winter [18]. Iona Miller writes:

> "Wherever we look, from the Microcosm to the Macrocosm, the sub-quantal to the Cosmic, chaos or non-linear dynamics and complexity is either right in sight or hidden just below the surface. Notions of form, pattern, geometry and structure can be found at the deepest levels of both matter and the psyche. Its domain lies at the edges of knowledge where our perceptions of structure and order end. Yet chaos reveals in its own depths, hidden degrees of order and structure that resonate with the soul and reveal to us the basic forms and structures repeated throughout nature and throughout our nature. Topology and geometrical relationships are a more fundamental way of understanding both matter and consciousness" [19]

Figure 10.6 The Analemma is the "figure 8" pattern the sun makes in the sky over the course of one year, due to the combination of the earth's tilt and orbit around the Sun. Credit: NOAA

So in the same way that we are discovering the secrets of the heavens and higher dimensions, we also learn about ourselves! The most advanced energy balancing techniques in the world will work with the following geometrical patterns

- Figure eight loops – infinity signs
- Diamond light body – diamonds
- Universal Calibration Lattice – toroidal multidimensional energy field
- Orbital Sweep - 8 petal spiral wave

The figure eight loops that radiate out from the chakras, are conduits that allow electrical charge to be distributed. They contribute to the self-balancing

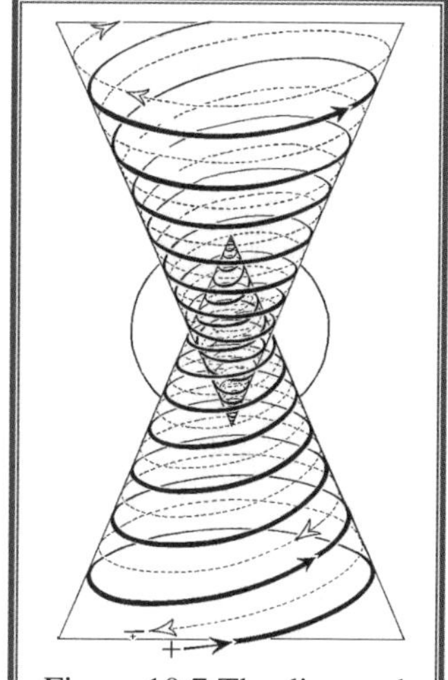
Figure 10.7 The diamond appears when spiralling energies meet.

and self-regulating nature of the UCL. In chaos theory, the figure-eight loop is one of the "strange attractors" known as Lorenz's Butterfly. This pattern allows energy adaptation and self-organization for evolutionary change. Also, the figure-eight is derived from the cross-section of a torus, a universal feature of electromagnetism. The Templates of Light are multi-dimensional. We can explain them by considering that higher dimensional energy travels in spirals and when these energies interacts in our dimension they focus to a point, as revealed by the research of Dr. Bevan Reid and Dr. Serge Barsamian, see figure 10.7. Secondly, this has to be combined with the universal principle of two opposite energy flows. Dr. Valery Uvarov reveals:

> "A living being is formed at the point (zone) of refraction of energy flows in the multi-layered energy system of the Creator"
>
> "For the Ancient Egyptian priests, BA denoted the focal point (of refraction) of an energy or light flow, that spread out evenly from it in all directions (globally and at once, without and within) — like the focal point of an optical system, refracting the flow of light entering an optical device from the environment outside. Both the photographic camera and the human eye function on this same principle" [20].

The "layers upon layers of light and energy" is the explanation for the emergence of the diamond, as there are refraction points associated with each layer. Furthermore, as inter-dimensional beings of light, our energy fields are toroidal, in accordance with aether theory. Yet, according to Professor Thomas F. Banchoff who is a geometer, when you project a three-dimensional torus in four-space, a diamond appears! See plate 34 for an artist's impression [21].

Our Diamond Reality Revealed

The following is from the beginning of the international bestseller, *The Power of Now* by Eckhart Tolle [22]. This book is greatly appreciated for the depth of wisdom and love that emanates from each page. With a simple question and answer format, it is based on the Tolle's experience of spiritual transformation. These paragraphs from the introduction reveal Tolle's moment of enlightenment, providing additional significance to this section.

The Power of Now Diamond

> "One night not long after my twenty-ninth birthday, I woke up in the early hours with a feeling of absolute dread. I had woken up with such a feeling many times before, but this time it was more intense than it had ever been. … I could feel that a deep longing for annihilation, for nonexistence, was now becoming much stronger than the instinctive desire to continue to live."
>
> "'I cannot live with myself any longer.' This was the thought that kept repeating itself in my mind. Then suddenly I became aware of what a peculiar thought it was. 'Am I one or two? If I cannot live with myself, there must be two of me: the 'I' and the 'self' that 'I' cannot live with.' 'Maybe,' I thought, 'only one of them is real.'"
>
> "I was so stunned by this strange realization that my mind stopped. I was fully conscious, but there were no more thoughts. Then I felt drawn into what seemed like a vortex of energy. It was a slow movement at first and then accelerated. I was gripped by an intense fear, and my body started to shake. I heard the words 'resist nothing,' as if spoken inside my chest. I could feel myself being sucked into a void. It felt as if the void was inside myself rather than outside. Suddenly, there was no more fear, and I let myself fall into that void. I have no recollection of what happened after that."
>
> "I was awakened by the chirping of a bird outside the window. I had never heard such a sound before. My eyes were still closed, and **I saw the image of a precious diamond**. Yes, if a diamond could make a sound, this is what it would be like. I opened my eyes. The first light of dawn was filtering through the curtains. Without any thought, I felt, I knew, that there is infinitely more to light than we realize... That day I walked around the city in utter amazement at the miracle of life on earth, as if I had just been born into this world."
>
> "For the next five months, I lived in a state of uninterrupted deep peace and bliss. After that, it diminished somewhat in intensity, or perhaps it just seemed to because it became my natural state. I could still function in the world, although I realized that nothing I ever did could possibly add anything to what I already had."

In the book, *Reality Revealed: The Theory of Multidimensional Reality* (1978), authors Douglas Vogt and Gary Sultan outlined a theory that is so thought provoking, that once it is seriously considered, it has to change our view of reality [23]. The theory does need to be revised in the light of recent scientific experiment, as several ideas were based on explaining prevailing theories, which have since been proven to be false. To the credit of Vogt & Sultan, if they had used more of their own theory to explain our reality, they would have come up with an even more startling model. One major assumption was accepting that the speed of light is a constant, which has been discredited by experiment. Another false assumption was accepting the Big Bang theory and the concept of homogeneity in the universe, which is also not observed. Nevertheless, "Multidimensional Reality" is highly relevant to diamond geometry and universal consciousness, so a brief summary is offered here.

The theory states that everything in the universe is made up of information, and is stored in a computer-like structure called the "diehold". The name "diehold" represents a place that holds the forms, "template" or "dies" (a metalworking term) which refers to type of mold or method of patterning, for more details see the small section, "What Does "The Diehold" Mean?" [24]. From now on we will use the term "Master Diamond Template" for reasons to follow.

What Does "The Diehold" Mean?

The term "diehold" seems to have been coined to describe a place (like the hold of a ship) which holds the forms, templates, or 'dies', (a metalworking term), of the patterns of reality. This means that the diehold is 'outside of reality', and so 'transmits' the information of existence, which organizes and gives rise to 'all of what is'. The expression, 'the die is cast' or 'the die has been cast', refers to a mold (die) which has been cast (made). Once the mold is made, everything that comes from it, will have the shape of the mold. 'The die is cast' thus means that a pattern has been laid down, and that subsequent events will conform to the pattern.

The Master Diamond Template represents Universal Consciousness, the perfect transmitter and receiver. This assertion is based on octahedron crystal geometry being the most perfect of the cube crystal group. There is perfect internal symmetry and an unusual growing characteristic that is not shared by any other geometry. At this point, we have to remember that scientists have absolutely no idea why crystals grow in the specific shapes with the angles the same for each element. These so-called inanimate crystals demonstrate Universal Intelligence! Vogt and Sultan suggested that this shape will have an effect on the expansion of the Universe and that a cosmological model can be based on this structure. Other researchers have had similar ideas, including Alexander S. Szalay and colleagues at Johns Hopkins University in Baltimore. They proposed that sound waves generated during the early history of the universe may have caused the periodic spacing observed in patterns of galaxy clusters and intervening voids. The suggestion is that only acoustic waves with certain frequencies became part of galactic structure. In 1997, these scientists stated that if they were right, the same architecture observed in galactic surveys should be apparent in the cosmic microwave background [25]. This theory has now been substantiated by direct observational evidence of the Cosmic Microwave Background, which displays diamond geometry as already outlined.

It is theorized that the Master Diamond Template resides in the first dimension, a place where there is no width no length, no time and space. The information from the Master Diamond Template is transmitted into the second dimension in the form of a "pulse modulation". The Second Dimension is the transmission dimension made up of pure information, which exists as magnetic lines of force. In the information state, magnetic fields predominate, but in the state of matter, the electrostatic fields predominate. Hence, the importance of the new theoretical understanding of the photon – "a messenger of light" – as pure static magnetic field. This also explains why we are seeing huge "spheres of light", they are just galactic sized "messengers of light" carrying information to transform the Earth! Curiously, the physicist Bibhas De, a student of Hannes Alfvén, suggests that the ultimate nature of the universe, can be symbolized by the magnetic field and another process with time variation that is NOT time [26].

All matter is made up of frequencies that represent the information of the system and exists in the third dimension. Only some of the frequencies are related to the actually make-up of matter and others are controlling frequencies. The crystal is the unique building block of this state of matter and all the remaining dimensions. Each element has its own frequency which forms unique angles associated with that element's unique crystal shape. (It is a fact that any geometrical form can be decomposed into a set of waves that describe the total potential in space and time. The mathematics to do this was discovered by Fourier, the 19th century French scientist.) A significant aspect to this theory is that there is a carrier-wave frequency from the second to the remaining dimensions where all the frequencies are superimposed for transmission. Magnetite (Fe_3O_4) is highlighted as a mineral made up mostly of iron that has the unique attribute of being the only natural magnet on the planet. When this natural magnet is grown in ideal conditions, it forms the octahedron shape. Conversely, if magnetism is mostly the carrier wave, then the shape it will produce will be the octahedron. Hence, it is theorized

The Octahedron Crystal

The octahedron shape is the most perfect of cube crystal group and the only crystal of the 32 groups, that has all perfect 111 faces. The octahedron shape is the only crystal in which the electrical resistance tensor is the same, no matter what direction the current is flowing through the crystal. That means that the power is dissipated in an octahedron crystal the same in any direction of current. The Octahedron because of these properties, is the most perfect receiver/transmitter on Earth [27].

that iron is very close or a first harmonic of the carrier wave frequency. This is backed up by spectral analysis revealing that iron has enough frequencies within it to be two elements, the carrier wave frequency and the element itself. As the transmitting signal arrives in the third dimension, it tries to form a shape based on the combined element frequency information and the carrier wave frequency, which will then manifest itself as the specific angles of the crystal. It is interesting to note that, 82 percent of all the good conductors of electricity form octahedron crystals under perfect growing conditions. The vector angle of energy formed by the carrier wave frequency is hence adopted as 51° 51' 14.3", the angle of a pyramid based on pi, see figure 10.8. Thus the recent phenomenon of what has been called 'diamond shaped' orbs, which indicates the perfection of the primordial energy being sent from the galactic center and now arriving on Earth. Next, we will very briefly mention the properties of the remaining dimensions.

- The fourth dimension is where living things exists and there exists a wide range of potential. The greater the potential, the more intelligence and ability to gather information using the senses. There is some occasional ability to exhibit abilities of the next dimension. Greater potential is measured by the amount of "charge".

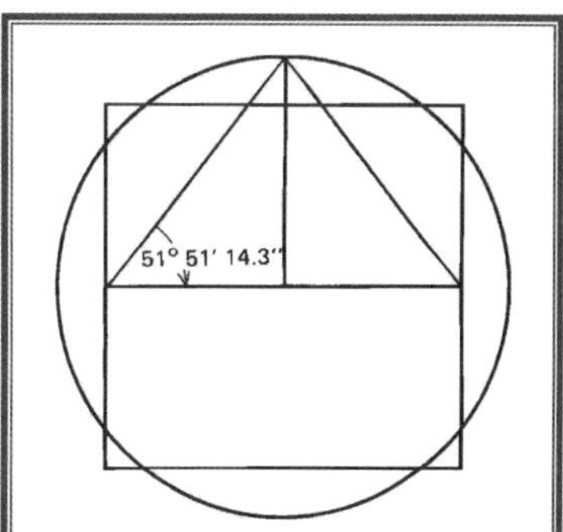

Figure 10.8 The Pi Pyramid. Here the height of a pyramid based on pi (π) is the same as the radius of a circle whose circumference is the same as the base of the pyramids.

- The fifth dimension allows an intelligence to perceive more information without the need to use fourth dimensional senses. A fifth-dimensional being can also manipulate information that makes up third dimensional matter.

- A sixth dimensional individual would be able to move objects in space and time, yet be in the form of a fourth dimensional being. A sixth dimensional being is able to recreate third and fourth dimension matter, at will.

- A planet is a seventh dimensional entity! Now this is strange concept, but Vogt and Sultan argue that planets have to be highly placed in the evolutionary scale to function.

- A star is an eight dimensional entity that has the ability to become a black hole and go back into the first dimension!

Pyramid Reality

There are so many aspects of this theory that are truly thought provoking in the light of the information presented in this book. The subject of pyramids is highlighted here, and scientific validation will be provided, courtesy of Russian pyramid research. Pyramids, seem to have the ability to reconfigures things back to how they are supposed to work, that is they make things more perfect. Pyramids that are based on pi, replicate the Master Diamond Template, so they are the same perfect transmitters and perfect receivers, a tuned circuit. So, an object inside a pyramid will attract it's own frequencies as information, delivered by the carrier wave from the Master Diamond Template. Those frequencies will never arrive distorted. It will make no difference what is put in the pyramid because the object's frequencies will NEVER be distorted by the pyramid shape and so the signal for the element arrives perfect. The object will receive information to make it up stronger. Hence, for people, plants or food etc. under pyramids, the frequencies that make them up are enhanced whilst the signals for disease are overcome. As the individual or object receives more information, the stronger the capability to re-balance. Another observation about pyramids is that they produce a resonance or frequency inside [28]. German scientists, Born and Lertes, found this to be in the microwave range. What's more, things placed inside pyramids become "charged". The charge remains for various lengths of time, even after being taken from the pyramid, and water retains this "charge" the longest. This is explained as the microwave frequencies being either part of the carrier wave frequency or a product of it. With water, it is the oxygen molecule that is being charged, since the oxygen molecule is the element in the water that forms the octahedron crystal.

Here, we can make a connection to the work of Bevan Reid and Sergei Barsamian. They found that a characteristic of space was that it had the property of memory [29]. So, an influence such as a 10kg mass of lead, was found to affect the form of crystalline structures viewed under the microscope. This influence was seen as a wavelike interference pattern coming from the mass of lead. The significance being that the wave effect persisted when the lead was removed. It was also observed, this wave effect had altered the structure of some protein albumin in the solution containing the crystalline matter. Continuing the experiment with cultures of mouse fibroblasts in bovine serum, he found some cell cultures, with the 10kg of lead again in the laboratory space, died at an accelerated rate compared to the normal mortality rate. After the influence was removed, fresh cell cultures died at the same accelerated rate. This property of space to retain an influence, even after the primary agent has been removed, is also a property of magnetic fields, now called "Magnetic Memory". Significantly, the *shape* of the lead was a factor in respect of the amount of influence the same mass of lead could exert. When lead was cut into shapes with many sharp points the influence diminished. The conclusion was that the sharp edges disturbed the flow of "virtual" energy.

Again, there is the recent discovery that strings of DNA will *spontaneously* fold into octahedron [30]. The octahedron shape is now being hailed as a step forward in the quest to use DNA nanoscale templates, that can be used to make materials molecule-by-molecule and structures that form microscopic machines. According to researchers, the straight strands can be coaxed to self-replicate, making it possible to quickly produce large numbers of octahedrons. Other three-dimensional DNA shapes must be synthesized chemically rather than biologically. Curiously, there is NO explanation offered as to what encourages the DNA to take on the octahedron shape.

The theory of *Multidimensional Reality* explains a host of phenomena including, atoms and subatomic particles, light, magnetism, geomagnetism, tornadoes, the psychic phenomena, and astronomy. Vogt and Sultan conclude that the Great Pyramid was built to "tell us the most important secret about our existence – that the information that makes everything exists is a structure like a pyramid." It may be more correct to state:

The source of our reality is a structure like a pi octahedron.

Vogt & Sultan also discuss the point of existence and the need for a soul to evolve to higher states of consciousness. In their terminology, this means evolving to a higher potential and thus holding more charge. The wisdom is profound. Being aware of galactic cycles, this is their message:

> "If an individual has evolved to the knowledge of what existence truly is, he can evolve himself to the next higher dimension, this being the fifth or even the sixth dimension. He can do this only during the time of the reversal, when vast amounts of potential are available to him. For an evolved soul, this is the only time in which to live."

Maybe this explains why there are so many highly evolved souls incarnating at this time, who some have called, "Indigos".

Making the World A Better Place with Pyramid Energy

In the past, there have been pyramid researchers who have helped to create awareness of the strange and powerful energies that focus inside pyramids. These researchers include, the Frenchman Antoine Bovis, who in the 1930s discovered

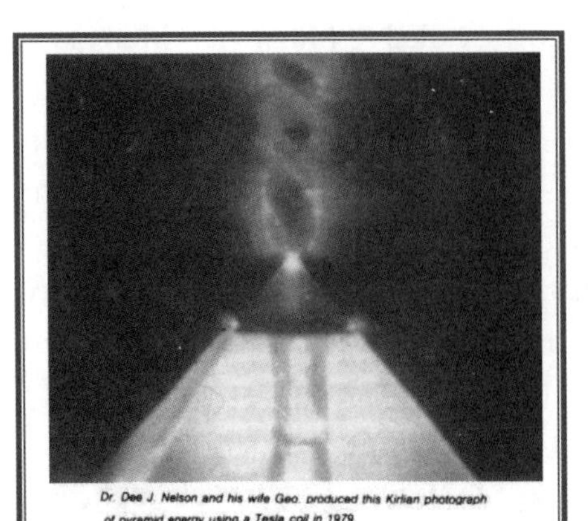

Figure 10.9 Pyramid Energy Experiment. Kirlian photograph of pyramid using a Tesla coil in 1979. Notice the braided energy coming off the apex! Courtesy: Doug Benjamin

that stray cat's and dogs found dead inside the pyramids did not decay but in fact became dehydrated and mummified. He quickly realized the orientation of a model pyramid was important, so he conducted a variety of experiments. Similarly, in 1935 John Hall carried out research with model pyramids. Using a copper ring and wires, he showed that an electric charge was emitted from the apex of the model pyramid. In the 1940s, Karl Drbal, a Czech radio technician was the first to place a razor blade in the model pyramid, and discover that dull razor blades become sharpened in a pyramid. Dr. Patrick Flanagan, was one of the first people to scientifically study pyramids, and he published the first book on this subject called *Pyramid Power* (1973). He believed there was energy coming from the pyramid and which he called "biocosmic energy." Joe Parr conducted hyperspace experiments and Dan Davidson another pyramid researcher, wrote the book *Shape Power* (1977) [31]. In 1979, pyramid researchers Mary and Dean Hardy of Allegan, Michigan produced the image shown in figure 10.9.

As outlined above, individual researchers took the initiative to conduct research into the unusual effects of the pyramid shape. It is only fairly recently, that large-scale experiments by creditable scientific establishments have been undertaken. In January 2001, Russian and Ukranian pyramid research was published on the website Gizapyramid.com by Dr. John DeSalvo of The Giza Pyramid Research Association, as a way to quickly distribute knowledge to the West. The author of this fascinating study, was Dr. Volodymyr Krasnoholovets, one of the top theoretical physicists at the Institute of Physics in Kiev, Ukraine [32]. This institution is part of the National Academy of Sciences of Ukraine and was one of the leading scientific centers in the former USSR and a leading military research association. The report contained research details of Russian pyramids built by Alexander Golod, now Director of a State Defense Enterprise in Moscow. Pictures were also sent by Anatoli Golod, son of Alexander Golod and these were also posted on the internet. Since this time, Dr. John DeSalvo has published *The Complete Pyramid Sourcebook* (2003), which gave more clarity and even more surprising details of the Russian/Ukranian research [33].

Starting in 1989, a total of about 25 different pyramids were built in 8 different locations in Russia and the Ukraine [34]. In particular, near Moscow in Russia, the two largest pyramids were constructed to a height of 22m (72 ft), and weighed 25 tons and the other was 44m (144 ft) and weighed 55 tons see figure 10.10. The largest pyramid, completed in 1999, was constructed 200 miles north west of Moscow, and cost over a million dollars. Prototypes had determined that no metal could be used in the construction of these pyramids and so fiberglass, was chosen, as it would be strong enough to withstand high wind. The pyramids have about a 73-degree angle, which was chosen by Alexander Golod to take advantage of the Golden Ratio. The pyramids were aligned to the North/Polar Star and built away from populated areas in the countryside. A group of pyramids were even built in an oil field in Bashkiriya, southern Russia to test the effect of a complex of pyramids on the physical and chemical properties of oil. When Alexander Golod was asked why he built the pyramids, he replied:

> **"I have children, I have a grandson, I do it for them. These pyramids are an instrument to make the world a better place to live and benefit mankind."**

Future building plans include the construction of a pyramid to a height of 88m (288ft). Golod states that the larger the pyramid, the great the effect it produces. Soon after the construction of the 44m pyramid near Moscow, botanists noticed ***extinct*** flowers starting to grow nearby and new streams appeared [36]. As you can imagine, this has completely mystified botanists! Also, not anticipated was the observation of strange atmospheric effects, that started whilst this pyramid was being built. The 22m Lake Seliger pyramid was planned to be composed of 30 main layers or sections of fiberglass. At the completion of the 11th section, Air Force radar picked up a column of ion particles coming off the pyramid apex and in fact, the energy was measured to extend 2000m or over 1 mile high. As the pyramid construction continued, the ion column still remained and at the completion of the pyramid, a special weather balloon was launched to measure this energy phenomenon. Several months later, the ozone layer was observed to have improved over Russia.

Figure 10.10 44m (144ft) Pyramid near Moscow. Courtesy: ABO Company [35].

Various Russians authorities have shown support for the building of the pyramids and related projects. In October 1998, permission was granted to allow crystals and a kilo of rocks that had been placed in one of the Russian Pyramids, to be taken aboard the Russian Mir Space Station, where they remained on board for over a year [37]. Cosmonaut Afanasiev was even allowed to take crystals, that had been imbued with pyramid energy, onto the International Space Station for a short 10 day period.

> **Alexander Golod believed that the energy fields produced by these crystals and rocks, would benefit both the space stations and possibly the entire world.**

The pyramids have become a huge tourist attraction with millions of visitors. On fair weather days, 5,000 visitors can be expected at the largest 44m pyramid, with people queuing to be allowed to go inside the pyramid. On one New Year's Eve, 20,000 people visited the 44m pyramid. People from all over Russia, including government officials, cosmonauts, the rich and famous visit the largest pyramid and spend time inside it, this pyramid is simply loved by the Russian people. Various research teams from the Russian Academy of Sciences carried out a variety of experiments in these pyramids, with surprising results. Areas of research included medicine, ecology, agriculture, chemistry and physics.

The specific details have been included in Appendix IV, based on a summary of the *Russian and Ukranian Pyramid Research* detailed in Dr. Krasnoholovets' paper. The following is a brief outline of the most interesting discoveries.

- Improved immune response against viruses, bacteria and carcinogens.
- Psychiatric studies showed positive improvement in human behavior, and indicates that the energy had a spiritual component. Helps to overcome addiction problems.
- Poisons and toxins because less harmful, viruses and bacteria become significantly less damaging.
- Burial of radioactive waste incorporating pyramids lose their radioactivity. Valery Uvarov states in his book, The Wands of Horus, "burials of radioactive waste incorporating pyramids lose their deadly properties" [38].
- Items kept inside the pyramids, even rocks and crystals had an immune enhancing effect, to the extent that rocks place in the pyramids could be used to combat influenza epidemics, when placed in rings around the neighborhood.

- Oil well production rates were improved due to oil purification, contaminated wells were also cleared of heavy metals and salty water could be made to be drinkable.
- Water refusing to turn to ice in temperatures as low as -38° C, or -6° F if left undisturbed.
- Pyramid energy had the ability to balance and distribute electrical charge.
- Purification and hardening of artificial diamonds
- Seeds kept in a pyramid for 5 days had a 20 to 100-percent increase in their yield, plants did not get sick and they were not affected by droughts. A yield of wheat in a field near the 12 meter pyramid built in the settlement Ramenskoe of the Moscow region increased four times after the pyramid was built.
- Improvement of the Ozone layer by a column of "unknown" energy that seem to create a vortex that was 300 km wide around the pyramid.
- Pyramids had the ability to dissipate the energetic buildup that would normally create sudden, violent earthquakes. Instead of seeing one large and powerful quake, several hundred tiny earthquakes were registered instead.
- The pyramids seem to shielding against severe weather.

The Emergence to the Fifth World

The Russian experiments clearly demonstrate how geometry can create fields that have powerful ordering effects. The pyramids seem to focus energy from higher dimensions to encourage evolutionary change and higher states of consciousness. Hence, we see greater balance, harmony, compassion, healing (mental, emotional and physical), abundance, and purification. Extinct flowers and streams re-appearing suggests that old morphogenetic patterns were re-established, a form of healing. The suggestion that the ozone layer was repairing itself, is indicative of the existence of very high energies [39]. We live in a highly complex biosystem where changes have a domino effect, it is unknown what the effect of these large pyramids will have in the long term, but the initial effects are very encouraging. It is pertinent to mention that the appearance of extinct flowers is the fulfilment of Hopi Prophecy [40]. This is from *The Book of the Hopi,* by Frank Walters. We find:

> "The Emergence to the future Fifth World has begun. It is being made by the humble people of little nations, tribes, and racial minorities. You can read this in the earth itself. Plant forms from previous worlds are beginning

> to spring up as seeds. This could start a new study of botany if people were wise enough to read them. The same kinds of seeds are being planted in the sky as stars. The same kinds of seeds are being planted in our hearts. All these are the same, depending how you look at them. That is what makes the Emergence to the next, Fifth World."

The question still remains: WHY are the Russians building these pyramids and what does this all mean? The answer to this question may found by the writing of the enlightened Dr. Valery Uvarov. In his informative book, *The Wands of Horus,* the Russian perspective, emphasizes the role of pyramids in evolutionary progress:

> "The actual idea of using the Golden Section in architecture today, together with the creation of "complexes of pyramidal energy structures", is the chief element in solving the problems of the ecology of housing, the ecology of the mental environment, and in the process of coming to an understanding of the world. This is the very key issue, recognition and implementation of which might become the start of our ascent to the next rung of evolution." [41]
>
> The pyramid is:
>
> - A powerful cosmic antenna;
> - **A model in stone of the energy structure of the human being and of the universe, using the latter's energy mechanism**;
> - A very powerful generator of cosmic energies operating on various planes.
>
> Pyramidal energy structures, whose positioning should be decided with reference to the energy qualities of the location, open up the following possibilities:
>
> 1. Tapping into natural flows of cosmic energy, the organization and stimulation of evolutionary processes in the biosphere and in human consciousness.
> 2. Correction of the human energetic structure, making it possible to stimulate internal energetic, bio-physical and physiological processes, which in turn provide the opportunity to discover and activate the inner resources of the human psyche, increasing psychic potential.
> 3. A positive influence on the immune and nervous systems, leading to their improvement.
> 4. An improvement of mankind's energo-ecological environment, an increase and improvement of the energy state at the pyramid's location and, as a consequence of the spread of pyramidal structures throughout

the world, a re-organization of the planet's energy structure within the next 10-15 years.

Pyramidal Energy Structures may play a decisive role in the fate of the new generation, changing their level of awareness. *[Bold added for emphasis, end of excerpts.]*

By the building of pyramids, the Russian authorities are demonstrating that they are acutely aware that the evolution of mankind is at hand. It seems that the Russians involved in these enterprises, are specifying their intent to create a balance between the aetheric forces of the Cosmos and the Earth, hence facilitating and influencing change in a positive way. Another question must be asked: are we seeing a demonstration of the most enlightened nation on Earth?

Did the Great Pyramid Tune the Earth diamond?

One of the Seven Wonders of the World is the Great Pyramid of Giza, see figure 10.11. For thousands of years, people have been speculating about the meaning and purpose of the most magnificent architectural work in existence. The Giza pyramid is composed of 2 ½ million blocks of granite and limestone, which weigh 2 to 70 tons each. The base of the pyramid covers 13 acres and it has a volume of 90 million cubic feet. It is 454 feet high, equivalent to a 48-story building. Each side slopes upward at an angle of 51° 51' and each side has an area of 5 ½ acres, while less than a fiftieth of an inch separates the blocks with optical precision. There are many other facts that add to the enigma. The Great Pyramid not only reflects the Earth in volume and area but also in weight, the estimated mass of 5.955 Million tons is approximately one billionth of the estimated mass

Figure 10.11 The Great Pyramid at Giza, Egypt.
Photograph by Egyptologist, Ludwig Borchardt, circa 1929.

of the Earth. There are many messages encoded in the design of the pyramid but the dimensions very clearly tell us that the Great Pyramid is meant to represent the Earth.

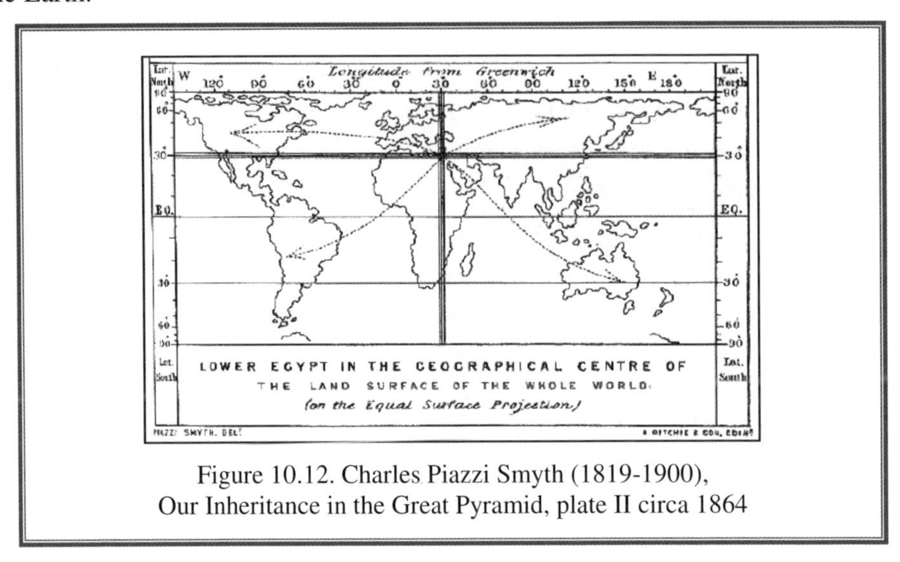

Figure 10.12. Charles Piazzi Smyth (1819-1900),
Our Inheritance in the Great Pyramid, plate II circa 1864

The Great Pyramid in Egypt is EXACTLY at the geographical center of the total landmass of the Earth, see figure 10.12. In fact, the Great Pyramid is a scale model of the Earth at a ratio of 1: 43,200. William R. Fix in his book "Pyramid Odyssey" made this calculation and he found that this 1: 43,200 ratio is true to an accuracy of one or two millimeters in 480 feet, the height of the pyramid. It is also shown that the height of the Pyramid is in direct relation to the polar radius of the Earth by this ratio. What's more, the perimeter at the sockets at the base has the same ratio to the world's best estimates of the circumference of the Earth at the Equator. The mathematician Stan Tenen has even shown that the Great Pyramid of Giza is built in harmony with the molecular structure of its materials [42]. Tenen knows of no other structure on Earth that fits this pattern. Clearly, such a harmonic connection between "micro" and "macro" would only further enhance the pyramid's effects. This is a comment by a pyramid researcher:

> "If one is to send a message the prime requirement is of course that people will read it, it is no good putting it in a bottle, throwing it in the ocean and then hoping it will be found. One must place the message somewhere where it simply cannot be missed, a place so significant that its very location makes a notable statement in itself." [43]

There can be no doubt, the builders of the great pyramids knew exactly what they were doing!

Hundreds of books have been written about the Great Pyramid, highlighting the mystery of this magnificent architectural wonder. Yet, it is possible to highlight one book that seeks to de-mystify and enlighten and has possibly taken our understanding of the pyramid at Giza to a new level. Christopher Dunn is a master craftsman and engineer who has worked with machines for thirty-five years. His interest in the Great Pyramid was sparked when he read Peter Tompkins book, *Secrets of the Great Pyramid* and those of other researchers who queried "official" theory. Dunn was intrigued by the precise nature of the measurements and tolerances measured by pyramid researchers. When he carefully examined the data, he decided the only reason for such small ranges of variation in the physical dimensions of the structure was because it was built as a machine. He started to view photographs and diagrams of the interior of the Great Pyramid as blueprints and so he decided to back engineer the structure, based on the premise that any viable theory concerning the function of the pyramid would have to explain all the architectural features and anomalies. Following twenty years of study, Dunn published his conclusions in a book called *The Giza Power Plant, Technologies of Ancient Egypt* [44]. In summary, he makes the following statement:

> "If my power plant theory was based on evidence from a singular exhibit or a few artifacts, critics and skeptics could rightly attribute that evidence to pure coincidence. However, I have amassed a plethora of facts and deductions based on sober considerations of the design of the Great Pyramid and nearly every artifact found within it that, when taken together, all support my premise that the Great Pyramid was a power plant and the King's Chamber its power center. Facilitated by the element that fuels our sun (hydrogen) and uniting the energy of the universe with that of the Earth, the ancient Egyptians converted vibrational energy into microwave energy. For the power plant to function, the designers and operators had to induce vibrations in the Great Pyramid that was in tune with the harmonic resonant vibrations of the Earth. Once the pyramid was vibrating in tune with the Earth's pulse it became a coupled oscillator and could sustain the transfer of energy from the Earth with little or no feedback. The three smaller pyramids on the east side of the Great Pyramid may have been used to assist the Great Pyramid in achieving resonance, much like today was use smaller gasoline engines to start large diesel engines."

Here are a few facts that give us reason to believe that the Great Pyramid could be considered a "Power Plant":

- Outer faces of the Great Pyramid slightly concave – architectural feature to harness aetheric energy. The only pyramid in the world like this.

- Evidence of "state of the art" machine-tooling. We do not have the technology on the planet to rebuild the Great Pyramid. Attempts to reproduce scale models have been embarrassing failures.
- The "Grand Gallery" shows evidence that it was actually a massive acoustic chamber filled with 27 vertical rows of Helmholtz resonators (bowl-like objects that select out a particular frequency from a complex sound while maximizing energy transfer). Curiously, 30,000 precision-machined stone vessels, with a similar geometry to those used in the aerospace industry today, were found in chambers under the Step Pyramid at Saqqara, Egypt! The pyramid explorer Petrie also found pieces of similar stoneware at Giza.
- Evidence that the interior chambers experienced extreme heat.
- The "Queen's Chamber" – walls, ceilings, and floor, as well as the passageway that led to it – covered in ½ inch of a salty material and originally had a "foul" smell. Conclusion, this was a chemical reaction chamber.
- The "King's Chamber" is a technological wonder. Five rows of 43 blocks of granite weighing 70 tons each! A resonant cavity designed to vibrate at F-sharp chord (a main frequency of the Earth) and produce electrical energy through the piezoelectric effect.
- Evidence of explosion in the King's Chamber but NOWHERE ELSE! Cracked granite and black soot.

It is not within the scope of this book to examine all Dunn's research, it is enough to draw attention to the fact that from a technological point of view, the Great Pyramid of Giza appeared to have features that suggest a functional use. Even though there is some debate about a few points, Chris Dunn has received praise the world over for his endeavors. However, there is one thing that haunts Dunn and he admits: "What did they do with the energy they produced? Where are the machines?" The problem being acknowledged, is that there is no evidence of how this energy was delivered and utilized. Dunn to his credit does suggest that this design could be used to draw off energy from seismically active regions of the Earth in a controlled fashion, thereby stabilizing the planet. As a result of Dunn's research, there have been suggestions that the Pyramid was designed as a weapon or a Tesla type device to transmit electrical energy. Yet, Dunn's research clearly shows us why the machine was called "Pyramid", the Greek translation means "Fire-in-the-middle!" A five cornered resonant crystal concentrates cosmic energy at the center. This means that, in the Great Pyramid, energy concentrated in the center would radiate from the tip, as well as create a mirror image pyramid pointing down! [45] The Great Pyramid was designed to replicate a pi octahedron and therefore act as a perfect receiver and transmitter.

The concentrated energy in the center created an etheric double, making up a pi octahedron, reflecting the Master Diamond Template!

In metallurgy and crystallography, the crystal twin is defined as: "A portion of a crystal in which the lattice is a mirror image of the lattice of the remainder of the crystal" [46]. There is also the concept of the reciprocal lattice or reciprocal space. Professor William Tiller et al. point out in the book *Conscious Acts of Creation: The Emergence of New Physics,* that Membrane theory (the most recent version of String Theory), has introduced the concept of direct and reciprocal space and the idea of a new type of physics which would allow an interchange of charge. This has been called the "Duality of Dualities" [47].

Metaphysical sources have always stated that the Great Pyramid was a place for raising consciousness via initiations. The concept of initiations or frequency attunements taking place *inside* the Great Pyramid, does not necessarily mean being physically present. If this did occur, it was only after the Great Pyramid had become defunct. The evidence shows that the Egyptians did not need to enter the Great Pyramid to benefit from the balanced energies produced. If you look at statues and images of the priests and pharaohs of Ancient Egypt, most often you see them wearing strange headwear called "concentrators", see figure 10.13. Russian sources suggest that these "concentrators" were designed to stimulate the pineal gland and hypothalamus, and work in combination with the powerful aetheric energies generated by the Great Pyramid and the Wands of Horus. The consensus of pyramid researchers is that when the Great Pyramid was fully functional, the surrounding energy field would have been enormous. We must conclude, that with the balanced energies generated by the Great Pyramid and the balancing effect of the Wands, we may have found the reason why some of the Pharaohs are reported to have lived so long.

Figure 10.13
The Concentrator!
Egyptian headwear

Again, we find this rather curious statement by Dr. Valery Uvarov in the appendix of the first edition of the book, *The Wands of Horus:* "The core of the planets using gravitational, electromagnetic and other means of interaction (including resonance) communication is achieved between planetary and galactic systems, joining the whole Universe into a single energo-informational space."

We do not know with any certainty HOW the Great Pyramid was used, but the evidence shows that a tremendous effort of technological supremacy was required to design and build the Great Pyramid that CANNOT be matched today. Whatever the role of the Great Pyramid, the purpose had to be very important and what could be more important that the stability of planet Earth? Whoever built the Great Pyramid, may have been aware of periodic explosions from the Galactic core or comets that could appear that could de-stabilise Earth. Is that not worth trying to influence the Earth's core to maintain balance? We know that torsion fields carry information and they can be minuscule in comparison to the electromagnetic field and gravitation, yet, they make a difference. We must remember here too that NASA monitors plasma streaming in and out of the poles via the polar cusps, on it's way down to the Earth's core carrying energy and thus information. So programming the core as a way to communicate with the planetary and galactic systems, seems a worthy function for the Great Pyramid. Hence, maybe we can conclude that one of the functions of the Great Pyramid was to tune the core of planet Earth!

Tuning the Earth Diamond: The Diamond Vision

The Great Pyramid can still be considered to be operational, as the pyramid shape still acts as a receiver and transmitter. Yet, the balance of energies may not be calibrated to serve humanity at the highest possible level. As our planet is in a state of flux, there is a tremendous need for humans to realise their power and assist the planet to balance. Humans can take responsibility, and this achieved by strengthening our *Signal Power* and using the power of intent to send balanced energies down to the core of the Earth. This is urgent and the Mayan Elders are currently pleading with people of higher consciousness to "make the balance". The Mayans are concerned that catastrophes will escalate if the required percentage of humanity do not make enough difference. Carlos Barrios, Mayan Elder and a spokesman for the Mayan Elders in Guatemala, has been giving regular interviews to Mitch Battros, the owner of the www.earthchangestv.com website [48]. The following prophecy is the forecast of how things will get worse if the balancing is not achieved.

"First there was water (tsunami), then there was air (hurricanes), then there will be dirt (earthquakes), then there will come fire (volcanoes)".

Carlos Barrios

Mayan Elders are now most worried about major volcanic activity. This can be backed up with hard science. The U.S. Lawrence Livermore National Laboratory has a mission to ensure national security and apply science and technology to the important issues of our time. They conclude that Earth will self-regulate and deal with climate change [49]. Using 12 new state-of-the-art climate models, researchers found that ocean warming and sea level rise in the 20th century were substantially reduced by the 1883 eruption of the Krakatoa volcano in Indonesia. Volcanic aerosols blocked sunlight and caused the ocean surface to cool. We must conclude that if large-scale volcanic eruptions occur, global food production will suffer due to the lack of sunlight and this will bring further hardship for humanity.

The Diamond Vision

Whilst the author was working with a client and *Tuning the Diamonds*, the client, started to remember a very poignant dream. It is included here with permission, because it is highly relevant to the message of the Mayan Elders.

> "I found myself in a different world, walking along a broad curved path that was paved with slabs and gradually rising. To the left of me was a wall at waist height. Out of curiosity, I walked towards the wall and I found myself gazing into a huge canyon. I looked to the right of me and there were stone white domed buildings. I was drawn to inspect these strange igloo-like buildings with round windows. As I touched the smooth stone that looked like marble, I was surprised to find that the stone felt warm to the touch and not cold as I had anticipated. I continued walking on the path and eventually it led to an enormous and magnificent temple. Like the other buildings in this strange world, it was white and glistening. The entrance consisted of two huge pillars and a colonnade that lead into a grand central hall. Before I was allowed into this sacred place, I was obliged to change my clothes. I was given a priestly robe that looked like linen but felt like silk. My garment appeared white but in the light it reflected many different colors."

> "When I entered the hall, I looked up and saw that the central part of the ceiling was open. Below, in front of me was a huge diamond that was being slowly adjusted. As I gazed around, I realized there were many more large diamonds and other geometrical crystals of different colors, arranged in a circle around the central diamond. Each was assigned guardians, their purpose was to continuously adjust these beautiful objects. In a moment, I saw energy and light stream down through the open gap in the ceiling, consequently, the large central diamond deflected the energy towards each of the crystals. This was the arrival of an expected event. As my dream moved forward in time, I learnt the reason why each crystal was given guardians.

My attention was drawn to the guardians for the red crystal who were not fulfilling their role of making the adjustments. When the energy came again and struck the central crystal and subsequently the surrounding crystals, the consequence of the red crystal not being tuned was immediately apparent. I saw an image of violent volcanic activity and earthquakes. The responsibility given to the guardians meant that their role was vital. They were needed to continuously adjust the crystals and keep *Tuning the Diamonds*."

Anne-Tora Svanes, Norway, circa 1989

We have been promised chaos, but chaos with a purpose!

We know that change is occurring. Nobel prize winner Ilya Prigogine, the Russian born Belgium chemist, suggested that a system in balance and functioning well is difficult to change. However, if a system falls into disorder, change becomes more and more feasible and finally inevitable. At that point, the least bit of coherent order can bring back the whole disorderly array to a new state of balance. Which direction that takes, depends on the nature of the chaotic attractor that lifts the chaos into its new order [50]. The attractor is the "magnetic" force that pulls a system towards it [51]. Here we can state, the people of higher consciousness are required to be in balance and strongly influence what happens on planet Earth to create the Golden Age for the future of mankind.

Lee Carroll gave an example of humanity tuning the Earth diamond on a massive scale, caused by the outpouring of compassion after the Asian Tsunami that occurred in December 2004 [52].

"There was so much compassion created at that time, in that one week, the Earth has never seen anything like it in your lifetime. Billions of Humans were involved with a compassion that instantly went to the core of the planet. It went into the Earth and it's still there. It changed the actual energy of where you walk and it planted a seeds that will grow that will indeed emerge later in Israel, and those surrounding Israel."

In many ways, the ongoing Earth changes can also be considered a test of "spiritual intelligence". The following quote comes from a channeled message, dated April 2006, given by Tom Kenyon who is also the source for the first quote in this book. He is a highly regarded enlightened Master and Shaman, author, psychologist and sound healer. We are told:

"No one can say for certain, what your future will be like—either individually or collectively, because there is always the possibility for conscious choice at any moment. And conscious choice or intent can and does alter the quantum field of consciousness itself and thus eventually even physical reality (if the power of choice or intent is strong enough)."

"And so it is that we do not predict your future. We are only saying what we see in your timeline unless you collectively make different choices in how you live your lives and how you deal with each other and the Earth."

"In many ways, survival is an intelligence test. In this light, we would say that the cosmic test of increased spiritual evolution is putting you and everyone else under extreme pressure. Nothing less than an upward movement in global consciousness will suffice. Nothing less than spiritual mastery will allow you to pass through the eye of the needle that is upon you. Those who master the new vibratory realms of consciousness and find ways to express them in physical reality—in how they live their lives—these will be the stewards who bring in the new age and the new world." *[End of excerpts]* [53]

Here, the reference to the "eye of the needle" is quite interesting. It reminds us of the parable told by Jesus of the rich man and his attempts to gain access to the Kingdom of Heaven. It is known that the original text was poorly translated and a better version would be, a rich man is like an overloaded camel trying to pass through a narrow gate. Since there are many sources today referring to 11:11 and notions of a "window of opportunity" or "gate" or even a "stargate". It would seem that this message was meant for initiates. In modern day metaphysical language, this equates to having too much karmic baggage which results in incoherent and unbalanced energy fields that stop us from reaching our full potential.

In closing, the final thoughts can be summarized as follows:

Greater balance will bring greater internal coherent order, this will result in greater *Signal Power*, which can be used to powerful effect. To this end, there are diamonds to tune and this book tries to highlight those diamonds!

The diamond crystalline inner core, which scientists think could modify the Earth's magnetic field is also a massive receiver and transmitter. When we connect to the Earth, we in effect transmit a signal to this giant receiver which then transmits out into the Universe. We can choose to tune the diamonds in our personal energy fields and then act to tune the Earth diamond with our clear intent for balance. As part of our spiritual evolution, we have to take more responsibility and that occurs by consciously, "Tuning the Diamonds". The End

Appendix I

PLANETOPHYSICAL STATE OF THE EARTH AND LIFE

By DR. ALEXEY N. DMITRIEV*

Published in Russian, IICA Transactions, Volume 4, 1997
English Presentation Sponsored By: THE MILLENNIUM GROUP,
January 8, 1998

http://www.tmgnow.com/

*Professor of Geology and Mineralogy, and Chief Scientific Member,
United Institute of Geology, Geophysics, and Mineralogy,
Siberian Department of Russian Academy of Sciences.
Expert on Global Ecology, and Fast -Processing Earth Events.

Russian to English Translation and Editing:
by A. N. Dmitriev, Andrew Tetenov, and Earl L. Crockett

Summary Paragraph

Current PlanetoPhysical alterations of the Earth are becoming irreversible. Strong evidence exists that these transformations are being caused by highly charged material and energetic non-uniformity's in anisotropic interstellar space which have broken into the interplanetary area of our Solar System. This "donation" of energy is producing hybrid processes and excited energy states in all planets, as well as the Sun. Effects here on Earth are to be found in the acceleration of the magnetic pole shift, in the vertical and horizontal ozone content distribution, and in the increased frequency and magnitude of significant catastrophic climatic events. There is growing probability that we are moving into a rapid temperature instability period similar to the one that took place 10,000 years ago. The adaptive responses of the biosphere, and humanity, to these new conditions may lead to a total global revision of the range of species and life on Earth. It is only through a deep understanding of the fundamental changes taking place in the natural environment surrounding us that politicians, and citizens a like, will be able to achieve balance with the renewing flow of PlanetoPhysical states and processes.

INTRODUCTION

Current, in process, geological, geophysical, and climatical alterations of the Earth are becoming more, and more, irreversible. At the present time researchers are revealing some of the causes which are leading to a general reorganization of the electro-magnetosphere (the electromagnetic skeleton) of our planet, and of its climatic machinery. A greater number of specialists in climatology, geophysics, planetophysics, and heliophysics are tending towards a cosmic causative sequence version for what is happening. Indeed, events of the last decade give strong evidence of unusually significant heliospheric and planetophysic transformations [1,2]. Given the quality, quantity, and scale of these transformations we may say that:

The climatic and biosphere processes here on Earth (through a tightly connected feedback system) are directly impacted by, and linked back to, the general overall transformational processes taking place in our Solar System. We must begin to organize our attention and thinking to understand that climatic changes on Earth are only one part, or link, in a whole chain of events taking place in our Heliosphere.

These deep physical processes, these new qualities of our physical and geological environment, will impose special adaptive challenges and requirements for all life forms on Earth. Considering the problems of adaptation our biosphere will have with these new physical conditions on Earth, we need to distinguish the general tendency and nature of the changes. As we will show below, these tendencies may be traced in the direction of planet energy capacity growth (capacitance), which is leading to a highly excited or charged state of some of Earth's systems. The most intense transformations are taking place in the planetary gas-plasma envelopes to which the productive possibilities of our biosphere are timed. Currently this new scenario of excess energy run-off is being formed, and observed:

In the ionosphere by plasma generation.
In the magnetosphere by magnetic storms.
In the atmosphere by cyclones.

This high-energy atmospheric phenomena, which was rare in the past, is now becoming more frequent, intense, and changed in its nature. The material composition of the gas-plasma envelope is also being transformed.

It is quite natural for the whole biota of the Earth to be subjected to these changing conditions of the electromagnetic field, and to the significant deep alterations of Earth's climatic machinery. These fundamental processes of change create a demand within all of Earth's life organisms for new forms of adaptation. The natural development of these new forms may lead to a total global revision of the range of species, and life, on Earth . New deeper qualities of life itself may come forth, bringing the new physical state of the Earth to an equilibrium with the new organismic possibilities of development, reproduction, and perfection. In this sense it is evident that we are faced with a problem of the adaptation of humanity to this new state of the Earth; new conditions on Earth whose biospheric qualities are varying, and non-uniformly distributed. Therefore the current period of transformation is transient, and the transition of life's representatives to the future may take place only after a deep evaluation of what it will take to comply with these new Earthly biospheric conditions. Each living representative on Earth will be getting a thorough "examination," or "quality control inspection," to determine it's ability to comply with these new conditions. These evolutionary challenges always require effort, or endurance, be it individual organisms, species, or communities. Therefore, it is not only the climate that is becoming new, but we as human beings are experiencing a global change in the vital processes of living organisms, or life itself; which is yet another link in the total process. We cannot treat such things separately, or individually.

1.0 TRANSFORMATION OF THE SOLAR SYSTEM

We will list the recent large-scale events in the Solar System in order to fully understand, and comprehend, the PlanetoPhysical transformations taking place. This development of events, as it has become clear in the last few years, is being caused by material and energetic non-uniformity's in anisotropic interstellar space[2,3,4]. In its travel through interstellar space, the Heliosphere travels in the direction of the Solar Apex in the Hercules Constellation. On its way it has met (1960's) non-homogeneities of matter and energy containing ions of Hydrogen, Helium, and Hydroxyl in addition to other elements and combinations. This kind of interstellar space dispersed plasma is presented by magnetized strip structures and striations. The Heliosphere [solar system] transition through this structure has led to an increase of the shock wave in front of the Solar System from 3 to 4 AU, to 40 AU, or more. This shock wave thickening has caused the formation of a collusive plasma in a parietal layer, which has led to a plasma overdraft around the Solar System, and then to its breakthrough into interplanetary domains [5,6]. This breakthrough constitutes a kind of matter and energy donation made by interplanetary space to our Solar System.

In response to this "donation of energy/matter," we have observed a number of large scale events:

A series of large PlanetoPhysical transformations.

A change in the quality of interplanetary space in the direction of an increase in its interplanetary, and solar-planetary transmitting properties.

The appearance of new states, and activity regimes, of the Sun.

1.1 A Series of Large PlanetoPhysical Transformations.

The following processes are taking place on the distant planets of our Solar System. But they are, essentially speaking, operationally driving the whole System.

Here are examples of these events:

1.1.1 A growth of dark spots on Pluto [7].

1.1.2 Reporting of auroras on Saturn [8].

1.1.3 Reporting of Uranus and Neptune polar shifts (They are magnetically conjugate planets), and the abrupt large-scale growth of Uranus' magnetosphere intensity.

1.1.4 A change in light intensity and light spot dynamics on Neptune [9,10].

1.1.5 The doubling of the magnetic field intensity on Jupiter (based upon 1992 data), and a series of new states and processes observed on this planet as an aftermath of a series of explosions in July 1994 [caused by "Comet" SL-9] [12]. That is, a relaxation of a plasmoid train [13,14] which excited the Jovian magnetosphere, thus inducing excessive plasma generation [12] and it's release in the same manner as Solar coronal holes [15] inducing an appearance of radiation belt brightening in decimeter band (13.2 and 36 cm), and the appearance of large auroral anomalies and a change of the Jupiter - Io system of currents [12, 14].

Update Note From A.N.D Nov. 1997:

A stream of ionized hydrogen, oxygen, nitrogen, etc. is being directed to Jupiter from the volcanic areas of Io through a one million amperes flux tube. It is affecting the character of Jupiter's magnetic process and intensifying it's plasma genesis.{Z.I.Vselennaya "Earth and Universe" N3, 1997 plo-9 by NASA data}

1.1.6 A series of Martian atmosphere transformations increasing its biosphere quality. In particularly, a cloudy growth in the equator area and an unusual growth of ozone concentration [16].

Update Note: In September 1997 the Mars Surveyor Satellite encountered an atmospheric density double that projected by NASA upon entering a Mars orbit. This greater density bent one of the solar array arms beyond the full and open stop. This combination of events has delayed the beginning of the scheduled photo mission for one year.

1.1.7 A first stage atmosphere generation on the Moon, where a growing natrium atmosphere is detected that reaches 9,000 km in height [17].

1.1.8 Significant physical, chemical and optical changes observed on Venus; an inversion of dark and light spots detected for the first time, and a sharp decrease of sulfur-containing gases in its atmosphere [16].

1.2 A Change in the Quality of Interplanetary Space Towards an Increase in Its Interplanetary and Solar-Planetary Transmitting Properties.

When speaking of new energetic and material qualities of interplanetary space, we must first point out the increase of the interplanetary domains energetic charge, and level of material saturation. This change of the typical mean state of interplanetary space has two main causes:

1.2.1 The supply/inflow of matter from interstellar space. (Radiation material, ionized elements, and combinations.) [19,20,21].

1.2.2 The after effects of Solar Cycle 22 activity, especially as a result of fast coronal mass ejection's [CME's] of magnetized solar plasmas [22].

It is natural for both interstellar matter and intra-heliospheric mass redistribution's to create new structural units and processes in the interplanetary domains. They are mostly observed in the structured formation of extended systems of magnetic plasma clouds [23], and an increased frequency of the generation of shock waves; and their resulting effects [24].

A report already exists of two new populations of cosmic particles that were not expected to be found in the Van Allen radiation belts [25]; particularly an injection of a greater than 50 MeV dense electron sheaf into the inner magnetosphere during times of abrupt magnetic storms [CME's], and the emergence of a new belt consisting of ionic elements traditionally found in the composition of stars. This newly changed quality of interplanetary space not only performs the function of a planetary interaction transmission mechanism, but it (this is most important) exerts stimulating and programming action upon the Solar activity both in it's maximal and minimal phases. The seismic effectiveness of the solar wind is also being observed [26,27].

1.3 The Appearance of New States and Activity Regimes of the Sun.

As far as the stellarphysical state of the Sun is concerned, we must first note the fact that significant modifications have occurred in the existing behavioral model of the central object of our solar system. This conclusion comes from observations and reportings of unusual forms, energetic powers, and activities in the Sun's functions [20,21], as well as modifications in it's basic fundamental properties [28]. Since the end of the Maunder minimum, a progressive growth of the Sun's general activity has been observed. This growth first revealed itself most definitely in the 22nd cycle; which posed a real problem for heliophysicists who were attempting to revise their main explanatory scenarios:

1.3.1 Concerning the velocity of reaching super-flash maximums.
1.3.2 Concerning the emissive power of separate flashes.
1.3.3 Concerning the energy of solar cosmic rays, etc.

Moreover, the Ulysses spacecraft, traversing high heliospheric latitudes, recorded the absence of the magnetic dipole, which drastically changed the general model of heliomagnetism, and further complicated the magnetologist's analytic presentations. The most important heliospheric role of coronal holes has now become clear; to regulate the magnetic saturation of interplanetary space. [28,30]. Additionally, they generate all large geomagnetic storms, and ejection's with a southerly directed magnetic field are geo-effective [22]. There is also existing substantiation favoring the solar winds effects upon Earth's atmospheric zone circulation, and lithospheric dynamics [31].

The 23rd cycle was initiated by a short series of sunspots in August 1995 [32], which allows us to predict the solar activity maximum in 1999. What is also remarkable, is that a series of class C flares has already happened in July 1996 . The specificity and energy of this cycle was discussed at the end of the 1980's [23]. The increased frequency of X-Ray flux flares which occurred in the very beginning of this cycle provided evidence of the large-scale events to come; especially in relation to an increase in the frequency of super-flashes. The situation has become extremely serious due to the growth in the transmitting qualities of the interplanetary environment [23, 24] and the growth of Jupiter's systems heliospheric function; with Jupiter having the possibility of being shrouded by a plasmosphere extending over Io's orbit [13].

As a whole, all of the reporting and observation facilities give evidence to a growth in the velocity, quality, quantity, and energetic power of our Solar System's Heliospheric processes.

Update Note 1/8/98: The unexpected high level of Sun activity in the later half of 1997, that is continuing into present time, provides strong substantiation of the above statement. There were three "X" level Goes 9 X-Ray Flux events in 1997 where one was forecasted; a 300% increase. The most dramatic of these, a X-9.1 coronal mass ejection on November 6, 1997, produced a proton event here on Earth of approximately 72 hours in duration. The character, scale, and magnitude of current Sun activity has increased to the point that one official government Sun satellite reporting station recently began their daily report by saying, "Everything pretty much blew apart on the Sun today, Jan. 3,1998."

2.0 THE EARTH REORGANIZATION PROCESSES

The recorded and documented observations of all geophysical (planetary environmental) processes, and the clearly significant and progressive modifications in all reported solar-terrestrial physical science relationships, combined with the integral effects of the antropohenedus activity in our Solar System's Heliosphere, [33,34], causes us to conclude that a global reorganization and transformation of the Earth's physical and environmental qualities is taking place now; before our very eyes. This current rearrangement constitutes one more in a long line of cosmo-historic events of significant Solar System evolutionary transformations which are caused by the periodic modification, and amplification, of the Heliospheric-Planetary-Sun processes. In the case of our own planet these new events have placed an intense pressure on the geophysical environment; causing new qualities to be observed in the natural processes here on Earth; causes and effects which have already produced hybrid processes throughout the planets of our Solar System; where the combining of effects on natural matter and energy characteristics have been observed and reported.

We shall now discuss global, regional, and local processes.

2.1 The Geomagnetic Field Inversion.

Keeping clearly in mind the known significant role of the magnetic field on human life, and all biological processes, we will outline the general features of this changing state of the Earth's geomagnetic field. We have to remind ourselves of the many spacecraft and satellites that have registered the growth of heliospheric magnetic saturation in recent years [11,18,35]. The natural response of the Earth to this increased saturation level reveals itself in its dipole intensity, its magnet "c" poles localization, and in its electromagnetic field resonance processes [36]. Earth is number one among all of the planets in the Solar System with respect to its specific ability regarding the magnetization of matter [6].

In recent years we have seen a growth of interest by geophysicists and magnetologists, in general, to geomagnetic processes [37-40], and specifically, to the travel of Earth's magnetic poles [41,42]. They are particularly interested in observing the facts surrounding the directed, or vectored, travel of the Antarctic magnetic pole. In the last 100 years this magnetic pole has traveled almost 900 km towards, and into, the Indian ocean. This significant shift by the magnetic poles began in 1885. The most recent data about the state of the Arctic magnetic pole (which is moving towards the Eastern Siberian world magnetic anomaly by way of the Arctic Ocean) reveals that this pole "traveled" more than 120 km during the ten year period 1973 through 1984, and 150 km during the same interval, 1984 through 1994. This estimated data has been confirmed by direct measurement (L. Newwitt. The Arctic pole coordinates are now 78.3 deg. North and 104.0 deg. West) [42].

We must emphasize that this documented polar shift acceleration (3 km per year average over 10 years), and its travel along the geo-historic magnetic poles inversion corridor (the corridor having been established by the analysis of more than 400 paleoinversion sites) necessarily leads us to the conclusion that the currently observed polar travel acceleration is not just a shift or digression from the norm, but is in fact an inversion of the magnetic poles; in full process. It is now seen that the acceleration of polar travel may grow to a rate of up to 200 km per year. This means that a polar inversion may happen far more rapidly than is currently supposed by those investigators without a familiarity with the overall polar shift problem.

We must also emphasize the significant growth of the recognized world magnetic anomalies (Canadian, East-Siberian, Brazilian, and Antarctic) in the Earth's magnetic reorganization. Their significance is due to the fact that these world anomalies constitute a magnetic source that is almost independent from Earth's main magnetic field. Most of the time, the intensity of these world magnetic anomalies substantially exceeds all of the residual non-dipole component; which is obtained by the subtraction of the dipole component from the total magnetic field of the Earth.[48]. It is the inversion of the magnetic fields process which is causing the various transformations of Earth's geophysical processes and the present state of the polar magnetosphere.

We also have to take into account the factual growth of the polar cusp's angle (i.e. The polar slots in the magnetosphere; North and South), which in the middle 1990's reached 45 degrees (by IZMIRAN data). [Note: The cusp angle was about 6 degrees most of the time. It fluctuates depending upon the situation. During the last five years, however, it has varied between 25 and 46 degrees.] The increasing and immense amounts of matter and energy radiating from the Sun's Solar Wind, and Interplanetary Space, by means previously discussed, has began to rush into these widened slots in the polar regions causing the Earth's crust, the oceans, and the polar ice caps to warm[27].

Our study of geomagnetic field paleoinversions, and their after effects, has lead us to the unambiguous, and straight forth, conclusion that these present processes being observed are following precisely the same scenarios as those of their distant ancestors. And additional signs of the inversion of the magnetic field are becoming more intense in frequency and scale. For example: During the previous 25 million years, the frequency of magnetic inversions was twice in half a million years while the frequency of inversions for the last 1 million years is 8 to 14 inversions [43], or one inversion each 71 to 125 thousand years. What is essential here is that during prior periods of maximum frequency of inversions there has also been a corresponding decrease in the level of oceans world-wide (10 to 150 meters) from contraction caused by the wide development of crustal folding processes. Periods of lessor frequency of geomagnetic field inversions reveals sharp increases of the world ocean level due to the priority of expansion and stretching processes in the crust. [43-44]. Therefore, the level of World's oceans depends on the global characteristic of the contraction and expansion processes in force at the time.

The current geomagnetic inversion frequency growth phase may not lead to an increase in oceanic volume from polar warming, but rather to a decrease in ocean levels. Frequent inversions mean stretching and expansion, rare inversions mean contraction. Planetary processes, as a rule, occur in complex and dynamic ways which require the combining and joining of all forces and fields in order to adequately understand the entire system. In addition to the consideration of hydrospheric redistribution, there are developing events which also indicate a sudden and sharp breaking of the Earth's meteorological machinery.

2.2 Climate Transformations.

Since public attention is so closely focused on the symptoms of major alterations, or breakdowns, in the climatic machinery, and the resulting and sometimes severe biospheric effects, we shall consider these climatic transformations in detail. Thus, while not claiming to characterize the climatic and biospheric transition period completely, we will provide a recent series of brief communications regarding the temperature, hydrological cycle, and the material composition of the Earth's atmosphere.

The temperature regime of any given phase of climatic reorganization is characterized by contrasts, and instabilities. The widely quoted, and believed, "Greenhouse Effect" scenario for total climatic changes is by far the weakest explanation, or link, in accounting for this reorganization. It has already been observed that the growth in the concentration of CO2 has stopped, and that the methane content in the atmosphere has began to decrease [45] while the temperature imbalance, and the common global pressure field dissolution has proceeded to grow.

There were reports of a global temperature maximum in 1994, and the almost uninterrupted existence of an "El-Nino" like hydrological effect. Satellite air surface layer temperature tracking [49,50] allowed the detection of a 0.22 degrees C global temperature variation (within a typical specific time period of about 30 days) that correlated with recorded middle frequency magnetic oscillations. The Earth's temperature regime is becoming more, and more, dependent on external influences. The representative regulating processes, or basis, of these general climatic rearrangements are:

2.2.1. A new ozone layer distribution.
2.2.2. Radiation material (plasma) inflows and discharges through the polar regions, and through the world's magnetic anomaly locations.
2.2.3. Growth of the direct ionospheric effects on the relationship between the Earth's meteorological (weather), magnetic, and temperature fields.

There is a growing probability that we are moving into a rapid temperature instability period similar to the one that took place 10,000 years ago. This not so ancient major instability was revealed by the analysis of ice drilling core samples in Greenland [51]. The analysis of these core samples established:

2.2.4.That annual temperatures increased by 7 degrees centigrade.
2.2.5.That precipitation grew in the range of 3 to 4 times.
2.2.6.That the mass of dust material increased by a factor of 100.

Such high-speed transformations of the global climatic mechanism parameters, and its effects on Earth's physical and biospheric qualities has not yet been rigorously studied by the reigning scientific community. But, researchers are now insisting more, and more, that the Earth's temperature increases are dependent upon, and directly linked to, space-terrestrial interactions [52,53]; be it Earth-Sun, Earth-Solar System, and/or Earth-Interstellar.

At the present time there is no lack of new evidence regarding temperature inversion variations in the hydrosphere [oceans]. In the Eastern Mediterranean there have been recordings of a temperature inversion in depths greater than two kilometers from a ratio of 13.3 to 13.5 degrees centigrade to a new ratio of 13.8 to 13.5; along with a growth in salinity of 0.02% since 1987. The growth of salinity in the Aegean Sea has stopped, and the salt water outflow from the Mediterranean Basin to the Atlantic has diminished. Neither of these processes, or their causes, has been satisfactorily explained. It has already been established that evaporation increases in the equatorial regions causes a water density increase which results in an immediate sinking to a greater depth. Ultimately this would force the Gulfstream to reverse its flow. A probability of this event happening is confirmed by other signs as well as multiparameter numeric models [53]. Therefore the most highly probable scenario for the European Continent is a sharp and sudden cooling. Elsewhere, the Siberian region has been experiencing a stable temperature increase [58] along with reports from the Novosibirsk Klyuchi Observatory of a constant growth of up to 30 nanoteslas per year of the vertical component of the magnetic field. This growth rate increases significantly as the Eastern Siberian magnetic anomaly is approached.

Update Note 1/8/98: The National Oceanic and Atmospheric Administration reported today, 1/8/98, that 1997 was the warmest year on record since records began in 1880, and that nine of the warmest years since that time have occured in the last eleven years.

2.3 Vertical and Horizontal Ozone Content Redistribution.

Vertical and horizontal ozone content redistribution is the main indicator, and active agent, of general climatic transformations on Earth. And, evidence exists that ozone concentrations also have a strong influence upon Earth's biospheric processes. Widespread models for "ozone holes" being in the stratosphere [7 to 10 miles above Earth] (Antarctic and Siberian) are receiving serious corrective modifications from reports of vertical ozone redistribution, and its growth in the troposphere [below 7 miles]. It is now clear that the decrease in our atmosphere's total ozone content is caused by technogeneous [industrial, human designed, pollution], and that the total ozone content in general has serious effects upon the energy distribution processes within Earth's gas-plasma [atmospheric] envelopes [54].

Stratospheric, tropospheric, and surface layer ozone's are now being studied [55,56]. Photodissociation [the process by which a chemical combination breaks up into simpler constituents] of ozone, controls the oxidizing activities within the troposphere. This has created a special atmospheric, physio-chemical, circumstance by which the usual tropospheric concentrations, and lifetimes, of carbon monoxide, methane, and other hydrocarbon gases are modified and changed. So, with the established fact that a statistically significant rise in the ozone concentrations has taken place in the tropospheric layers between 5 and 7 miles, and with the addition, and full knowledge, of ozone's oxidizing properties, we must conclude that a basic and fundamental alteration of the gas composition and physical state of Earth's atmosphere has already begun.

There are continuing reports of diminishing regional stratosphere ozone concentrations [25 to 49% or more above Siberia (57)], and of global decreases of ozone content in altitudes of 20-26 miles; with the maximal decrease of 7% being at 24 miles [55]. At the same time, there is no direct evidence of a growth of UV radiation at the ground surface [58]. There are, however, a growing number of "ozone alerts" in large European cities. For example, in 1994 there were 1800 "ozone alerts" in Paris. In addition, remarkably high concentrations of surface layer ozone were registered in the Siberian Region. There were ozone concentration splashes in Novosibirsk that exceeded 50 times the normal level. We must remember that ozone smell is noticeable in concentrations of 100 mkg/m3; i.e. at 2 to 10 times the normal level.

The most serious concern of aeronomists comes from the detection of H02 that is being produced at an altitude of 11 miles by a completely unknown source or mechanism. This source of HO2 was discovered as a result of the investigation of OH/HO2 ratios in the interval between 4.35 and 21.70 miles in the upper troposphere and stratosphere. This significant growth of HO2, over the course of time, will create a dependence on this substance for the ozone transfer and redistribution process in the lower stratosphere[56].

The submission of the ozone's dynamic regime and space distribution to the above unknown source of HO2, signifies a transition of Earth's atmosphere to a new physico-chemical process. This is very important because non-uniformity's in the Earth's ozone concentrations can, and will, cause an abrupt growth in temperature gradients, which in turn do lead to the increase of air mass movement velocities, and to irregularities of moisture circulation patterns[46,59]. Temperature gradient changes, and alterations, over the entire planet would create new thermodynamic conditions for entire regions; especially when the hydrospheres [oceans] begin to participate in the new thermal non-equilibrium. The study [53] supports this conclusion, and the consideration of a highly possible abrupt cooling of the European and North American Continents. The probability of such a scenario increases when you take into account the ten year idleness of the North Atlantic hydrothermal pump. With this in mind, the creation of a global, ecology-oriented, climate map which might reveal these global catastrophes becomes critically important.

3.0 THE ARRIVAL OF NEW CONDITIONS AND CONSEQUENCES

Considering the totality and sequential relationship of transient background, and newly formed processes, brought about by the above stated cosmogenic and anthropogenic PlanetoPhysical transformations and alterations of our weather and climatic systems, we find it reasonable to divide matters into their manifest (explicit) and non-manifest (implicit) influences upon Earth's environment.

3.1 The Manifest or Explicit Consequences.

The classes or categories of effects brought about by the Earth's current stage of reorganization are very diverse. Most often, however, they tend to the transient high-energy type of event. Based on the results of the Yokohama Conference (Fall 1994,) they can be called "significant catastrophes". There are nine types of "significant catastrophes:"

Catastrophes by type: For the period of 1963-1993

Years	total	Annual	total	annual	total	annual
1963-1967	16	3.2	39	7.8	89	17.8
1968-1972	15	3.0	54	10.8	98	19.6
1973-1977	31	6.2	56	11.2	95	19
1978-1982	55	11.0	99	19.8	138	27.6
1983-1987	58	11.6	116	23.2	153	30.6
1988-1992	66	13.2	139	27.8	205	41.0
	241	8.0	503	16.8	778	25.5

In addition, we must point out the abrupt growth of meteorological/weather catastrophes in recent years. In the Atlantic region alone there were 19 cyclones in 1994; 11 of which became hurricanes. This is a 100 year record [60]. The current year, 1996, is especially laden with reports of flooding and other types of meteocatastrophes. The dynamic growth of significant catastrophes shows a major increase in the rate of production since 1973. And in general, the number of catastrophes has grown by 410% between 1963 and 1993. Special attention must be focused on the growing number and variety of catastrophes, and to their consequences.

	Number	$ Damage(Billions)	Deaths
Flooding	76	162	202,000
Hurricanes	73		153,000
Drought	53	167	
Frost	24		
Storms	6		
Epidemics	100		133,000
Earthquakes	20		102,000
Starvation	18		
Landslides			54,000

Damage >1% of Casualties>1%
gross national product of population. > 100 deaths.

One must keep in mind that the growing complexity of climatic and weather patterns signals a transformation tending towards a new state, or as Academician Kondratyev says, data indicates that we are moving in the direction of climatic chaos. In reality this transition state of our climatic machinery is placing new requirements upon Earth's entire biosphere; which does include the human species. In particular, there are reports from Antarctica that show a dramatic reaction by vegetation to the recent changes in climate; there were 700 species found growing in 1964 and 17,500 in 1990 [61]. This increase in Earth's vegetative cover provides evidence of the biosphere's reaction to the ongoing process of climatic rearrangement.

The overall pattern of the generation and movement of cyclones has also changed. For example, the number of cyclones moving to Russia from the West has grown 2.5 times during the last 10 years. Increased ocean levels caused by the shedding of ice from the polar regions will lead to sharp changes in coast lines, a redistribution of land and sea relationships, and to the activation of significant geodynamic processes. This is the main characteristic of those processes leading to a new climatic and biospheric order.

3.2 The Non-Manifest or Implicit Consequences.

Implicit consequences are those processes which are below the threshold of usual human perception, and are therefore not brought to our common attention. Instrument recordings, and even direct observations, of these phenomena throughout Earth's electromagnetic field provides evidence that an immense transformation of Earth's environment is taking place. This situation is aggravated by the fact that in the 1990's anthropogeneous (human) power production/usage increased to (1-9)E+26 ergs/per year which means it reached the conservative energetic production/usage values of our planet. For example, Earth's annual energy consumption is comprised of (1-9)E+26 ergs for earthquakes, (1-9)E+24 for geomagnetic storms, and (1-9)E+28 for heat emission [54].

There already are technogeneous effects upon the functional state of Earth's electromagnetic skeleton being registered and recorded. A seven-day technogeneous cycle for geomagnetic field dynamic parameter variations was revealed in 1985 [62,63]. This cycle has affected many of the short cycles in Solar-terrestrial relationships. More than 30% of middle magnetosphere disturbances are caused by power production, transmission, and consumption. The Van Allen radiation belt has abruptly lowered above the East Coast of the US from 300 km to 10 km. This process is associated with electricity transmission from the Great Lakes to the South along a magnetic meridian, and usage of the ionosphere-resonance frequency (60Hz) of energy consumption [63]. There is also a registered coherence between the gutter qualities of the Brazilian magnetic anomaly, and the "Hydro-Quebec" power production system. Combined techno-natural electromagnetic processes in megalopolises are very complex and as yet unstudied. A 1996 study of mortality from cardiovascular diseases in St. Petersburg, Russia uncovered a direct connection between the city's power consumption and mortality.

Moreover, the increase in the frequency, and scope, of natural self-luminous formations in the atmosphere and geospace forces us to wake up, and take notice [64,65,66]. The processes of generation, and the existence of such formations, spreading all over the Earth, represents a remarkable physical phenomenon. What is most unusual about these natural self-luminous formations is that while they have distinct features of well-known physical processes, they are in entirely unusual combinations, and are accompanied by process features which cannot be explained on the basis of existing physical knowledge. Thus, features of intense electromagnetic processes are being found in the space inside and near these natural self-luminous objects. These features include:

3.2.1. Intense electromagnetic emissions ranging from the micrometer wave band through the visible diapason, to television, and radio wavelengths.
3.2.2. Electric and magnetic field changes such as electric breakdowns, and the magnetization of rocks and technical objects.
3.2.3. Destructive electrical discharges.
3.2.4. Gravitation effects such as levitation.
3.2.5. Others.

All of the qualities of this class of phenomena are requiring the development of new branches of modern physics; particularly the creation of a "non-homogeneous physical vacuum model" [67]. An advancement of the sciences in this direction would allow us to reveal the true nature of these objects, which are acting apparently, and latently, upon our geological-geophysical and biospheric environment, and on human life [68].

Therefore, we must first take into account all of the newly developed processes and states of our geological-geophysical environment. These processes, for the most part, manifest themselves in the hard-to-register, and observe, qualities of the Earth's electromagnetic skeleton. This data also concerns the geophysical and climatic meanings of Solar-terrestrial and planetary-terrestrial interactions. This is especially true of Jupiter which is magnetically conjugate to our planet. The totality of these planet-transforming processes develops precipitately, ubiquitously, and diversely. It is critical that politicians be informed and trained to understand these global relationships between the totality of natural and anthropogeneous activities, and there fundamental causes and effects [69]. A compelling need exists to commence a scientific study which would delineate the problems associated with Earth's current transformational processes, and the effects they will have on global demographic dynamics [70]. The sharp rise of our technogeneous system's destructive force on a planetary as well as a cosmic scale, has now placed the future survival of our technocratic civilization in question [33,7]. Additionally, the principle of Natures supremacy [72] over that of humanities current integral technogeneous and psychogenic activities and results, becomes more, and more, apparent.

CONCLUSIONS

The situation that has been created here in our Heliosphere is of external, Interstellar, cosmic space origin,and is herein assumed to be caused by the underlying fundamental auto-oscillation, space-physical, processes of continuous creation that has shaped, and continues to evolve our Universe. The present excited state of our Heliosphere exists within the whole, or entire, organism that makes up the Solar System; the Sun, Planets, Moons, Comets, and Asteroids, as well as the plasmas, and/or electromagnetic mediums, and structures, of Interplanetary Space. The response to these Interstellar energy and matter injections into our Heliosphere has been, and continues to be, a series of newly observed energetic processes and formations on all of the Planets; between the Planets and their Moons, and the Planets and the Sun.

Earth's ability to adapt to these external actions and transference's is aggravated, made more difficult, by the technogeneous alterations we have made to the natural quality, or state, of our geological-geophysical environment. Our Planet Earth is now in the process of a dramatic transformation;by altering the electromagnetic skeleton through a shift of the geomagnetic field poles, and through compositional changes in the ozone, and hydrogen, saturation levels of its gas-plasma envelopes. These changes in the Earth's physical state are being accompanied by resultant climatic/atmospheric, and biospheric, adaptation processes. These processes are becoming more and more intense, and frequent, as evidenced by the real time increase in "non-periodic transient events"; ie., catastrophes. There are reasons favoring, or pointing to, the fact that a growth in the ethical, or spiritual quality, of humanity would decrease the number and intensity of complex catastrophes. It has become vitally important that a world chart be prepared setting forth the favorable, and the catastrophic, regions on Earth taking into account the quality of the geologic-geophysical environment, the variety and intensity of cosmic influences, and the real level of spiritual-ethical development of the people occupying those areas.

It is reasonable to point out that our Planet will soon be experiencing these new conditions of growing energy signifying the transition into a new state and quality of Space-Earth relationship. The living organisms of those regions of Earth having the major "inlets", or attractions, for cosmic influences will be taking the lead in evolving life's appropriate reactions, or processes, to these new conditions. These zones of vertical commutations and energy transfers are already becoming the heart, or hotbeds, in the search for new systems of adaptation and mutual transformation. The general list of these zones includes the polar regions, the eastern continental extremities of the equatorial regions [Caribbean, Madagascar, Philippines, Yellow Sea, etc.], and the inner continental zones tending to folding and uplifting [Himalayas, Pamir-Hindukush, Altay-Sayan systems, etc.]

The most significant of these areas are the helio-sensitive zones which have intense responses to geoeffective solar activities [Note #1]; responses that include the very dramatic and unusual manifestation of non-homogeneous vacuum, or classical non-mechanical ether, domain structures. These structures, or objects, then interact with the heliosensitive zones producing deep and powerful effects upon the environment such as the alteration of seismic activities, and chemical compositions. Because these non-homogeneous vacuum domain objects display not-of-this-physical-world characteristics such as "liquid light" and "non-Newtonian movement" it is difficult not to describe their manifestations as being "interworld processes". It is important to note that those heliosensitive zones that exhibit middle and large scale processes are also those that are closely associated with these "interworld processes" produced by physical vacuum homogeneity disturbances.

Such disturbances cause, and create, energy and matter transfer processes between the ether media and our three-dimensional world. The multitude of such phenomena, which is rich in it's quality and variety, is already growing quickly. Hundreds of thousands of these natural self-luminous formations are exerting a increasing influence upon Earth's geophysic fields and biosphere. We suggest that the presence of these formations is the mainstream precedent to the transformation of Earth; an Earth which becomes more and more subject to the transitional physical processes which exist within the borderland between the physical vacuum and our material world.

All of this places humanity, and each one of us, squarely in front of a very difficult and topical problem; the creation of a revolutionary advancement in knowledge which will require a transformation of our thinking and being equal to this never-before-seen phenomena now presencing itself in our world. There is no other path to the future than a profound internal experiential perception and knowledge of the events now underway in the natural environment that surrounds us. It is only through this understanding that humanity will achieve balance with the renewing flow of the PlanetoPhysical States and Processes.

End Paper

NOTES

1. Since the Earth is a large very highly organized organism, each of its structural units or territories such as, mountain systems, rivers, tectonic faults, ore deposits, oil fields etc. plays a certain functional role in its life, and in its connections with the outer world. For example, iron ore deposits support the climate stability because they perform the connection between the electrical activity in the atmosphere, and the electrical activity beneath the Earth's surface.
2. Nowadays we all know the works of Tschizhevsky who discovered, and proved in the 1920's, that deep and various connections exist between Solar activity and various life processes. Using vast historical and statistical material he showed that Solar activity acts as an accelerator and moderator upon the whole biosphere, which manifests in the frequency and quantity of : births, deaths , harvests, epidemics, heart attacks, emergencies, bank crashes, catastrophes, suicides, populations growths and decreases, etc., etc.
3. Since different zones of Earth have different functions in the Earth organism, their response to Solar activity is also different. For example, the polar regions are first to react to Solar disturbances, which we know well in the form of magnetic storms, auroras, and nowadays, in ocean warming at the 75 degree North latitudes. We also know other places which demonstrate intense reactions to different kinds of solar activity; that's what we call heliosensitive zones.Such reactions include local electromagnetic disturbances, low-latitude auroras, and specific changes in the pattern of magnetic field variations on the short term scale. There are also long-term reactions in the state of the biosphere. One of our colleagues, Ildar Mingazov, found, in studying the distribution and frequency of different types of diseases in various regions, that the intensity of disease frequency in correlation with solar activity varies between regions, and is maximal for heliosensitive zones (for example, cardiovascular diseases). (Notes by: Andrew Tetenov)

References are available at http://www.tmgnow.com/

Appendix II

The Cosmic String Tutorial

In 1976, Thomas Kibble, a theoretical physicist at Imperial College, London made the hypothesis that when matter first condensed shortly after the Big Bang, it gathered around long thin "cracks" in the fabric of space-time, the cracks he called "cosmic string". He postulated the possibility of this defect formation, when he realized that in a cooling universe, such a phase transition would not necessarily proceed in an orderly fashion. Rather, there would appear domain-separate regions where the boundary is marked by a structure called a domain wall. Due to the properties of Higgs fields (loosely analogous to a magnetic or electrical field in space), when mismatched domains come together, the Higgs field adjusts so as to concentrate the discontinuity into a line rather than a wall. This then becomes a string defect, an incredibly thin filament of false vacuum that then produces these cosmic strings.

Other scientists have also theorized about the existence of these *strings.* Alejandro Gangui in an article in America Scientist (May – June 2000) described cosmic string and recent work that indicates that they may conduct great amounts of electrical current [1]. The theory has many aspects that seem to match observations in the cosmos.

> "As imagined by physicists, cosmic strings are exceedingly narrow filaments of primordial material, strands of a trapped, unconverted phase left over from the early moments of cosmic history. They have extraordinary energies, move at velocities approaching that of light and curve space around themselves. Through their gravitational interactions they can draw matter together to form large-scale structures such as galaxies or clusters of galaxies, and push matter around to give such structures bulk drift velocities."
>
> "Moreover, realistic particle-physics models predict that at a certain stage of their evolution these strings can develop tremendous electric currents, effectively becoming electrically conducting-actually superconducting-wires of astrophysical dimensions. This notion could help to explain some puzzles of observational cosmology. The currents would generate primordial magnetic fields that could give rise to the observed magnetic fields in galaxies today. Currents would also stabilize small loops of cosmic string against decay; such loops might still survive, forming so-called non-baryonic dark matter-the as-yet-undetected matter thought to occupy much of the modern universe."

These theories could be tested with liquid crystals and later with the discovery of superfluidity in helium-3. This has provided a kind of experimental confirmation of cosmological topological defect theory, increasing the credibility of these ideas. In 1996, Ville Ruutu and collaborators in Helsinki succeeded in heating up a volume of superfluid helium-3 with thermal neutrons to just above the transition temperature, then cooling it back through the superfluid transition. They observed copious production of quantized vortices in their advanced experiments with helium-3. These scientists even probed the internal microscopic structure of the vortices, which forms a close analogy to cosmic strings whose internal structure allows the motion of particles, and thus electric currents, along them.

Interestingly, the existence of a current allows the loop configuration as a whole to rotate. Such currents also allow the existence of stable loops of fixed microscopic size, in which the angular momentum of the current balances string tension. These stationary-loop solutions were dubbed "vortons" by Richard L. Davis and Paul Shellard in 1988. Vortons do not radiate energy in a classical way, even though they are oscillating electromagnetic structures. At large distances these vortons look like point masses with quantized electric charge, a hundred times the charge of the electron and angular momentum. They are very much like particles but their size is found by multiplying their charge number by the string thickness, essentially some 14 orders of magnitude smaller than the classical electron radius. Even so, a vorton would be still be some 20 orders of magnitude heavier than the electron.

Outstanding astrophysical problems may perhaps be explained with the help of these superconducting cosmic strings. The first concerns how galactic magnetic fields are generated. Magnetic fields are produced when an electrically charged object moves in space, precisely what cosmic strings are and what they do. Missing dark energy can be accounted for by cosmic strings, being high density, they would also be high in mass but are only detectable by their gravitational radiation.

Cosmic strings look like they also offer a solution to the extremely high energy particles which constantly assault the Earth's atmosphere. Gangui states that superconducting cosmic strings offer two ways to deliver extremely energetic particles. Firstly, they may directly emit particles with tremendous energies, or, secondly tiny loops of superconducting cosmic string, which would be misinterpreted as ordinary but very energetic particles. According to Kibble, with all the cosmic activity the Earth is experiencing today, his theory which is over twenty years old, is currently experiencing a revival [2]. Kibble remarks, “string theory cosmologists have discovered cosmic strings lurking everywhere in the undergrowth”.

Cosmic Strings demonstrated in a Swimming Pool?

The Falaco Effect as a topological defect, first noticed by Professor Emeritus, R M Kiehn from the Physics Department, University of Houston in a swimming pool in March 1986. The concept was first presented at the Austin Meeting of Dynamic Days in Austin, January 1987, and caused some interest among topologists. The easily reproduced experiment helps us to understand topological phenomena, which is now understood to be universal, and will appear at all levels from the microscopic to the galactic [3].

Falaco Solitons is the scientific term given to vortices, or swirls that can be made with a frisbee in a swimming pool [4]. The frisbee imparts kinetic energy and distributed angular momentum, to the fluid in the form of a pair of Rankine Vortices. In a few seconds with bright sunlight, the concave Rankine depressions, will produce black spots at the bottom of the pool [5]. [Kiehn 1992]. See figures 1 & 2. The surface distortion is a pair of dimple-like depressions of a few millimeters **but unseen to the eye is a one dimensional defect or string that appears to connect the pair** of surface two dimensional defects at their vertices. The stable shape of the connecting string is in the form of a circular arc. Kiehn describes this as a 1-dimensional defect, or string, that can be made visible by injecting dye drops near a dimple vertex. Though, if the string is dynamically severed, the two surface defects disappear with a pop!

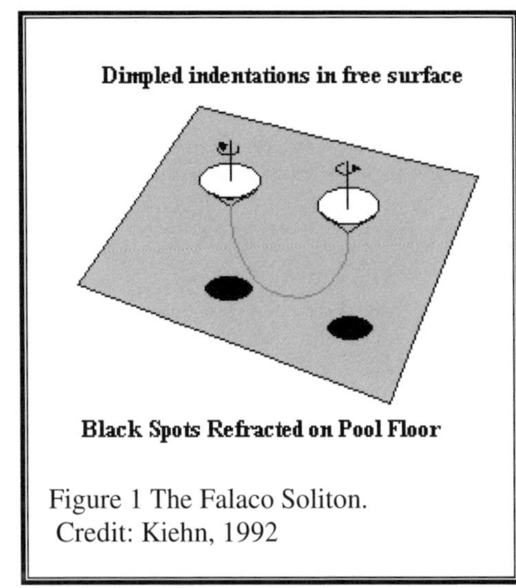

Figure 1 The Falaco Soliton.
Credit: Kiehn, 1992

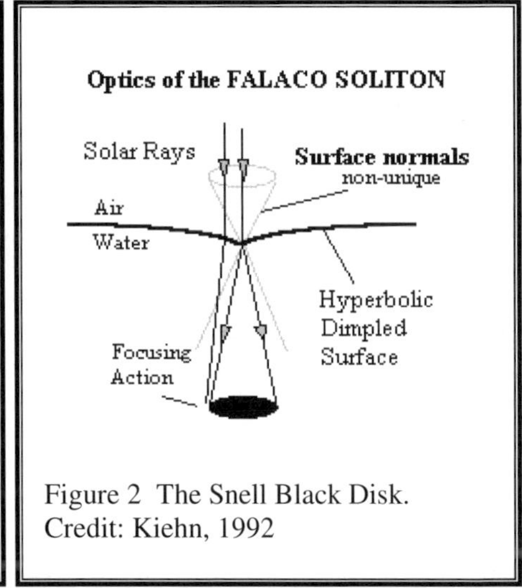

Figure 2 The Snell Black Disk.
Credit: Kiehn, 1992

In reality the description of a 1-dimensional defect, or string that can be produced is a mathematical abstraction and what must exists is an energetic structure, another vortex, such as the “invisible” lines of the magnetic force, or a wormhole. The point is, Kiehn has provided an experiment that anyone can do that demonstrates how vortices can be connected by cosmic strings. This applies on all levels from the microscopic to the macroscopic. At the macroscopic level, the vortices are represented as planets and stars. Cosmic strings demonstrated in the swimming pool provides a novel way to learn the rules of the universe!

Notes:

1 Gangui A, Superconducting Cosmic Strings: These relics from the early universe could be the answer to many astrophysical conundrums, American Scientist, pages 254-263, May-June 2000.
Copy of article at URL: http://www.iafe.uba.ar/relatividad/gangui/SCS.html

2 Kibble T.W.B., Cosmic Strings Reborn? Imperial/TP/041001, Oct 2004
http://arxiv.org/PS_cache/astro-ph/pdf/0410/0410073.pdf

3 Falaco Solitons
http://www22.pair.com/csdc/car/carfre10.htm

4 Kiehn R M, The Falaco Soliton: Cosmic Strings in a Swimming Pool, Physics Department, University of Houston
http://www22.pair.com/csdc/pdf/falaco97.pdf
http://arxiv.org/abs/gr-qc/0101098

5 The black spots on the bottom of the pool are created from the Snell refraction of a surface of rotational symmetry with negative Gauss curvature.

Appendix III

The New Balance Hormones

This is an excerpt from the following research paper:

Rollin McCraty, Ph.D., Mike Atkinson, Dana Tomasino, B.A., and Raymond Trevor Bradley, Ph.D. *The Coherent Heart: Heart-Brain Interactions, Psychophysiological, Coherence, and the Emergence of System-Wide Order, HeartMath* Research Center, Institute of HeartMath, Publication No. 06-022. Boulder Creek, California, 2006, Institute of HeartMath, 14700 West Park Ave., Boulder Creek, CA 95006

Printed with permission from Dr. Rollin McCraty, Director of Research at the Institute of HeartMath.

Heart Coherence - Biochemical Interactions

In addition to its extensive neurological interactions with the brain and body, the heart also communicates with the brain and body biochemically, by way of the hormones it produces. Although not typically thought of as an endocrine gland, the heart in fact manufactures and secretes a number of hormones and neurotransmitters that have a wide-ranging impact on body as a whole.

The heart was reclassified as part of the hormonal system in 1983, when a new hormone produced and secreted by the atria of the heart was discovered. This hormone has been variously termed atrial natriuretic factor (ANF), atrial natriuretic peptide (ANP), or atrial peptide. Nicknamed the "balance hormone" and playing an important role in fluid and electrolyte homeostasis, it exerts its effects on the blood vessels, kidneys, adrenal glands, and many of the regulatory regions of the brain.58, 59 In addition, studies indicate that atrial peptide inhibits the release of stress hormones,109 reduces sympathetic outflow,110 plays a part in hormonal pathways that stimulate the function and growth of reproductive organs,111 and may even interact with the immune system.112 Even more intriguing, experiments suggest that atrial peptide can influence motivation and behavior.113

Several years following the discovery of atrial peptide, a related peptide hormone, with similar biological functions, was identified. This was called brain natriuretic peptide (BNP) because it was first identified in porcine brain. It soon became clear, however, that the main source of this peptide was the cardiac ventricle rather than the brain, and brain natriuretic peptide is now sometimes called B-type natriuretic peptide.60

Armour and colleagues also found that the heart contains a cell type known as intrinsic cardiac adrenergic cells. These cells are so classified because they synthesize and release catecholamines (norepinephrine, epinephrine, and dopamine), neurotransmitters once thought to be produced only by neurons in the brain and ganglia outside the heart.62 More recently still, it was discovered that the heart also manufactures and secretes oxytocin, commonly referred to as the "love" or social "bonding hormone". Beyond its well-known functions in childbirth and lactation, recent evidence indicates that this hormone is also involved in cognition, tolerance, trust, complex sexual and maternal behaviors, as well as in the learning of social cues and the establishment of enduring pair bonds. Remarkably, concentrations of oxytocin produced in the heart are in the same range as those produced in the brain.61

In a preliminary study (10 participants), we examined changes in the blood concentrations of oxytocin and atrial peptide before and after 10 minutes of maintaining the psychophysiological coherence mode, which was generated by a loving emotional focus. Figure 24 displays the results. While an increase in oxytocin was observed, it was not statistically significant, although this would be likely with a larger number of research subjects. On the other hand, despite the small number of cases, the decrease in atrial peptide was significant. Though unexpected, this is an interesting result. As atrial peptide release is directly related to the stretch and contractile force of the atrial wall of the heart, these data suggest that cardiovascular efficiency increases during the psychophysiological coherence mode.

Heart Hormones Before and After Coherence

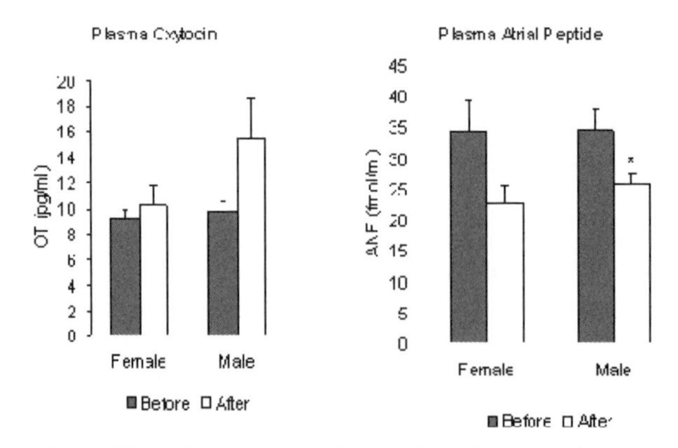

Figure 24. Balance Heart Hormones before and Coherence. Courtesy Heartmath Institute

Figure 24. Oxytocin and atrial peptide changes during heart rhythm coherence. Graphs show changes in blood levels of oxytocin and atrial peptide for male and female subgroups from a resting baseline mode to after maintaining the coherence mode for 10 minutes.

In addition to changes in the amount of a heart hormone released into the blood affecting cellular and psychological systems, there is also evidence that the temporal pattern of the hormonal release has substantial effects independent of the amount of the hormone released. It has been known for some time that neurotransmitters, hormones, and intracellular "second messengers" are released in a pulsatile fashion. Pulsatile patterns of secretion are observed for nearly all of the major hormones, including ACTH, GH, LH, FSH, TSH, prolactin, beta-endorphin, melatonin, vasopressin, progesterone, testosterone, insulin, glucagon, renin, aldosterone, and cortisol, among many others.

Recent studies by German endocrinology researchers Georg Brabant, Klaus Prank, and Christoph Schofl have shown that, in much the same way that the nervous system encodes information in the time interval between action potentials, biologically relevant information is also encoded in the temporal pattern of hormonal release, across time scales ranging from seconds to hours.114 As most heart hormones are released in synchronicity with the contractions of the heart, there is a rhythmic pattern of hormonal release that tracks the heart rhythm.

This is particularly relevant to our discussion of coherence, as it suggests that changes in heart rhythm patterns-such as those generated during psychophysiological coherence-impact the brain and body in yet another way: that is, they change the pattern of hormonal pulses released by the heart. Although the influence of these changes in hormonal pulse patterns on biological, emotional, and behavioral processes is still unknown, it is likely that the transmission of such hormonal information constitutes another pathway by which the effects of psychophysiological coherence on health, well-being, and performance are mediated.

Appendix IV

Russian & Ukranian Pyramid Research

The following is a summary of the experiments detailed in Dr. Krasnoholovets' paper that represent over 20 years of research. Any reference to experiments directed by Alexander Golod were actually performed by a team of researchers from the Scientific Manufacturing Union Gidrometpribor in Russia.

Medical Research

#1 Strengthening of the Immune System

- Professor Klimenko and Dr. Nosik from Ivanovskii R&D Institute of Virology, which is part of the Russian Academy of Medical Science, studied the effect of pyramids on molecules used in immunity. These molecules which exist in our bodies are immunoglobulins. They fight infections, viruses, and bacteria that may enter our body. These researchers took a specific kind of immunoglobulin (called venoglobulin) and placed it in the pyramid for several days. They wanted to see if the pyramids effect would change the ability of this molecule to help fight harmful viruses in the body. Then, they obtained a specific virus (encephalomyocarditis) from a mouse. They placed both the immunoglobulin and this virus together in a culture (a dish with nutrients). They also had a control group of immunogobulins that had *not* been placed in the pyramid with the mouse virus. The results showed that the immunoglobulin that *was* placed in the pyramids inhibited the viruses by more than 3 times. This was a significant result and shows that the immunoglobin was affected by being placed in the pyramids. This could have an important potential for strengthening the bodies immune system against viruses.

#2 Fortifying the Healing Benefits of Glucose and Water

- The team of Prof. A.G. Antonov from the Russian R&D Institute of Pediatrics, Obstetrics and Gynecology tested the effects of a solution of 40% glucose in distilled water after it had been stored in the pyramid. By administering only 1 ml of the glucose to 20 different newborn babies with low health measurements, their levels of health were seen to rapidly increase up to normal levels even for the most sickly babies. Subsequently, the researchers discovered that the glucose was not necessary, and the same effect could be produced by simply using 1 ml of ordinary water that had been stored in the pyramid.

#3 Increased Immune Response by Living Organisms

- Another study was performed by Dr. N.B. Yegorova at the Mechnikov R&D Institute within the Russian Academy of Medical Science. This study, monitored the benefits on living animals placed inside the pyramid and mice were used for the experiments. The mice were divided into an experimental and a control group and were both injected with a specific bacteria known as S.typhimurium, which is a deadly bacterium in mice and only requires a hand full of cells to cause death. At various lengths of time after exposure in the pyramids, the mice were infected with this salmonella typhimurium and their survival rate was recorded over the course of a month. By the twenty-fifth day of observation practically all the control animals had died. However, among the groups exposed in the pyramids 35-40% survived.

- In other experiments, mice were exposed to various carcinogens. The experimental group drank water from the pyramid whereas the control group drank ordinary water. The mice drinking the pyramid water had significantly fewer tumors develop than the mice drinking the ordinary water.

- Dr. Yuri Bogdanov et al. conducted studies on behalf of the Joint-stock Company, "Scientific and Technological Institute of Transcription, Translation and Replication" (TTR), in Kharkiv, Ukraine. Dr Bogdanov particpated in the choice of location of several large pyramids in Russia. He found that rabbits and white rats exposed to the pyramid gained 200% more endurance and their blood gained a higher concentration of leukocytes, or white blood cells.

#4 Positive Human Behavioral Changes

- A psychiatric study was conducted where a quantity of salt and pepper was stored inside the pyramid. This salt and pepper was later removed and fed continually to about 5000 people in different jails in Russia. Amazingly, within a few months there was a dramatic improvement in behavior, and the most violent behavior almost completely disappeared compared to a control group. This is one of the more important points, as it validates the idea that energy generated by the pyramid is "spiritual energy" and that as a person is exposed to higher intensities, there is a propensity for greater feelings of love and compassion for others.

- Other studies with people of alcoholism and drug addiction have shown that if they are given pyramid stored glucose intravenously or distilled water orally, significant improvement can be made in combating addiction. The results show the effect pyramids have on mental processes.

- Alexander Golod's team also determined that poisons and other toxins become less destructive to living systems after even a short term of exposure in the pyramid. Pathogenic viruses and bacteria become significantly less damaging to life after being held in the pyramid

- Since the end of 1997, Alexander Golod supervised the distribution of chunks of granite and crystal, which had been exposed to pyramid energy, and these were circulated around Moscow and the Moscow region in ring formations. By the beginning of 1999, 40 such rings were created, containing between 50 and 300 rocks with total weight from 20 to 200 kg. It is anticipated that the odds of an appearance of epidemics will drop with each year. In the previous two winters prior to the experimental results being announced to the West via the internet in January 2001, the drop in influenza epidemics had already been recorded. Specifically, it was also noted that the effect is more pronounced, for younger age groups.

- Psychotropic drugs have less of an effect on people either staying inside a pyramid or within close range of a pyramid.

Chemistry and Physics Studies

#1 Oil Production Increase

- In Golod's experiments with a series of pyramids built over a number of oil wells. It was discovered that the viscosity of the oil under the pyramids decreased by 30%, while the production rate accordingly increased by 30% compared to the surrounding wells. There was a decrease in the amount of unwanted materials in the oil, such as gums, pyrobitumen and paraffin. These results were confirmed by the Gubkin Moscow Academy of Oil and Gas.

#2 Water Will Not Freeze Unless Disturbed

- Plastic bottles of distilled water were kept in the pyramid over a period of three winter months. During this time, the air temperature in the pyramid sank as low as -38° C, or -6° F. Thermometers inside the bottles revealed that the temperature of the water was the same as the below-freezing air temperatures surrounding them, yet the water remained in a liquid form and would not turn into ice! However, if the water in any of the bottles was shaken or bumped in any way, it would immediately start crystallizing and quickly turn into a block of ice. Golod and his associates have videotaped these results.

#3 Change of Electrical Resistance

- Prof. V.I. Kostikov and Dr. A.C. Katasonov from the R&D Institute "Graphite" within the Russian Academy of Sciences performed various studies on the changes in electrical resistance that can be induced by a pyramid structure. In one example, a pyrocarbon material was tested that normally had a resistance of 5 to 7 micro-ohms. After a one-day stay in the pyramid, the material became 200% more resistant to electric current, which is a highly abnormal effect for pyrocarbon. Irradiating the same material with ~1019 neutrons/m2 would only change the resistance of the pyrocarbon by about 5% in comparison. Similarly, silicon semiconductors would have an exponential lowering of their electrical resistance, moving from 105 to 104 ohms/cm, and high-temperature superconducting materials would lose their superconductive properties after a one-day stay in the pyramid.

#4 Balancing Electrical Charge Distribution

- A group of researchers from the All-Russian Electrotechnical Institute in Moscow conducted an experiment to demonstrate how pyramid-charged rocks could dissipate strong electric charges, rendering them less harmful. The setup involved two identical systems, an experimental and a control, which involved a flat metallic plate that was zapped by positively-charged electric blasts. In the experimental system, seven 100-gram chunks of granite that had been stored inside the pyramid were then placed on the flat plate in a one-meter wide ring. The researchers discovered that there were five times more burn marks on the control plate as opposed to the experimental plate. It seems that the rocks exposed to the torsion fields in the pyramid were much more capable of distributing electrical charges.

- Golod also found radioactive materials held inside a pyramid would decay more rapidly than expected.

#5 Better Artificial Diamonds

- Artificial diamonds that were synthesized within the pyramid turned out harder and purer than they would otherwise. Again, this suggests that torsion-waves are of central importance in the forming of chemical bonds to create a crystal. Dr. Yuri Bogdanov also found that:

- The half-life of radioactive carbon was altered; The crystallization patterns of salts would change; Concrete would change in its strength;

- In addition, Dr. Bogdanov performed many laboratory studies on medicinal preparations, fungi and so forth. In the city of Kiev, Dr. Bogdanov studied how matter interacts with different torsion-field patterns created by various pyramid shapes, and these investigations also studied how the consciousness of the person would affect these energy fields. These studies were performed by a torsion-wave detecting device that he named the "Tesey". This device allows the user to detect peculiar properties in a particular geological feature, energetic "breathing" activity in the Earth, as well as the torsion effects of various buildings including pyramids. These results were discussed on the Conference on Problems of Harmonization of Mankind, held in Kiev, and were subsequently published

#6 Light Generation and Razor Blade sharpening

- Dr. Krasnoholovets built a small and simple resonator to study these pyramid effects. Within this small resonator, a KIO3*HIO3 crystal experienced a greater clustering of hydrogen atoms in the crystal. Rare gases and the surface of metals were also seen to have a photoelectric effect while in the resonator, meaning that they were producing light.

- Furthermore, Dr. Krasnoholovets replicated previous experiments by studying the effects on a razor blade within a resonator. This comprised of placing two blades one aligned east to west, and the other perpendicular to the Earth's magnetic field in which a piece of the edge was removed and stored away from the resonator. Under scanning electron microscope JSM, the edge of the razor blade from the resonator was seen to take on a smoother, less angular form over time. (This confirms again why the large outdoor pyramids could not use metal in their construction.) The other sample, also stayed in the pyramid for a month and was orientated north-south. The coarse structure was well preserved, "thus a sharpening effect of the edge."

Agricultural Studies

Increased Crop Production

- In Golod's agricultural experiments, seeds were kept in a pyramid for 1 to 5 days before being planted. More than 20 different seed varieties were planted across tens of thousands of hectares. In all cases, the seeds from the pyramid had a 20 to100-percent increase in their yield, plants did not get sick and they were not affected by droughts. Even the amount of toxiferous matters in plants was measured and shown to be sharply decreased. When small rocks that had been previously placed in a pyramid were then consequently placed in a ring around a crop, similar results were also obtained.

- It was also noted that the yield of wheat in a field near the 12 meter pyramid built in the settlement Ramenskoe of the Moscow region increased four times after the pyramid was built.

Environmental Studies

#1 Water Purification

- Dr. Yuri Bogdanov also built a complex of pyramids in a town near the Arkhangelsk region of Russia with the permission of the local government. In this case, strontium and heavy metals that had contaminated a well were able to be cleared by the effects of the pyramids, similar to how unwanted materials were filtered out of oil in the above example. In the town of Krasnogorskoe near Moscow, a pyramid was constructed that would reduce the amount of salt in water, again making it more drinkable.

#2 "Unknown Energy" Appears Above The Pyramid

- In Golod's experiments with the Joint-stock company "R&D Institute TTR", they conducted studies of the air above the pyramid with a Russian instrument similar to radar known as a "military locator." A column of "unknown energy" was detected at a width of 500 meters and a height of 2000 meters.

- Further studies confirmed that a larger circle of this energy surrounded the area above the pyramid in a 300-kilometer-wide range, with the highest concentration being directly above the apex of the pyramid. Golod's team calculated that if such an energy column were to be produced electromagnetically, it would require all the energy of the various power plants in Russia combined.

- Several months after the 22m Lake Seliger pyramid was built, the ***Ozone layer was observed to have improved*** in the atmosphere in Russia. The electrical energy from the pyramid could be harnessed by a capacitor that was placed at the apex of the pyramid and the capacitor would spontaneously take on a charge. Furthermore, pieces of the capacitor assembly were seen to break away and rise into the air on the energetic column that the pyramid was producing. People working near the top of the pyramid would start to experience dizziness and nausea, and need to be taken some distance away from the pyramid for these effects to subside.

#3 Less Extreme Seismic & Weather Activity

- Teams from the Russian National Academy of Sciences also studied the earthquake data from the areas surrounding the pyramids and compared it to earlier data before the pyramids were built. They discovered that the pyramids have the ability to dissipate the energetic buildup that would normally create sudden, violent earthquakes. Instead of seeing one large and powerful quake, several hundred tiny earthquakes are registered instead. Furthermore, the atmosphere surrounding the pyramid seems to be shielded from severe weather as well, causing an overall decrease in the amount of violent weather patterns. This suggests the role of pyramids for ***balancing*** electromagnetic or aetheric energies streaming onto a planet.

Notes:

Krasnoholovetz, et al., *Russian Pyramid Studies, 2001,* http://www.gizapyramid.com

Chapter Notes

Introduction

1. Connor S, *Disaster Planning: Norway builds a 'doomsday vault'*, The Independent Online, 12 January 2006, http://news.independent.co.uk/environment/article338009.ece
   ♦Pearce F, *Doomsday vault to avert world famine*, New Scientist, 12 January 2006 http://www.newscientist.com/article.ns?id=mg18925343.700

Chapter 1
The Electromagnetic Universe

1. Carlowicz M. J. & Lopez R. E. *Storms from the Sun: The Emerging Science of Space Weather*, Joseph Henry Press (2002)
2. Hildner E, *What is Space Weather, And Who Should Forecast It*, Before The Subcommittee on Environment, Technology and Standards Committee on Science, U.S. House of Representatives, October 2003
   www.house.gov/science/hearings/ets03/oct30/hildner.pdf
3. From the report: "We were completely surprised by the highly unusual and unexpected composition in this CME," Gloeckler says. His team observed, for example, that the density of 4He+ [a form of charged helium] was almost as high as the density of 4He++ for several hours. "Such large 4He+/4He++ratios, persisting for hours, have never been observed in the solar wind before," they write. They also observed high increases of helium and heavier ions in the CME plasma. The unusual composition of the CME lasted an exceptionally long time, they write… "This is certainly not an average solar wind but an anomalous situation," Gloeckler says.
   Bartlett, Kristina. *ACEing the sun*. American Geophysical Union / Geotimes News Notes, April 1999. www.geotimes.org/apr99/newsnotes.html
4. *The Winners! Top 10 Sun Images from SOHO*, Helical Coronal Mass Ejection which was observed by the LASCO C2 coronagraph on June 2, 1998.
   www.space.com/scienceastronomy/soho_top10_winners_031125-9.html
5. *The Sun's twisted mysteries,* Particle Physics and Astronomy Research Council Release, Spaceflightnow.com, September 1, 2002, www.spaceflightnow.com/news/n0209/01sun/
6. *Cosmic Rays From The Sun*, The Millennium Group
   www.tmgnow.com/repository/solar/cosmicrays.html
7. Carlowicz M. J. & Lopez R. E. *Storms from the Sun: The Emerging Science of Space Weather*, Joseph Henry Press (2002), Pg 184
8. *Interplanetary "Day After Tomorrow?" An Enterprise Mission Hyperdimensional Report* by Richard C. Hoagland David Wilcock May 2004
   www.enterprisemission.com/_articles/05-14-

2004_Interplanetary_Part_1/Interplanetary_1.htm
♦Bosman A N, *New Universe*, 2004, phoenix.akasha.de/~aton/NU2.html

9. Shaviv N J, Veizer J, *Celestial driver of Phanerozoic climate?*: GSA Today, v. 13, no. 7, p. 4–10. 2003, www.fathersforlife.org/articles/gunter/Kyoto_10.htm
www.deas.harvard.edu/climate/pdf/shaviv-2003.pdf
also here at www.envirotruth.org/docs/Veizer-Shaviv.pdf

10. Scientific institutions where scientists debunk the commonly held views of global warming include, Harvard University, the Smithsonian Institute, the European Space Agency, Lawrence Livermore National Laboratory in California, at the Schroeder Institute for Research in Cycles of Solar Activity in Nova Scotia and a variety of Canadian and international universities.
Gunter L, *Cosmic ray flux zaps pro-Kyoto types: New study puts paid to overheated theories on climate change*, Edmonton Journal, July 2003
www.sepp.org/weekwas/2003/Jul12.htm
♦Petition by the Oregon Institute of Science and Medicine signed by over 17,000 scientists, engineers and physicians, who oppose adoption of the Kyoto Protocol, see links at: *The Other Side of the Global Warming Debate: The Myth that the Majority of Scientists Support the Global Warming Theory.*
personals.galaxyinternet.net/tunga/OSGWD.htm
♦Svensmark H, *Influence of Cosmic Rays on Earth's Climate*, Solar-Terrestrial Physics Division. Danish Meteorological Institute, Lyngbyvej 30. DK-2100 Copenhagen, Denmark, 1997) http://www.tmgnow.com/repository/global/CREC.html
♦Svensmark H & Calder N, *The Chilling Stars: A New Theory of Climate Change*, Icon Books Ltd, 2007
♦& Singer F & Avery D T, *Unstoppable Global Warming - Every 1500 Years,* Rowman & Littlefield Publishers, Inc, 2007
♦*First Global Connection Between Earth And Space Weather Found*, September 9, 2006 http://www.nasa.gov/centers/goddard/news/topstory/2006/space_weather_link.html
♦*Getting closer to the cosmic connection to climate,* Danish National Space Center Press Release, 3 October 2006, http://www.spacecenter.dk/research/sun-climate/other/getting-closer-to-the-cosmic-connection-to-climate

11. Dmitriev A N, *Planetophysical State of the Earth and Life. (1997)*
www.tmgnow.com/repository/global/planetophysical.html

12. Peratt A, *Challenges to common sense*, Los Alamos National Laboratory
public.lanl.gov/alp/plasma/AtHomeChall.html

13. Talbott D & Thornhill W, *Thunderbolts of the Gods*, Mikamar Publishing, 2004
www.thunderbolts.info/pdf/01.1PART%20I_Ch1.pdf
Scott D, *Electrical Plasma,* www.electric-cosmos.org/electricplasma.htm

14. Peratt A L & Green J C, "*On the evolution of interacting magnetized galactic plasmas*," Astrophys. Space. Sci.,. vol. 91, pp. 19-33, 1983.
♦Peratt A L, *Evolution of the Plasma Universe: I. Double Radio Galaxies, Quasars, and Extragalactic Jets*, IEEE Trans. Plasma Sci. Vol. PS-14, N.6, pp.639-660, December 1986
♦Peratt A L, Evolution of the Plasma Universe: II. The Formation of Systems of Galaxies, IEEE Trans. Plasma Sci. Vol. PS-14, N.6, pp.763-778, December 1986
♦Peratt, Anthony L., "Physics of the Plasma Universe". Springer-Verlag, 1991

15. *Flashes in the Sky: Scientists Trace Effects of Lightning Thousands of Miles into Space,* NASA Goddard Space Flight Center, 03.08.05
www.nasa.gov/lb/vision/universe/solarsystem/lightning_in_space.html
Than K, Space Tornado! Cosmic Front Packs a Punch, Space.com, 12 January 2006
space.com/scienceastronomy/060112_space_tornado.html

16. *Prediction #1: Big Bang a Big Loser in 2005: You'd never know it from official news releases, but the Big Bang is broken and can't be fixed.* Thunderbolts Picture of the Day, Dec 27 2004, www.thunderbolts.info/tpod/2004/arch/041227prediction-bigbang.htm

17. *Hannes Alfvén (1908-1995)*, public.lanl.gov/alp/plasma/people/alfven.html

♦The 200-krone note, Norges Bank Website
www.norges-bank.no/english/notes_and_coins/200kr.html

18. Jago L, *The Northern Lights*, Hamish Hamilton, London 2001
♦Jago L, *The Serialisation of "The Northern Lights"*, www.lucyjago.com

19. *Kristian Birkeland in the Norwegian Aurora Polaris Expedition 1902-1903*. Published by Christiana, Norway, Aschehoug, Secs. 1 and 2, 1908, 1913.

20. Potemra, T. A., *Observation of Birkeland currents with the TRIAD satellite*, Astrophysics and Space Science, vol. 58, no. 1, Sept. 1978, p. 207-226. Navy-NSF-supported research.
Potemra, T. A., *Field-aligned (Birkeland) currents*, (URSI, USAF, NASA, et al. International School for Space Simulations, 2nd, Kapaa, HI, Feb. 4-15, 1985) Space Science Reviews (ISSN 0038-6308), vol. 42, Dec. 1985, p. 295-311. NSF-Navy-DNA-supported research. (SSRv Homepage), 10/1985
♦*Orbiting observatory SOHO finds source of high-speed "wind" blowing from the Sun*, European Space Agency, sohowww.nascom.nasa.gov/gallery/ESAPR/info01.html/
In 1984 astronomers found an example of Birkeland currents on a galactic scale. Working with the Very Large Array radio telescope, they discovered an arc of radio emission some 120 light-years long near the center of the Milky Way. The structure is made up of narrow filaments typically 3 light-years wide and running the full length of the arc. The strength of the associated magnetic field is 100 times greater than previously thought possible on such a large scale, but the field is nearly identical in geometry and strength with computer simulations of Birkeland currents in studies of galaxy formation. For informations see
♦*The Plasma Universe—Theory and Background*
public.lanl.gov/alp/plasma/plasma.universe.intro.html

21. Science, Vol. 210, 5 Dec 1980, p. 1108
Dermott S F, *The 'braided' F-ring of Saturn*, Nature 290, 454 - 457 (09 April 1981)
www.nature.com/nature/journal/v290/n5806/abs/290454a0.html;jsessionid=C21CB320453E2DEC5815815AF13DA8EC
♦Saturn's F-ring was discovered by Pioneer 11 in 1979. Photos of the F-ring taken by Voyager 1 showed three separate strands that appear twisted or braided. At higher resolution, Voyager 2 found five separate strands in a region that had no apparent braiding, and surprisingly revealed only one small region where the F-ring appeared twisted. The photopolarimeter found the brightest of the F-ring strands was subdivided into at least 10 strands. Voyager Saturn Science Summary, May 4, 1990,Courtesy of: NASA/JPL
www.solarviews.com/eng/vgrsat.htm
♦Schilling, *Ring Riddles Baffle Saturn Scientists*, ScienceNOW 2005: 4
sciencenow.sciencemag.org/cgi/content/full/2005/906/4

22. Hecht J, *Science: Planet's tail of the unexpected Premium*, New Scientist.com, Magazine issue 2084, 31 May 1997, www.newscientist.com/article/mg15420842.900.html

23. Alfvén H, *Electricity in Space*, (First published in 1948 in the book The New Astronomy , Chapter 2, Section III, page 74 –79), www.catastrophism.com/texts/electricity-in-space/index.htm

24. For many years, astronomers made upside down maps of the Moon, because that was the way the Moon appeared in their telescopes! Even in recent textbooks on astronomy, one can see photographs of the Moon that are upside down. Planetary astronomers prefer to have the north at the top of a map, however, and gradually most lunar maps have appeared in that orientation!
Lecture 13 - Light and the Electromagnetic Spectrum: The Astronomer's Tools
www.astro.lsa.umich.edu/users/cowley/intro2.html

25. Olson W P, et al., *Electric Fields in Earth Orbital Space*, Report number: A055201, McDonnell Douglas Astronautics Co Hunting Beach CA, June 1981
www.stormingmedia.us/05/0552/A055201.html
NASA Selects Teams for Space Weather Mission and Studies, NASA News, RELEASE: 06-286 (Corrected), 31 July, 2006,
http://www.nasa.gov/home/hqnews/2006/jul/HQ_06286_SMD_SUN_RADIATION.html

26. Alfvén H, *Plasma physics, space research and the origin of the solar system*, Nobel

Lecture, December 11, 1970, nobelprize.org/physics/laureates/1970/alfven-lecture.pdf

27. Ballou Newbrough J, *Oahspe: A Kosmon Bible* [1882] (based on 3rd edition of 1912) www.sacred-texts.com/oah/oah/index.htm
28. *Cygnus Loop, Thunderbolts Picture Of The Day*, Aug 31, 2005 www.thunderbolts.info/tpod/2005/arch05/050831cygnusloop.htm
29. Here it is recommended to reference the work of Paul Laviolette, *Galactic Evolution and Subquantum Kinetics*. From his website it reads;
"Subquantum kinetics predicts that matter is continuously created throughout the universe, with the matter creation rate being highest in the vicinity of already existing matter. Furthermore it predicts that galaxies should progressively grow in size with the passage of time since they are formed by matter being created primarily in their central nucleus and being propelled outward by galactic core explosions. Dr. LaViolette published this prediction on two occasions, in 1985 (LaViolette, IJGS, p. 335) and in 1994 (LaViolette, Subquantum Kinetics, p. 118). Also see LaViolette, Beyond the Big Bang, p. 94.
♦See his website for further information and validation of his predictions. www.etheric.com/LaViolette/Predict2.html
♦Lerner E J, *The Big Bang Never Happened*, Vintage Books, 1992 (pg 46-49)
30. Lineweaver C H & Davis T M, *Baffled by the expansion of the universe? You're not alone,* Scientific American, March 2005
♦Abstract: A critical look at the very old big bang problems (of the singularity, smoothness, horizon, and flatness) and the failed solutions of inflation theory; newer Big Bang problems relating to missing mass (as required for a flat inflationary universe), the age of the universe, radiation from the "decoupling" ("smearing" of black body spectrum), a contrived Big Bang chronology, the abundance of light elements, and red shift anomalies; and problems, newer yet, regarding inconsistencies of red shift interpretation, curved space, inflation theory, the decelerating expansion of a Big Bang universe, and some additional logical inconsistencies of Big Bang theory are presented.
Mitchell W C, *The Big Bang Theory Under Fire*, Physics Essays Volume 10, Number 2, June 1997
31. Plasma Introduction. Technical overview I, www.plasmacosmology.net/tech.html#
♦ Scott D, *The Electric Sky: A Challenge to the Myths of Modern Astronomy*, Mikamar Publishing, 2006
32. Bearden, T. E. *"Dark Matter or Dark Energy?"*, Journal of New Energy, 4(4), Spring 2000, p. 4-11.
In the above paper Bearden discusses the prevailing theories of universe creation. For some time, astronomers and astrophysicists have known that there is insufficient mass to account for the gravity that is observed to be holding the distant galaxies together, as shown by observed star movements in them. Some nine-tenths of the gravity is still unexplained by the predicted matter (now fully observed and accounted). This is called the "dark matter" problem, where some form of matter previously unknown must be present and involved. Bearden points out the discrepancy of a vast source of EM energy ignored for a century by electrodynamicists. This energy is in fact present in the neighborhood of every EM field interaction, and therefore is present at all interactions in the astronomical entities involved in those distant galaxies. Bearden believes that since this ignored component is a normal EM energy flow, it also must produce gravitational field. Hence it must be at least a factor in producing, and may produce all of, the missing gravity.
33. Scott D, *Missing Dark Matter!!*, www.electric-cosmos.org/darkmatter.htm
♦ Scott D, *The Electric Sky: A Challenge to the Myths of Modern Astronomy*, Mikamar Publishing, 2006
34. Milan W, *Shall the WIMPs Inherit the Universe?* Special for SPACE.com 28 February 2000, www.space.com/scienceastronomy/generalscience/dark_matter_000228.html
35. Thornhill W, *Science heading for a big bang,* www.holoscience.com/news/science_bang.htm.
36. Kaufmann W, *The Most Feared Astronomer on Earth*, Science Digest, 89[6]:76-81,117, July 1981.

♦Boerner R, *The Suppression of Inconvenient Facts in Physics*, 2003
http://www.world-mysteries.com/sci_supr.htm
♦Arp is Right! Others are catching up!
McDonald K, *Discovery By UCSD Astronomers Poses A Cosmic Puzzle: Can A 'Distant' Quasar Lie Within A Nearby Galaxy?*, January 10, 2005
http://ucsdnews.ucsd.edu/newsrel/science/mcquasar.asp

37. Van Flandern T, *'The top 30 problems with the big bang'*, Meta Research, www.metaresearch.org/cosmology/top10BBproblems.asp
38. *An Open Letter to Closed Minds,* Holoscience News & Articles: 12 April 2004 www.holoscience.com/news.php?article=zj49j0u7
♦Arp H, *What is redshift?*, www.electric-cosmos.org/arp.htm
39. *Prediction #1: Big Bang a Big Loser in 2005*, Dec 27, 2004 www.thunderbolts.info/tpod/2004/arch/041227prediction-bigbang.htm
♦Thornhill Wal, *The True State of the Universe* Holoscience News: 27 October 2004, www.holoscience.com/news.php?article=0auycyew
40. *Universe in crisis as experts question Big Bang model*, PHYSORG.COM, July 07, 2005, www.physorg.com/news4999.html
♦Ratcliffe H, *The First "Crisis in Cosmology" Conference*, Held in Moncao, Portugal, June 23 – 25, 2005, www.s8int.com/bigbang5.html
41. *Electrical Birthing of Stars*, Mar 04 2005, www.thunderbolts.info/tpod/2005/arch05/050304starbirth.htm
42. Pratt D, *Big Bang, Black Holes, and Common Sense,* ourworld.compuserve.com/homepages/dp5/
bang.htm
43. Pratt D, *Black holes: fact or fiction?,* ourworld.compuserve.com/homepages/dp5/bol.htm
44. *Black Hole Blows Bubble Between The Stars*, Spacedaily.com, Aug 11, 2005 www.spacedaily.com/news/blackhole-05u.html
45. *Black holes tear logic apart*, 7 March 2004, www.holoscience.com/news.php?article=tyybhrr8
♦Stenger R, Is black hole theory full of hot air?, CNN Sci-Tech, January 22, 2002 archives.cnn.com/2002/TECH/space/01/22/gravastars/
46. *Anatomy of a Galaxy in Evolution,*public.lanl.gov/alp/plasma/anatomy.html
47. Janka H, et al., *Short Gamma-Ray Bursts- New Models Shed Light on Enigmatic Explosions*, Max-Planck-Institute for Astrophysics
www.mpa-garching.mpg.de/mpa/research/current_research/hl2004-9/hl2004-9-en.html
♦Shiga D, *Mysterious quasar casts doubt on black holes,* NewScientist.com news service, 27 July 2006
http://space.newscientist.com/article.ns?id=dn9620&feedId=online-news_rss20
48. *Pathological Science*, en.wikipedia.org/wiki/Pathological_science
Langmuir's talk on Pathological Science (December 18, 1953)
www.cs.princeton.edu/~ken/Langmuir/langmuir.htm
49. Haisch B, Rueda A, *"A Quantum Broom Sweeps Clean"*, Mercury, Vol. 25, No. 2, March/April 1996, p12, www.calphysics.org/haisch/mercury.html
♦*The Universe trapped in its own web*, Physorg.com, April 04, 2006 www.physorg.com/news63354975.html
♦Trujillo I, Carretero C, Patiri S G, *Detection of the Effect of Cosmological Large-Scale Structure on the Orientation of Galaxies*, The Astrophysical Journal, volume 640, part 2 (2006), pages L111–L114, 2006 March 16
50. *Magnetism—Molder of the Universe*, public.lanl.gov/alp/plasma/mag_fields.html
51. *The Remarkable Slowness of Light*, Holoscience.com, 2 September 2002, www.holoscience.com/news/slow_light.html
52. Carroll L, *The Cosmic Lattice – Part I*, New Hampshire - November 97
kryon.com/k_26.html
Carroll L, *Letters from Home* (Kryon Book 7), The Kryon Writings, Inc. 1999
53. Carroll L, *Co-creation Explained - "Singing in the Choir"*, Toronto, Canada September

21, 2002, www.kryon.com/k_chaneltoronto.html
Carroll L, *A New Dispensation: (Plain Talk For Confusing Times)*, (Kryon Book 10), The Kryon Writings, Inc. 2004

54. Miller E, Dupke, R A and Bregman J N, *Hot Baryons in Supercluster Filaments,* Department of Astronomy, University of Michigan, Ann Arbor, MI 48109, USA, May 2004 www.arxiv.org/PS_cache/astro-ph/pdf/0407/0407487.pdf
55. Gangui A, *Superconducting Cosmic Strings: These relics from the early universe could be the answer to many astrophysical conundrums*, American Scientist, pages 254-263, May-June 2000. Copy of article at www.iafe.uba.ar/relatividad/gangui/SCS.html
56. Klarreich E, *Navigating Celestial Currents: Math leads spacecraft on joy rides through the solar system*, Science News Online, Vol. 167, No. 16 , p. 250, April 16, 2005 www.sciencenews.org/articles/20050416/toc.asp
57. Frank D, (Tony) Smith, Jr , *Gamma Ray Bursts and CETI*, eprint arXiv:astro-ph/9302008, 02/1993, arxiv.org/PS_cache/astro-ph/pdf/9302/9302008.pdf
58. Schwarzschild, Bertram, *Compton Observatory data deepen the gamma ray burster mystery*, Physics Today (ISSN 0031-9228), vol. 45, Feb. 1992, p. 21-24, 02/1992 adsabs.harvard.edu/cgi-bin/nph-bib_query?bibcode=1992PhT....45b..21S&db_key=AST&data_type=HTML&format=
59. Battaner E, Florido E, *The egg-carton Universe*, December 23, 2005 arxiv.org/PS_cache/astro-ph/pdf/9802/9802009.pdf
60. Battaner E, *The Fractal octahedron network of the large scale structure*, Astronomy and Astrophysics, Vol. 334 No. 3, p. 770-771.
link.springer.de/link/service/journals/ 00230/tocs/t8334003.htm
or xxx.lanl.gov/PS_cache/astro-ph/pdf/9801/9801276.pdf
61. Whitehouse D, *Map reveals strange cosmos*, BBC News Online science, 3 March, 2003, http://news.bbc.co.uk/2/hi/science/nature/2814947.stm
Multipole vector information, www.phys.cwru.edu/projects/mpvectors/
62. Chown M, *"Axis of evil' warps cosmic background*, New Scientist, 22 October 2005 www.newscientist.com/article.ns?id=dn8193&&feedId=online-news_rss20
63. Wilcock D et al., *The "Matrix" is a Reality,* ascension2000.com/04.10.03.htm
64. McKee M, *Moon-sized crystal revealed in star's heart,* NewScientist.com news service, 17 February 2004, www.newscientist.com/article.ns?id=dn4692
65. *The Plasma Universe* – NASA 1995
liftoff.msfc.nasa.gov/academy/universe/plasma_univ.html
66. A theory published in February 1994, "Inertia as a Zero-Point Field Lorentz Force", suggests that inertia is nothing but an electromagnetic side-effect, building on an earlier work [Puthoff, 1989]. Both of these works rely on the perspective that all matter is fundamentally made up of electrically charged particles, and they rely on the existence of Zero Point Energy.
Haisch, B., Rueda, A., and Puthoff, H.E., *Inertia as a Zero-Point Field Lorentz Force*, In Physical Review A, Vol. 49, No. 2, p. 678- 694, (FEB 1994)
♦Puthoff,H.E., *"Gravity as a zero-point-fluctuation force",* In Physical Review A, Vol. 39, N. 5, (A89-33278), p. 2333-2342, (Mar 1, 1989).
67. Seife C, Distant Spacecraft Seem To Be Showing No Respect For The Laws Of Physics, New Scientist Magazine, September 1998 www.mufor.org/antigrav4.html
It could be that a new theory first revealed in a news article published in December 1994 which challenges Einstein's general theory of relativity is correct. The theory claims that the Einstein field equations need a slight correction. It is claimed that the Einstein equations can only predict the behavior of simple one-body problems (where only one gravitating mass exists whose affect on an inconsequential test particle is described). For two-body or n-body problems, this new theory shows that the Einstein equations are inadequate. The required correction is that another term must be added to the matter tensor, specifically a term for the stress-energy tensor of the gravitational field itself. This suggests that gravitational fields have an energy and momentum of their own. Hence why

NASA occasional lose their spacecraft!

♦Peterson, I., *A New Gravity?, Challenging Einstein's General Theory of Relativity*, In Science News, Vol. 146, p. 376-378, (Dec 3, 1994).

♦Yilmaz, H., *Toward a Field Theory of Gravitation*, In Il Nuovo Cimento, Vol. 107B, no. 8, p. 941-960, (Aug 1992).

68. From Thunderbolts Picture of the Day:
Comet Schwassmann-Wachmann 3 Disintegrates, May 05, 2006
http://www.thunderbolts.info/tpod/2006/arch06/060505cometbreakup.htm
Comet Schwassman-Wachmann 3 Disintegrates (2): Predictions of the Electric Model, May 08, 2006, http://www.thunderbolts.info/tpod/2006/arch06/060508cometbreakup2.htm
When Comets Break Apart,Jan 19, 2006
http://www.thunderbolts.info/tpod/2006/arch06/060119comets.htm

Chapter 2
The Sun-Earth-Core Connection

1. Sami K. Solanki, et al. *Unusual activity of the Sun during recent decades compared to the previous 11,000 years,* Nature, 28 October 2004
♦McKee M, *Sunspots more active than for 8000 years*, NewScientist.com news service 27, October 2004, www.newscientist.com/article.ns?id=dn6591
2. Hogan J. *Sun More Active than for a Millennium.* New Scientist, November 2, 2003. www.newscientist.com/news/news.jsp?id=ns99994321
3. Suplee, Curt. *Sun Studies May Shed Light on Global Warming.* Washington Post, Monday, Oct. 9, 2000, pg. A13. www.washingtonpost.com/wp-dyn/articles/A35885-2000Oct8.html
4. *NASA Study Finds Increasing Solar Trend that can Change Climate.* NASA Goddard Space Flight Center. March 20, 2003. www.gsfc.nasa.gov/topstory/2003/0313irradiance.html
5. Odenwald Dr S, *The 23rd Cycle: Learning to live with a stormy star*, Columbia University Press, 2000, Online version, www.solarstorms.org/S23rdCycle.html
6. Britt R R, *Solar super-flare amazes scientists.* Space.com / MSNBC.com, Nov. 6, 2003. www.msnbc.com/news/984388.asp?cp1=1
7. By using Earth's atmosphere as a giant X-ray detector, the luminosity was determined from radio monitoring of the upper atmosphere.
Biggest ever solar flare was even bigger than thought, Press Release Spaceref.com, Monday, March 15, 2004, www.spaceref.com/news/viewpr.html?pid=13844
8. Whitehouse D, *What is Happening to the Sun?* BBC News Online, Tuesday, November 4, 2003. http://news.bbc.co.uk/2/hi/science/nature/3238961.stm
9. Allen J, *Satellite Anomalies Talk*, September 2000 - Collage of Papers showing headlines including the Day the Bleepers Died, www.ngdc.noaa.gov/stp/SCOSTEP/Slide5.htm
10. Allen J, *Satellite Anomalies Talk - Killer Electrons*, September 2000 www.ngdc.noaa.gov/stp/SCOSTEP/Slide26.htm
11. Allen J, *Satellite Anomalies Talk - Chronologies of Satellite failures*, September 2000 www.ngdc.noaa.gov/stp/SCOSTEP/Slide3.htm, www.ngdc.noaa.gov/stp/SCOSTEP/Slide4.htm
♦*Space events diary*, July - September, 2002, SSC's Space Systems Division www.ssc.se/data/content/DOCUMENTS/2004105133157749023.pdf
12. Britt R, *No Safe Place for Satellites*, Space.com,15 December 2004 www.space.com/scienceastronomy/solar_storms_041215.html
♦Steigerwald B, *Flashes in the Sky: Lightning Zaps Space Radiation Surrounding Earth,* NASA Goddard Space Flight Center, 03.08.05
www.nasa.gov/vision/universe/solarsystem/image_lightning.html
13. Schirber M, *Earth's Lightning Zaps Space Too*, LiveScience, 08 March 2005 www.livescience.com/forcesofnature/050308_lightning_space.html
14. A large fraction of global communication systems are in Low Earth Orbit (LEO) altitude and Geostationary (GEO) altitude, in the equatorial ionosphere, located in the vicinity of electric

currents that are subject to “disturbed ambient magnetic field conditions”
Satellite orbits: LEO Low Earth Orbit is between 400 - 1500 miles / 640 - 2400 kilometers
MEO Mid Earth Orbit is between 6000 - 12000 miles / 9600 - 19200 kilometers
GEO Geosynchronous Orbit is at 22300 miles 35,680 kilometers
Barfield, J. N.; Saflekos, N. A.; Sheehan, R. E.; Carovillano, R. L.; Potemra, T. A. Three-dimensional observations of Birkeland currents, Journal of Geophysical Research (ISSN 0148-0227), vol. 91, April 1, 1986, p. 4393-4403. Research supported by the Southwest Research Institute. 04/1986
adsabs.harvard.edu/cgi-bin/nph-bib_query?bibcode=1986JGR....91.4393B&db_key=AST

15. Space Environmental Impacts on DoD Operations, Air Force Space Forecast Center (AFSFC), 01 Oct 2003
152.229.169.35/pubfiles/afspc/15/afspcpam15-2/afspcpam15-2.pdf
16. In March 1994, an inter-agency infrastructure was set up to support a National Space Weather Service (NSWS) in the United States of America. The following agencies were included: the Department of Defense, National Aeronautics and Space Administration (NASA), National Oceanic and Atmospheric Administration (NOAA), and the National Science Foundation (NSF). A major element in the NSWS infrastructure is continuous, real-time receipt of essential data. Currently, the Space Environment Service Center (SESC) and the Air Force Space Forecast Center (AFSFC) receive energetic particle, solar X-ray, magnetometer, trapped particle, and precipitating particle data from Geostationary Operational Environmental Satellite (GOES), the Television and Infra-red Observing Satellite, and the Defense Meteorological Satellite Program. From ground observatories they obtain near-real-time solar optical, solar radio, neutron monitor, geomagnetic radiometer and ionosonde data.
Ogunade S.O. *Advances in space weather monitoring: implications for life on Earth*, Department of Physics, Obafemi Awolowo University Ile-Ife, Nigeria
www.saao.ac.za/~wgssa/as4/ogunade.html
17. *Blast Wave Blows Through the Solar System*, NASA NEWS, 07.08.04
www.nasa.gov/vision/universe/solarsystem/0708_flare.html
18. Hitt D, *Staring at the Sun*, NASA explores¸ 3rd February 2005
www.nasa.gov/audience/foreducators/k-4/features/F_Staring_at_the_Sun.html
19. Karash Y, *Key Russian Space Officials, Mir Designers Rebuff Station Rescue Attempts*, Space.com, 19 February 2001
www.space.com/missionlaunches/missions/mir_deorbit_update_010219.html
20. Phillips Dr T, *A New Kind of Solar Storm*, NASA News, June 10, 2005:
science.nasa.gov/headlines/y2005/10jun_newstorm.htm
In this article it refers to a theory called, “Magnetic Reconnection. Plasma scientists complain it is one of the most misguided theoretical ideas that astronomers ever derived from the mistaken belief that there are no electric currents in space.”
21. *The Myth of Magnetic Reconnection*, Thunderbolts Picture of the Day, Jul 20, 2005,
www.thunderbolts.info/tpod/2005/arch05/050720magnetic.htm
♦In April 1999, the “Wind” satellite flew right through “the reconnection region” as the process was occurring. While flying tailward through the magnetosphere (away from Earth), Wind’s instruments detected jets of plasma racing toward Earth. Part-way through the journey, the jets stopped and Wind detected unusual electric currents and magnetic signatures that were predicted to occur at the point of reconnection. Some time later, as Wind kept flying away from Earth, the spacecraft detected that jets of plasma flow in the exact opposite direction of the previous flows, racing away from the planet. The event was comparable to a plane flying through the eerie, calm eye of a hurricane. This observation clearly demonstrates the known behavior of plasma in a magnetic field and the phenomenon of a “Double Layer”. See Glossary “Magnetic Reconnection” and “Double Layer”.
22. *Solar Myth: With solar minimum near, the sun continues to be surprisingly active*, Science@Nasa , 5th May 2005
science.nasa.gov/headlines/y2005/05may_solarmyth.htm

23. *NASA Aids in Resolving Long Standing Solar Cycle Mystery*, March 6, 2006 RELEASE: 06-087, www.nasa.gov/home/hqnews/2006/mar/HQ_06087_solar_cycle.html
24. Davidson K, *Huge solar storms could zap Earth, scientists warn: Next sunspot cycle may disrupt power*, communications, March 7, 2006 www.sfgate.com/cgi-bin/article.cgi?file=/c/a/2006/03/07/MNGAFHJJL91.DTL
25. Britt R, *How the Sun Shines: New Evidence Pins Down Elusive Core Action*, Space.Com News, 03 April 2003 www.space.com/scienceastronomy/sun_shine_030403.html
    ♦ *Proposal for SOHO Solar Maximum Science Program*, May 1, 1997 soi.stanford.edu/results/2001_MDI_sr_review/soho_solar_maximum_proposal.pdf
    N° 01-99 - Paris, 3 February 1999
    ♦ *Orbiting observatory SOHO finds source of high-speed "wind" blowing from the Sun* sohowww.nascom.nasa.gov/gallery/ESAPR/info01.html/
    ♦ Since the initial discovery of the honeycombed shaped coronal holes, a press release from the ESA/NASA tells us that "They observed solar wind flowing from funnel-shaped magnetic fields which are anchored in the lanes of the magnetic network near the surface of the Sun."Solar Wind Originates in Coronal Funnels: The ESA/NASA SOHO spacecraft determines the origin of the fast solar wind in the magnetized atmosphere of the Sun www.mpg.de/english/illustrationsDocumentation/documentation/pressReleases/2005/pressRelease20050421/
26. Carroll L, *The Cosmic Lattice – Part II*, Live Kryon Channel - New Hampshire - November 98, kryon.com/k_29.html
    Carroll L, *Letters from Home* (Kryon Book 7), The Kryon Writings, Inc. 1999
27. The Institute for Solar Physics is operated as an independent institute, under the auspices of the Royal Swedish Academy of Sciences, www.astro.su.se/English/groups/solar/solar.html In May 2002, the Swedish 1-m Solar Telescope started operation with its full aperture [at Roque de los Muchachos, La Palma. During the first few months of operation they collected many solar images with unprecedented spatial resolution
    De Pontieu B, Erdélyi R, James S P, Solar chromospheric spicules from the leakage of photospheric oscillations and flows, Nature 430, 536-539 (29 July 2004) | doi: 10.1038/nature02749, dx.doi.org/10.1038/nature02749
28. Dwivedi, B.N., & K.J.H. Phillips. *Paradox of the sun's hot corona*. Scientific American 284(June):40. 2001.
29. Scott D, *The Electric Sun*, www.electric-cosmos.org/sun.htm
30. Evans J C, *Physics and Structure of Stars*, Physics & Astronomy Department, George Mason University, physics.gmu.edu/~jevans/astr103/CourseNotes/ Text/Lec05/Lec05_pt1_txt_stellarPhysics.htm
    ♦ Scott D, Sudbury Neutrino Observatory Report an Analysis, www.electric-cosmos.org/sudbury.htm
31. Dmitriev A N, *Planetophysical State of the Earth and Life. 1997*, www.tmgnow.com/repository/global/planetophysical.html
32. *Electric Currents and Transmission Lines in Space,* Los Alamos National Laboratory Website, public.lanl.gov/alp/plasma/elec_currents.html
33. The James McCanney Website, www.jmccanneyscience.com/
34. Since the 1950s, the standard comet model has been that comets are "dirty snowballs". Large lumps of rock and ice, but the data and observation show otherwise. The most surprising feature being that the comets are producing X-rays which can only be attributed to temperatures in the range of millions of degrees Kelvin! Satellite and space probes have repeated given observations proving comets are highly electrical in nature and are not "dirty snowballs". The Comet Tempel collision on the 4th July 2005 quickly turned into an embarrassing silence from NASA and then a series of conflicting reports from various research establishments associated with NASA. A copper projectile, was fired into Comet Tempel, which produced two flashes and a cloud of "talcum powder" type material, which was totally unexpected from a frozen mass of ice and rock! The standard comet model is now at near death, especially as the only "on target" predictions were from proponents of the Electric universe model! In one report, the Comet Tempel rendezvous which cost $333

million, was dismissed as "an anomaly" by a NASA spokesperson!
♦McCandless D, *They Sing the Comet Electric*, Wired News, Aug. 02, 2005
www.wired.com/news/space/0,2697,68258,00.html
♦Goodwing G, *TMG Proven Again: Comet Borelly is Dry!*
www.tmgnow.com/repository/cometary/borrelly.html

35. McCanney J M, *The Nature and Origin Of Comets and The Revolution of Celestial Bodies*, www.tmgnow.com/repository/cometary/ori1.html
♦McCanney J M, *Dynamics Of A Small Comet*, Millenium Group
www.tmgnow.com/repository/cometary/smcomet.html
♦McCanney, J. M.: 1981, The Moon and the Planets 24, 349-53.
♦McCanney, J. M.: 1983, KRONOS IX-1, 17-39.
♦McCanney, J. M.: 1984, KRONOS IX-3, 60-85.
♦McCanney, J. M.: 1985, KRONOS, X-2, 42-53.
36. McCanney J, *Electric High-Ways to the Stars*, The Edge Newspaper, Jan 2004, www.edgenews.com/issues/2004/01/mccanney.html
37. Website: www.TheSpectrumNews.org, E-mail address: thespectrum@tminet.com
Telephone: 1-877-280-2866 toll-free (US & Canada); 1-661-823-9696 (all others)
Regular mail: PO Box 1567, Tehachapi, CA 93581
38. McCanney J M, et al., *"Cosmic Rays From The Sun: A Millenium Group Discovery"*, July 4, 1998, www.tmgnow.com/repository/solar/cosmicrays.html
♦McCaney J*, Principia Meteorologia - The Physics of Sun-Earth Weather,*
www.jmccanneyscience.com/WeatherBookCoversandTableofContents.htm
39. *Is The Sun An Iron-Rich Powerhouse*, Nov 18 2003,
www.spacedaily.com/news/solarscience-03zl.html
♦Than K, *Record Set for Hottest Temperature on Earth: 3.6 Billion Degrees in Lab*, LiveScience, 08 March 2006
http://www.livescience.com/technology/060308_sandia_z.html
40. Ghosh A, "*Velocity-dependent inertial induction: a possible tired-light mechanism"*, Apeiron 9-10, 35-44, 1991
Link provided here for a series of articles about the Big Bang and redshift controversy.
www.fixall.org/bigbang/bigblackbang.htm
41. Aspden H, *Energy Science Tutorial Note 10: Tifft's Discovery*, 1997,
www.energyscience.org.uk/tu/tu10.htm
♦Apsden writes: "Cosmologists, lacking insight into the structure of the aether, have missed seeing the important analogy that can be drawn between the aether and the ferromagnet, namely its domain structure. Just as magnetic polarization is reversed in adjacent magnetic domains within iron, so the electric polarization is reversed in adjacent domains in space. The evidence comes from the sequence of geomagnetic reversals that have geological record in the Earth's crust, evidence which tells us that periodically our Earth traverses along with the sun a space domain boundary, such boundaries being spaced at distances measured in hundreds of light years."
♦Aspden H, *The Physics of Creation*, Sabberton Publications, Southampton, England, 2003
Aether Structure, chapter 7, online edition www.aspden.org/books/2edpoc/2edpocch7.pdf
42. Responses to "Susskind Interview at New Scientist"
www.math.columbia.edu/~woit/wordpress/?p=312
43. Shemansky, D.E. Vitae. University of Southern California.
http:// ae-www.usc.edu/bio/dons/ds_biosk.html
44. *How Do clouds Form?* www.ghcc.msfc.nasa.gov/lisotd_old.html
Kanipe J, A Cosmic Connection, NATURE|Vol 443|14 September 2006
45. *Tornadoes as Electric Discharge*, Oct 13, 2004
www.thunderbolts.info/tpod/2004/arch/041013tornado-electric-discharge.htm
♦Dmitriev A N, Dyatlov V L, Merculov V I, Electrogravidynamic Concept of Tornadoes, The Millennium Group, www.tmgnow.com/repository/planetary/tornado.html
46. Pfeiffer T, *Etna Volcano Photographs*, June 2001

www.decadevolcano.net/photos/etna0601_2.htm

47. There has been decades of research by scientists who have found a clear connection between planetary alignments, solar activity and Earth weather. A good synopsis of research can be found at: www.justgoodtiming.com/id45.htm.
♦A highly successful weather prediction company that uses sunspot counts and solar cycles to predict months and months in advance is run by meteorologists Piers Corbyn at www.weatheraction.com
48. Battros M, *Interview with Paul Barys, Chief Meteorlogist*, Tennessee Channel 3 Eyewitness News Storm Alert Team, 11th April 2006
49. Zabarenko D, *More strong Katrina-like hurricanes reported*, Reuters, 15 Sep 2005 Source: www.alertnet.org/thenews/newsdesk/N14677798.htm
50. Solomon L, *The hurricane expert who stood up to UN junk science*, Financial Post, December 08, 2006
http://www.canada.com/nationalpost/financialpost/story.html?id=95efa8fe-638b-4058-95c3-60343f461cac
51. Barry P L & Phillips T, *Lots of Lightning in 2005 Hurricanes Baffles Scientists,* Science@NASA, 10 January 2006
www.livescience.com/forcesofnature/060110_hurricane_lightning.html
52. *First Global Connection Between Earth And Space Weather Found*, September 9, 2006
http://www.nasa.gov/centers/goddard/news/topstory/2006/space_weather_link.html
♦Bishop, R L, et al., *An investigation of possible coupling between the passage of a tropical storm and the local ionosphere*, American Geophysical Union, Spring Meeting 2005, abstract #SA23B-06, 05/2005 adsabs.harvard.edu/cgi-bin/nph-bib_query?bibcode=2005AGUSMSA23B..06B
&db_key=AST&data_type=HTML&format=
♦*Living with a Star: Opportunities for Geospace Science*,
lws.gsfc.nasa.gov/missions/geospace/geospace_objectives.htm
♦*Living with a Star: Sun-Earth Connection Missions*
ds9.ssl.berkeley.edu/LWS_GEMS/resource/sun_e.htm
♦Marren, K, *APL to Implement NASA Geospace Missions*: Part of Living With a Star program, projects will study sun's effects on Earth, VOL. 32, NO. 23, The Gazette Online, The Newspapers of the John Hopkins University, February 24, 2003
www.jhu.edu/~gazette/2003/24feb03/24star.html
♦Grebowsky J M,Yee J, *Preparing for the Living With a Star Ionosphere-Thermosphere Storm Probe I Mission I,* www.agu.org/meetings/sm05/sm05-sessions/sm05_SA13B.html
53. *Electric Earthquakes*, Holscience.com, 21 December 2005
www.holoscience.com/news.php?article=36uyr9nx
Bleier T, Freund F, *Earthquake Alarm*, IEEE journal, SPECTRUM, December 2005
www.spectrum.ieee.org/dec05/2367
Freund laments: "The peer review system often creates near-insurmountable hurdles against the publication of data that seem contrary to long-held beliefs."
♦Freund F T, *Rocks That Crackle and Sparkle and Glow: Strange Pre-Earthquake Phenomena*, Journal of Scientific Exploration, Vol. 17, No. 1, pp. 37–71, 2003
www.scientificexploration.org/jse/articles/pdf/17.1_freund.pdf
♦Playfair, G L, *The Cycles of Heaven: Cosmic Forces and What They are Doing to You*,
♦Caymaz G, *Know Thyself Book III: Findings of a Searcher*, Ankara, Turkey, privately published, 1998
54. Observation evidence proved that such large currents existed and in 1984, Farhad Yusef-Zadeh of Columbia University, and colleagues at the Very Large Array radio telescope in Zoccoro, New Mexico, discovered large-scale magnetic vortex filaments at the heart of our own Milky Way galaxy. This discovery convinced a number of astrophysicists, especially those already familiar with the work on solar system plasma, of the reality of current filaments in space. The alignments and shape of the galactic filaments simply could not have been created by gravity.

♦Lerner E J, *The Big Bang Never Happened*, Vintage Books, 1992

♦C. Illert. *Formulation and solution of the classical seashell problem.* Il Nuovo Cimento, 11 D(5):761–780, 1989

♦Foundations of Theoretical Conchology, www.hadronicpress.com/biology.htm

55. Kruger A, *Construction And Deployment Of An ULF Receiver For The Study Of Schumann Resonance In Iowa,* College of Engineering, The University of Iowa, www.iihr.uiowa.edu/projects/schumann/Index.html
56. Johnson C, *Source of the Earth's Magnetic Field*, University of Chicago, 1997, www.mb-soft.com/public/tecto2.html
57. The super-continent Pangaea that existed approximately 220 million years ago was studied in 1976 by Athelstan Spilhaus, a consultant working for the National Oceanographic and Atmospheric Administration (NOAA). Spilhaus found that the Pangaea break-up occurred along equidistant lines forming the edges and points of a tetrahedron, a geometric shape composed of four equilateral triangles.
Jochmans J, *Earth: A Crystal Planet*? Atlantis Rising, 25 Oct 2002
58. Awo Fa'lokun Fatunmbi, Odu and the Concept of History, Part IV: The African Perspective, Awo Study Center, www.awostudycenter.com/Articles/art_oduhist4.htm
59. Cathie B, *The Harmonic Conquest of Space*, Nexus Magazine, Oct 1994 www.whale.to/m/cathie.html
60. Kovalenko K, *A Russian Theory of the Energy Grids*, The Spirit of Maat, Vol. 2, No. 4 www.spiritofmaat.com/archive/nov2/thegrids.htm
61. The crystal rays creates on the surface a matrix made up of the icosahedron or 20 sided figure with the dodecahedron or 12 sided figure superimposed.
62. Jochmans J, *Earth: A Crystal Planet?* Atlantis Rising, 25 Oct 2002
63. Sky Vaja obtainable from The Tibetan Foundation, www.tibetanfoundation.org
64. Articles 1. *A Spinning Crystal Ball*, Scientific American, October 1996 2. *Earth's Core Crystal*, CNN - July 1996 3. *Coffee H, Getting to the Core of the Matter* 4. *Crystal at the Center of the Earth: A Seismic Adventure* www.crystalinks.com/corecrystal.html
65. Stixrude L & Cohen R E, *Constraints on the crystalline structure of the inner core-mechanical instability of bcc iron at high-pressure*, Geophys. Res. Lett., 22, 125128, 1995a.
♦Stixrude, L., and R. E. Cohen, *High-pressure elasticity of iron and anisotropy of Earth's inner-core*, Science, 267, 1972-1975, 1995b.
♦Hecht J, *The Giant Crystal at the Heart of the Earth*, New Scientist, January 22, 1994, p17
♦*Earth's Core Rotates Faster Than Its Crust, Scientists Say*, NSF Press Release, August 26th, 2005
http://www.nsf.gov/news/news_summ.jsp?cntn_id=104359&org=OLPA&from=news
66. Tromp J, *Inner-Core Anisotropy and Rotation*
Annual Review of Earth and Planetary Sciences, May 2001, Vol. 29, Pages 47-69
67. Cromie W J, *Putting a New Spin on Earth's Core*, Harvard Gazette, August 15 1996 www.news.harvard.edu/gazette/1996/08.15/PuttingaNewSpin.html
68. Dmitriev A.N., Dyatlov V.L., Litasov K.D, Physical Model of Kimberlite Pipe Formation: New Constraints From Theory of Non-Homogenous Physical Vacuum, Extended Abstracts of the 7th International Kimberlite Conference, Cape Town, South Africa,1998, (p.196-198) http://www.tmgnow.com/repository/planetary/kimberlite.html
69. Dmitriev A N, *Planetophysical State of the Earth and Life*. (1997) www.tmgnow.com/repository/global/planetophysical.html
70. Dmitriev A.N. et al. *Plasma generation in energy-active zones* (Russian) Novosibirsk, Rus.Acad.Sci.Sib.Branch Geol.Geophys.Inst. 1992. (in Russian
71. *Who Does a Plasma Focus Device Work?*, Black holes tear logic apart, Holoscience News, 07 March 2004, www.holoscience.com/news.php?article=tyybhrr8
72. Frank L A & Sigwarth J B, "*Atmospheric Holes and Small Comets,*" p 1-28 v 31 n 1 Reviews of Geophysics. February, 1993.
♦L.A. Frank and J.B. Sigwarth. "*Influx of small comets into Earth's upper atmosphere,*" in Instruments, Methods, and Missions for the Investigation of Extraterrestrial Microorganisms,
♦Richard B. Hoover, Editor, Proceedings of SPIE Vol. 3111, p 238-248 (1997).

♦ "Small Comet" discovery papers, images, articles and comment.
smallcomets.physics.uiowa.edu/pdf/

73. Frank L A & Huyghe P, *The Big Splash*, Birch Lane Press, 1990.
The Original Discovery- Excerpt from "The Big Splash"
smallcomets.physics.uiowa.edu/blackspot.html
74. *Cosmic Rain from Space* – Laura Lee Show, Interview with Dr Louis Frank,
www.lauralee.com/index.cgi?search=frank&range=Audio+on+Demand&x=18&y=11
75. Visits to S.E.A.T at the United Nations, 1995, 1996, 1998, 2005, 2006 & 2007, see
www.kryon.com
♦Carroll L, *The End Times* (Kryon Book 1), The Kryon Writings, Inc. 1993
♦Carroll L, *Don't Think Like a Human: Channelled Answers to Basic Questions* (Kryon Book 2), The Kryon Writings, Inc.1994
♦Carroll L, *Alchemy of the Human Spirit: A Guide to Human Transition into the New Age* (Kryon Book 3), The Kryon Writings, Inc. 1995 pg. 168
76. The story the author refers to as "The Hyperdimensional You've been Framed" was a major scoop for UFO researchers Nice article here:
Farrell M, *The Smoking gun Still Smokes*, www.thelosthaven.co.uk/Smokinggun.html
77. *Scientists explain UFO sightings*, The Telegraph online, 07/05/2006
http://www.telegraph.co.uk/news/main.jhtml?xml=/news/2006/05/07/uufo.xml
♦Project Report, Daily Express (UK), 15 May 2006
http://www.nickpope.net/project_condign.htm
78. *Unidentified Aerial Phenomena (UAP) in the UK Air Defence Region*
http://www.mod.uk/DefenceInternet/FreedomOfInformation/PublicationScheme/SearchPublicationScheme/UnidentifiedAerialPhenomenauapInTheUkAirDefenceRegion.htm
79. *The Condign Report, Britain's Secret U.F.O. Study,* http://www.uk-ufo.org/condign/index.htm, http://www.uk-ufo.org/condign/condscan.htm
80. Watson N, *It's Official: UFOs Are Just UAPs*, May, 10, 2006
http://www.wired.com/news/technology/space/0,70862-0.html?tw=rss.technology
81. Dmitriev, AN, et al., *Planetophysical Function of Vacuum Domains*
(Geology institute UIGGM, Mathematics institute SB RAS, Gorno-Altaisk state University.)
www.tmgnow.com/repository/planetary/pfvd.html

Chapter 3
Earth's Changing Electromagnetic Environment

1. Major Jenkins J, *Maya Cosmogenesis 2012: The True Meaning of the Maya Calendar End-Date.* Santa Fe, N. M.: Bear & Co., 1998
♦Willard Van De Bogart W, *The Portal into the Heart of Creation : A review of John Major Jenkin's book: Maya Cosmogenesis 2012*
www.earthportals.com/Portal_Messenger/izapa.html
2. Major Jenkins J, *Galactic Alignment: The Transformation of Consciousness According to Mayan, Egyptian, and Vedic Traditions*, (Inner Traditions International, 2002)
♦Willard Van De Bogart W, The Alignment Generation: A review of John Major Jenkins' book Galactic Alignment: The Transformation of Consciousness According to Mayan, Egyptian, and Vedic Traditions,
www.earthportals.com/Portal_Messenger/alignment2012.html
3. *The Galactic Center Radio Arc*, Astronomy Picture of the Day, 2002 May 21
antwrp.gsfc.nasa.gov/apod/ap020521.html
♦Beryllium 10 is produced in the atmosphere by cosmic rays which readily attach to aerosols. This gets snowed out onto ice caps, leaving a clear signal in the ice core of variations in the cosmic ray flux.
Solar Effects on the Climate, ENVI2150: Climate Change: Scientific Issues - Lecture 9
http://www.env.leeds.ac.uk/envi2150/oldnotes/lecture9/lecture9.html
4. Biographical information for Paul A. LaViolette, Ph.D
www.earthchangestv.com/tvguests/biolaviolette.htm

♦LaViolette, P. A. *Earth Under Fire.* Alexandria, VA: Starlane Publications, 1997.

♦LaViolette, P. A. *Galactic Explosions, Cosmic Dust Invasions, and Climatic Change. Ph.D. dissertation,* Portland State University, Portland, Oregon, August 1983.

♦LaViolette, P. A. *"The terminal Pleistocene cosmic event: Evidence for recent incursion of nebular material into the Solar System."* Eos 64 (1983): 286. American Geophysical Union paper, Baltimore, Maryland.

♦LaViolette, P. A. *"Elevated concentrations of cosmic dust in Wisconsin stage polar ice."* Meteoritics 18 (1983): 336. Meteoritical Society paper, Mainz, Germany.

♦LaViolette, P. A. *"Evidence of high cosmic dust concentrations in Late Pleistocene polar ice (20,000 - 14,000 Years BP)."* Meteoritics 20 (1985): 545.

♦LaViolette P A, *"Cosmic ray volleys from the Galactic Center and their recent impact on the Earth environment."* Earth, Moon, and Planets 37 (1987): 241.
Download the above paper from URL below:
adsabs.harvard.edu/cgi-bin/nph-
bib_query?bibcode=1987EM%26P...37..241L&db_key=AST&high=40c54fe18502618

♦LaViolette, P. A. "Galactic core explosions and the evolution of life." Anthropos 12, (1990): 239 - 255.

♦LaViolette, P. A. "Anticipation of the Ulysses interstellar dust findings." Eos 74(44) (1993): 510 - 511.

♦Oort, J. H. "The Galactic Center." Annual Reviews of Astronomy & Astrophysics 15 (1977): 295.

♦*Superwave Theory Predictions and their Subsequent Verification*, The website of Dr LaViolette, www.etheric.com/LaViolette/Predict.html

5. Corliss W R, *Iridium And Mass Extinctions*, Science Frontiers #8, Fall 1979. © 1979-2000, www.science-frontiers.com/sf008/sf008p11.htm

   ♦Mass Extinction underway: The World Wide Web's Most Comprehensive Source of Information on the Current Mass Extinction at www.well.com/user/davidu/extinction.html
6. Daly S, *The Man Who Fell From Earth: Paul LaViolette hears a warning from space,* Washington Free Weekly, August 2000, www.cyberspaceorbit.com/bluecosmic.htm
7. Combs A, Goerner S, *Consciousness As A Self-Organizing Process: An Ecological Perspective*, www.sourceintegralis.org/Art%20Self-Org.html
8. Alford A, *The Mystery of Homo Sapiens*
   www.eridu.co.uk/Author/human_origins/article3.html
9. Cosmic Radiation and Clouds, Swiss Federal Institute of Aquatic Science and Technology, EAWAG News 58, January 2005, http://www.eawag.ch/publications/eawagnews/ www_en58/en58e_screen/en58e_beer_clouds_s.pd
10. Voight et al., A Map of Recent Positive Selection in the Human Genome, Department of Human Genetics, University of Chicago, March 7, 2006
    biology.plosjournals.org/perlserv/?request=get-
    document&doi=10.1371/journal.pbio.0040072

    ♦Keely J, *Evidence that human brain evolution was a special event*, Howard Hughes Medical Institute, 28-Dec-2004
    www.eurekalert.org/pub_releases/2004-12/hhmi-eth122804.php
11. From a Bruce Lipton article he writes:
    "An important paper by H. F. Nijhout (BioEssays 12:441, 1990) reveals that "When a gene product is needed, a signal from its environment, not an emergent property of the gene itself, activates expression of that gene." Simply stated, a gene can not turn itself on or off, it is dependent upon a signal from its environment to control its action. This fact totally invalidates the concept of the Primacy of DNA."

    ♦Lipton B, *The Biology of Complementary Medicine, Complementary and Alternative Medical Association*, www.camaweb.org/library/misc/biology_of_CAM.php

    ♦# Over 100 references which back up the new paradigm understanding of electromagnetic fields influencing cell physiology.
    Lipton B, *The new Biology*, 2005, www.brucelipton.com/newbiology.php

♦*DNA & the Environment* – Laura Lee Show, Interview with Bruce Lipton
http://www.lauralee.com/audio/asf/041701.asf
♦ Recent studies show evolutionary changes taking place in ***decades***
"Over the past 40 years, animal species have been extending their range toward the poles and populations have been migrating, developing or reproducing earlier."
"These expansions and changes have often been attributed to 'phenotypic plasticity,' or the ability of individuals to modify their behavior, morphology or physiology in response to altered environmental conditions....phenotypic plasticity is not the whole story. Studies show that over the past several decades, rapid climate change has led to heritable, genetic changes in animal populations."
♦***Recent, rapid climate change is driving evolution of animal species***., Astrobiology.com, June 8, 2006 http://www.astrobiology.com/news/viewpr.html?pid=20053
♦Franks et al. say their results *"provide evidence for a rapid, adaptive evolutionary shift in flowering phenology after a climatic fluctuation," which "adds to the growing evidence that evolution is not always a slow, gradual process but can occur on contemporary time scales in natural populations," and, we would add (as was the case in this study), in response to real-world climatic changes.*
♦ *Evolutionary Adaptations to Climate Change*
www.co2science.org/scripts/CO2ScienceB2C/articles/V10/N22/EDIT.jsp
♦ ♦ *The Specter of Species Extinction: Will Global Warming Decimate Earth's Biosphere?*
www.co2science.org/scripts/CO2ScienceB2C/education/reports/extinction/extinction.jsp

12. Carroll L, *The New Beginning: 2002 and Beyond*, (Kryon Book 9), The Kryon Writings, Inc. 2002 pg 221
13. *NYU Physicist Isolates First Source Of Ultra-High Energy Cosmic Rays*, Spacedaily.com News 2nd February 2005,
www.sciencedaily.com/releases/2005/02/050201104007.htm
♦*Auger experiment could resolve mystery of high-energy cosmic rays*, University of Chicago News Office, Feb. 16, 2003
www-news.uchicago.edu/releases/03/030216.rays.shtml
♦An excerpt from the article Superconducting Cosmic Strings
"Particles with such energies cannot easily move through intergalactic space, which, far from being empty, is pervaded by cosmic background radiation fields, including the microwave background as well as diffuse radio backgrounds. From the perspective of particles moving faster than some critical velocity, these fields look like bunches of very damaging photons, which degrade the particle's energy through collisions and scattering. For example, a proton that reaches Earth's atmosphere with the necessary energy to explain these ultra-energetic events could not have come from farther away than about 30 million parsecs, according to a result known as the Greisen-Zatsepin-Kuz'min (GZK) cutoff."
"One might therefore conclude that the ultra-high-energy cosmic rays must come from sources that are close (astrophysically speaking) to our galaxy. However, unusual and energetic objects like quasars and active galactic nuclei are mostly too far away. The high-energy particles remain a mystery because when one looks back in the direction they came from, there is nothing nearby that could have given them the necessary kick! So what are they, and how did they manage to reach us?"
"For the time being, standard astrophysics seems unable to answer these questions, and in fact essentially states that we should not receive any such rays. As Ludwik Celnikier from the Observatoire de Paris-Meudon has said, comparing cosmological dark matter to ultra-high-energy cosmic rays: The former is a form of matter which should exist, but until further notice doesn't, whereas the high-energy rays are particles which do exist but perhaps shouldn't."
Gangui A, *Superconducting Cosmic Strings: These relics from the early universe could be the answer to many astrophysical conundrums*, American Scientist, May-June 2000, pages 254-263, www.iafe.uba.ar/relatividad/gangui/SCS.html
14. Gawin J, et al., *Lodz Extensive Air Shower Array*, The Andrzej Soltan Institute for Nuclear

Studies Cosmic Ray Laboratory in Lodz (Poland), 2000, www.u.lodz.pl/english/r2000/Report-1.html, www.ipj.gov.pl/common/annual2002/p7/default.htm

15. Pierre Auger Observatory – Overview, www.auger.org/overview.html
Kotulak R, *Cosmic rays are enigma, for now*, Chicago Tribune, November 13, 2005 www.orlandosentinel.com/news/custom/space/orl-rays1305nov13,0,3361059,email.story?coll=orl-news-headlines-space
16. Marciniak B, *Earth: Pleiadian Keys to the Living Library*, Bear & Company, Inc,1995
17. *Marciniak B, Path of Empowerment: Pleiadian Wisdom for a World in Chaos, Inner Ocean Publishing, 2004*
18. Frank D. (Tony) Smith, Jr , *Gamma Ray Bursts and CETI*, eprint arXiv:astro-ph/9302008, 02/1993, arxiv.org/PS_cache/astro-ph/pdf/9302/9302008.pdf
19. Faal S, *Unknown Energy Surges Continue to Hit Planet, Global Weather Systems in Chaos*, (By: Sorcha Faal, and as reported to the Russian Academy of Sciences), December 22, 2004, www.whatdoesitmean.com/index601.htm
♦ Also reported Eskimo concerns of the strange "lightness at noon".
Lean G, *Mysterious Light Brightens Arctic*, The Independent UK, December 19, 2004, www.whatdoesitmean.com/index595.htm
20. Steensma B, Galactic Mayan Time-Science Project on Planet Earth, January 2001 http://www.gaianxaos.com/2012.htm
♦Calleman C J, *The Mayan Calendar: And the Transformation of Consciousness*, Bear & Company, 2004
21. McFadden S, *Steep Uphill Climb to 2012:Messages from the Mayan Milieu*, 2002, www.chiron-communications.com/communique%207-10.html
22. *ESA's Hipparcos finds rebels with a cause,* ESA Media Relations Division, 20 October 2004, http://www.esa.int/esaSC/Pr_23_2004_s_en.html
23. Daglis I A, et al., *The terrestrial ring current: Origin, formation, evolution, and decay.* Rev. Geophys., 37, 407-438, 1999, www.sat2.space.noa.gr/~daglis/rev.pdf
24. The Van Allen belts are most intense along the equator, and effectively absent over the poles. At the equator the lower Van Allen Belt dips down low over the South Atlantic Ocean and are about 1,000 km high over the Central Pacific Ocean. The lower Van Allen belt, can be considered to be between 400 - 7700 km above the Earth's surface. The outer Van Allen Belt, is between 10,000 - 51,500 km above the Earth's surface.
Galactic Winds Blow Away Idea of 'Island Universe', University of Maryland, College Park November 21, 2003, universe.nasa.gov/press/2003/031121a.html
25. *The Exploration of the Earth's Magnetosphere*: An educational web site by David P. Stern and Mauricio Peredo (since 1995), www-spof.gsfc.nasa.gov/Education/Intro.html
26. Bushby T, *The Secret in the Bible*, The Stanford Publishing Group and Joshua Books, 2003 Pg 255
27. Plasma physicists and mythologists have gathered a highly impressive collection of data and information to clearly demonstrate that the ancients drew what they were seeing in the sky or wrote accounts of catastrophic world events caused by plasma phenomena. This new understanding has been of great interest to mythologists. I recommend the work of Anthony Peratt, David Talbott and Wallace Thornhill. See the following book preview.
Thunderbolts of the Gods by David Talbott and Wallace Thornhill – Book Preview www.thunderbolts.info/tb-book-preview.htm
♦*Thunderbolts of the Gods* by David Talbott and Wallace Thornhill – unedited excerpts www.bibliotecapleyades.net/esp_thunderboltgods.htm
28. It is very difficult to assess historic records of the EEJ because it was so insignificant, scientists did not have strict criteria for measurements. Even though research have been done for over the 50 years [Egedal 1947] and [Chapman 1951]. The varying models for analyzing data were not consistent and different groups of scientists took different measurements related to the current flow and magnetic field values. The EEJ varies enormously depending on time of day, magnetic dip latitude, longitude and whether there is a geomagnetic storm affecting the readings. The EEJ is very often depicted "on quiet

days" and so the author has made the attempt to provide one parameter for comparison. From 1967-69 data Onwumechili has done some anaylsis of data taken from POGO satellite data. The mean eastward current intensity J A/km is given as 162 (pg 214 & pg 192). Onwumechili and Agu (1981) have reported peak current densities of 200 - 300 A/km. Multi-satellite data from 2001 (Oersted, Champ and SAC-C) reported by Geeta Jadhav, R. Rajaram and Mita Rajaram, from the Indian Institute of Geomagnetism, now report average peak current densities between 200 - 400 A/km but in fact the graphs show longitudinal variations from 350 - 750 A/km. This is the problem, averaging data is very deceptive! What is more, the scientists do not report that these were considered "quiet days," "average days" or "storm class" days. This is the reason the author has chosen to report the response to the increased EEJ and not the actual data itself. The maxim here is the, "Actions speak more loudly than data!"

♦Onwumechili C A, *The Equatorial Electrojet*, Gordon and Breach Science Publishers, 1997

♦*Multi-satellite observations of the Equatorial Electrojet: Slides and Transcripts*, AGU Spring Meeting, 2002
www.dsri.dk/multimagsatellites/virtual_talks/jadhav/jadhav.html
An alternative respresentation of the EEJ.

♦*The Equatorial Electrojet*, Dr. H. McCreadie [Kyoto University]
kagi.coc21.kyoto u.ac.jp/en/tidbit/tidbit27.html

29. Maeda, H.; Iyemori, T.; Araki, T.; Kamei, T. New evidence of a meridional current system in the equatorial ionosphere, 1982GeoRL...9..337M
adsabs.harvard.edu/cgi-bin/nph-bib_query?bibcode=1982GeoRL...9..337M&db_key=PHY&high=422de4171d16066
30. Langel, R. A.; Purucker, M.; Rajaram, M. The equatorial electrojet and associated currents as seen in Magsat data 1993JATP...55.1233L
adsabs.harvard.edu/cgi-bin/nph-bib_query?bibcode=1993JATP...55.1233L&db_key=PHY&high=422de4171d16066
31. International Association of Geomagnetism and Aeronomy (IAGA), International Association of Geomagnetism and Aeronomy, Minutes on success of IEEY
www.agu.org/iugg/comp-ren/iugg-cr-48.html
32. The African magnetotelluric stations where placed along a 1200-km-long meridian profile, between Lamto (latitude 6.2°N, Côte d'Ivoire) to the south and Tombouctou (latitude 16.7°N, Mali) to the north.
V. Doumouya, J. Vassal, Y. Cohen, O. Fambitakoye, M. Menvielle
Equatorial electrojet at African longitudes: first results from magnetic measurements, Annales Geophysicae (1998) 16: 658 - 676
www.copernicus.org/EGU/annales/16/6/658.htm
33. Savage D, *NASA Sounding Rocket Campaign to Study Ionosphere with Brazil*, RELEASE: 94-126, Wallops Flight Facility, Wallops Island, Va.
www.scienceblog.com/community/older/archives/D/archnas2095.html
34. *IAGA Resolutions1963-2003*, XXI IUGG General Assembly, Boulder, USA, 1995
www.iugg.org/IAGA/iaga_pages/pdf/IAGA_Resolutions_v8.pdf
35. Anomaly Studies in Asia (PREASA) Program, umlcar.uml.edu/PREASA/preasa.htm
36. Kobea A T, et al. *Equatorial electrojet as part of the global circuit: a case-study from the IEEY,* Annales Geophysicae (1998) 16: 698 - 710
www.copernicus.org/EGU/annales/16/6/698.htm
37. Fraser B. J. et al., *Australian Space Research: The Fedsat Microsatellite*, CRC for Satellite Systems, Department of Physics, University of Newcastle, Callaghan, NSW, 2308, Australia, www.ips.gov.au/IPSHosted/NCRS/wars/wars2000/invited/fraser.pdf
38. This interview is referenced but the MP3 file is unavailable. Mitch Battros interview with Dr. Ernest Hildner, Earthchanges TV, October 2, 2003, www.earthchangestv.com
♦Battros M, *Solar Rain The Earth changes have begun*, Earth changes Press, 2005

39. Stephens T, *NASA Satellite Observes Mysterious Earth Energy*, NASA News, Feb. 22, 2005 RELEASE: 05-054
www.nasa.gov/home/hqnews/ 2005/feb/HQ_05054_Earth_Energy.html
40. Stephens T, Weintraub R A, *Flashes in the Sky: Earth's Gamma-Ray Bursts Triggered by Lightning*, NASA News, Feb. 17 2005
♦ *Gamma Rays From Thunderstorms?* Duke News, May 2, 2005
www.dukenews.duke.edu/2005/05/gammabolt.html
41. *The True State of the Universe,* Holoscience.com, 27 October 2004
www.holoscience.com/news.php?article=0auycyew
♦ Koskinen H et al, *Space Weather and Interactions with Spacecraft Summary report of Study of plasma and energetic electron environment and effects* (SPEE) SPEE-FR-2.0 European Space Agency (ESA) Technology Research Programme
www.ava.fmi.fi/spee/docs/spee-final1.pdf
♦ *ESA sees stardust storms heading for Solar System,* ESA News Press Release, August 18, 2003, http://www.esa.int/esaSC/Pr_13_2003_s_en.html
42. The study of the construction of Alaska pipeline underneath the auroral electrojet promoted extensive investigation of GICs in the pipelines (Campbel, 1978; 1980), in Finland (Viljanen, 1989) and in Argentina (Osella et al., 1997) and the equatorial electrojet influence on pipelines (Ogunade, 1986). From these studies the most severely affected areas of a pipeline network were identified. In general , the pipcline-to-ground voltages are greatest at areas of non-uniformity in the system: at the ends, bends and junctions of the pipeline. However, variations in material or pipe diameter also encourage voltage differences. Experience shows that geomagnetically induced voltages are greater in long pipelines than in short pipelines.
aurora.fmi.fi/gic_service/english/about_ground_effects.html
43. Odenwald S, *The 23rd Cycle: Learning to live with a stormy star*, Columbia University Press, 2000. www.solarstorms.org/S23rdCycle.html
GICs and pipelines referenced in Chapter 8
www.solarstorms.org /SWChapter8.pdf
♦ *Solar Weather and Satellites,* www.slatewiper.com/solarwind.shtml
44. Barringer F, *Oil Spill Raises Concerns on Pipeline Maintenance*, The New York Times, March 20, 2006,
www.nytimes.com/2006/03/20/national/20spill.html?ex=1143694800&en=7799d16f3c595745&ei=5070
45. 4-17 September 2005 Solar Storm Period
"During the first half of September 2005, a period of increased solar activity occurred that rivaled the number and magnitude of flares produced during the "Halloween" storm in October-November of 2003. The presence of NOAA active region 808 produced a total of 115 flares of GOES C-class or higher, including 26 M-class and 10 X-class flares.... The largest of the flares, a GOES X17.0 flare that occurred on September 7, 2005, was the largest flare that has occurred since the X28+ flare on November 4, 2003, and was just smaller than the X17.2 flare that occurred on October 28, 2003. This X17.0 flare was the 4th largest observed X-ray flare since GOES started making flare observations in 1986."
lasp.colorado.edu/sorce/september_2005_flares/sorce_news_Sept05.html
46. *Solar Minimum Explodes: Solar minimum is looking strangely like Solar Max. NASA* Headline News, 9.15.05, science.nasa.gov/headlines/y2005/15sep_solarminexplodes.htm
47. *Solar Weather and Satellites*, ideaworx.com/slatewiper/solarwind.htm
48. Kappenman J G, Radasky W A, *Learning to Live in a Dangerous Solar System: Advanced Geomagnetic Storm Forecasting Technologies allow the Electric Power Industry to Manage Storm Impacts*, Metatech Corp. www.metatechcorp.com/aps/electro.htm
www.metatechcorp.com/aps/AAAS_Press_Brief.htm,
Rastogi R. G. *Electromagnetic induction by the equatorial electrojet*
Geophysical Journal International, Volume 158 Issue 1 Page 16 - July 2004
doi:10.1111/j.1365-246X.2004.02128.x
www.blackwell-synergy.com/links/doi/10.1111/j.1365-246X.2004.02128.x/abs/

49. As early as 1920 Nobel Prize winning British physicist C.T.R. Wilson, the inventor of the Wilson Cloud Chamber, saw "diffuse fan-shaped flashes of greenish color extending upward into the clear sky...". He speculated then than such discharges between cloud tops and the ionosphere might be a normal accompaniment of lightning discharges to earth, but ones that are only visible only under very special conditions, representing an unknown component of the global electrical circuit.
Vaughan O H & Lyons W A, *What's Up There: A Brief History of Sprites, Jets, and Elves* www.knology.net/~skeetv/myobs.htm
50. *Sprite Gallery showing tentacles,* www.physicstoday.org/pt/vol-54/iss-11/captions/p41cap4.html
51. Lyons W A, et al., *The Hundred Year Hunt for the Sprite* www.fma-research.com/Papers&presentations/100YR.htm
52. Muir H, *Giant lightning jets discovered*, New Scientist report [vol 178 issue 2401 - 28 June 2003, page 16] by: www.newscientist.com/article.ns?id=mg17824011.800
53. Russell S, *Seeking evidence that electrical bolt may have doomed Columbia*, San Francisco Chronicle, 2nd October 2003, www.cincypost.com/2003/02/10/shbolt021003.html
54. Williams E R, *Sprites, Elves, and Glow Discharge Tubes: The venerable field of gaseous electronics underlies the understanding of a lightning-like phenomenon of spectacular extent, shape, and color.,* www.physicstoday.org/pt/vol-54/iss-11/p41.html
55. The red sprite photograph was actually taken in 2001.
Bettwy M, *Scientists Seek Sprite Light Source*, NASA Goddard Space Flight Center, 06.07.05 www.nasa.gov/vision/earth/environment/sprites.html
56. Thornhill W, *The Balloon goes up over lightning!* 29 January 2002 www.holoscience.com/news/balloon.html
57. *Earth: A Self-repairing Capacitor*, Sep 27, 2004 www.thunderbolts.info/tpod/2004/arch/040927earth-capacitor.htm
58. Layson L, *Sprites, Blue Jets and Tibetan Dakinis*, Morphogenesis - Priestessing on the edge of chaos, 20 Feb 2003
morphogenesis.info/newslog2.php/__show_article/_a000144-000010.htm
♦ *Welcome To a celebration of the Female Spirit as manifest in the Dakini,* www.dakini.demon.co.uk/index2.htm
59. *Indian National Report for IUGG 2003*, Indian National Science Academy www.iugg.org/indiancr.pdf
60. Williams E R, *Sprites, Elves, and Glow Discharge Tubes: The venerable field of gaseous electronics underlies the understanding of a lightning-like phenomenon of spectacular extent, shape, and color.* www.physicstoday.org/pt/vol-54/iss-11/p41.html
♦ Huang, E., E. et al. *Criteria for sprites and elves based on Schumann resonance observations*, *J. Geophys.Res.*, *104*, 16943-16964. (1999)
www-star.stanford.edu/~vlf/bibliography/sprites.bib
61. ♦ Carroll L, *Alchemy of the Human Spirit: A Guide to Human Transition into the New Age* (Kryon Book 3), The Kryon Writings, Inc. 1995 pg. 170
♦ Sudden Narrow Temperature Inversion-Layer Formation in ALOHA-93 as A Critical-Layer-Interaction Phenomenon, http://www.lv.psu.edu/tuh4/thesis/chapter_7.htm
62. Fosar G & Bludorf F, *Transition to the age of frequencies: Schumann waves, weather and mind control,* www.fosar-bludorf.com/archiv/schum_eng.htm
63. Carroll, L *Perceptions of Masterhood*, The Pacific Ocean, September 8, 2003, www.kryon.com/k_chanelhawaii103.html
64. *2004 Incoherent Scatter Coordinated Observation* Dayswww.haystack.edu/schedules/worldays_2004.html
♦ *The Plasma Tutorial: What is Plasma,* www.hmo.ac.za/Space_Physics/tut/tut.html
65. K. Schlegel K, Fuellekrug M, *Schumann Resonance Parameter Changes during High Energy Particle Precipitation,* Max-Planck-Institut fuer Aeronomie Max-Planck-Str. 2 D-37191 Katlenburg-Lindau Germany, 1998
www.agu.org/pubs/abs/jc/1998JC900077/tmp.html
66. Rosalie Bertell, is a consultant on top-level environment issues with Provincial and Federal

Governments, unions and citizen organizations. She has written two books, *No Immediate Danger: Prognosis for a Radioactive Earth* and *Planet Earth: The Latest Weapon of War*
♦Bertell R, *The Background of the HAARP Project*, November 5, 1996 www.earthpulse.com/haarp/background.html
♦Manning J & Begich Dr.N, *Angels Don't Play This HAARP*: Advances In Tesla Technology, Earthpulse Press, 2nd Edition, Eight Printing, 2004
♦Dmitriev A, Planetophysical State of the Earth and Life. (1997) www.tmgnow.com/repository/global/planetophysical.html

67. Roach J, *Earth's Magnetic Field Is Fading,* National Geographic News, September 9, 2004, news.nationalgeographic.com/news/2004/09/0909_040909_earthmagfield.html
68. Whitehouse D, *Earth buffeted by big solar flare*, BBC News Online, 30 October, 2003, http://news.bbc.co.uk/1/hi/sci/tech/3223739.stm
69. More specifically, electrically-conducting fluid flowing across magnetic-field lines induces an electric current, and this generated current supports its own associated magnetic field. Depending on the geometrical relationship between the fluid flow and the magnetic field, the generated magnetic field can reinforce the pre-existing magnetic field, in which case the dynamo is said to be 'self-sustaining'
A Brief Introduction To Geomagnetism, U.S. Geological Survey geomag.usgs.gov/intro.html
70. Scientific Challenges: Magnetic Field Dynamics, Solid Earth Science Working Group (SESWG) solidearth.jpl.nasa.gov/PAGES/mag02.html
71. William J. Broad, *Fast decline of magnetic field hints at reversal*, The Mercury News / NYT, 13 Jul 2004, www.energybulletin.net/1045.html
72. Schoonakker B, *Something weird is going on below us: Satellites in low-Earth orbit over Southern Africa are already showing signs of radiation damage*, Sunday Times - New Zealand, 18th July 2004, www.sundaytimes.co.za/2004/07/18/news/news14.asp
♦www.mayanmajix.com/art1251.html
73. *Magnetic Storm Transcript*, PBS Airdate: November 18, 2003 www.pbs.org/wgbh/nova/transcripts/3016_magnetic.html
74. Monastersky R, *Earth's magnetic field follies revealed.* Science News, 1995. Ref. 9
75. Snelling A, *The 'principle of least astonishment'!,* Technical Journal TJ 9(2):138–139 August 1995, www.answersingenesis.org/tj/v9/i2/astonishment.asp
Related Research papers
♦Coe R S, Prévot, M and Camps, P, *New evidence for extraordinarily rapid change of the geomagnetic field during a reversal. Nature,* 374:687–692. 1995
♦Prévot M, Mankinen E A, Grommé C S, Coe R S, *How the geomagnetic field vector reverses polarity.* Nature, 316:230–234, 1985.
♦Mankinen E A, Prévot M, Grommé C S, Coe R S, *The Steens Mountain (Oregon) geomagnetic polarity transition*, 1. Directional variation, duration of episodes, and rock magnetism. Journal of Geophysical Research, 90:10,393–10,416, 1985.
♦Prévot M, Mankinen E A, Coe R S, Grommé C S, *The Steens Mountain (Oregon) geomagnetic polarity transition*, 2. Field intensity variations and discussion of reversal models. Journal of Geophysical Research, 90:10,417–10,448, 1985.
♦Coe R S, Prévot M, *Evidence suggesting extremely rapid field variation during a geomagnetic reversal.* Earth and Planetary Science Letters, 92:292–298, 1989.
76. LaViolette P, *Predictions Part I - Superwave Theory Predictions and their Subsequent Verification – Prediction 9*
www.etheric.com/LaViolette/Predict.html
♦ Recently, there has been a new suggestion on how magnetic poles can be flipped by microwave radiation.
77. *Solar Storms, Arctic Winds Swirl In A Double Dip Cone Of Ozone Loss*, 24 Jun 2005 www.spacedaily.com/news/ozone-05h.html
78. LaViolette P, *Lunar Evidence of Past Solar Activity*, Excerpt from Paul LaViolette's 1983 Ph.D. dissertation "Galactic Explosions, Cosmic Dust Invasions, and Climatic Change"

From Chapter 4, Section 4.7 "Planetary Evidence", 1983
www.etheric.com/Superwave/Ch4.html
Astrophysicist James Mccanney estimates one coronal mass ejection (CME,) caused by a passing comet, to be 5 million miles long. Fortunately, it was not aimed directly at Earth!

79. Marciniak B, Earth: *Pleiadian Keys to the Living Library*, Bear & Company, 1995, Pg207
80. Section heading quote: Earth's Core Rotates Faster Than Its Crust, Scientists Say, NSF Press Release, August 26th, 2005
http://www.nsf.gov/news/news_summ.jsp?cntn_id=104359&org=OLPA&from=news
♦ "Scientists Now Admit that the Proposed Dynamo Theory, which is Supposedly Generating the Earth's Magnetic Field, is Insufficient. Current estimates indicate that the inferred heat flow from the core is not enough to drive the dynamo over most of the Earth's history. Viscosity values are orders of magnitude to high and the rotation is too slow. However, long held theories are very hard to let go of, and so, they are now considering a core with potassium, instead of the core of hydrogen fusion presented here." [Holme, R. (2004) A Fuel-Efficient Geodynamo? Nature Vol. 429, p. 137].
♦Pasichnyk R M, *The Vital Vastness: Our Living Earth* , Writer's Showcase Press, 2002
www.livingcosmos.com/earth.htm
81. Wilcock, *Large-Scale Geometric Energy Forms,* D Divine Cosmos: Chapter 5, ascension2000.com/DivineCosmos/05.htm
82. Burch, J. L., *Energetic particles and currents - Results from Dynamics Explorer*, Reviews of Geophysics (ISSN 8755-1209), vol. 26, May 1988, p. 215-228. (RvGeo Homepage), 05/1988
83. The Sun is the primary source of torsion as it has 99.86% of the total mass of the Solar System. In 1970, Saxel and Allen showed that during a solar eclipse, the presence of the moon shields the Sun's radiant torsion fields, and this causes an increase in the period of oscillation for a torsion balance. Meteorologists V.S. Kazachok, O.V. Khavroshkin and V.V. Tsyplakov were able to repeat this experiment during the 1976 solar eclipse and produce the same effect, which they then published in 1977.
♦Saxel E J & Allen M A, Solar eclipse as "seen" by a torsion pendulum. Phys.Rev.D, V.3, N.4, pp.823-825., 1970
♦Kazachok V S, Khavroshkin O V & Tsyplakov V V, *Behavior of atomic and mechanical oscillators during a solar eclipse.* Astronomichesky Tsirkuliar (Astronomical Circular), N.943, 1977, pp.4-6 (in Russian).
84. Johnson C, *Source of the Earth's Magnetic Field*, University of Chicago, 1997
www.mb-soft.com/public/tecto2.html
85. *The Vatican Observatory,* clavius.as.arizona.edu/vo/R1024/VO.html
86. Consolmagno G, *Brother Astronomer: Adventures of a Vatican Scientist*, McGraw-Hill,
♦Consolmagno G, *A Jesuit's scientific and spiritual discoveries in Antarctica*
http://www.companysj.com/v163/midnight.html
87. Comet Neat Video: soho.nascom.nasa.gov/bestofsoho/Movies/CometNeat/c2002v1.mpg

Chapter 4
Getting The Facts Straight

1. Suzar, *Blacked Out Through Whitewash*, suzar.com/BOTW/BOTW-ch1d-pages7-8.html
2. Schjelderup B, *The Periscope: Book One The Way To The Middle*, Periscope Vision, 2003
3. Brancazio P J, The Nature of Physics, Macmillan Publishing, New York. 1975, Pg 328
4. Beaty W J, *What is "Electricity"?* amasci.com/miscon/whatis.html
5. This book has been included in my references because it is a book written by an Electrical Engineer for non-scientists. It critiques the arguments and theories presented by standard models and presents an alternative explanation called "The expansion theory". Obviously this is a challenge to the scientific community who have dubbed it "pseudo-science", the normal rebuff. When presented with solid arguments, it is difficult to not accept the notion that the current theories do not stand up to scrutiny. In contrast to the mainstream scientific

community, the popular response to *The Final Theory* (as measured by Internet bookseller feedback) has been overwhelmingly favorable.
McCutcheon M, The Final Theory: Rethinking our Scientific Legacy, Universal Publishers, Published 2002

6. Wilcock D, *The Science of Oneness*, Chapter 5 Aether, Electromagnetism and Free Energy ascension2000.com/ConvergenceIII/c305.htm
7. DePalma B, *De Palma on Free Energy,* www.sumeria.net/free/dpalma1.html
♦Walters R, Scientists Claim To Tap The Free Energy Of Space www.freerepublic.com/focus/f-news/1234848/posts
8. Aspden H, *The Aspden Effect, Lecture No. 30*, 2002 www.energyscience.org.uk/le/Le30/le30.html
♦Aspden H, *Energy Science: An Introductory Overview, 2004* www.aspden.org/books/Es/esbookoverview.pdf
9. New Energy News, vol. 5, no. 4, Aug. 1997
♦Wilcock D, *The Science of Oneness: Harnessing The Conscious Aether ESP and Magnetism –A New Model of Gravity,* ascension2000.com/ConvergenceIII/c03-aether.htm
10. Von Reichenbach C, *Vital Force,* J.S Redfield, Clinton Hall, New York, 1851
Reichenbach's Letters on Od and Magnetism, F.D. O'Bryne, B.A. (London), 1852, republished by Mokelumne Hill, California, 1964.
11. The Van Allen Radiation Belt is described as a torus of energetic charged particles (plasma) around Earth, held in place by Earth's magnetic field. Yet the facts reveal this cannot be strictly true. The lower Van Allen Belt is about 7700 km above the earth's surface. According to the Encyclopedia Britannica, they are most intense along the equator, and effectively absent over the poles. They dip to 400 km over the South Atlantic Ocean, and are about 1,000 km high over the Central Pacific Ocean. The new understanding of the figure-8 magnetic field explains why between August and September 1958, the US Navy exploded three fission type nuclear bombs 480 km above the South Atlantic Ocean, in the part of the lower Van Allen Belt closest to the earth's surface.
♦Davis A R, Rawls W C, *Magnetism and its Effect on the Living System*, Acres, Kansas City.
12. Davis A R & Rawls W. C. The Magnetic Effect, Acres USA, 1999
13. Now we can make an interesting comparison here. The news of a tornado photographed in space gave the astronomers another puzzle to consider. This "stunning" phenomena created "triangular shockwaves," similar to the wake left by a speeding boat, as it moved through clouds of dust in space. This provides us with another example of seeing universal principles (magnetism) at work on the macro and micro scale, "as above, so below."
Than K, Space Tornado! Cosmic Front Packs a Punch, Space.com, 12 January 2006. space.com/scienceastronomy/060112_space_tornado.html
14. Brennan P, The Biomagnetic Revolution, What it Means to You www.magnetlabs.com/articles/biomagrev.htm
15. Schneider D, Some Levity in Physics, Science Observer, April 1999 www.americanscientist.org/template/AssetDetail/assetid/26612#26822
♦ Berry M V & Geim A K, "Of Flying Frogs and Levitrons", European Journal of Physics, v. 18, p. 307-313 (1997). www.science.ru.nl/hfml/frog-ejp.pdf
♦Magnet Levitation at your fingers, Nature 400, 323-324 (July 22 1999), awww.hfml.ru.nl/nature-july22v400.pdf
♦Simon M D & Geim A K, Diamagnetic levitation: Flying frogs and floating magnets, Journal of Applied Physics, Vol 87 No. 9, 1st May 2000 www.physics.ucla.edu/marty/diamag/diajap00.pdf
16. Ostrander S. & Schroeder L. Psychic Discoveries The Iron Curtain Lifted, Marlowe & Company, New York, 1997.
17. Becker, R. & Selden G. The Body Electric William Morrow & Company Inc, 1985 pg 233
18. Waechter R L, Qi and Bioelectromagnetic Energy, York University, 2002 www.e-budo.com/forum/attachment.php?attachmentid=6337

19. Pankratov S. Meridians Conduct Light. Germany: Raum & Zeit; 1991. www.photonstimulator.com/Article%20Russian.htm
20. Hunt V, Infinite Mind. Los Angeles: Malibu Press, 1995
21. Tiller W, Science and Human Transformation: Subtle Energies, Intentionality and Consciousness, Walnut Creek, CA: Pavior 1997
22. Hunt V et al., *A Study of Structural Integration from Neuromuscular, Energy Field and Emotional Approaches*, University of California, Los Angeles, 1977, www.somatics.de/HuntStudy.html
    ♦Hunt V, *Electronic evidence of auras, chakras in UCLA study.* Brain/Mind Bulletin, Mar 29, 3(9): 1-2, (1978)
    ♦Hunt V, *Scientific research on psychic energies at the Department of Kinesiology*, UCLA. J. Holistic Health, 6: 47-54., (1982)
    ♦Bruyere, R.L., *Wheels of Light: Chakras, Auras and the Healing Energy of the Body*, Simon & Schuster, New York 1989, 1991, 194 The Rolf Study – Appendix I
23. Solomon J & Solomon G, *Harry Oldfield's Invisible Universe*, Thorsens 1998 Pg. 131
24. Solomon J, *Harry Oldfield Interview – Inventor of Electro-Scanning and Polycontrast Interference Photography* www.positivehealth.com/permit/Articles/Energy%20Medicine/solomn41.htm
25. Alvino G, *The Human Energy Field in Relation to Science, Consciousness, and Health,* www.vxm.com/21R.43.html
26. ♦*Health on the Edge: Visionary Views of Healing in the New Millennium*, Tarcher/Putnam
    ♦Trivieri L, *The Human Energy Field – An Interview With Valerie Hunt*, Ph.D., The Health Plus Letter Vol. 1, No.1, July, 8, 2003, www.1healthyworld.com/ezine/Vol1No1.cfm
27. Beaty W, *What is a spark?* 1996, www.amasci.com/miscon/whatis2.html
28. Barber, S. *The Promise of Bioenergy Fields: An end to all Disease - An Interview with Dr Valerie Hunt*, www.spiritofmaat.com/archive/nov1/vh.htm
29. Cestnick C. *Healing Through Unconditional Love- The Higher Self and The Light Body*, Jan 2005, www.emaxhealth.com/26/1115.html
30. For further details see, Appendix A Biofield: Connecting Web Between Physical & Subtle Realm, Appendix B Self-Organizing Systems: Active Information In The Human-To-Human Connection, Appendix C Physical Model of the Biofield by Andrej Detela, Appendix D Self-Organization Within Complex Quantum States by Andrej Detela
    ♦Dubro, P & Lapierre D, *Elegant Empowerment: Evolution of Consciousness*, Platinum Publishing, 2002
31. Ho M, *The Rainbow and the Worm: The Physics of Organisms* (2nd Edition), The Open University, UK,
    ♦Ho M, *The Entangled Universe*, YES! Positive Futures Network, Spring 2000 www.yesmagazine.org/article.asp?ID=329
32. There is evidence that all the major constituents of living organisms may be liquid crystalline – lipids of cellular membranes, DNA in chromosomes possibly all proteins, especially cytoskeletal proteins, muscle proteins and proteins in the connective tissues such as collagens and proteoglycans (macromolecules that are part protein and part carbohydrates). Mae-Wae Ho cites evidence of nuclear magnetic resonance (nmr) studies of muscles in living human subjects provided evidence of their "liquid-crystalline like" structure.[Kreis & Boesch, 1994]
33. *Laser, Science History Study Guide,* www.bookrags.com/sciences/sciencehistory/laser-woi.html
34. Hughes M, *Assessment Of Health Effects From Exposure To Power-Line Frequency Electric And Magnetic Fields U.S. Department of Labour* www.niehs.nih.gov/emfrapid/html/EMF_DIR_RPT/Dir_Comments/CD_Files/VOL2/emf2_083.pdf
35. Smith C. W, *Electromagnetic effects in humans*. In Fröhlich H (Ed) Biological coherence and response to external stimuli. Springer-Verlag, Berlin, 1988
36. Smith C. & Best S., *Electromagnetic Man. Health & Hazard in the electrical environment.*

Palgrave Macmillan, 1989
37. Scott-Mumby, K. *Virtual medicine,* Thorsens/Harper Collins, London , 1999
♦Gerber, R. M.D. *Vibrational Medicine: The #1 Handbook of Subtle-Energy Therapies*, Bear & Company, Rochester, Vermont 2001
38. Good article with well over 100 references which back up the new paradigm understanding of electromagnetic fields influencing cell physiology.
Lipton B, *The new Biology*, 2005, www.brucelipton.com/newbiology.php
39. ♦Benveniste J, et al*: Transfer of the molecular signal by electronic amplification*, FASEB J 8:A398, 1994 (abstract).
Nature 1988;333: 816-8[CrossRef][ISI][Medline] - original report published in Nature
♦Obituary Jacques Benveniste, BMJ 2004;329:1290 (27 November), doi:10.1136/bmj.329.7477.1290, bmj.bmjjournals.com/cgi/content/full/329/7477/1290
40. Becker R O, *Cross Currents: The Promise of Electromedicine, the Perils of Electropollution,* Jeremy P. Tarcher, 1990
41. Bearden T, *The Priore Machine and Phase Conjugation* www.cheniere.org/books/aids/priore.htm
♦Bearden, T *A Non-Technical Description of the Priore Process,* November 9th, 2000 www.cheniere.org/books/aids/priorenontech.htm
♦ Bateman J, Office of Naval Research Report R-5-78
♦Priore A, *Method of Producing Radiations for Penetrating Living Cells,* US Patent # 3,280,816
♦Priore A, *Treatment of a Patient by Negative Ions,* French Patent # 2,408,357
♦Bird C & Bearden T, *Background of Antoine Prioré and L'Affaire Prioré,* www.rexresearch.com/priore/priore.htm
♦Bearden T E, *The Case of Antoine Priore and His Therapeutic Machine: A Scandal in the Politics of Science*,
42. Ryan B, *Cancer Research - A Super Fraud?,* www.pnc.com.au/~cafmr/online/research/cancer.html
43. Bell F, *Rays of Truth – Crystals of Light, Pyradyne Publishing, 1998*
44. Diver S. & Kueper G. *Radionics in Agriculture,* May 1997 home.earthlink.net/~gkuepper/index/Radionics.htm
The link above includes references and provides 'Further Readings On Agricultural Radionics' (19 books) and 'General Readings and Workbooks On Radionics' (29 works)
45. Annex G, *IEE Guidance Document on EMC & Functional Safety,* www.iee.org.uk/PAB/EMC/core.htm
46. *Bryant E, PSA: Beware of Cosmic Rays,* 1 June 2006 www.audiportal.com/index.php?option=com_content&task=view&id=379&Itemid=68
♦Martin M, *Cosmic rays damage automotive electronics*, Planet Analog, 1 June 2006 http://planetanalog.com/features/showArticle.jhtml?articleID=188700453
47. Grant L. (Editor), *Electrical Sensitivity News* Vol1, No.4 J/A 1996
♦Hillert L et al., *Hypersensitivity to electricity: working definition and additional characterization of the syndrome*. J. Psychosom. Res., 47, 429-38, 1999

Chapter 5
Mind & Body Electromagnetic Balance

1. Dossey L, *Healing Happens,* 1995 Utne Reader, no.71 (Sept/Oct)
Ader R et al. Psychoneuroimmunology, 2nd edition SanDiego: Academic Press, 1990
2. Pearsall, P. 1998. *The Heart's Code*. New York: Random House
3. Pearsall P, *The Heart Remembers* www.findarticles.com/p/articles/mi_m0NAH/is_n2_v27/ai_20353562
4. *Female kidney turns lumberjack on to housework*, Ananova News, 16th January 2006, www.ananova.com/news/story/sm_1685466.html
5. Pert C, *Molecules of Emotion: Why You Feel the Way You Feel,* Scriber, 1997

♦Kandel E R, *A new intellectual framework for psychiatry.* Am J Psychiatry, 1998;155:457- 469.

6. *A Rational Decision? Don't Bet On It* , www.pcipr.com/RSNA/news/thinking.asp
   ♦Ramachandra V S, Phantoms in the Brain: Probing The Mysteries Of The Human Mind, Harper Perennial, 1998
7. McCraty R,Childre D.*The appreciative heart:The psychophysiology of positive emotions and optimal functioning.*Boulder Creek,CA:HeartMath Research Center,Institute of HeartMath, Publication No.02-026,2002.
   ♦McCraty R.*The energetic heart:Bioelectromagnetic interactions within and between people* .Boulder Creek,CA:HeartMath Research Center,Institute of HeartMath, Publication No.02-035,2002.
   ♦*Head Heart Interactions*, Heartmath Institution
   www.heartmath.org/research/science-of-the-heart/soh_20.html
8. McCraty R, Atkinson M, Tomasino D, *Modulation of DNA Conformation by Heart-Focused Intention*, HeartMath Research Center, Institute of HeartMath, Publication No. 03-008. Boulder Creek, CA, 2003.
   www.heartmath.org/research/research-intuition/Modulation_of_DNA.pdf
9. McCraty, R Ph.D., Atkinson M, Bradley R T, *Electrophysiological Evidence of Intuition: Part 1. The Surprising Role of the Heart*, The Journal Of Alternative And Complementary Medicine Volume 10,Number 1,2004,pp.133 –143, www.heartmath.org/research/research-intuition/Intuition_Part1.pdf
   ♦McCraty R , Atkinson M, Bradley R T, *Electrophysiological Evidence of Intuition: Part 2. A System – Wide Process?* The Journal Of Alternative And Complementary Medicine Volume 10,Number 2,2004,pp.325 –336
   www.heartmath.org/research/research-intuition/Intuition_Part2.pdf
10. Lacey J & Lacey B, *Two-Way Communication between the Heart and the Brain: Significance of Time within the Cardiac Cycle.* American Psychologist (February 1978): 99-113
11. Armour J A, Srdell, J *Neurocardiology.* Oxford University Press: New York, 1994. www.heartmath.org/store/e-books/index.html
12. The "Little Brain in the Heart", The Institute of Heartmath
   http://www.heartmath.org/research/our-heart-brain.html
   Mercogliano C & Debus K, *An Interview with Joseph Chilton Pearce*, Journal of Family Life magazine, Vol. 5 #1 1999
   www.appliedmeditation.org/The_Heart/articles_joseph_chilton_pearce.shtml
13. Cantin M, et al. *The heart as an endocrine gland.* J Hypertens Suppl.1984 Dec;2(3):S329-31.
   www.ncbi.nlm.nih.gov/entrez/query.fcgi?cmd=Retrieve&db=PubMed&list_uids=6100743&dopt=Abstract
   ♦Cantin M, Genest J. *The heart as an endocrine gland.* Sci Am. 1986 Feb;254(2):76–81.
   Connections Between the Heart and the Brain
   www.primordia.net/articles/CGB%20Connections%20Between%20the%20Heart%20and%20the%20Brain.htm
14. Pearsall P, *The Heart Remembers*, Natural Health, March-April 1998
   www.findarticles.com/p/articles/mi_m0NAH/is_n2_v27/ai_20353562
15. Goswami, S S, *Layayoga: The Definitive Guide to the Chakras.* London: Routledgeand Kegan Paul, 1980
16. Heading *The Gate of Heaven* inspired from chapter 12
   Gaffney M H, *Gnostic Secrets of the Naassenes: The Initiatory Teachings of the Last Supper*, Inner Traditions Rochester, Vermont, 2004
17. Sannella, L., *The Kundalini Experience*, Integral Publishing, California, 1987
18. *Chilton Pearce J, The Biology of Transcendence: A Blueprint of the Human Spirit,* Park Street Press Rochester Vermont, 2002
19. Ibid page 4, & 64-73
20. Walters F, *Book of the Hopi,* Ballentine Books Inc. New York, 1963

21. Becker, R. M.D. *Cross Currents: The Promise of Electromedicine, The Perils of Electropollution* Jeremy P. Tarcher / Putnam 1990 Pg 69
22. David Cohen, first to succeed in detecting the magnetic alpha rhythm from the brain [Cohen, 1968], and he was also the first scientist to detect the MEG signal with a point contact SQUID [Cohen, 1972]
    ♦In Electroencephalography & Magnetoencephalography, the head is modeled as concentric spheres, Malmivuo, 1980
    butler.cc.tut.fi/~malmivuo/bem/bembook/12/12.htm Pg 201
23. Shine, B. *Mind to Mind: The Secrets of Your Mind Energy Revealed*, Corgi Books, 1989
24. Zh Nevropatol Psikhiatr Im S S Korsakova., *Interhemispheric correlations of electric activity of the brain in late depression* 1992;92(1):88-92.
    www.ncbi.nlm.nih.gov/entrez/query.fcgi?cmd=Retrieve&db=PubMed&list_uids=1319661 &dopt=
25. Cromie W J, *Depressed get a lift from MRI - Brain scanners please manic-depressives*, Harvard News Office, January 2004,
    www.news.harvard.edu/gazette/2004/01.22/01-depression.html
26. George M S, *Stimulating The Brain*, Scientific America, 2003
    www.ists.unibe.ch/sciam.pdf copy www.musc.edu/psychiatry/fnrd/tmssciam.pdf
27. Null, G. *Biomagnetic Healing*, www.garynull.com/Documents/magnets.htm
28. *Magnetic Fields Decrease Seizure Frequency In Some Patients*, 2-21-2000
    www.pslresearch.com/dgtraffic/dgtraffic.html
    ♦ www.rense.com/politics6/mag.htm
29. Miller R & Miller I, *The Schumann Resonances and Human Psychobiology*, Extracted from Nexus Magazine, Volume 10, Number 3 (April-May 2003), © 2002, 2003
    www.nexusmagazine.com/articles/schumann.html
    Additional Scientific References:
    ♦Cherry Dr N, *'Schumann Resonances, a plausible biophysical mechanism for the human health effects of Solar/Geomagnetic Activity'* (2002)
    ♦Cherry Dr N, *'Human intelligence: The brain, an electromagnetic system synchronised by the Schumann Resonance signal'* (2003).
    ♦Cherry N, *Health Effects of Electromagnetic Radiation: Evidence for the Australian Senate Committee*, Lincoln University, New Zealand, 8th September 2000,
    www.energyfields.org/science/CWTI.Cherry_literature_review_9.2000.doc
    ♦Dr Neil Cherry (1946 -2003) held the position of Associate Professor of Environmental Health at Lincoln University in New Zealand. In 2000, he wrote a 120 page review of 188 research papers on electromagnetic radiation (EMR), he was later rewarded for his work with the highest honour that can be attained by a civilian.
    Cherry Environmental Health Consulting Ltd, www.neilcherry.com
    ♦Cherry N, Lincoln University 25/4/2000, www.whale.to/b/cherry.doc
30. Schienle A et al., Biological Effects of Very Low Frequency (VLF) Atmospherics in Humans: A Review
    Journal of Scienti®c Exploration, Vol. 12, No. 3, pp. 455±468, 1998
    http://www.scientificexploration.org/jse/articles/pdf/12.3_schienle_stark_vaitl.pdf
31. Corliss W R, *An invisible information superhighway?* Science Frontiers ONLINE, No. 104: Mar-Apr 1996, www.science-frontiers.com/sf104/sf104p14.htm
32. Washnis, G. J. & Hricak, R. Z. *Discovery of Magnetic Health*. Rockville, MD: Nova Publishing Company, (1993).
33. Kirschvink JL, Kobayashi-Kirschvink A, Woodford BJ: *Magnetite biomineralization in the human brain,* Proc Natl Acad Sci U S A 89:7683-7687, 1992.
34. www.affs.org/html/biomagnetism.html
35. Associated Press, Omaha World-Herald. *Tiny Crystal Magnets Found in Human Brain.* May 12, 1992.

Chapter 6
Making Sense of Consciousness

1. From issue 2438 of New Scientist magazine, 13 March 2004
Opposites Detract, Mind Power News – Online extracts of New Scientist article
www.mindpowernews.com/035.htm
2. Ostrander S. & Schroeder L. *Psychic Discoveries Behind The Iron Curtain*, Marlowe & Company, New York, 1971.
3. *Who Was Paracelsus?* www.paracelsusclinic.com/paracelsus.asp
4. Russell Targ and Harold Puthoff, "Information transmission under conditions of sensory shielding," in Nature, Volume 251, 1974;
♦Russell Targ and K. Harary, *The Mind Race*, New York: Villard Books, 1984;
♦Harold E. Puthoff and Russell Targ, *"A perceptual channel for information transfer over kilometer distances: historical perspective and recent research"* Proceedings of the IEEE, Vol. 64, 1976.
5. Davis, Eric W. *Teleportation Physics Study*, Edwards Air Force Research Laboratory, Contract Number F04611-99-C-0025, www.fas.org/sgp/eprint/teleport.pdf
6. Ostrander S. & Schroeder L. *Psychic Discoveries: The Iron Curtain Lifted*, Marlowe & Company, New York, 1997.
7. Professor William Tiller is well known for his research conducted into the power of consciousness and intent.
Tiller W, *Science and Human Transformation: Subtle Energies, Intentionality and Consciousness*, Walnut Creek, CA: Pavior 1997
♦Tiller W, Dibble W.E, Kohane M J, *Conscious Acts of Creation*, Pavior 2001
8. Becker, R. & Selden G. *The Body Electric,* William Morrow & Company Inc, 1985 pg 266
9. Ho M, *The Entangled Universe*, YES! Positive Futures Network, Spring 2000
www.yesmagazine.org/article.asp?ID=329
10. Einstein, A., Podolsky, B., Rosen, N., (1935) *"Can Quantum Mechanical Description of Reality be Considered Complete?"* *Physical Review*, vol. 47, pp. 777- 780.
11. Rincon, Paul, *Teleportation goes long distance*, BBC News, 18 August, 2004
http://news.bbc.co.uk/2/hi/science/nature/3576594.stm
12. Goswami A, *The Self-aware Universe. How Consciousness Creates the Material World*, Tarcher, 1995
13. Hamilton C, *An Interview with Amit Goswami* [Abridged] twm.co.nz/goswam1.htm
14. Grinberg-Zylberbaum, J., Delaflor, M., Attie, L., and Goswami, A. (1994) *"The Einstein-Podolsky-Rosen Paradox in the Brain: the Transferred Potential."* *Physics Essays,7, pp 422. ♦Orme-Johnson et al, 1982; ♦Grinberg-Zylberbaum, 1988
15. Popper K, Eccles J C, *The Self and Its Brain: An Argument for Interactionism*, Springer International, London, 1977.
♦Holmes C, *The Heart of Doctrine: Mystical Views of the Origin and Nature of Human Consciousness -- Neurological Enigmas*, www.zeropoint.ca/heartIII5neuro.htm
♦♦*Is your brain really necessary?* www.alternativescience.com/no_brainer.htm
♦Dr. John Lorber (1915–1996), neurology professor at the University of Sheffield in the United Kingdom collected research data concerning several hundred people who functioned quite well with practically no "detectable brains."
Dr. Patrick Wall, professor of anatomy at University College, London, stated that there existed "scores" of accounts of people existing without discernable brains.
www.20k.de/postnuke//modules.php?op=modload&name=News&file=article&sid=313
16. Pribram K, *Languages of the Brain: Experimental Paradoxes and Principles in Neuropsychology,* Prentice-Hall, New Jersey, 1971.
♦Pribram K, *Brain and Perception: Holonomy and Structure in Figural Processing*, Hilldale, New Jersey, 1991
♦Boyd R N, *The Fabrics of Consciousness*, ITC Journal, No.11, twm.co.nz/fabriconsc_boyd.html

17. *The Universe as a Hologram*, twm.co.nz/hologram.html
18. Dr. Slawinski asserts a death flash of electromagnetic radiation that is measurable in all living things. He believes this may be how science will answer the age old question of what happens to one at death.
    Slawinski J, *Electromagnetic Radiation and the Afterlife*. Journal of Near-Death Studies, 6(2), 79-93. Human Sciences Press, 1987 pg79
    ♦Russian Experiments were conducted by Russian Dr Sergeyev.
    Ostrander S. & Schroeder L. Psychic Discoveries Behind The Iron Curtain, Marlowe & Company, New York, 1971.
19. McFadden J, *Synchronous firing and its influence on the brain's electromagnetic field: evidence for an electromagnetic field theory of consciousness"*, Journal of Consciousness Studies, vol.9,pp.23-50., 2002
20. Dr. John Lorber (1915–1996), neurology professor at the University of Sheffield in the United Kingdom collected research data concerning several hundred people who functioned quite well with practically no brains at all. Upon careful examination, he described some of the subjects as having no "detectable brains."
    Dr. Patrick Wall, professor of anatomy at University College, London, stated that there existed "scores" of accounts of people existing without discernable brains.
    ♦Lewin R, *Is Your Brain Really Necessary?* Science 210, December 12, 1980
    ♦Is *Your Brain Really Necessary?*, Alternative Science News, September 9, 2002. http://www.alternativescience.com/no_brainer.htm
    ♦For a more scientific analysis of this issue see:
    Bearden T E, *Gravitobiology: The New Biophysics*, Tesla Book Company, 1991
21. Pockett S, *The Nature of Consciousness: A Hypothesis*. (Lincoln, NE: Writers Club Press), 2000.
22. E Abbott, *Flatland: A Romance of Many Dimensions*, Dower Publications, New York, 1952 6th Ed., Revised
23. Kaku M, *Hyperspace: A Scientific Odyssey through Parallel Universes*, Time Warps & the 10th Dimension, Oxford University Press, New York, 1994
24. Davis E W. *Teleportation Physics Study, Edwards Air Force Research Laboratory*, Contract Number F04611-99-C-0025, www.fas.org/sgp/eprint/teleport.pdf
25. For details of fourth spatial dimension see: [Reichenbach, 1957;Rucker, 1977, 1984]. Ultimate components of our nervous system are actually higher dimensional see: [Hinton, 1888, 1904; Rucker, 1977]. Four dimensional consciousness: [Rucker, 1977, 1984]
26. Yurth, *David Seeing Past The Edge*, chap. 10 The Seething Sea of Infinite Potential zpenergy.com/modules.php?name=Forums&file=viewtopic&p=351
    ♦Hagelin J., *Is Consciousness the Unified Field? A Field Theorist's Perspective,* Maharishi International University, Fairfield, Iowa.
27. Kaku M, *Hyperspace and a Theory of Everything:What lies beyond our 4 dimensions?* www.mkaku.org/articles/hyper_and_toe.shtml
28. *On The Evolution of String Theory To Membrane Theory,* scienceweek.com/1998/sw980123.htm
29. M-theory postulates an 11-dimensional space-time, inhabited not only by one-dimensional strings but also by two-dimensional membranes, three-dimensional 'blobs' (three-branes), up to and including nine-dimensional entities, not forgetting anti-branes and zero-branes.
    ♦Overbye D, *String Theory, at 20, Explains It All (or Not),* The New York Times December 7, 2004,
    http://www.nytimes.com/2004/12/07/science/07stri.html?ex=1260075600&%2338;en=fd15a74e2dca3af0&%2338;ei=5090&
30. *Physics' greatest endeavour is grinding to a halt: The hunt for a theory of everything is going nowhere fast*, New Scientist Magazine issue 2529, 10 December 2005 http://www.newscientist.com/channel/fundamentals/quantum-world/mg18825293.200-editorial-physics-greatest-endeavour-is-grinding-to-a-halt.html
    ♦Woit P, *Not Even Wrong: The Failure of String Theory and the Search for Unity in Physical Law*, Basic Books, 2006

31. Aspden H, *"Physics Without Einstein: A Centenary Review"* www.aspden.org/books/pwecent/pwecent2005.pdf

32. The Correas U.S. patents are numbered 5,416,391 (issued May 16, 1995), 5,449,989 (issued September 12, 1995) and 5,502,354 (issued March 26, 1996).
♦Aspden H, Opinion On Correa Invention Energy Conversion System, European PatentAttorney, February 13, 1996, www.aetherometry.com/aspden_opinion.html

33. The parameters were accurate derivations for the fine-structure constant [the dimensionless constant combining Planck's constant, the electron charge, and the speed of light, all parameters of the vacuum], for the proton-electron and muon-electron mass ratios, and for the gravitational constant.
From the paper referenced below, the abstract reads: "A comparison is made of theoretical values of various authors for the fine-structure constant, for the proton-electron and muon-electron mass ratios, and for the gravitational constant. It is shown that a lattice ether theory developed by Aspden gives the best overall agreement with experiment."
Dr. D. M. Eagles entitled, *A Comparison of Results of Various Theories for Four Fundamental Constants of Physics,* published in the International Journal of Theoretical Physics, v. 15, pp. 265-270 (1976).
Aspden also writes: "Leading experts, R. S. Van Dyck, Jr., F. L. Moore, D. L. Farnham and P. B. Schwinberg, involved in making such measurements reported in 1985 their findings in Int. J. Mass Spectrometry and Ion Processes, 66, p. 327 they stated: "A comparison is made of theoretical values of various authors for the fine-structure constant, for the proton-electron and muon-electron mass ratios, and for the gravitational constant. It is shown that a lattice ether theory developed by Aspden gives the best overall agreement with experiment." The experts wrote, "The value that they [Aspden and Eagles] calculate is remarkably close to our experimentally measured value (i.e. within two standard deviations) This is even more curious when one notes that they published this result several years before direct precision measurements of this ratio had begun. "They had measured the proton-electron mass ratio to within a precision of 41 parts in a billion and this measurement was reported some 10 years after we had presented the theoretical value derived from aether theory.

34. *Cubic From & diamonds*, bestinhonolulu.com/Facets/Pages/Facets_General/Science.htm
♦Aspden H, The Crystalline Vacuum, Energy Science Essay No. 13, 1998 www.energyscience.org.uk/essays/ese13.htm

35. 30 January 1998, issue of SCIENCE, vol. 279, pp 675-676 and pp. 686-689

36. Valigra L, *MIT physicists create new form of matter*, MIT News Office, June 22, 2005 web.mit.edu/newsoffice/2005/matter.html

37. Dan Davidson writes, "Space is envisioned as a superfluidic medium, nonviscous, relatively frictionless, massless and continuous. It can be modeled as a particulate superfluid with average interaction spacing of L. Essentially, this is a new definition of the aether."
Tewari P, *Space is the Absolute Reality, International Conference on Space-Time Absoluteness*, Genoa, Italy, July 1982.

38. Einasto J et al, *A 120-Mpc periodicity in the three-dimensional distribution of galaxy superclusters,* Nature 385, 139-141, 09 Jan 1997
♦Kirshner R P, *The universe as a lattice*, Nature 385, 120, 09 Jan 1997.
♦Chu R, The ccp and hcp family of structures derived from interpenetrating lattices http://www.verbchu.com/crystals/ccp_lattices.html

39. Dr Harold Aspden's websites: www.aspden.org, www.energyscience.org.uk
Aspden H, *Aetheric Science Papers*, Sabberton Publications, Southampton, England, 1996

40. After Planetary scientists thought that they had considered and eliminated all possible planetary-scale energy sources, they declared "by default" that Jupiter's internally-generated energy was left over from planetary formation some 4.5 billion years ago. This is explanation does not make sense as Jupiter is 98% a mixture of hydrogen and helium, both of which transfer heat quite efficiently.

41. Hoagland R, & Torun E, *The "Message of Cydonia": First Communication from an*

Extraterrestrial Civilization? 1989, www.enterprisemission.com/message.htm
♦Hubble's New "Runaway Planet": A Unique Opportunity for Testing the Exploding Planet Hypothesis and ... Hyperdimensional Physics Part I
http://www.enterprisemission.com/hyper1.html

42. The following Resource link is provided with fifty articles related to the Aether. *Theories of the Aether Articles relating to the Emergence of Scientific Theories of the Cosmic Aether,* Web Publication by Mountain Man Graphics, Australia, www.mountainman.com.au/aether.html
Knot Theory's Odd Origins Volume: 94 Number: 2 Page: 158 DOI: 10.1511/2006.2.158
www.americanscientist.org/template/CreateToken?type=PDF&assetid=49811
43. According to classical physics the electrons should radiate away their energy and spiral into the nucleus, as this does not occur quantum mechanics was invented to explain away the actual observations.
The following book brings together papers by a number of authors with different views on the electron. Simulik V, (editor), What is the electron?, Montreal : Apeiron, 2005.
44. Puthoff H E, *Ground State of Hydrogen as a Zero-Point Fluctuation-Determined State*, Physical Review D Vol. 35, No 10. pp. 3266-69, May 1987.
Kanarev Ph. M. *Planck's Constant and The Model of the Electron*, Journal of Theoretics www.journaloftheoretics.com/Links/Papers/Kanarev-Electron.pdf
45. Weinstock *M, Scientists Claim To Break Speed-of-Light Barrier* Space.com 19 July 2000, www.space.com/scienceastronomy/generalscience/faster_than_c_000719.html
46. The Speed of Light and the Einstein Legacy: 1905-2005, Reginald T Cahill (Flinders University) www.arxiv.org/ftp/physics/papers/0501/0501051.pdf
There have always been doubts about Relativity and it appears that where it really matters, Einstein's legacy is questionable. So we find that in the practical world of GPS atomic clocks, they refuse to completely obey Einstein's theory! See reference below.
♦Boerner R, The Suppression of Inconvenient Facts in Physics, 2003
http://www.world-mysteries.com/sci_supr.htm
47. *An Introduction to Zero-Point Energy*, The California Institute for Physics and Astrophysics (CIPA), www.calphysics.org/zpe.html
48. Maclay, G.J., Fearn, and Milonni, *"Of some theoretical significance: implications of Casimir effects",* European Journal of Physics, 22 (2001), pp. 463-469.
49. Bortman H, *Energy unlimited*, New Scientist magazine, 22/1/2000.
www.quantumfields.com/bortman.htm
NASA Breakthrough Propulsion Physics (BPP), Project Public Information Site
www.grc.nasa.gov/WWW/bpp/
Puthoff, Dr. H. E. *Quantum Vacuum Fluctuations: A New Rosetta Stone of Physics?* Institute for Advanced Studies (512) 328-5751, www.ldolphin.org/zpe.html
50. Battaglia, John-Michael "The Wilhelm Reich Story" by © 1993
www.orgone.org/articles/ax6bjmbt.htm
51. *Boeing tries to defy gravity,* 29 July, 2002, BBC News,
http:// news.bbc.co.uk/2/hi/science/nature/2157975.stm
52. J. Hutchison, *"The Hutchison Effect Apparatus,"* Proc. of the 1st Int. Symp. on New Energy, Denver, p. 191, May 1994.
53. Bearden T.E. *Flaws in Classical EM Theory*
www.cheniere.org/misc/flaws_in_classical_em_theory.htm
54. Alfvén H, *Plasma physics, space research and the origin of the solar system*, Nobel Lecture, December 11, 1970, nobelprize.org/physics/laureates/1970/alfven-lecture.pdf
55. Kenyon T & Sion J, *The Magdalen Manuscript,* Publisher ORB Communication P.O. Box 98, Orcas, WA 98280
56. Davis, Eric W. *Teleportation Physics Study*, Edwards Air Force Research Laboratory, Contract Number F04611-99-C-0025, www.fas.org/sgp/eprint/teleport.pdf
57. Salla M, *Teleportation Physics Study An Analysis Of Its Exopolitical, Implications*:www.exopolitics.org/Exo-Comment-27.htm
Copy, www.rense.com/general62/TELEPO.HTM

58. *Hoagland & Wilcock on Coast to Coast* 15/16 May 2004 www.enterprisemission.com/_articles/05-22-2004_Bell_Interviews_123/Bell%20InterviewPartTwo1.htm www.enterprisemission.com/_articles/05-22-2004_Bell_Interviews_123/Bell%20InterviewPartThree.htm

Chapter 7
Balancing in Chaos

1. Hunt V, *Infinite Mind: The science of human vibrations*. Malibu, CA: Malibu Press. (1995)
2. Free V, *Healing With Light*, Atlantis Rising Magazine, www.atlantisrising.com/issue6/ar6healing1.html
3. Dorman L I. et al., *Cosmic Ray Forbush-Decreases as Indicators of Space Dangerous Phenomena and Possible Use of Cosmic Ray Data for their Prediction,* binary.stelab.nagoya-u.ac.jp/ICRC1999/root/vol6/s2_1_22.pdf
   ♦*Earth's Magnetic Field Affects Humans*, Items 44, 45, 48, 49, 50, 51, 54 www.justgoodtiming.com/id45.htm
4. Zaitsev Y, *Solar flares Affect Humans*, RIA Novosti, en.rian.ru/analysis/20050721/40947085.html
5. Kay RW. *Geomagnetic storms: association with incidence of depression as measured by hospital admission.* British Journal Psychiatry 1994 164(3): 403-9.
   ♦Scientists seek link between solar flares and strokes,Kerala News,25 Apr 2006 http://www.newkerala.com/news2.php?action=fullnews&id=48240
6. Moore C, *Sunspot Cycles and Activist Strategy: Welcome to the height of the 11.5 year sunspot cycle,* www.rumormillnews.com/cgi-bin/archive.cgi?noframes;read=5854
7. Odenwald S, *Solar Storms, Special to The Washington Post*, March 10, 1999 solar.physics.montana.edu/press/WashPost/Horizon/1961-031099-idx.html
8. *Astronauts' Children Unlikely to Inherit Cosmic Ray-Induced Genetic Defects,* Brookhaven National Laboratory,April 14, 2005 www.bnl.gov/bnlweb/pubaf/pr/PR_display.asp?prID=05-43
9. *Spiral Waves Break Hearts: New Research Stresses the Importance of Communication Between Cardiac Cells*, American Institute of Physics www.aip.org/isns/reports/2002/036.html
10. Otani N F, *Cardiac Bioelectricity*, Cornell University vivo.library.cornell.edu/entity?home=1&id=6326
11. Fenton FH, Cherry EM, Hastings HM, Evans SJ, *Multiple mechanisms of spiral wave breakup in a model of cardiac electrical activity,* Chaos. Sep;12(3):852-892. PMID: 12779613, 2002 arxiv.org/ftp/nlin/papers/0204/0204040.pdf
   ♦NF Otani, *"A primary mechanism for spiral wave meandering,"* Chaos Vol. 12 No.3 2002, 829–842, pg 838, diagram 7b. scitation.aip.org/getabs/servlet/GetabsServlet?prog=normal&id=CHAOEH000012000003000829000001&idtype=cvips&gifs=yes
12. W. Ludwig: *Informative Medizin.* Essen 1999 - it may be obtained by contacting AMS GmbH in Germany Wastl, Dr. Gregory J., DC The Medisend Super and Magnetic Field Therapy www.drwastl.com/files/medisend_super.htm additional reference material
   ♦*The Discovery of the Schumann Resonance*, www.earthbreathing.co.uk/sr.htm
13. Rutger Wever, introduced various electric and magnetic fields into his completely shielded room. Only one had any effect on the amorphous (out-of-rhythm) cycles. An infinitesimal electric field pulsing at 10 hertz dramatically restored normal patterns to most of the biological measurements. Wever concluded that this frequency in the micropulsations of the earth's electromagnetic field was the prime timer of biocycles. In light of this work, the fact that 10 hertz is also the dominant frequency of the EEG (electrical current of the brain) in all animals becomes another significant bit of evidence that every creature is

hooked up to the earth electromagnetically through its DC system –
♦ Becker R, *The Body Electric: Electromagnetism and the Foundation of Life,* 1985 pg248
14. Elektromagnetische Schwingungen bestimmen unser Leben!
www.magnetmed.de/html/magnetfeldtherapie.html
15. Gagnon T A, and Rein G, *'The Biological Significance Of Water Structured With Non-Hertzian Time Reversed Waves,* Journal U.S.Psychotronics Assoc.7/1989
www.cellatroniks.com/uspa.htm & www.bodyvibes.com/scalar.htm
16. Hunt V, *Bioscalar Energy: The Healing Power*
www.bioenergyfields.org/index.asp?SecId=4&SubSecid=44
17. Tesla received two patents for this radiant energy device; U.S. Patent No. 685,957 - Apparatus for the Utilization of Radiant Energy and U.S. Patent No. 685,958 - Method of Utilizing Radiant Energy. Both these patents were filed on March 21, 1901 and granted on November 5, 1901. In these patents he explains:
"The sun, as well as other sources of radiant energy throw off minute particles of matter positively electrified, which, impinging upon the upper plate, communicate continuously an electrical charge to the same. The opposite terminal of the condenser being connected to ground, which may be considered as a vast reservoir of negative electricity, a feeble current flows continuously into the condenser and inasmuch as the particles are ...charged to a very high potential, this charging of the condenser may continue, as I have actually observed, almost indefinitely, even to the point of rupturing the dielectric."
www.nuenergy.org/alt/tesla_energy.htm
♦ Freund F T, *Rocks That Crackle and Sparkle and Glow: Strange Pre-Earthquake Phenomena*, Journal of Scientific Exploration, Vol. 17, No. 1, pp. 37–71, 2003
18. Gardner P & Osborn G, *The Serpent Grail: The Truth behind the Holy Grail, the Philosopher's Stone and the Elixir of Life,* Watkins Publishing, London, 2005
19. Uvarov V, *The Wands of Horus*, New Version 2004 Updated
www.wandsofhorus.biz/txt/txt_15e.html
20. The "KA_BA" Principal,Uvarov V, The Wands of Horus, 2001Version,
www.wands.ru/en_old/footnotes.html
21. Dunn J, *Apophis (Apep), the Enemy of Re*
www.touregypt.net/featurestories/apep.htm
22. The "Apophis Factor, Uvarov V, The Wands of Horus, New Version 2004,
www.wandsofhorus.biz/txt/lnk_002e.html
23. Straiton V, The Celestial Ship of the North. New York: Albert & Charles Boni, 1927 pg 167-168

Chapter 8
Strengthening Your Energy Field IS Spiritual Evolution

1. Goodheart G, *Applied Kinesiology*, Privately published, 1976
Diamond J, Your Body Doesn't Lie, New York: Warner Books, 1979.
2. Hawkins D, *Power vs Force: The Hidden Determinants of Human Behavior*, Hay House, Inc. 1995, 1998, 2002
Hawkins D, *The Eye Of The I: From Which Nothing is Hidden*, Veritas Publishing, 2001
3. Coombs A, *Consciousness: Chaotic and Strangely Attractive*, University of North Carolina at Asheville, Dynamical Psychology 1995, www.goertzel.org/dynapsyc/1995/COMBS.html
4. McClain C, *Near-death survivors show brain-wave abnormality*, study finds, Arizona Daily Star 6th January 2004, neardeath.home.comcast.net/nde/001_pages/84.html
5. *Investigating truth,* Kindred Spirit Magazine
www.kindredspirit.co.uk/articles/6834-david-hawkins.html
6. *Transforming Anger: The HeartMath Solution for Letting Go of Rage, Frustration, and Irritation,* www.heartmath.com/company/proom/pr/transforming_anger.html
7. *Spirituality and Healing: Selected Bibliography*
www.healthyroads.com/mylibrary/data/pelletier/chapter11/p_selectedbibliographych11.asp

8. Pham M T, *"The Logic of Feeling,"* Journal of Consumer Psychology, Vol. 14 (4), 360-369. (2004), www.columbia.edu/~tdp4/JCP2004.pdf
9. Raghunathan, et. al, *Informational Properties of Anxiety and Sadness, and Displaced Coping*, Journal of Consumer Research, Vol. 31 March 2006, www.columbia.edu/~tdp4/JCR2006.pdf
Kenyon T & Essene V, The Hathor Material: Messages from An Ascended Civilization, 1996
10. Henry W, *Secrets Of The Cathars: Why the Dark Age Church Was Out to Destroy Them,* (originally published in *Atlantis Rising*, Dec. 2002)
www.williamhenry.net/documents/secrets_of_the_cathars.pdf
♦Henry W, *One Foot In Atlantis: The Secret Occult History of WWII and It's Impact On New Age Politics*, Earthpulse Press, 1998
11. Dubro *P, The Universal Calibration Lattice*, EMF Chapter from Kryon Book 7, www.emfbalancingtechnique.com/emfchapter.html
Dubro, P & Lapierre D, *Elegant Empowerment: Evolution of Consciousness*, Platinum Publishing, 2002
12. Researchers at Kennedy Krieger Studying Efficacy of Energy Therapy, Press Release. 10th June 2003, www.kennedykrieger.org/kki_news.jsp?pid=2327
♦McGrath C, *Hands that Heal: Researchers at Kennedy Krieger investigate whether energy therapy can benefit children with developmental disabilities.*
www.kennedykrieger.org/kki_touch_article.jsp?pid=2560
13. Marciniak B, *Path of Empowerment: Pleiadian Wisdom for a World in Chaos, Inner Ocean Publishing, 2004*
14. Hermann R., *Integrating and Igniting The Diamond Ray Flame,* March 2007 www.ronnastar.com
15. Fenn C., *Crossing the Threshold ~ Activating the Infinity Codes,* August 2007 http://astrotribe.tribe.net/thread/63e543a6-ee22-422e-a506-8b2544ec17ad
16. *The System of W. B. Yeats's A Vision,* www.yeatsvision.com
17. Kenyon T, *Earth Changes and Holons*, www.tomkenyon.com
18. *Holonic Concepts* hms.ifw.uni-hannover.de/public/Concepts/concepts.htm
19. *What is the Seth material?* www.newworldview.com/library/Seth_material.html?s=
20. Friedman N & Wolf F A, *Bridging Science and Spirit: Common Elements in David Bohm's Physics, the Perennial Philosophy and Seth*
♦Amber Allen Publishing Inc, Author Pages - Jane Roberts
www.amberallen.com/?s=/authors/author_pages/jane_roberts.ws
21. Dubro P, EMF Chapter from Kryon Book 7
emfbalancingtechnique.com/reading/kryon_emf_chapter.php
♦Dubro P & Lapierre D, *Elegant Empowerment: Evolution of Consciousness*, Platinum Publishing, 2002 Pages 69-70
22. Wilcock D, *The Shift of the Ages*, Chapter 6, The Seth Entity and Conscious units ascension2000.com/Shift-of-the-Ages/shift06.htm
23. Freeman W J, *Emotion is Essential to All Intentional Behaviors*, Department of Molecular & Cell Biology,University of California at Berkeley CA, 1998
♦Lewis M D & Granic I (Eds).*Emotion, Development, and Self-Organization: Dynamic Systems Approaches to Emotional Development*, Cambridge U.K.: Cambridge University Press, 2000. Chapter 8, pp. 209-235.
sulcus.berkeley.edu/wjf/CE.%20Neurodynamics.and.Emotion.pdf
24. Ostrander S. & Schroeder L. *Psychic Discoveries The Iron Curtain Lifted*, Marlowe & Company, New York, 1997
25. Roberts J, *Seth Speaks: The Eternal Validity of the Soul,* (1970), Roberts J, Unknown Reality: Volume One, (1977)
♦Roberts J, *The Nature of the Psyche: The Human Expression,* (1979).
26. Paramahansa Yogananda, *Autobiography of a Yogi*, Self-Realization Fellowship, 1946
27. Martin B, *Subtle Energy Research for Alternative Healing*, Vibrant Living Newsletter, January 2004, www.subtleenergysolutions.com/newsletter-role-research.html#2
♦Besant, Annie, Leadbeater CW, *Occult chemistry*, 3rd edn. Kessinger Publishing Company, Montana, 1951

28. Phillips S, *Extrasensory Perception of Quarks*, Theosophical Publishing House, London, UK
29. Sarkar P R, *Microvitum -- The mysterious Emanation of Cosmic Factor* home.versatel.nl/microvita/
30. Cummins G, *Beyond Human Personality*: www.freewebs.com/1library/personality-cummins.htm
31. Narby J, *The cosmic Serpent: DNA and The Origins of Knowledge,* Phoenix 1998
32. Ibid pg 126.
♦Popp F A et al. *Recent Advances in Biophoton Research*, World Scientific, Singapore, 1992
♦Popp F A et al.. *Biophoton emission: New evidence for coherence and DNA as a source.* Cell. Biophys. 6. p. 33-52. 1984.
33. Narby J, *The cosmic Serpent: DNA and The Origins of Knowledge*, Phoenix 1998 pg 38
34. Popp FA, *On the coherence of ultraweak photoemission from living tissues. In Disequilibrium and Self-Organization,* C.W. Kilmister, D. Reidel (Eds.). MA, 1986.
35. From the paper called *The DNA-wave Biocomputer,* we find the following description: "The *quantum holographic* DNA-wave biocomputer model describes the morphology and dynamics of DNA, as a self-calibrating antenna working by phase conjugate adaptive resonance capable of both receiving and transmitting quantum holographic information stored in the form of diffraction patterns (which in MRI can be shown to be *quantum holograms*). The model describes how during the development of the embryo of the DNA's organism, these holographic patterns carry the essential holographic information necessary for that development. This would explain the almost miraculous way the multiplying assembly of individual cells is coordinated across the entire organism throughout every stage of its development."
♦Peter P. Gariaev, et al, *"The DNA-wave Biocomputer",* MS Institute for the Control of Sciences, Russian Academy of Sciences, Moscow , 2002
Russia www.rialian.com/rnboyd/dna-wave.doc
36. Burr H S, *The Fields of Life: Our Links with the Universe,* Ballantine Books, New York, 1972
37. Balfour M, *Energy Matters by Mark How the Energy Body Governs Life's Processes* www.atozen.net/articles/energy_matters.html
38. Dr Serge Barsamian, World Chairman of the New York based Bio-dielectrics (Bio-energy field) Committee and author of 'Physics Today' (available in the Russian language only).
Dr Barsamian has developed the Dielectric Diagnostic Analyser (DDA), an advanced device for the early detection of diseases, which include cancer and AIDS. It employs sensitive computerised techniques to quickly reveal EM disturbances in the cytoplasm (the protoplasm outside the nucleus) of living cells as well as in the human bio-energy field.
The DDA is thus able to determine the very beginning of the development of a disease prior to its clinical or physical appearance, which should be seen as a secondary effect.
Being used today in Russian, German and other European clinics and medical institutes, there are innumerable hospitals, clinics and research institutions throughout Russia and Europe, employing EM principles based on Dr Barsamian's research for the actual control of disease with high accuracy and success.
39. S.T. Barsamian & S.P Barsamian, *"A Morphogenic Process in Low-Energy Electromagnetic Fields",* Journal of Biological Physics, Stillwater, Oklahoma, 1988
40. Balfour M, *Sign of the Serpent – Key to Life Energy*, UBS Publishers' Distributors PVT. Ltd, 2002
41. A list of elements that form octahedron crystals when grown in ideal growing conditions.
1. carbon (the diamond) 2. chromium 3. germanium 4. lead 5. manganese 6. oxygen 7. palladium 8. platinum 9. strontium
42. This is based on Wilcock's understanding of a rare book by "Rama Prasad's , entitled *Nature's Finer Forces: The Science of Breath and the Philosophy of the Tattvas* (1894).
♦Wilcock D, *The Science of Oneness: Vedic Yoga, Seth And Multidimensional Cosmology* ascension2000.com/ConvergenceIII/c314.htm
43. Bearden, T *A Non-Technical Description of the Priore Process: Extraordinary Biology,* November 9th, 2000
www.cheniere.org/books/aids/priorenontech.htm

44. More details about Bevan Reid's original work can be found in the book
Oliver A J, *Thinkerman, and the accident of knowing,* (1999), pp 32 – 35 reference found at:
www.godlikeproductions.com/bbs/aitem.php?message=266505&show=0104&PHPSESSID=2c0f06cfcdd883ffe0bbb1cb71071982
♦See Appendix I – Dielectrics: An Evolutionary Process in the Detection of Disease, for further details of Dr Sergei Barsamian's work.
♦Balfour M, *Sign of the Serpent: Key to Life Energy*, UBS Publishers, 2002
45. The interview given by Valerie Hunt can be found as a chapter in the following book and also online at the Healthyworld.com website.
♦*Health on the Edge: Visionary Views of Healing in the New Millennium*, Tarcher/Putnam
Trivieri L, *The Human Energy Field – An Interview With Valerie Hunt*, Ph.D., The Health Plus Letter Vol. 1, No.1, July, 8, 2003
www.1healthyworld.com/ezine/Vol1No1.cfm

Chapter 9
Universal Energy

1. Bearden is credited with giving a new kind of unconventional non-electromagnetic field meaning and definition. These fields still require to be incorporated into electromagnetic theory in general. (Bischof, 1995, 1998).
2. Sheldrake R, *A new A Science of Life,* Park Street Press; Reprint edition, 1995
♦Sheldrake R , *The Presence of the Past: Morphic Resonance & the Habits of Nature'*, Inner Traditions International; Reprint edition 1995
3. Sheldrake R, *The Sense of being Stared At: And Other Aspects Of The Extended Mind*, Three Rivers Press, 2004)
4. Weathersby K, *Hootenanny Editor Ken Weathersby talks with Rupert Sheldrake*
www.hootenanny.com/hoot/3/sheldrake.html
5. Grad-Shafranov Equation:
Interestingly, when an axisymmetric toroidal plasma is in equilibrium (forces balance and the plasma is stationary) the magnetic field may be written in terms of a scalar potential, which obeys a magnetohydrodynamic-equilibrium equation known as the Grad-Shafranov Equation.
http://plasmadictionary.llnl.gov/terms.lasso?-MaxRecords=1&-SkipRecords=2&-SortField=Term&-SortOrder=ascending&ABC=G&page=detail
♦In a remarkable press release dated May 2007, British plasma astrophysicists from the Centre for Fusion, Space and Astrophysics at University of Warwick, announced that they had found fractal patterns in the solar wind, which occur when the Sun was at the peak of the solar cycle. This fractal signature was explained as coming from the complex magnetic field of the sun. However further studies are needed before we can state that there proof that the Sun is "programming" the Earth & our solar system via the solar wind.
Astrophysicists find fractal image of Sun's 'Storm Season' imprinted on Solar Wind
Centre for Fusion, Space and Astrophysics, University of Warwick, 24th May 2007
http://www2.warwick.ac.uk/newsandevents/pressreleases/astrophysicists_find_fractal/
6. Experiments conducted in the Institute of Material Research, in Kiev, Ukraine, established that torsion radiation produced by mechanically rotating magnets are able to alter the inner structure of any substance (it's spin structure) and this could only be duplicated by psychics. See reference below for details of further research and anomalous energy.
♦Nachalov Yu.V. &. Sokolov.A.N *Experimental investigation of new long-range actions: Analytical review,* www.amasci.com/freenrg/tors/doc17.html
7. Wilcock, D Divine Cosmos: *The Breakthroughs of Dr. N.A. Kozyrev,* 2002
ascension2000.com/DivineCosmos/01.htm
♦Levich A P, *Reviews and Comments: A Substantial Interpretation of N A Kozyrev's Conception of Time,*
www.chronos.msu.ru/EREPORTS/levich_substan_inter/levich_substan_inter.htm
8. In an analytical review, Nachalov and Sokolov listed the following terms: "Time emanation",

"O-emanation" or "Orgone", "N-emanation", "Mon-emanation", "Mitogenetic emanation", "Z-emanation", "Chronal field", "M-field", D-field", "biofield", "X-agent", "Multipolar energy", "Radiesthesietic emanation", "Shape power", "Empty waves", "Pseudomagnetism", "Gravity field energy", "Electrogravitation", "Fifth force", "Antigravitation", "Free energy". The author's prize for the best name has to be "X-agent", for the X factor!

9. From the mid-fifties to the late 1970s, N.A.Kozyrev and other astronomers were puzzled by signals from stars that indicated the electromagnetic waves (light) had a component that could not be shielded by metal screens. Furthermore, this component caused a variation in readings. The detection of the *true* position of a star could be interpreted if the anomalous radiation had velocities billions of times greater than the speed of light. In the late 1980s and 1990s a shielded telescope with a Kozyrev-type detector inside, registered signals coming from the visible position of each star, the true position, and also a position symmetrical to the visible position of a star relative to it's true position. This fact was interpreted as a detection of the future position of stars! Hence scientists started to postulate that these mysterious torsion fields could propagate not only in the future but in the past as well!
Akimov A.E., Shipov A E, Torsion Fields and their Experimental Manifestations, 1996
www.amasci.com/freenrg/tors/tors.html

10. Wilcock D, *The Breakthroughs of Dr. N.A. Kozyrev,* Divine Cosmos:2002
ascension2000.com/DivineCosmos/01.htm
♦Levich A P, Reviews and Comments: A Substantial Interpretation of N A Kozyrev's Conception of Time
www.chronos.msu.ru/ereports/levich_substan_inter/levich_substan_inter.htm
♦Sciama, D.W., *On the analogy between charge and spin in general relativity*, Recent Developments in General Relativity, (Pergamon+PWD, Oxford), 1962, 415.
♦Sciama, D.W., *The physical structure of general relativity*, Rev. Mod. Phys. 36 (1964), 463 and 1103.

11. Dr Emoto's website, www.masaru-emoto.net/english/entop.html
Suddath R, *Water's Remarkable Expressions*, Edge News,
www.edgenews.com/issues/2002/03/suddath.html

12. Cherednichenko I N, *The Natural Phenomena of AntiGravitation and Invisibility in Insects due to the Grebennikov Cavity Structure Effect (CSE),* Biophysics Laboratory, Institute of Human Pathology and Ecology, Russian Academy of Medical Science
www.keelynet.com/greb/greb.htm

13. Sannella, L., *The Kundalini Experience,* Integral Publishing, California, 1987

14. Krishna, Gopi. *Kundalini - The Evolutionary Energy in Man.* Second ed. Boulder, Colorado: Shambala Publications, 1970.
♦Krishna, G., *The Secret of Yoga*, Harper and Row, New York, 1972
♦Krishna, Gopi. *Higher Consciousness - The Evolutionary Thrust of Kundalini.* First ed. New York: The Julian Press, 1974.
♦Krishna, Gopi. *The Awakening of Kundalini.* First ed. New York: E. P. Dutton, 1975.
♦Krishna, Gopi. *The Riddle of Consciousness.* First ed. New York: Kundalini Research Foundation, 1976.
♦Krishna, G., *The Dawn of a New Science*, Kundalini Research and Publication Trust, New Delhi, 1978
♦Krishna, Gopi. *Living With Kundalini.* First ed. Boston: Shambhala, 1993.
♦Krishna, Gopi. *The Evolution of Higher Consciousness.* First ed. New Delhi: UBS Publishers Distributors Ltd. 1994.

15. The Osho Spiritual organisation, www.osho.com

16. Hunt V, *Mind Mastery Meditations: A Workbook for the "Infinite Mind",* Malibu Publishing , 1997

17. Ostrander S & Schroeder L, *Psychic Discoveries – The Iron Curtain Lifted*, Souvenir Press Ltd, 1997

18. Gagnon T.A. & Rein G, *'The Biological Significance Of Water Structured With Non-Hertzian Time Reversed Waves',* Journal U.S.Psychotronics Assoc.7/1989

www.cellatroniks.com/uspa.htm & www.bodyvibes.com/scalar.htm

19. Gagnon T A & Rein G, *'The Biological Significance Of Water Structured With Non-Hertzian Time Reversed Waves'*, 1989
♦Hutchison M, Megabrain Report Vol. 1, No. 1
www.beyond-the-illusion.com/files/Mind-Control/General/brn-hv.txt
20. Bearden T E, *James Clerk Maxwell*, The Tom Bearden Website, www.cheniere.org/references/maxwell.htm
21. Bearden T E, *"Possible Whittaker Unification of Electromagnetics, General Relativity, and Quantum Mechanics,"* (Association of Distinguished American Scientists 2311 Big Cove Road, Huntsville, Alabama, 35801)
22. Patten T & Hutchison M, *Interview with Lt. Col. Thomas E.*, "Megabrain Report". 4-Feb-1991. twm.co.nz/beard_interview.htm
23. *"Significance of Electromagnetic Potentials in Quantum Theory,"* The Physical Review, Vol. 115, No. 3, pp. 485-491; August, 1959
24. Hoagland R, *Hubble's New "Runaway Planet":A Unique Opportunity for Testing the Exploding Planet Hypothesis and ... Hyperdimensional Physics Part II* www.enterprisemission.com/hyper2.html
25. Healing Studies and Clinical Reports
www.wholistichealingresearch.com/Research/Studies.asp
26. Cerutti E, *Mystic with the Healing Hands: The Life Story of Olga Worrall*, Harper & Row, 1977
27. Oschman J L, *Energy Medicine, The Scientific Basis,* Harcourt Publishers Ltd, 2000
28. Gerber R, *Vibrational Medicine: The #1 Handbook of Subtle-Energy Therapies*, Bear & Company, Rochester, Vermont 2001
29. R. Miller, *"Methods of Detecting and Measuring Healing Energies,"* in Future Science, ed. S. Krippner and J. White (New York: Doubleday & Co. 1977), pp. 431-444
30. Smith J., *The Influence on Enyzme Growth by "Laying-on-of-Hands,"* The dimensions of Healing:A symposium (Los Altos, CA: Academy of Parapsychology and Medecine), 1972.
♦Davis A R, Rawls W C, *The Rainbow in Your Hands*, Halcyon House, September 1995
31. Cade M. & Coxhead N., *'The Awakened Mind: Biofeedback and the Development of Higher States of Awareness'*, pub: Element Books, 1996 reprint
♦Maginley D, *Healing Energies,*
www.intuitivetimes.ca/Articles/artresearchhelaingenergies.htm
♦Wise A, The High Performance Mind: Mastering Brainwaves for Insight, Healing, and Creativity, Tarcher/Putnam, 1996,
32. David Hudson could only identify the ormus elements when he employed a world class spectroscopist trained in West Germany, a laboratory at Cornell University and Soviet spectroscopy techniques he found in a book called, *The Analytical Chemistry of the Platinum Group Elements* by Ginsberg, published by the Soviet Academy of Sciences. In that book, he found that a 300 second burn is required to read elements properly. The standard at that time was only 15 seconds, hence that is why these elements had not been discovered in the West! Superconductivity and Modern Alchemy: Has the Philosopher's Stone Been Found?
www.subtleenergies.com/ORMUS/presentations/portland.htm
♦List of Hudson's Presentations, videotapes
www.subtleenergies.com/ORMUS/presentations/present.htm
33. Details of British Patent filed obtained by David Hudson
www.subtleenergies.com/ormus/patents/patents.htm
♦David R. Hudson: Orbitally Rearranged Monoatomic Elements (ORMEs) British Patent # GB 2,219,995 A (December 28, 1989) UK Class: C1A &c International Class: C21D
Non-Metallic, Monoatomic Forms of Transitional Elements
Invented by David Radius Hudson
Concord Research Corp., 15650 North Black Canyon Hwy., Phoenix, AZ 85023
www.rexresearch.com/ormes/ormes.htm
34. How could a small percentage of the earth's matter be comprised of material which heretofore has been completely undiscovered? Basically, there has been a fundamental flaw in theory of

analytical chemistry. None of the detection techniques of analytical chemistry can detect monatomic elements. They can only detect elements by interacting with their valence electrons. But because the valence electrons of monatomic atoms are unavailable, the atoms are unidentifiable. To detect a monatomic element requires that you first convert it from its monatomic state to its normal state to allow the element to be detected with conventional instrumentation. As a result, this phase of matter has existed in "stealth mode," right under the noses of scientists without detection until very recently! Monatomic Elements (ORMES) www.crucible.org/monatomic_elements.htm
♦ Special Properties of the "Transition Group Elements" www.luminet.net/~wenonah/new/hudson.htm

35. Encyclopedia: Crystal Habit, www.sciencedaily.com/encyclopedia/crystal_habit
See also, Magnetite en.wikipedia.org/wiki/Magnetite
Coetzee H, Biomagnetism and Bio-Electromagnetism: The Foundation of Life, [Originally published in Future History, Volume 8], www.affs.org/html/biomagnetism.html
36. ORMUS Related Scientific References:
www.subtleenergies.com/ormus/research/research.htm#Supercon
www.halexandria.org/dward477.htm
37. *The Wonderful World of Advanced Materials*, Dr. John V. Milewski, Professional Engineer. www.luminet.net/~wenonah/new/milewski.htm
38. For further photographs and information please see Dr Milewski's website.
Milewski J V, *ORMUS IS A GAS*, 3/18/04, www.luminet.net/~wenonah/hudson/ormusgas.htm
Contact details for Dr John V. Milewski at 505-856-6259, 2881 Tramway Place NE, Albuquerque NM 87122
39. *Gamma Rays From Thunderstorms?* Duke News, May 2, 2005
www.dukenews.duke.edu/2005/05/gammabolt.html
www.sciencedaily.com/releases/2005/05/050502190314.htm
40. Yam P, *The Spectra of Super Deformed Nuclei*, Scientific American, October 1991, p. 26, ORMUS Related Scientific References
www.subtleenergies.com/ormus/research/research.htm
41. LaViolette,P.A.,1983a.Galactic Explosions, Cosmic Dust Invasions and Climatic Change,Ph.D. dissertation, Portland State University,Portland,Oregon,763 pp.
♦ LaViolette,P.A.,1983b.*Elevated concentrations of cosmic dust in Wisconsin Stage polar ice.* Meteoritics 18:336-337.
♦ LaViolette,P.A.,1985.*Evidence of high cosmic dust concentrations in Late Pleistocene polar ice (20,000 -14,000 Years B.P.).*Meteoritics,20:545-558.
♦ LaViolette,P.A.,1987a.*Cosmic-ray volleys from the Galactic Center and their recent impact on the Earth environment.Earth Moon Planets*,37:241-286.
♦ LaViolette,P.A.,2003.*Galactic superwaves and their impact on the Earth,* Starlane Publications, Niskayuna,NY.
♦ LaViolette,P.A.,2005.*Solar Cycle Variations in Ice Acidity at the End of the Last Ice Age:Possible Marker of a Climatically Significant Interstellar Dust Incursion.Planetary Space Science*,53:385 -393.
♦ *Superwave Theory Predictions and their Subsequent Verification*, Predictions 5 & 6 www.etheric.com/LaViolette/Predict.html
42. Gangui A, Superconducting Cosmic Strings: These relics from the early universe could be the answer to many astrophysical conundrums, American Scientist, May-June 2000, pages 254-263, www.iafe.uba.ar/relatividad/gangui/SCS.html
43. *Goo found on space station vents,* CNN News, January 26, 2005
www.cnn.com/2005/TECH/space/01/26/space.walk.ap/
♦ *Spacewalking Astronauts Install Mini-robotic Arm, Find Goo On Vents* www.kotv.com/main/home/stories.asp?whichpage=1&id=76706
♦ Oberg J, *Spacewalk thruster incident alarms NASA - Coordination breakdown could have led to toxic exposure,* NBC News, Jan. 31, 2005, www.msnbc.msn.com/id/6890895/
44. ♦ *Orbiting observatory SOHO finds source of high-speed "wind" blowing from the Sun*

sohowww.nascom.nasa.gov/gallery/ESAPR/info01.html/
♦Carroll L, Letters from Home (Kryon Book 7), The Kryon Writings, Inc. 1999

45. *Predicting catastrophic transitionsm*, University of Chicago Press Journals, 22 May 2007 http://www.firstscience.com/home/news/breaking-news-all-topics/predicting-catastrophic-transitions_29347.html
46. *Russian DNA Discoveries*, www.quantumbalancing.com/news/russian_dna.htm
♦Fosar G & Bludorf F, *"Vernetzte Intelligenz"* ISBN 3930243237,
The book is only available in German You can reach the authors here: www.fosar-bludorf.com
♦Garjajev P. P. Der wellengenetische Code. 1997, ISBN 5-7816-0022-1 (in Russian.)
♦*Quantum phenomena in biology*, TWM Quantum phenomena in biology twm.co.nz/quant_biology.htm
47. Experiments successfully transformed, for example, frog embryos to salamander embryos simply by transmitting the DNA information patterns and these worked with no side effects! Gariaev .P, Wave Genome, Public Profit, Moscow, 1994 (279 pages, in Russian).
♦Gariaev,,P.,Tertishny,G.and Leonova,K.(2001*), "The Wave: Probabilistic and Linguistic Representation of Cancer and HIV"*, Journal of Non-Locality and Remote Mental Interactions (JNLRMI),vol.I,no.2,May 2002
This is similar to the work of a Australian team of researchers Dr. B. L. Reid and Dr. S. Barsamian, and their colleagues where experimental studies could positively verify pattern and form transmission at a distance. An unexplored information field was discovered and they could demonstrate how this could effect both living cells and inert crystalline matter.
♦ST & SP Barsamian , *A morphogenic Process in Low Energy Electromagnetic Fields'*, Journal of Biological Physics, Stillwater; OK~ USA. 1988.
It is very interesting that both sets of research are now currently focusing on cures for cancer.
48. Gariaev P, et al., *"The DNA-wave Biocomputer"*, MS, Institute for the Control of Sciences, Russian Academy of Sciences, Moscow, Russia, and Wave Genetics, Inc., Toronto, Canada, 2002, www.rialian.com/rnboyd/dna-wave.doc
49. Ibid. reference [42]
50. Poponin V, *The DNA Phantom Effect: Direct Measurement of A New Field in the Vacuum Substructure,* TWM, twm.co.nz/DNAPhantom.htm
51. Dandliker P J, Holmlin R E, BartonMarch J K, *Oxidative Thymine Dimer Repair in the DNA Helix Science,* 275 (5305):1465, 1997
52. *Iridium-based cancer technique attracts medical attention,* 20th April 2004 www.platinum.matthey.com/media_room/1082476803.html

Chapter 10
The Master Diamond Template

1. Cox S, *Cracking the Da Vinci Code: The Facts Behind the Fiction,* Michael O'Mara Books
2. Brown D, *The Da Vinci Code*, Random House, 2003
Dramatic Day At 'Da Vinci' Trial, CBS News, March 7, 2006
www.cbsnews.com/stories/2006/03/07/entertainment/main1379394.shtml
3. Delarue M, *Un Pharaon republicain: Enquetes*, Jacques Grancher, Paris, 1999
Picknett L & Prince C, *The Sion Revelation: Inside the Shadowy World of Europe's Secret masters*, Time Warner Books, 2006 pg 462-467
4. Ibid Translation from French by English authors, Lynne Picknett & Clive Prince
5. Hamilton III W. F, *The Cosmic Matrix,* www.astrosciences.info/Matrix.htm
6. It is now believed that the Greeks were not the originators of these concepts. A collection of Neolithic stones at least 3,000 years old, unmistakably show the same basic "platonic" shapes. These are now kept at the Ashmolean Museum, Oxford, UK.
7. *The Platonic Solids*, www.dartmouth.edu/~matc/math5.geometry/unit6/unit6.html
The Platonic solids www.goldenmeangauge.co.uk/platonic.htm
8. *Torroidal space: Dynamic Expressive Surface Topology*
harmonicresolution.com/Toroidal%20Space.htm

9. Davidson D A, *Shape Power*, Rivas Publishing, 1977
Bentov I, *A Brief Tour of Higher Consciousness,* Destiny Books, 2000
10. Clark C, *Modeling Blends Science with Art*, Technology at a Glance quarterly newsletter, National Institute of Standards and Technology
www.nist.gov/public_affairs/taglance/tag99fall/99fall.htm#Bose
11. *How Dan Brown cracked the code,* The Sun-Herald, December 20, 2004
www.smh.com.au/news/Books/How-Dan-Brown-cracked-the-code/2004/12/19/1103391631441.html?oneclick=true
12. *Mystical Blaze, Dimensional Concept,* www.mysticalblaze.com/OtherDimenConcept.htm
13. *Saul-Paul Sirag Interview With Dr. Jeffrey Mishlove*, March 29, 1999
www.mishlove.com/transcripts/sirag.htm
♦ Sirag S, *Hyperspace Reality,* www.williamjames.com/sirag.htm
♦ Sirag S, "*Consciousness: a Hyperspace View,"* Appendix in the following:
Mishlove J & Sirag S, *Roots of Consciousness: The Classic Encyclopedia of Consciousness Studies,* Revised and Expanded,2nd. Ed., Marlowe,1993
14. Wilcock D, *The Sequential Perspective*, *Divine Cosmos*, Chapter 4. Published 6/4/2, Latest Updates 10/28/04, http://www.sandrelli.net/The%20Divine%20Cosmos.pdf
15. *Unique Crystal Creation from Swarovski to Beautify GIA*, Business Wire, Oct. 3, 2002, http://www.panapress.com/newswire.asp?code=746
♦ *World's Largest Crystal Octahedron from Swarovski to Cap GIA Tower,* Nov. 01, 2002 http://www.gia.edu/newsroom/issue/2798/1382/insider_newsletter_details.cfm#6
16. Alex Grey main website: www.alexgrey.com
17. *Venus and The Pentagram, Grand Lodge of British Columbia and Yukon freemasonry.* bcy.ca/anti-masonry/venus.html
18. *Astronomy Picture of the Day*, 2002 July 9, antwrp.gsfc.nasa.gov/apod/ap020709.html
19. Miller I & Swinney G, *Chaos Theory & Complex Dynamical Systems: Its Emergence in Human Consciousness and Healing,* 2001,
www.geocities.com/iona_m/ChaosTheory/CTintro.html
20. 1st paragraph of quote. Uvarov V, *The Wands of Horus*, New Version 2004 Updated www.wandsofhorus.biz/txt/txt_15e.html
2nd paragraph of quote: The "Apophis" factor details taken from: Uvarov V, The Wands of Horus, 2001Version, www.wands.ru/en_old/footnotes.html
21. Banchoff T & Cervone D, In and Outside the Torus, alem3d.obidos.org/en/torusio/
22. Tolle E, *The Power of Now: A guide to Spiritual Enlightenment,* Hodder & Stoughton, 2001
23. Vogt D, Sultan G, *Reality Revealed: The Theory of Multidimensional Reality*, Vector Associates, San Jose, CA, 1978
24. Explanation for "Diehold" given by Gene Pool, www.nonduality.com/gene14.htm
25. Cowen R, *Sound waves may drive cosmic structure*, Science News, 1/11/1997
26. Essays on: Physics in the Twenty-first Century by Bibhas De
www.geocities.com/bibhasde/magmass.html
27. Encyclopedia: Crystal Habit, www.sciencedaily.com/encyclopedia/crystal_habit
♦ See also, Magnetite en.wikipedia.org/wiki/Magnetite
Coetzee H, Biomagnetism and Bio-Electromagnetism: The Foundation of Life, [Originally published in Future History, Volume 8] www.affs.org/html/biomagnetism.html
The faces of an octahedron make equal intercepts, positive and negative, on all three axes and therefore have Miller indices (111)
28. Kerrell B & Goggin K, *The Guide to Pyramid Energy*, Santa Monica, Pyramid Power V, 1975.
29. Oliver A J, *Thinkerman, and the accident of knowing*, 1999, pp 32 – 35
www.godlikeproductions.com/bbs/aitem.php?message=266505&show=0104&PHPSESSID=2c0f06cfcdd883ffe0bbb1cb71071982
30. *DNA folds into paired pyramids*, Technology Research News, 04.13.04 www.alwayson-network.com/comments.php?id=P3666_0_6_0_C
31. Davidson D A, *Shape Power*, Rivas Publishing, 1997
32. Volodymyr Krasnoholovets & Associates, On The Way To Disclosing The Mysterious Power Of The Great Pyramid, www.gizapyramid.com/DrV-article.htm

33. DeSalvo J. *The Complete Pyramid Source Book*, Authorhouse, 2003 www.authorhouse.com/BookStore/ItemDetail.aspx?bookid=17006
34. According to the www.pyramidoflife.com, the no. of pyramids built in Russia & Ukraine is 50, but no independent verification can be found.
35. Photograph of pyramid courtesy of ABO Company who help to organize excursions to the Pyramid near Moscow. info@ABO.RU www.abo.ru/english.html
36. *Pyramid of Life: Tests and Experiments,* www.pyramidoflife.com/eng/tests_experiments.html
37. *Press Release: International Partnership For Pyramid Research* www.gizapyramid.com/russian/press-release.htm
38. Uvarov V, *The Wands of Horus*, Third Edition - December 2001 www.neilos.com.au/pdf/Wands_of_Horus_English_3rd_Edition.pdf
39. This information is from a letter from 1994 letter from Dr Eastlund to a concerned Australian who was worried about the impact of HAARP
Manning J & Begich Dr.N, Angels Don't Play This HAARP: Advances In Tesla Technology, Earthpulse Press, 2nd Edition, Eight Printing, 2004 Pg 38
40. *Frank Walters & Oswald White Bear Fredericks, The Book of the Hopi,* Penguin Books; Reprint edition (June 1, 1977)
♦ *The Prophecies of the Hopi People*, Excerpts at Morgana's Observatory www.dreamscape.com/morgana/pan.htm
41. Uvarov V, *The Wands of Horus*, Internet published, Updated version 2004 www.wandsofhorus.biz/
42. The vast majority of blocks that make up the pyramid are limestone, which is primarily a calcium carbonate [CaCO3] crystal. The calcium carbonate molecule has an approximately 52-degree angle in its shape. This is known as a "cleavage angle" and means that when pure calcium carbonate crystals are split, they will tend to split along this 52-degree angle. Therefore, Tenen claims, the slope angle of the pyramid brings its entire shape into harmony with the molecules of the matter that makes it up.
Wilcock D The Divine Cosmos, chapter 9, Harnessing Torsion Waves and Consciousness, 2002, 2004, ascension2000.com/DivineCosmos/09.htm
43. Tatler J, *The Great Pyramid - Reflections in Time*, doncol.org/Pyramid/pyrmindx.htm
44. *Dunn C, The Giza Power Plant: Technologies of Ancient Egypt, Bear & Company, 1998,* p.219
45. Millardo, *About Atlantis*, www.millardo.us/about_atlantis.html
46. Glossary of Metallurgical Terms, www.armco.com.br/en/glossario_t.php
47. Tiller W et al., *Conscious Acts of Creation: The Emergence of New Physics, Pavior, 2001*
48. Battros M, *A Treat For Thanksgiving – Transcript of Interview with Mayan Elder Carlos*, Earth Changes TV Newsletter, November 21st 2005 www.mayanmajix.com/art2094.html
49. *Volcanic eruption cut warming in 20th century*, mongabay.com, February 9, 2006 news.mongabay.com/2006/0209-volcano.html
50. Prigogine I, Stengers I, *Order Out Of Chaos*, Bantam, 1984
51. Briggs J, F David Peat, *Turbulent Mirror*, Harper Perennial, 1990
52. Carroll L, "Current Events", Washington DC, April 10, 2005 www.kryon.com/k_chanelDC05.html
53. Kenyon T, *A Catalytic and Volatile Phase of Global Transformation*, The Hathors, Spain, 3.17.06, www.tomkenyon.com/hathors/hathors8.html

Glossary

- **A- and K-index:** Geomagnetic activity indices, high indices (K:>5 or A:>20) means stormy conditions with an active geomagnetic field. Classification of K-indices are as follows: K0=Inactive, K1=Very quiet, K2=Quiet, K3=Unsettled, K4=Active, K6=Major storm, K7=Severe storm, K8=Very severe storm, K9=Extremely severe storm. As with the K-index, the higher the A-index, the more unstable propagation becomes. Classification of A-indices are as follows: A0 - A7 = quiet, A8 - A15 = unsettled, A16 - A29 = active, A30 - A49 = minor storm, A50 - A99 = major storm, A100 - A400 = severe storm
- **Action at a distance:** 1. The interaction of two objects which are separated in space with no known mediator of the interaction. This term was used most often with early theories of gravity and electromagnetism to describe how an object could "know" the mass (in the case of gravity) or charge (in electromagnetism) of another distant object. 2. With the Electric or Plasma Universe theories, action at a distance denotes that an object like a comet can create a reaction at the Sun and/or create affects on Earth without a direct physical impact like that suggested by an asteroid hit.
- **Aharonov-Bohm Effect:** Phenomenon whereby interfering electromagnetic potentials can produce effects on charged particle systems, even at a distance and in the absence of the electromagnetic force fields.
- **Alignment:** The act and state of establishing a resonant unity of consciousness. Energetic transference.
- **Angstrom [A]:** A unit of length equal to 1 x 10-8 centimeters; used chiefly to express short wavelengths (e.g., X-ray wavelengths).
- **Assay:** A chemical analysis of a substance to determine its components.
- **Astronomical Unit (AU):** An Astronomical Unit is approximately the mean distance between the Earth and the Sun. It is a derived constant and used to indicate distances within the solar system. It is approximately 150 million km or 93 million miles.
- **Aurora:** The term given to the glow created when energetic particles from space strike Earth's upper atmosphere, or ionosphere.
- **Auroral Electrojet:** An electric current that flows in the auroral zone at E-layer altitudes caused by the interaction of the plasma in the Solar Wind with the Earth's magnetosphere. The current flows down earthwards at the morning side of the Earth's ionosphere, around the polar regions and up spacewards at the evening side of the ionosphere. It is most intense during geomagnetic disturbances.
- **Balance:** 1. A harmonious process of the optimum flow of energy between all dynamic systems within the whole. 2. To create equilibrium at the mental, physical, emotional and spiritual level to maximise well-being.
- **Big Bang:** A theory of cosmology in which the expansion of the universe is presumed to have begun with a primeval explosion.

- **Birkeland Current:** In the presence of a magnetic field, the motion of plasmas will form filamentary structures. Plasma ions assume the form of a filament to flow through the plasma exactly along the magnetic field lines
- **Biomagnetism:** A science which involves the mapping of weak magnetic fields in the human body (heart, brain, spinal cord) using a SQUID (super conducting quantum interference device). See also Magnetocardiography (MCG) and Magnetoencephalography (MEG)
- **Blood-Brain Barrier:** A group of cells that form a special, impermeable lining in the blood vessels of the brain which prevents toxic substances in the blood from entering the brain.
- **Bow Shock:** This is the huge shock wave in front of the magnetic field of the Earth that results from the very fast solar wind from the Sun ramming into the Earth's magnetic field.
- **Caldera:** Crater formed by an explosion or collapse of a volcanic vent.
- **Calibration:** A process to adjust, tune, strengthen, gauge and bring into a higher level of harmonious relationship or alignment with the whole-being. The attainment of stable and balanced states between interrelated patterns.
- **Capacitor:** A device for accumulating and storing electric charge.
- **Celestial Equator:** Imaginary line projected into the sky dividing the northern and southern hemispheres of the sky.
- **Charge:** The property of a matter that determines all electromagnetic interactions in a system and can be either positive or negative.
- **Chromosphere:** The layer of the solar atmosphere lying between the photosphere and the corona characterized by a rapid rise in temperature with height from the photosphere's temperature of 7,000 degrees Kelvin to about 2 million degrees in the corona. It is approximately 4,000 km thick, so it is really a relatively 'thin layer' on the Sun (whose photosphere's radius is about 700,000 km). The chromosphere is not visible to the naked eye because, even though it is hotter than the photosphere, it is very tenuous.
- **Cooper Pairs:** These are pairs of electrons with complementary spins. When the electrons pair, their magnetic vortices connect directly producing an entity with a large electric component and a small magnetic component: photons. The magnetic energy pulls the two electrons together, while the electric component pushes them apart, keeping them separated and maintaining their complementary spin. An additional axis of rotation then develops, and this is what gives the Cooper pair some properties of a photon. When in a superconductor, the Cooper pairs are held in the nodal orbits by the reconfigured Coulomb Force of the High Spin nucleus.
- **Corona:** The very extended region of low density and high temperature gas which forms the outermost layer of the sun. Much of the solar X-ray and radio emission originates in the corona. The corona extends far into interplanetary space and becomes the solar wind.
- **Coronal Hole:** A region of low particle density and open magnetic field lines in the solar corona. The holes are thus a primary source of high-speed particle streams superimposed on the background "solar wind". These streams can cause geomagnetic storms if they impact the Earth's magnetosphere. Since holes may persist for several months and the solar rotation period is only 27 days, coronal holes are closely related to recurrent geomagnetic storms. (Also see "Geomagnetic Storms".)

- **Coronal mass ejection (CME):** Ejection of plasma and magnetic field from the Sun, usually observed by optical telescopes with the Sun blocked off, where tens of trillions of tons of predominantly hydrogen plasma at velocities approaching more than 1000 km/s. Also called solar mass ejection.
- **Corpuscular Radiation:** Radiation consisting of particles, specifically atomic particles such as protons (hydrogen nuclei), electrons, neutrons, and alpha particles (helium nuclei). Also known as "Particulate Radiation".
- **Cortex :** One of the major components of the brain. The cortex is divided into four lobes (frontal, parietal, temporal, occipital), it contains the sensory and motor areas.
- **Cosmic Background Radiation: B**ackground radiation from the Universe is strongest in the frequency range 3 x 10^8 to 3 x 10^{11} Hertz and was first discovered to be coming from all directions in the sky in 1965. It is believed to be the cosmologically redshifted radiation released by the Big Bang itself.
- **Cosmic Lattice:** The energy of the universe. It is found throughout the universe, including all dimensions and is the common denominator of the unified energy source. It passes through all matter and is available all the time, it also holds unlimited energy, tremendous power and contains conscious love. The Cosmic Lattice responds to human consciousness and intent through a series of magnetic resonant frequencies. The Universal Calibration Lattice (UCL), permanently establishes a powerful connection to the Cosmic Lattice. Also see "The Universal Calibration Lattice (UCL).
- **Cosmic Radio Noise:** Radio waves emanating from extraterrestrial sources.
- **Cosmic Rays:** Very high-energy particulate radiation that permeates interstellar space; primarily protons (85 percent) and alpha particles (13 percent), with some heavier particles (oxygen, silicon, iron, etc.) 2 percent. Cosmic rays can cause "single event upsets (SEUs)" on satellites. They are also a significant radiation hazard to aircrews at high altitudes (about 20 km).
- **Crystalline:** The ordering of atomic structure such that the atoms and molecules that comprise a crystal are arranged in definite patterns. When people talk about crystals, they usually are referring to solid pieces of matter that are bounded by regularly arranged flat faces. Crystal faces result as the solid grows by adding atoms in a completely orderly, repetitive, 3-dimensional array called its atomic structure. Scientists call a substance crystalline if it possesses an atomic structure, whether it exhibits external faces or not.
- **Crystal Habit:** The general shape of a crystal determined both by the atomic structure of the crystal and by the environment in which the crystal grows. Because of variability in the growth environment, natural crystals rarely grow in ideal geometric shapes. Nevertheless the angular relationships between crystal faces will always provide evidence of the symmetrical relationships between crystal faces.
- **Dedifferentiation:** The process where a mature, specialized cell returns to its original, embryonic, unspecialized state. See also "Differentiation" and "Redifferentiation".
- **Dendritic:** Intergrowth of crystals in the shape of slender divergent branches like a plant.
- **Diamagnetic materials:** Materials that are repelled from a magnetic field but not magnetized.
- **Dielectric:** Dielectric materials can be made to hold an electrostatic charge while dissipating minimal energy in the form of heat. 1. It is a poor conductor of electricity i.e., the electrical conductivity is zero or near zero. 2. A dielectric material is an

electrical insulator. Glass, porcelain, mica, rubber, plastics dry air, vacuums and some liquids and gases are dielectric.

- **Differentiation:** The process in which a cell matures from a simple embryonic type to a mature, specialized type in the adult. See also "Dedifferentiation" and "Redifferentiation".
- **D-Layer [D-Region]:** A daytime layer in the ionosphere between about 50 and 90 km altitude. During solar flares, the D-layer may be enhanced and lowered by an increased flux of X-ray radiation.
- **Dipole Equator:** The "dip equator" is defined by where the Earth's magnetic field lines are inclined zero degrees to the Earth's surface. The dip equator does not correspond exactly to the "geomagnetic equator", since the dip system includes local variations in the near-Earth magnetic field.
- **DNA:** The molecule in cells that contains genetic information.
- **Doppler Shift:** A displacement in the observed frequency of a radiated signal caused by relative motion between an emitter and receiver.
- **Double-Layer:** The isolating wall called a double layer (DL) between the two halves of any electrical plasma.
- **Dst index:** A measure of variation in the geomagnetic field due to the equatorial ring current.
- **E-Layer [E-Region]:** The ionospheric region between 90 km altitude and about 120 to 140 km.
- **Electromagnetic Radiation [EM]:** Energy propagated through space or a material medium in the form of oscillating electric and magnetic fields.
- **Electromagnetic Smog:** The background of extremely weak artificial EM radiation that fills the normal modern environment.
- **Electromagnetic Spectrum:** The ordered array of electromagnetic radiation, extending from the shortest gamma rays, through X-rays, ultraviolet waves, visible light, infrared waves, and on to radio waves.
- **Electron:** A negatively charged particle typically found orbiting the nucleus of an atom.
- **Electron Volt [eV]:** A measure of energy (1 eV = 1.602 x 10 -19 joules).
- **El Niño:** A significant increase in sea surface temperature over the eastern and central equatorial Pacific that occurs at irregular intervals, generally ranging between two and seven years. This is part of a larger-scale phenomenon arising from coupled ocean–atmosphere interactions. La Niña is the name given to a significant decrease in sea surface temperature ("cold events") in the central and eastern equatorial Pacific and occurs on a more sporadic basis.
- **Entrainment:** See "Resonant Entrainment"
- **EPR Paradox:** This draws on a phenomenon predicted by quantum mechanics, known as quantum entanglement, to show that measurements performed on spatially separated parts of a quantum system can apparently have an instantaneous influence on one another. This effect is now known as "nonlocal behavior"
- **Equatorial Electrojet:** An ionospheric electric current at E-layer altitudes (between 100 and 120 km), centered over the "dipole equator" and roughly 10 degrees latitude in width. It is driven by the dynamic action of a daytime westward drift of free electrons across geomagnetic field lines.
- **Equinox:** The event when twice a year the sun crosses the celestial equator and the length of day and night are equal. See celestial equator.

- **Esotericism:** The esoteric world-view considers that there are secrets to existence and the meaning of life, which are not easily understood and therefore not appropriate for the general public, who also remain largely uninterested in them.
- **Evolution:** From the Latin word meaning the 'unrolling of a scroll'. Referring to genetic change that occurs over time to adapt to environmental stimulus and energetic changes. Over time simple organisms develop into more complex ones, each better adapted to its environment that its predecessor. Spiritual evolution is the occurrence of genetic and hormonal changes to facilitate the multidimensional development of human beings.
- **F-Layer [F-Region]:** The ionospheric region between about 130 and roughly 1000 km altitude.
- **Filament [Solar]:** A ribbon like mass of relatively high density, low temperature gas suspended in the upper chromosphere and/or the lower corona by magnetic fields. (Also see "Prominence"& "Birkeland Current".)
- **Flux:** The amount of something (protons, X-rays, radio energy, etc.) passing through a specified area in a given time period.
- **Fractal:** Geometrical objects that are self-similar under a change of scale.
- **"Frozen-in Magnetic Fields":** Idea that plasmas are perfect conductors and, as such, a magnetic field would have to be "frozen" inside it. The electrical conductivity of any material, including plasma, is determined by two factors: the density of the population of available charge carriers (the ions) in the material, and the mobility of these carriers. In any plasma, the mobility of the ions is extremely high. Electrons and ions can move around very freely in space. But the concentration (number per unit volume) of ions available to carry charge may not be at all high if the plasma is a very low pressure (diffuse) one. So, although plasmas are excellent conductors, they are not perfect conductors. Weak electric fields can exist inside plasmas hence magnetic fields are not frozen inside them.
- **Galactic Cosmic Rays:** High-energy particulate radiation originating from outside the solar system. (Also see "Cosmic Rays".)
- **Galaxy:** A vast formation of plasma clouds that contain electrical currents and occasional, widely distributed small points of matter as nebulae, stars and planets.
- **Gamma:** A unit of magnetic field strength (1 gamma = 1 x 10 -5 gauss = 1 nanotesla). The average surface strength of the geomagnetic field is about 0.5 gauss, while the average strength of the Interplanetary Magnetic Field (IMF) is roughly 6 x 10 -5 gauss (or 6 gamma).
- **Gamma Rays [nuclear x–rays]:** May be emitted from radioactive substances. They are quanta of electromagnetic wave energy similar to but of much higher energy than normal x-rays. The gamma ray region of the electromagnetic spectrum merges into the adjacent lower energy x-ray region. Gamma rays have been more commonly associated with nuclear processes.
- **Gamma Ray Bursts:** Intense flashes of gamma rays detected at energies up to 10^(6) electron volts.
- **Ganglia:** Plural form of ganglion. Ganglion are a group of nerve cell bodies in the Central Nervous System (CNS) or Peripheral Nervous System (PNS.
- **Gene:** A portion of a DNA molecule structured so as to produce a specific effect in the cell.
- **Geomagnetic Coordinates:** A system of spherical coordinates ("geomagnetic latitude and longitude").
- **Geomagnetic Disturbance:** See "Geomagnetic Storm".

- **Geomagnetic Equator:** The terrestrial great circle that is everywhere 90 degrees from the geomagnetic poles.
- **Geomagnetic Field:** The magnetic field in and around the earth. The intensity of the magnetic field at the earth's surface is approximately 32,.000 nT at the equator and 62,000 nT at the north pole (the place where a compass needle points vertically downward). The geomagnetic field is dynamic and undergoes continual slow secular changes as well as short-term disturbances. The geomagnetic field is most often approximated by a centered dipole field, with the axis of the dipole inclined to the earth's rotational axis by about 11.5 degrees.
- **Geomagnetic Poles:** The intersections with the Earth's surface of the axis of the best-fit centered dipole of the magnetic field approximating the source of the actual geomagnetic field of the Earth. The geographic position of the geomagnetic North Pole is approximately 79 N, 70 W. The geographic position of the geomagnetic South Pole is approximately 79 S, 110 E.
- **Geomagnetic Storm:** A widespread disturbance in the Earth's geomagnetic field. (Also see "Substorm".)
- **Geostationary Orbit:** See "Geosynchronous Orbit".
- **Geosynchronous Orbit:** The orbit of any equatorial satellite with an orbital velocity equal to the rotational velocity of the Earth, and thus a period of 23 hours, 56 minutes.
- **Global Positioning System [GPS]:** A network of earth-orbiting satellites used for precise position-finding in surveying and navigation. It is made up of 18 to 24 satellites, each carrying atomic clocks, to provide a receiver anywhere on earth with extremely accurate measurements of its own three-dimensional position, velocity, and time.
- **Global Warming:** An increase in the average temperature of the Earth's surface.
- **Grand Unified field Theory:** A theory describing the unification of gravity with the other elementary forces in physics, i.e., the weak force, the strong force and the electromagnetic force.
- **Gyroscope:** An instrument that maintains an angular reference direction by virtue of a rapidly spinning mass. A gyroscope is little more than a flywheel that spins around an axis. But once the wheel is set spinning, the axis of the gyroscope will keep pointing in the same direction as long as no other force comes along to reorient it. This effect depends on a principle of physics known as the conservation of angular momentum.
- **Hermeticism:** An ancient spiritual, philosophical, and magical tradition
- **Hertz [Hz]:** A unit for measuring the frequency of electromagnetic radiation equal to one cycle per second.
- **High Frequency [HF]:** The 3 to 30 MHz radio wave band. Normally used for long distance communication by refraction in the F-layer of the ionosphere.
- **Hologram:** An individual piece called a hologram contains the same information for the whole stored in a holographic manner. This concept extends to human beings being a hologram and that the Universe is also holographic
- **Holon:** Part of a system which is complete and consistent in itself, but is also a necessary integral part of a greater system which encompasses it. For example, an atom is a holon, which is complete in itself, but atoms can join together to form molecules. Molecules can be organized into a basic living cell. Cells are holons which can form a body organ. Body organs can form a complete being etc.

- **Homeopathy:** A system of medical treatment based on the theory that certain diseases can be cured by giving very small doses of substances which in a healthy person would produce symptoms like those of the disease.
- **Hyperspace:** Dimensions beyond the normal three-dimensional space and time.
- **Infrared [IR] Radiation:** Electromagnetic radiation with wavelengths between approximately 8000 Angstroms and 1 million Angstroms (or 0.01 cm).
- **Intent:** The determined and focused direction of will to a particular purpose. Intent is considered to be a real meta-physical force – a force beyond measurable orthodox physics. Intent acts to influence, alter, shape, modify, or create the 'information' fields and patterns that organize and shape our reality. Intent works with non-traditional electromagnetic fields to re-program information fields.
- **Interplanetary Magnetic Field [IMF]:** The magnetic field that originates from the magnetic fields found on the sun's surface, and which extends into interplanetary space. The IMF strongly influences the motion of charged particles in the solar wind.
- **Ion:** An atom that carries a positive or negative electric charge as a result of having lost or gained one or more electrons.
- **Ionize:** To cause an atom or molecule to lose an electron (e.g., by X-ray bombardment), and thus be converted into a positive ion and a free electron
- **Ionosphere:** The region of free electrons (plasma) located approximately 50-2,000 kilometers above Earth's surface and created by the action of extreme ultraviolet (EUV) sunlight on the gases of the upper neutral atmosphere. At certain times and locations the ionosphere can reach as low as about 35 km. The variation of electron density with height leads to the subdivision of the ionosphere into the D-, E-, and F-layers (or regions).
- **Karma:** Karma is a sum of all that an individual has done, is currently doing and will do. The effects of all deeds creates a life history that actively creates present and future experiences, thus making one responsible for one's own life. In belief systems that incorporate reincarnation, karma extends to all past and future lives as well.
- **Kelvin [K]:** A unit of measurement named after Lord Kelvin (1824-1907), a Scottish physicist and mathematician who calculated that molecular motion stops at -273 deg C. He called this temperature absolute zero, the lowest possible temperature.
- **Light-year:** The distance light travels in one year, about 5.9 trillion miles (9.5 trillion km), or almost 800 times the diameter of our solar system. The nearest star is about four light-years away.
- **Liquefaction:** The process of making or becoming liquid.
- **Magnetic field:** A region of space wherein any magnetic dipole (charged particle) would experience a magnetic force or torque. The magnetic field is often represented as the geometric array of the imaginary magnetic lines of force that exist in relation to magnetic poles.
- **Magnetic lines of force:** Imaginary lines so drawn in a region containing a magnetic field to be everywhere tangent to the magnetic field intensity vector if in vacuum or nonmagnetic material, or parallel to the magnetic induction vector if in a magnetic medium.
- **Magnetic Reconnection:** The widely held concept that magnetic fields that are heading in opposite directions can break and reconnect to each other. Plasma physicists refer to this theory as pseudoscience, magnetic field lines DO NOT EXIST they can only be used to provide an indication of the direction of the magnetic force exerted on a charge at a certain point, so they act like on like contours on a map!

- **Magnetocardiography [MCG]:** The recording of magnetic fields produced by electrical activity in the heart.
- **Magnetoencephalography [MEG]:** The recording of magnetic fields produced by electrical activity in the brain.
- **Magnetohydrodynamics (MHD):** The study of the dynamics of an electrically conducting matter in the presence of a magnetic field.
- **Magnetometer:** An instrument used to record the strength and orientation of the geomagnetic field as observed at a particular point on, or near, the Earth's surface.
- **Magnetopause:** The boundary surface between the interplanetary magnetic field (where the solar wind is present) and the Earth's magnetosphere.
- **Magnetosphere:** The area around the earth in which the planet's magnetic field exerts a stronger influence than the solar or interplanetary magnetic field. It extends 30,000 to 50,000 miles from the earth's surface. A prominent, feature of the magnetosphere is the Van Allen Belts. This magnetic cavity, impedes the direct entry of the solar wind plasma.
- **Magnetotail:** The portion of the magnetosphere in the anti-sunward direction. In the magnetotail, geomagnetic field lines are drawn out to great distances by the flow of the solar wind past the Earth
- **Megahertz [MHz]:** A measure of frequency equal to a million cycles per second.
- **Meissner Field:** A strong diamagnetic field, unique to superconductors, that causes them to be repelled by an external magnetic field.
- **Metaphysical:** Derived from the Greek meta ta physika, "after the things of nature". Meaning the philosophy or study explaining inherent or universal elements of reality, which are not easily discovered or experienced in our everyday life. As such, it is concerned with explaining the features of reality that exist beyond the physical world and our immediate senses.
- **MeV [Million Electron Volts]:** A measure of energy (1 MeV = 1.602 x 10 -13 joules).
- **Mindbody:** A term denoting the inherent unity of the body and mind as a single, interdependent phenomena of human existence.
- **Monoatomic:** Molecules with only one atom.
- **Nebula:** Latin for "cloud". A cloud of interstellar gas and dust.
- **Neo-cortex:** Part of the outermost layer of our brains. It is responsible for our highest mental functions (e.g. planning and strategy formation/execution).
- **Neurotransmitter:** A chemical used to carry the nerve impulse across the synapse.
- **Neutrino:** A particle with no charge, subject only to the weak force.
- **Neutron:** An electronically neutral subatomic particle with a mass 1839 times that of an electron.
- **Nonlocality:** In quantum mechanics this refers to the property of entangled quantum states in which both the entangled states "collapse" simultaneously upon measurement of one of their entangled components, regardless of the spatial separation of the two states. This "spooky action at a distance" is the content of Bell's theorem and the EPR paradox.
- **Occam's [Ockham's] Razor:** Principle attributed to the 14th century logician and Franciscan friar; William of Occam. The principle states that "Entities should not be multiplied unnecessarily." Scientists have re-interpreted this phrase to mean, "when you have two competing theories which make exactly the same predictions, the one

that is simpler is the better." Or, "The simplest explanation for some phenomenon is more likely to be accurate".

- **Paradigm:** A widely held framework of thinking or way of viewing the world that is not easy to transcend even in the face of compelling evidence. A world-view, pattern, or model, including the assumptions, concepts, values, and practices that define how an intellectual or scientific community proceeds on a daily basis.
- **Paradigm Shift:** A fundamental change in concepts, or worldview governing scientific research.
- **Paramagnetic:** Materials attracted to a magnetic field, but not magnetized.
- **Penumbra:** The gray portion of a sunspot that may surround the black "umbra". It is the portion of a spot where magnetic fields are less intense, causing the temperature (and thus brightness) of the sunspot to be closer to that of the overall photosphere.
- **Photon:** Normally defined as a quantum of electromagnetic energy. A particle of light. A photon is the quantum of energy released when an electron goes from an outer orbital to a lower orbital in the atom. In depth analysis of the photon by Dr Myron Evans suggests that the photon is a magnetic dipole and Bibhas De defines the photon as, "a finite structure in empty space, made entirely of static magnetic field."
- **Photosphere:** The sun's visible surface as seen in white (integrated) light. The photosphere is a region of high opacity, responsible for the continuous spectrum of solar electromagnetic radiation. Sunspots are located in the photosphere. The average temperature in the photosphere is about 6,000 deg Kelvin (or 11,000 deg F).
- **Pi:** Relationship between the radius and area of a circle given as Pi = A/r2. Pi = 3141592653589793...
- **Piezoelectric:** A substance that converts mechanical stress into electrical energy, producing an electrical current when deformed by pressure or bending.
- **Plank Length:** The uncertainty principle of quantum mechanics prevents any certain measurement shorter than the Planck length of about 10^{-33} centimeters.
- **Plasma:** In an ordinary gas each atom contains an equal number of positive and negative charges; the positive charges in the nucleus are surrounded by an equal number of negatively charged electrons, and each atom is electrically "neutral." A gas becomes a plasma when the addition of heat or other energy causes a significant number of atoms to release some or all of their electrons. The remaining parts of those atoms are left with a positive charge, and the detached negative electrons are free to move about. Those atoms and the resulting electrically charged gas are said to be "ionized." When enough atoms are ionized to significantly affect the electrical characteristics of the gas, it is a plasma.
- **Plasmasheet:** A sheet of hot (i.e., high energy), dense plasma running down the center of the magnetotail. The plasmasheet normally remains beyond geosynchronous orbit, except when it is forced inward during geomagnetic disturbances. (Also see "Magnetotail".)
- **Plasmasphere:** A doughnut-shaped region of cool (i.e., low energy), dense plasma surrounding the Earth. It may be considered an extension of the ionosphere. Like the ionosphere, it tends to co-rotate with the Earth. The Inner "Van Allen Radiation Belt" lies in the plasmasphere.
- **Polar Cap:** The area within about 20 degrees of the geomagnetic poles. It is susceptible to direct bombardment by high-energy solar particles deflected by the Earth's geomagnetic field and guided inward through cusps in the magnetosphere.

- **Polar Cusps:** Funnel like features (vortexes) in the magnetosphere over each geomagnetic pole. High-energy solar particles can be deflected by the Earth's geomagnetic field and guided in through the polar cusps, allowing the particles direct access to low altitudes over the polar caps.
- **Polarization:** The polarization of an electromagnetic wave is defined as the plane of vibration of its electric field. Polarization is defined in terms of the electric field because it interacts more strongly with matter than will the magnetic field.
- **Positive lightning:** Typically six to ten times more powerful than negative bolts and last around ten times longer. During a positive lightning strike, huge quantities of ELF and VLF radio waves are generated.
- **Potential:** Another name for voltage that exists that could potentially cause a current to flow if a circuit is completed.
- **Precession:** The earth is like a big spinning top or gyroscope pulled by the force of gravity towards the sun, and towards the moon. It is these two forces which cause the slow precession of the earth, and causing the solstices and equinoxes to move around Earth's orbit, completing a full orbit around the Sun every approx. 26,000 years.
- **Probe (Space):** An instrumented vehicle that is located in the upper atmosphere, space or upon another celestial body and used to obtain information about the specific environment.
- **Prominence:** A mass of relatively high density, low temperature gas suspended in the upper chromosphere and/or the lower corona by magnetic fields. It is seen as a bright, ribbon-like emission feature in H-alpha against the dark corona beyond the solar limb. (The corona appears dark in H-alpha since it is too hot to emit energy at that wavelength.) (Also see "Filament".)
- **Propagation:** When speaking of a radio wave, the motion of the wave through a medium like the ionosphere, where its path may be refracted, attenuated, or retarded.
- **Proton:** A positively charged subatomic particle (equivalent to a Hydrogen atom nucleus) with a mass 1836 times that of an electron.
- **Proton Flare:** Any flare that produces significant fluxes of greater than 10 MeV protons in the vicinity of the Earth.
- **Quaternion:** Expression comprised of the sum of four terms, one of which is real and three of which contain imaginary units, and that can be written as the sum of a scalar and a three-dimensional vector.
- **Quasar:** This is an acronym for quasi-stella radio sources (QSOs). Although their exact nature is controversial, they are commonly considered to be extremely distant, unusually bright nuclei of galaxies. Quasars have very large redshifts (i.e. the light they emit is strongly displaced toward the red end of the spectrum), so the light we see from them, is supposed to have been originally emitted when the universe was a fraction of its present age.
- **Quantum:** Any of the very small increments or parcels into which many forms of energy are subdivided.
- **Radio Waves:** Electromagnetic radiation at wavelengths longer than about 0.01 centimeters.
- **Receptor:** A specialized protein on a cell's surface that binds to substances that affect the activities of the cell. Specifically, in a nerve cell (neuron), neurotransmitters bind to receptors on the surface of the neuron. The binding of a neurotransmitter can have either excitatory or inhibitory effects on the neuron. Once a neurotransmitter is bound to a receptor, changes occur within the neuron that can result in the neuron sending messages to other neurons.

- **Redifferentiation:** The process in which a previously mature cell that has differentiated and become a mature, specialized cell again. type in the adult. See also "Dedifferentiation" and "Differentiation".
- **Redshift:** When the light an object emits is displaced toward the red end of the spectrum it is said to be redshifted. In general, photons of light that are emitted at a source, at one energy and detected by an observer at a lower energy are redshifted. Often, the redshift of an object can be measured by examining atomic absorption or emission lines in its spectrum.
- **Refraction:** The physical process of bending an electromagnetic wave (e.g., a ray of light or a radio wave) as it passes from one medium to another medium with a different index of refraction.
- **Relativistic:** Particles with sufficient energy to move at speeds that are an appreciable fraction (10 percent or more) of the speed of light.
- **Relativity [Einstein's Special theory of]:** Published in 1905, this is one of the foundational theories of modern physics. It states that the vacuum speed of light is the same for all observers in initial (non-accelerated) reference frames, and that time and space coordinates combine in a peculiar way when measured from different inertial systems. Exactly how this happens is described by a set of equations called the Lorentz Transformation.
- **Relativity [Einstein's General theory of]:** In 1916 Einstein expanded his Special Theory to include the effect of gravitation on the shape of space and the flow of time. He, proposed that matter causes space to curve. New thought defined space-time has as an invisible stream flowing ever onward, bending in response to objects in its path, carrying everything in the universe along its twists and turns.
- **REM:** The dosage of ionizing radiation that will cause the same biological effect as one roentgen of X-ray dosage.
- **Resonance:** The state of two connected systems which are in tune and vibrating in sympathy and harmony, resulting in an energy transfer. This can occur between two connected periodical processes with equal or multiple frequencies and biological systems. See "Resonant Entrainment".
- **Resonant Entrainment:** Resonant entrainment can be illustrated by a tuning fork (F1) designed to produce a specific frequency. When the tuning fork (F1) is struck (causing it to oscillate) and then brought into the vicinity of another tuning fork (F2) of the same frequency, the second tuning fork (F2) will begin to oscillate. F2 has been entrained and caused to resonate. The physics of entrainment apply to biosystems as well as electromagnetic brain waves. Two brains can be brought into resonance as a natural ability of nonlocal consciousness. This was conclusively proved by the Grinberg-Zylberbaum experiments.
- **Ring Current:** A westward electric current that flows above the geomagnetic equator; it is located in the Outer "Van Allen Radiation Belt". The ring current is produced by the drift (eastward for electrons and westward for protons) of trapped charged particles. This drift is superimposed on the spiraling motion of particles as they bounce between conjugate points. The ring current is greatly enhanced during geomagnetic storms by the injection of hot plasma from the magnetotail.
- **Solar Activity:** Transient perturbations of the quiet solar atmosphere. Sunspots, plage, filaments, prominences, and flares are all forms of solar activity.
- **Solar Cosmic Rays:** High-energy particulate radiation emitted by extremely energetic solar flares. (Also see "Cosmic Rays".)

- **Solar Cycle:** A quasi-periodic (roughly 11-year) variation in the general level of solar activity. (Also see "Sunspot Cycle".)
- **Solar Flare:** A rapid brightening in localized regions on the Sun's photosphere that is usually observed in the ultraviolet and X-ray ranges of the spectrum, and is often accompanied by gamma ray and radio bursts. Solar flares can form in a few minutes and last from tens of minutes to several hours in long-duration events.
- **Solar Maximum/Solar Minimum:** The activity peak/minimum in the 11-year "solar, or sunspot, cycle". (Also see "Sunspot Cycle".)
- **Solar Wind:** Flow of coronal plasma into interplanetary space.
- **Solstice:** Solstice means "Sun standing still". The two days called the Winter and Summer Solstice, when the Sun appears at its most southern or northern position along the horizon at sunrise and sunset and reaches its lowest or highest midday altitude for the year.
- **South Atlantic Anomaly:** A dip in the Earth's magnetic field which allows cosmic rays, and charged particles to reach lower into the atmosphere. The South Atlantic Anomaly is located over a large portion of South America, the South Atlantic and the Southern tip of Africa.
- **Space-time:** A union of space and time originally emerging from special relativity. Can be viewed as the "fabric" from which the universe is fashioned.
- **Speed of Light:** Defined as the speed at which electromagnetic radiation propagates in a vacuum, this is calculates to be 299 792 458 m/s (186,000 miles/second). Einstein's Special Theory of Relativity implies that nothing can go faster than the speed of light, however this is being seriously challenged by recent experiments.
- **Sprite:** Short-lived electrical discharge displaying luminous shapes, that are associated with large thunderstorms.
- **Steady State Theory:** Theory of the creation of the universe that says the universe has been and always will be like it is today. It assumes that the universe is uniform, infinite, and not expanding.
- **Strange Attractor:** A pattern of a pathway, in visual form, produced by graphing the behavior of a system. Most, nonlinear systems are unpredictable and yet patterned, it is called strange and since it tends to produce a fractal geometric shape, it is said to be attracted to that shape. The attractor is actually "a set of points such that all trajectories nearby converge to it". Here the pattern is more important than the evolving position or momentum, for as the system evolves, the exact same path is never repeated twice within the geometry of the attractor.
- **Substorm:** A full cycle in auroral activity, from quiet to highly active to quiet conditions. A geomagnetic storm can be thought of as a sequence of one or more substorms typically 1 to 3 hours in duration and separated by 2 to 3 hours
- **Sunspot:** A small spot on the sun's visible surface where the magnetic flux lines converge. Sunspots appear darker than the surrounding surface area because they are relatively cooler in temperature. Sunspots normally occur in magnetically bipolar groups, and are closely related to the level of solar activity.
- **Sunspot Cycle:** A quasi-periodic variation in the number of observed sunspots. The cycle exhibits an average period of 11 years, but past cycles have been as short as 8, or as long as 15, years. Generally there is a 4-year rise to a "Solar Maximum", followed by a gradual 7-year decline to a "Solar Minimum". Overall solar activity tends to follow the same 11-year cycle.
- **Superconduction:** The conduction of an electrical current by a specific material that under certain circumstances (generally very low temperatures) offers no resistance to

the flow. Such a current will continue undiminished as long as the necessary circumstances are maintained.

- **Superconductivity:** A property of many metals, alloys, and chemical compounds, by which their electrical resistivity vanishes and magnetic fields are expelled.
- **Superconductor:** Any material capable of exhibiting superconducting properties. Examples include iridium, lead, mercury, niobium, tin, tantalum, vanadium, and many alloys. Also known as a cryogenic conductor.
- **Superconducting Quantum Interference Device [SQUID]:** A sensor composed of a superconducting ring coupled with one or two Josephson junctions; applications include high-sensitivity magnetometers, near-magnetic-field antennas, and measurement of very small currents or voltages.
- **Superfluid Helium:** Liquid helium kept at temperatures near absolute zero and capable of flowing completely without friction through holes as small as 10-7 centimeters in diameter, with partical velocities less than a few centimeters per second.
- **Superluminal:** In a manner or with a speed faster than c, the theoretical speed of light in vacuum.
- **Supernova:** An extremely violent explosion of a star many times more massive than our Sun. During this explosion, the star may become as bright as all the other stars in a galaxy combined, and in which a great deal of matter is thrown off into space at high velocity and high energy.
- **Synapse:** A synapse is the tiny gap across which nerve impulses pass from one neuron (nerve cell) to the next.
- **Template:** A basic pattern or model, designed with the capability to be modified or changed to reflect individual uniqueness.
- **Transpersonal:** Something that goes beyond or transcends the merely personal or individual.
- **Ultraviolet [UV] Radiation:** Electromagnetic radiation with wavelengths between approximately 20 and 4000 Angstroms.
- **Umbra:** The dark core in a sunspot. It is the portion of a sunspot where magnetic fields are most intense, causing the temperature to be coolest (about 3900 degrees Kelvin) compared to the overall photosphere (6000 degrees Kelvin). (Also see "Penumbra".)
- **Universal Calibration Lattice [UCL]:** A multidimensional lattice structure of light and energy in the energy anatomy surrounding the human being.
- **Van Allen Radiation Belts:** Bands of highly energized particles, deep inside the magnetosphere of Earth, trapped by the magnetic field, which can cause hazard to spacecraft.
- **Visible Light:** That portion of the electromagnetic spectrum that is perceptible to the human eye, which includes wavelengths between about 4000 and 8000 Angstroms.
- **X-rays:** Electromagnetic radiation with a wavelength of between 0.05 and 20 Angstroms. X-rays impacting the Earth's atmosphere cause neutral gases to become ionized.
- **Z-pinch Effect:** A constriction of a plasma carrying a large current, caused by the interaction of that current with its own encircling magnetic field.

Index

Additional Notes

- The Bibliography for Tuning the Diamonds: Electromagnetism and Spiritual Evolution can be found at: www.joyfirepublishing.com/bibliography.html

- Book reviews can be found at: www.joyfirepublishing.com/bookreviews.html

- A discussion forum for Tuning the Diamonds can be found at: www.joyfirepublishing.com/forum/

- Joyfire Publishing is looking for distributors, for more details visit: www.joyfirepublishing.com/Joyfire_Distributors_Wanted.html